A GIFT FROM

Dave and Lois Knight

A

HUMBOLDT STATE UNIVERSITY

PARENT

SYMPOSIUM ON ANOMALIES, GEOMETRY, TOPOLOGY

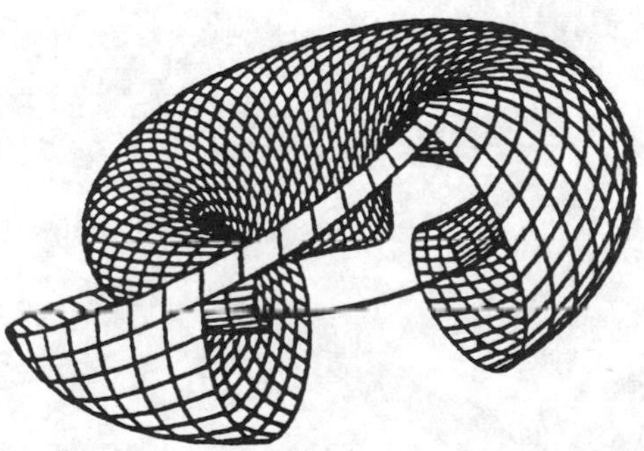

Symposium on Anomalies Geometry Topology

Edited by

William A. Bardeen
Alan R. White

Sponsored by

Argonne National Laboratory
Fermi National Accelerator Laboratory
University of Chicago

March 28-30, 1985

World Scientific

Published by

World Scientific Publishing Co. Pte. Ltd.
P. O. Box 128, Farrer Road, Singapore 9128

ISBN 9971-978-69-5
9971-978-72-5 pbk

Printed in Singapore by Singapore National Printers (Pte) Ltd.

SYMPOSIUM ON ANOMALIES, GEOMETRY, TOPOLOGY

ORGANIZING COMMITTEE

William A. Bardeen
Fermilab

Eric Braaten
Northwestern University

Peter G.O. Freund
University of Chicago

Yoichiro Nambu
University of Chicago

Alan R. White
Argonne National Laboratory

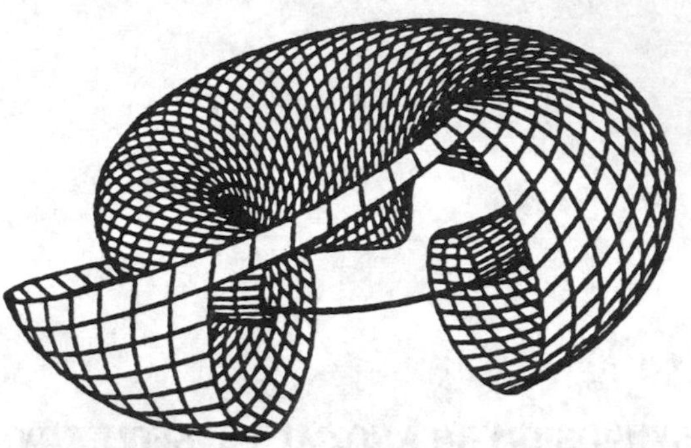

LOGO

The Symposium logo is a twisted scroll ring of a three dimensional nonlinear chemical wave. Scroll rings are observed in certain chemically active media. The scroll is produced by the central organizing axis which forms a ring. The scroll ring used for the logo has nontrivial topological structure due to the global twist in the wave structure. This image of a twisted scroll ring was produced by Arthur T. Winfree (Department of Biological Sciences, Purdue University) and Steven H. Strogatz (Division of Applied Sciences, Harvard University) and appears in their review article on organizing centres in Nature magazine. We wish to thank the authors for permission to use this intriguing figure as the symbol of our Symposium.

A.T. Winfree and S.H. Strogatz, "Organizing Centres for Three-dimensional Chemical Waves", Nature Vol. **311**, 611(1984).

A.T. Winfree, "Wavefront Geometry in Excitable Media", Physica **12B**, 32(1984).

A.T. Winfree and S.H. Strogatz, "Singular Filaments Organize Chemical Waves in Three Dimensions", Physica **8D**,35; **9D**,65; **9D**,333; **13D**,221.

CONTENTS

Special Topics Sessions

Anomaly Structure I - Paul Ginsparg, Chairman

Anomaly Structure II - Paul Ginsparg, Chairman

Superstrings I - Dan Friedan, Chairman

Superstrings II - Steve Shenker, Chairman

Compactification - Andrew Strominger, Chairman

Charge Fractionalization - A. Niemi, Chairman

Effective Lagrangians - E. Farhi, Chairman

Related Topics - C. Goebel, Chairman

Preface

Mathematics and particle physics have often gone their separate ways in an attitude of mutual "benign neglect", diverging in both methodology and language. This uncomfortable gap was bridged to a unique degree at the Argonne-Chicago-Fermilab sponsored Symposium on Anomalies, Geometry, and Topology, which took place at Argonne National Laboratory and the University of Chicago on March 28-30. More than 300 theoretical physicists and mathematicians met together to discuss problems of current excitement and to report on recent progress in an atmosphere of remarkably unguarded optimism. While the meeting had many high points, the focus of much of the excitement and optimism concerned superstring theories. In an overview, John Schwarz described how superstring theories are now making dramatic strides towards achieving the ultimate goal of a unified quantum theory of all interactions including gravity.

Of course, superstrings are not isolated theoretical constructs but sit naturally at the peak of a large pyramid of theoretical concepts developed during the past few years, none seeming to be the whole truth but each having elements of formal beauty and aspects of physical reality. These developments include GUTS, low energy supersymmetry, supergravity, Kaluza-Klein compactification, and finally superstrings. Each of these developments has motivated the next, addressing some of the remaining problems while making possibly more radical assumptions. Several speakers at the Symposium expressed the opinion that with this last doubling of the ante involving superstrings, winning the theoretical jackpot is all but a "sure thing"!

A unifying theme of the Symposium was the mathematical discipline of topology, which has intriqued particle theorists for a long time and led to developments in the study of magnetic monopoles, instantons, solitons, etc. In the last few years, however, the general relevance of topology to the understanding and computation of anomalies has become much more apparent. Anomalies are subtle quantum mechanical violations of the fundamental symmetries used to build the gauge field theories, which are the basis of current dynamical understanding of all interactions. Anomaly cancellation has been an important ingredient in the construction of self-consistent quantum field theories. However, anomalies have much broader implications from predictions for the π^0 decay rate to the existence of fractional charge excitations in polymers. Most recently, they have played a crucial role in developing the new versions of the quantum string model. The mathematical structure of anomalies and the new developments in superstring theories dominated discussions at the Symposium.

Anomalies were first discovered by Jack Steinberger in theoretical calculations of $\pi^0 \rightarrow \gamma\gamma$ decay amplitudes based on virtual proton loops. Anomalies have since proceeded from protons to quarks to strings. The simple perturbative calculations have led to precise theorems concerning fundamental physical processes. The original mathematical focus of anomalies concernec properties of Dirac operators and the related index theorems discovered by Atiyah and Singer. Recent developments have concerned theorems on spectral flow, homotopy, cohomology, and the complex structure of manifolds in four and higher dimensions.

Very recently, it has become possible to study the global gauge manifold structure of anomalies using these powerful topological techniques. As a result, anomalies have been computed outside the realm of perturbation theory by the use of spectral flow arguments (as in Witten's discrete gauge anomaly); a variety of anomalies in different spacetime dimensions were correlated using elegant differential geometry constructions based on cohomology(the cocycle descent sequence); and several new ones including the gravitational anomalies (the nonconservationof the energy-momentum tensor) were derived in a general context. This last development in turn proved crucial in computing a subtle gauge-gravitational anomaly cancellation in the intriguing superstring theory of Schwarz and Green. It is this particular cancellation discovered in the Fall of 1984 that opened the door to dramatic developments in the field and spurred the intense creative activity in the theoretical community, which has led to the first results reported at the Symposium.

While the fever of the Symposium was concentrated on superstrings, there were also many other exciting moments. The intense level of interaction between mathematicians and physicists was certainly a notable feature. Atiyah remarked in his talk that "I used to think mathematicians and physicists were very different. Physicists were interested in four dimensions only and never interested in unusual cases while mathematicians were always interested in general numbers of dimensions and the unusual cases". The Symposium demonstrated a joining together of mathematicians and physicists not only in the dimensions of their interest but also in specific mutual problems. Singer noted that three branches of mathematics - index theorems, complex manifolds, and Kac-Moody algebras - are all playing a role in current string theory. He also traced the history of anomalies in relation to the index theorems. Atiyah gave a general discussion of the phenomenon of spectral flow and its ramifications. Kac spoke on "112 constructions of the basic representation of the loop group of E_8", a topic of special interest to the development of the heterotic string. Yau discussed the general properties and constructions of Kahler manifolds including the celebrated Calabi-Yau manifolds used in initial attempts to compactify the extra dimensions of the superstring theories - even though explicit metrics for these manifolds remain to be constructed.

A major focus of the Symposium concerned the mathematical structure of anomalies. Orlando Alvarez and Bruno Zumino presented point-counterpoint on the role of cohomology in the understanding of anomaly structure. This theme was continued in the parallel sessions with talks by B. Grossman, Y.S. Wu, and D. Nemeschansky. H.-Y. Guo and B. Hou of the Peoples Republic of China also gave talks on the mathematical structure of anomalies. A mathematician's perspective on the physicist's formulation of anomalies was presented by J. Stasheff. Various aspects of anomalies and supersymmetry were discussed in a number of talks including those by L. Baulieu and P. Pasti. Ed Witten presented an analysis of global anomalies which could provide obstructions to defining consistent quantum theories beyond those implied by the usual anomalies. He showed that these obstructions do not arise for the superstring theory but may be important to the study of possible compactifications for the extra dimensions of the theory. Roman Jackiw summarized topological aspects of anomalies in defining quantum gauge field theories. He examined various cures for anomalous gauge theories including anomaly cancellation, gauge invariance as a second class constraint, and the abandonment of gauge invariance with the immediate confrontation of the obvious questions of renormalizability and unitarity.

Topological considerations have also illuminated how induced couplings (Wess-Zumino terms, Chern-Simons terms, etc...) reflect anomaly structure in effective lagrangians for QCD, the standard model, and other fundamental theories. Eric D'Hoker explored anomalies associated with the decoupling of heavy flavors and their impact on the spectrum of states of the standard model. A number of talks (C. Nappi, R. Mackenzie, A. Balachandran) covered recent developments in the theory of the Skyrme model for baryons where the latter appear as solitons of the meson field.

J.R. Schrieffer brought the condensed-matter physicist's perspective to the study of topological effects and reported on some examples (such as the solitons of polyacetylene or the fractional charges of the quantum Hall effect) which are actually observed in the laboratory. His talk illustrated the broad extent of anomalies and topological structure and provided a delightful anchor to the real world. This theme was continued in the parallel sessions by Mike Stone in a talk on topological structure and twists in the new phases of helium, He-A. Aspects of charge fractionalization were discussed in a number of talks with special emphasis on the relation to index theory provided by G. Semenoff and A. Niemi.

In a somewhat different vein, Gerard 't Hooft presented his work on the quantum mechanics and the tunnelling processes of black holes and argued that a new physical picture of the "interior" of a black hole may be necessary for a consistent interpretation of Hawking radiation. He also shouldered the role of skeptic in the evening panel discussion entitled "Philosophy, Strings, and the Answer *42*" by asking the sober questions of the average man in the [physics] street when first exposed to the zealots of the string.

't Hooft's balancing criticism not withstanding, this conference may well be remembered as the first meeting where superstring physics emerged as a dominant theme for the entire physics community.

Like Yang-Mills theory, string theories started life in the wrong context. Yang and Mills developed their theory in 1954 to describe the strong interactions of isospin. It took more than a dozen years for the theory to triumph as the fundamental basis for standard gauge theories of the electroweak theory of leptons and the strong interactions of quarks. String theories were formulated in 1970 by Nambu, and others as an elegant codification of the dual resonance structure of strong interaction amplitudes. The Regge behavior of the hadronic amplitudes was described in terms of the excitations of a massless, relativistic string. Although the development of quantum chromodymanics also led to a string picture of strong interactions, it soon became clear that the fundamental string theory could not be regarded as a satisfactory model of strong interactions. Lorentz invariance and unitarity forced the theory to exist in apparently unphysical numbers of spacetime dimensions, such as 26 or 10 and the strong interaction amplitudes did not have quite the Regge structure. Various techniques were adapted from the work of Kaluza and Klein to "compactify" the unwanted extra dimensions. In addition, an interesting new symmetry emerged from the string in 1971 (Neveu-Schwarz. Ramond), which connected fermions with bosons; eventually this symmetry was formulated as supersymmetry in the context of field theory. Despite heroic theoretical efforts and the intricate formal beauty, strings seemed to be without physical applications.

Then, in 1974, Scherk and Schwarz decided to apply strings to a totally different problem, namely the quantum theory of gravity. The relativistic string contained a massless, spin two excitation which was a phenomenological embarrassment in a hadron theory but could be identified as the graviton, the quantum of the gravitational field. The lowest order string amplitudes for the scattering of this massless quantum were shown to agree with those derived from Einstein's theory of gravity. This shift of focus to gravity entailed changing the Regge slope from the scale of strong interactions to that of the Planck scale, a decrease in size of about 38 orders of magnitude! In 1976, Gliozzi, Scherk and Olive realized that a projection of the fermionic strings produced a supersymmetric theory in ten dimensional space-time, thus the birth of superstrings. It was found that the infinite tower of massive states of the superstring could prevent the divergence effects of the quantum fluctuations. Hence, the superstring theory could succeed where field theory had failed: it could provide a "renormalizable" or, indeed, "finite" theory of gravity, supergravity, and lots more.

A complete string theory is now envisaged as including all interactions of the universe -- seen and unseen. Much of the work presented at the Symposium was aimed at identifying within the full theory plausible "low energy physics", that is, low with respect to 10^{19} GeV. First, gauge invariance is established through the anomaly cancellation mechanism of Schwarz and Green. This cancellation was demonstrated first for an SO(32) string theory although the possibility of a similar cancellation based on an $E_8 \otimes E_8$ gauge group was also noted. Peter Freund suggested that these symmetries could be viewed as arising from a tororidal reduction from twenty-six dimensions. An ingenious hybrid of older string theories which realizes either the SO(32) symmetry or the $E_8 \otimes E_8$ symmetry was developed by Gross, Harvey, Martinec, and Rohm and called the "heterotic string". This version of the new superstring theories has the most promising possibilities for "low energy phenomenology".

A major part of the technology of extracting low energy physics from the ten-dimensional superstring theories relies on the compactification of the additional six dimensions which are not observed. The emergence of a low energy GUT model based on the gauge group E_6 from the heterotic string is tentatitively suggested by the analysis of P. Candelas, G. Horowitz, A. Strominger, and E. Witten. This work was described in talks by both Gary Horowitz and Ed Witten who also discussed very recent results from Princeton. The number of families which emerge after the compactification manifold is found will be determined by an index theorem and one particular solution which yields four conventional families was presented! Future improvement in the formulation and compactification of superstring theories can be expected to come from the deeper understanding of finite two-dimensional sigma models with the geometry and topology of the compactification manifolds as emphasized in the talk of Luis Alvarez-Gaumé.

Many crucial issues for understanding the structure of superstrings were discussed. Attempts to provide a covariant, gauge invariant quantization of the superstring were the subject of much discussion with Tom Banks, Mike Kaku, and Warren Siegel all making presentations. Lars Brink emphasized the uniqueness of the superstring action in the light-cone functional formalism. There was general agreement that understanding the limitations or otherwise of light-cone quantization will be an important direction for future research.

The breakthrough achieved in superstring theory and the impact of the Symposium can perhaps be summarized by the following comments. Mike Green remarked "I feel the symmetry groups found for the superstring are very important but I am not yet convinced that one particular superstring theory is correct". Ed Witten commented "This was the first widely attended conference since the (superstring) revolution. Before this meeting the significance of the developments had not really sunk in for many people". David Gross expressed the greatest optimism and said "it is remarkable how easily recognizable features of low-energy physics emerge from superstrings. While I don't believe we have yet found the right route to low-energy, there appear to be no insuperable obstacles to deriving all known physics from the $E_8 \otimes E_8$ heterotic string".

Acknowledgments

The Symposium benefited from the combined efforts of many people. We wish to thank our sponsors, the High Energy Physics Division, the Division of Educational Programs, and the Board of Governors of Argonne National Laboratory, the Enrico Fermi Institute of The University of Chicago, and Fermi National Accelerator Laboratory. People vital to the organizational support, before, during, and after the meeting, include Joanne Day and Barb Angelos of Argonne, Jean Plese of Fermilab, and Lois Cox of the Fermi Institute. Finally we are grateful to the session chairmen for organizing such lively parallel sessions and to both the speakers and the participants for providing such a stimulating and enjoyable atmosphere during the entire Symposium. We hope this meeting has provided the basis for significant progress in developing our mathematical and physical understanding of the fundamental structure of our universe.

For the Organizing Committee

William A. Bardeen
Alan R. White

June, 1985

SYMPOSIUM ON ANOMALIES, GEOMETRY, TOPOLOGY

PLENARY SESSIONS

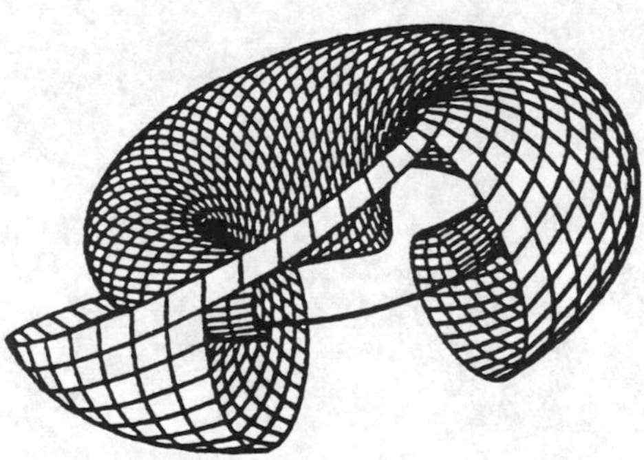

COHOMOLOGY AND FIELD THEORY[1,2]

Orlando Alvarez[3]
Department of Physics
and
Lawrence Berkeley Laboratory
University of California
Berkeley, CA 94720

ABSTRACT

The relationship between cohomology and the quantization of certain coupling constants in physics is discussed. A brief discussion is given about the relationship between cohomology and the Schrödinger wavefunction in field theories with quantized coupling constants.

1 Introduction

The relationship between charge quantization and topology goes back to Dirac [1]. In recent years, a flurry of research has gone into elucidating the relationships among geometry, topology and quantum field theory. In particular, physicists have discovered that homotopy arguments are very useful in understanding quantization conditions. It is also possible to use cohomology arguments to obtain the same quantization conditions. These ideas have been discussed in detail in a paper [2]. In this talk I present a brief introduction to the subject. I will also discuss the classification of Schrödinger wavefunctions in a quantum field theory. This seems to be intimately related to the Cech cohomology ideas used in the topological quantization arguments. The bulk of the wavefunction study is still unpublished [3].

There are three very familiar quantization conditions in quantum field theory: magnetic charge quantization [1], quantization [4] of the Yang-Mills mass term [5] and the quantization [6] of the coupling of the Wess-Zumino Lagrangian [7]. Part of the Lagrangian for each of these theories can be interpreted as a differential form. The Lagrangian will be written as the sum of two terms $\mathcal{L} = \mathcal{L}_0 + T$ where T is the term of topological significance and

[1]Invited plenary talk at the Symposium on Anomalies, Geometry and Topology, March 28-30, 1985

[2]This work was supported in part by the National Science Foundation under Contracts PHY81-18547; and by the Director, Office of High Energy and Nuclear Physics of the U.S. Department of Energy under Contract DE-AC03-70SF00098.

[3]Alfred P. Sloan Foundation Fellow

magnetic monopole	$\int T$	$\sim \int A_\mu \dot{x}^\mu \, dt$ $\sim \int A_\mu \, dx^\mu$
Y-M mass	$\int T$	$\sim \int \epsilon^{\mu\nu\rho} \operatorname{Tr}(A_\mu \partial_\nu A_\rho + \cdots) \, d^3x$ $\sim \int \operatorname{Tr}(A \wedge dA + \cdots)$
W-Z (d=2)	$\int T$	$\sim \int \epsilon^{\mu\nu} \operatorname{Tr}(\pi \, \partial_\mu \pi \, \partial_\nu \pi + \cdots) \, d^2x$ $\sim \int \operatorname{Tr}(\pi \, d\pi \wedge d\pi + \cdots)$

$\mathcal{L}_0$ includes the kinetic energy terms and interactions which will not concern us. The three "topological" Lagrangians for each of the theories are schematically presented in the table. The Lagrangians have the following in common:

1. $\mathcal{L}_0$ is globally defined.

2. T has special properties:

   (a) T may be interpreted as a differential form.

   (b) Under an appropriate transformation T changes by a total derivative.[4]

   (c) T is not globally defined.

The common properties of the topological part of the Lagrangian, denoted by T, will lead to the topological quantization conditions.

2 Dirac's Quantization Condition Revisited

In this section, the familiar Dirac quantization condition is derived in a manner illustrating Cech cohomological concepts. We will use a generalization of some ideas of Wu and Yang [8]. The methods of this section extend to higher dimensional cases.

Consider the motion of a point particle on a two dimensional sphere with a magnetic monopole residing at the center of the sphere. The classical Lagrangian for this system is

$$\mathrm{L} = \frac{1}{2}\left(\frac{dx}{dt}\right)^2 + \frac{1}{4e^2} F_{\mu\nu} F^{\mu\nu} + A_\mu \frac{dx^\mu}{dt}$$

The term of interest for us is the coupling of the vector potential to the velocity of the particle. This is the only term of topological interest and for the remaining part of this section we will completely disregard the kinetic energy terms. We would like to view this term as the line integral of the one form $A = A_\mu dx^\mu$ along the trajectory Γ of the particle:

$$\int_\Gamma A$$

This would be fine except for the fact that it is impossible to find an everywhere nonsingular vector potential over the entire sphere. Wu and Yang [8] pointed out how to

[4]This should remind the reader of the classical mechanics theorem about the equivalence of Lagrangians that differ by a total time derivative.

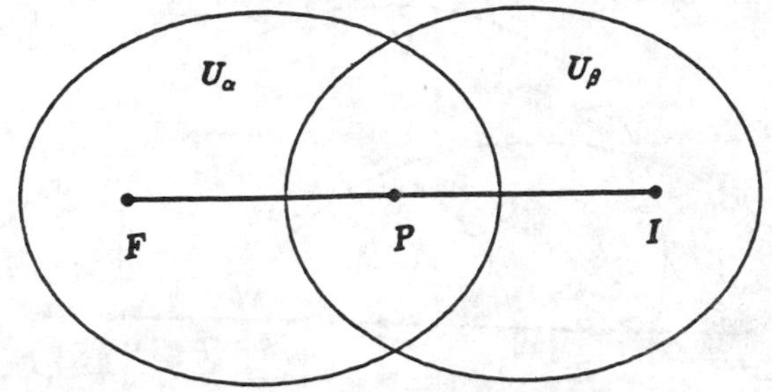

Figure 1: The worldline of the particle which begins at I and ends at F traverses two distinct coordinate patches. The point P is in the intersection of the two patches

modify the Lagrangian to take this into account. Cover the sphere with a collection of open sets $\mathcal{U} = \{U_\alpha\}$. On each open set choose a vector potential one form A_α. The subscript α on A_α is not a Lorentz index and refers to the open cover: $A_\alpha = A_{\alpha\mu}dx^\mu$. Consider the situation depicted in Figure 1 where one has a trajectory Γ that goes through a non-empty overlap $U_\alpha \cap U_\beta$. Let P be a point in the intersection. Naively one would write the vector potential contribution to the action as (remember that we are concentrating only on the term of possible topological interest)

$$I_P = \int_P^F A_\alpha + \int_I^P A_\beta$$

The problem with this definition is that it depends on the choice of the point P. To see this, consider another point Q in the overlap, construct I_Q and compute the difference $I_Q - I_P$:

$$I_Q - I_P = -\int_P^Q (A_\alpha - A_\beta)$$

We require knowledge of the gauge transformation on the overlap to evaluate the above. On each overlap it is necessary to specify a gauge transformation $\psi_{\alpha\beta}$ satisfying

$$d\psi_{\alpha\beta} = A_\alpha - A_\beta$$

Note that $-\psi_{\alpha\beta} = \psi_{\beta\alpha}$. Using the gauge transformation properties we see that:

$$I_Q - I_P = \psi_{\alpha\beta}(P) - \psi_{\alpha\beta}(Q)$$

In particular the quantity $I = I_Q + \psi_{\alpha\beta}(Q)$ is independent of the choice of point Q. More explicitly, I is given by

$$I = \int_Q^F A_\alpha + \psi_{\alpha\beta}(Q) + \int_I^Q A_\beta$$

This is the correct form of the action which was given by Wu and Yang. It seems to be a bit mysterious but its significance is more discernible by thinking about quantum mechanics.

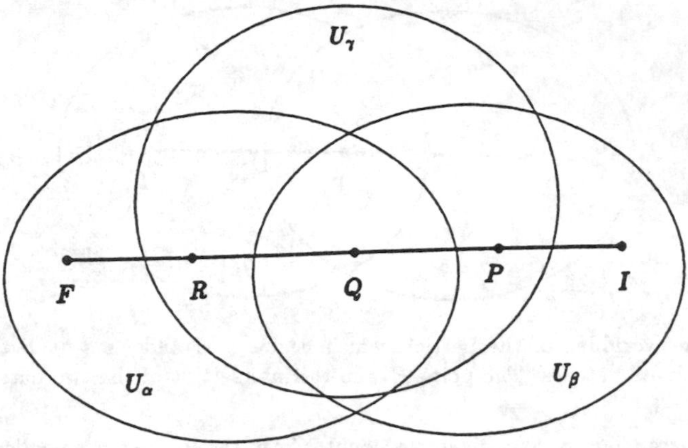

Figure 2: A third coordinate patch is introduced. The points P and R do not have to be in the triple intersection

According to the Feynman path integral formulation of quantum mechanics [9], the effect of a vector potential on propagation is to multiply the amplitudes by the exponential of the above equation. This is simply seen to be the amplitude for propagation in patch U_β, followed by a gauge transformation and terminating with the amplitude to propagate in the new gauge in patch U_α.

We now depart from the discussion of Wu and Yang and we ask the question, "What happens in a triple overlap?". The situation is depicted in Figure 2. Let us temporarily forget U_γ. The action is given by the Wu-Yang prescription. Remember that the value of the action is independent of the location of Q. Let us rewrite this term in such a way that contribution to the line integral from the part of the trajectory between P and R is expressed in terms of A_γ only. By using the gauge transformation law for the vector potential the action may be rewritten as:

$$\begin{aligned} I = \int_R^F A_\alpha + \psi_{\alpha\gamma}(R) + \int_P^R A_\gamma + \psi_{\gamma\beta}(P) + \int_I^P A_\beta \\ + \Big(\psi_{\alpha\beta}(Q) + \psi_{\beta\gamma}(Q) + \psi_{\gamma\alpha}(Q)\Big) \end{aligned} \quad (1)$$

This equation is reminiscent of the Wu-Yang prescription. It is of the form line integral, gauge transformation, line integral, gauge transformation, line integral, and a left over piece. It is important to note that the left over piece contains the only reference to the point Q. The other pieces are just the Wu-Yang prescription for going from patch U_β to patch U_γ and ending in patch U_α. We will see that the left over piece contains all the information required to obtain Dirac's quantization condition.

The first piece of information we need is that the gauge transformations must satisfy a consistency condition on triple overlaps. Consider the following three equations:

$$A_\alpha - A_\beta = d\psi_{\alpha\beta}$$
$$A_\beta - A_\gamma = d\psi_{\beta\gamma}$$
$$A_\gamma - A_\alpha = d\psi_{\gamma\alpha}$$

Add all three equations to obtain the result

$$d(\psi_{\alpha\beta} + \psi_{\beta\gamma} + \psi_{\gamma\alpha}) = 0$$

To proceed further we need a special condition on the cover we chose for the sphere. It is possible to choose a cover such that each U_δ is diffeomorphic to an open ball, and each non-empty finite multiple intersection is also diffeomorphic to an open ball [10].This means that the Poincaré lemma is valid in each multiple intersection. In particular, we reach the conclusion that on $U_\alpha \cap U_\beta \cap U_\gamma$ one has

$$\psi_{\alpha\beta} + \psi_{\beta\gamma} + \psi_{\gamma\alpha} = c_{\alpha\beta\gamma}$$

where $c_{\alpha\beta\gamma}$ is a constant over the entire triple overlap. Therefore equation (1) is independent of Q as required.

There is an important lesson that this exercise teaches us. The classical action is ambiguous up to a constant. A priori, one could use the Wu-Yang prescription to write an expression involving patches U_α and U_β only, or write an expression involving patches U_α, U_β, U_γ. The difference between these two expressions is a constant which does not affect the classical equations of motion.

This classical ambiguity leads to quantum mechanical inconsistencies unless certain conditions are imposed on the collection of all $\{c_{\alpha\beta\gamma}\}$. The best way to see this is through path integral quantization. Consider the contribution of a trajectory Γ to the non-relativistic propagator:

$$\exp\left(i\int_\Gamma A\right) \cdot K_{\text{free}}(\Gamma)$$

The only ambiguity arises in how one decides to evaluate the vector potential line integral. There is an ambiguous phase factor of $\exp(ic_{\alpha\beta\gamma})$. Such a potential ambiguity exists at each non-empty triple intersection of patches on the sphere. The only way to avoid this mishap is to require that each phase factor be equal to one. In other words one has to choose all $c_{\alpha\beta\gamma}$ to be $2\pi \times$ (integer). Later we will see that this statement contains topological information about the manifold. It states that if the manifold's second cohomology class contains the integers then a consistent quantum theory requires an appropriate coupling constant to be quantized. In fact, the collection $\{c_{\alpha\beta\gamma}\}$ defines a two cocycle.

The Dirac flux quantization condition is related to the two cocycle $\{c_{\alpha\beta\gamma}\}$. With a little work one can see that the total magnetic flux is given by

$$\int_{S^2} F = \sum_{V_{\alpha\beta\gamma}} c_{\alpha\beta\gamma}$$

where the sum is over all triple overlaps with $V_{\alpha\beta\gamma} = U_\alpha \cap U_\beta \cap U_\gamma \cap S^2$. We conclude that the total flux is given by

$$\int_{S^2} F = 2\pi \sum_{V_{\alpha\beta\gamma}} n_{\alpha\beta\gamma}$$

where the integer n is given by

$$c_{\alpha\beta\gamma} = 2\pi\, n_{\alpha\beta\gamma}$$

This is Dirac's quantization condition. We shall see that this condition generalizes in higher dimensions. Note that the quantization arose because of consistency conditions on triple overlaps of the different coordinate patches. There is a connection between the ambiguity in the classical action and the total flux through the sphere. In the case of a sphere, the construction given above is not necessary since one can cover the sphere with two coordinate patches, see Wu and Yang [8]. The above construction is valid for any manifold.

In this example, one finds that no further conditions are imposed by looking at quadruple or higher overlaps. This is not true in two dimensional field theories as we will see in the next section.

3 Cech Cohomology

Cech cohomology is the correct language for formulating the examples presented in the previous section. The machinery of Cech cohomology provides a means of cataloguing the necessary information required to extract the physics. In this section we will explain the relationship of Cech cohomology to the topology of the manifold, and we will also explain the cataloguing procedure. We will not present Cech cohomology in its most abstract setting. The general theory will be stripped down to a level sufficient to attack and solve the problems addressed in this talk. We assume the reader is familiar with the elementary aspects of simplicial homology [11], [12]. Namely, the concept of simplices, the existence of triangulations of a manifold, the notion of a chain (the formal sum of simplices), and the concept of the boundary of a chain. It is clear that the topology of the manifold will determine the allowed triangulations and that there are many possible triangulations. What is remarkable is that there are certain invariants which are independent of the triangulations. These invariants are the homology groups and their associated cohomology groups.

We will formulate Cech homology in a way that the connection to simplicial homology will be explicit. In all the manifolds we will consider it is always possible to choose an open cover $\mathcal{U} = \{U_\alpha\}$ such that each open set and each non-empty finite intersection is diffeomorphic to an open ball in $\mathbf{R}^n$ [10]. We will refer to these covers as *good covers*. At this stage we have already tailored Cech theory to some specifics we require. A major benefit of a good cover is that on each intersection the Poincaré lemma holds.

On each non-empty finite intersection define objects $U_{\alpha\beta}$, $U_{\alpha\beta\gamma}$, $U_{\alpha\beta\gamma\delta}$, etc. by

$$\begin{aligned} U_{\alpha\beta} &= U_\alpha \cap U_\beta \\ U_{\alpha\beta\gamma} &= U_\alpha \cap U_\beta \cap U_\gamma \\ U_{\alpha\beta\gamma\delta} &= U_\alpha \cap U_\beta \cap U_\gamma \cap U_\delta \end{aligned}$$

We define a formal orientation by requiring that $U_{\alpha\beta} = -U_{\beta\alpha}$, and likewise for the other objects. This good cover of the manifold defines a simplicial triangulation of the manifold. This is illustrated in Figure 3. In each open set U_α we choose a point in the interior, see Figure 3a . These points define the vertices of the triangulation. To each non-empty intersection we associate a one simplex, see Figure 3b . To each non-empty triple intersection

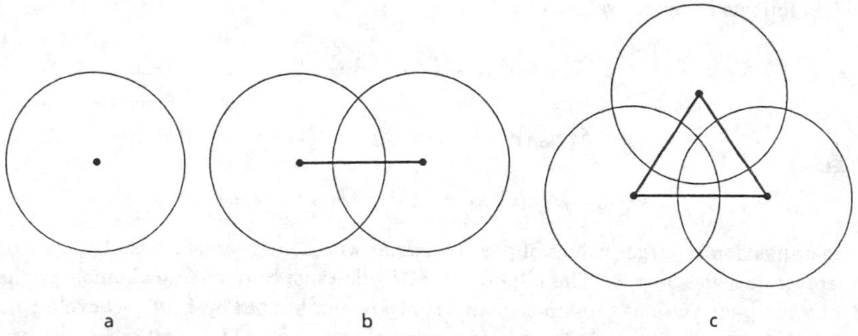

Figure 3: a: an open set and its associated vertex. b: two intersecting open sets and the associated segment. c: triply overlapping sets and the associated triangle.

we associate a two simplex, see Figure 3c . It is clear that the combinatorics of a good cover defines a simplicial triangulation of the manifold.

Our main interest is not Cech homology theory but Cech cohomology theory. For our purposes, Cech cohomology provides a systematic way of cataloguing information and a systematic way of dealing with singular fields configurations by avoiding the singularities. We will see how the ideas discussed in the previous sections may be discussed in the language of Cech cohomology.

A p-cochain with values in q-forms is an assignment of a nonsingular q-form to each p-chain. As an example consider the monopole. In that case we assigned to each open set U_α a vector potential A_α. The collection $\{A_\alpha\}$ is a zero cochain with values in one forms. We required that on U_α the vector potential A_α be nonsingular. A_α may be singular somewhere outside of U_α. This singularity is the famous Dirac string singularity. The collection of gauge transformations $\{\psi_{\alpha\beta}\}$ defines a one cochain with values in the zero forms.

Let us try to answer the following question, "When does a zero cochain define a global differential form?" Consider a zero cochain $\{\lambda_\alpha\}$. The zero cochain specifies a q-form on each open set in the cover. Assume $U_{\alpha\beta} \neq 0$, then on the overlap $U_{\alpha\beta}$ one must have $\lambda_\alpha - \lambda_\beta = 0$. If not then λ_α will not extend to λ_β. One can define a global differential q-form λ^{global} if and only if $\{\lambda_\alpha - \lambda_\beta\}$ vanishes identically. In other words, $\{\lambda_\alpha\}$ is a zero cocycle. This already gives us an inkling on what Cech theory will do for us. It will in certain situations allow us to piece local information into global information. We will see that Cech cohomology provides a systematic way for determining when local information can be pieced into less local information.

The coboundary operator δ is an operation between p-chains and (p+1)-chains. It is defined as follows for small values of p:

$$\delta\{A_\alpha\} = \{A_\alpha - A_\beta\}$$

$$\delta\{B_{\alpha\beta}\} = \{B_{\alpha\beta} + B_{\beta\gamma} + B_{\gamma\alpha}\}$$

$$\delta\{C_{\alpha\beta\gamma}\} = \{C_{\alpha\beta\gamma} + C_{\beta\gamma\delta} + C_{\gamma\delta\alpha} + C_{\delta\alpha\beta}\}$$

The generalization to larger values of p is straightforward. One can show that the coboundary operator satisfies $\delta^2 = 0$. The nilpotency of δ allows us to define a cohomology theory. We define the p-cocycles as those p-cochains that are annihilated by δ. A p-cocycle z is said to be *exact* if one can find a (p-1)-cochain y such that $z = \delta y$. The p-coboundaries are the image of the (p-1)-cochains under δ. Since δ is nilpotent, it follows that the p-coboundaries are a subset of the p-cochains. Therefore it is possible to define cohomology classes by taking the quotient of the cocycles by the coboundaries. Since a cocycle is defined by the condition $\delta z = 0$, the existence of non-trivial cohomology classes boils down to the question of whether every cocycle is exact. The answer is provided by the existence of a Poincaré lemma for the δ operator. This lemma states that if $p > 0$ then the equation $\delta z = 0$ for a p-chain z can always be "solved". Namely, there exists a (p-1)-cochain y such that $z = \delta y$. This seems to say that the cohomology classes are trivial. This is true except for a caveat which is related to the construction of y in the proof of the Poincaré lemma. This caveat will be used to constuct nontrivial cohomology classes called Cech cohomology classes. We will postpone the caveat until later. The p=0 case is the statement that a closed zero cochain defines a global differential form.

The final piece of formalism we need is the *tic-tac-toe* box [10]. We will be studying the so called *double chain complexes.* These ideas are best explained by looking at our magnetic monopole example. It will not be necessary to assume that the electrically charged particle moves on the surface of a sphere. The configuration space for the trajectory of the particle may be any compact manifold without boundary. In the box below we have included the vector potentials and the transition functions.

Ω^3					
Ω^2					
Ω^1		$\{A_\alpha\}$			
Ω^0			$\{\psi_{\alpha\beta}\}$		
d	$\uparrow$				
δ	$\rightarrow$	C^0	C^1	C^2	C^3

The rows correspond to the degree of the differential form. The notation Ω^q stands for the q-forms. The columns correspond to the degree of the cochain. The notation C^p stands for the p-cochains. The d operator moves us vertically and the δ operator moves us horizontally. Let us apply the d and the δ operations to the elements in the above box. We can operate again with d and δ and get zero since these operators are nilpotent. Notice that one of the entries is the gauge transformation law. Also, the operators d and δ commute.

$$
\begin{array}{cc|cccc}
\Omega^3 & & 0 & & & \\
\Omega^2 & & \{dA_\alpha\} & 0 & & \\
\Omega^1 & & \{A_\alpha\} & \delta\{A\}=\{d\psi\} & 0 & \\
\Omega^0 & & & \{\psi_{\alpha\beta}\} & \delta\{\psi_{\alpha\beta}\} & 0 \\
\hline
d & \uparrow & & & & \\
\delta & \rightarrow & C^0 & C^1 & C^2 & C^3
\end{array}
$$

Define quantities F_α by $F_\alpha = dA_\alpha$, and $c_{\alpha\beta\gamma}$ by $\delta\{\psi_{\alpha\beta}\} = \{c_{\alpha\beta\gamma}\}$. The above box thus becomes:

$$
\begin{array}{cc|cccc}
\Omega^3 & & 0 & & & \\
\Omega^2 & & \{F_\alpha\} & 0 & & \\
\Omega^1 & & \{A_\alpha\} & \delta\{A\}=\{d\psi\} & 0 & \\
\Omega^0 & & & \{\psi_{\alpha\beta}\} & \{c_{\alpha\beta\gamma}\} & 0 \\
\hline
d & \uparrow & & & & \\
\delta & \rightarrow & C^0 & C^1 & C^2 & C^3
\end{array}
$$

We immediately learn that the F_α is d-closed and it is also a zero δ-cocycle. This means that F_α defines a closed global differential form F, the electromagnetic field strength two form.

The other piece of information we learn from the tic-tac-toe box involves the $\{c_{\alpha\beta\gamma}\}$. These objects are d-closed and they define a two cocycle. Since locally closed zero form is given by a constant, the $\{c_{\alpha\beta\gamma}\}$ must define a two cocycle. All this information is shown in the box below.

$$
\begin{array}{cc|cccc}
\Omega^3 & 0 & 0 & & & \\
\Omega^2 & F & \{F_\alpha\} & 0 & & \\
\Omega^1 & & \{A_\alpha\} & \delta\{A\}=\{d\psi\} & 0 & \\
\Omega^0 & & & \{\psi_{\alpha\beta}\} & \{c_{\alpha\beta\gamma}\} & 0 \\
\hline
d & \uparrow & & & \{c_{\alpha\beta\gamma}\} & 0 \\
\delta & \rightarrow & C^0 & C^1 & C^2 & C^3
\end{array}
$$

The main conclusion is that given a collection of vector potentials $\{A_\alpha\}$ and transition functions $\{\psi_{\alpha\beta}\}$, the gauge transformation law $\delta A = \psi$, one can construct a closed global two form F and a locally constant two cocycle $\{c_{\alpha\beta\gamma}\}$. Since F is closed and global, it is a representative of the second DeRham cohomology class. Note that we wrote F "outside" the tic-tac-toe box. The reason is that even though F is closed, the Poincaré lemma is in general not valid globally. If something is outside the box then one has to be careful about applying the Poincaré lemma. We are not allowing singular vector potentials as acceptable solutions.

A similar thing happens with the Poincaré lemma for the δ operator. Note that the locally constant cocycle $\{c_{\alpha\beta\gamma}\}$ is exact. It is the δ of $\{\psi_{\alpha\beta}\}$. In general the ψ's will not be constant. The question is whether one can find a solution to the equation $\delta c = 0$ given by $c = \delta b$ where the $\{b_{\alpha\beta}\}$ are constants. In general, such a solution does not exist. This is the caveat we previously mentioned. There is no Poincaré lemma for the δ operator if one only uses locally constant cochains. This is analogous to not allowing singular differential forms in the Poincaré lemma for the d operator. In analogy to the previous case we write the c cocycle "outside" the box. One has to be careful in applying the Poincaré lemma outside the box. The Cech cohomology classes are defined by looking at locally constant cocycles and asking whether they are exact within the class of locally constant cocycles. The two cocycle c is a representative of the second Cech cohomology class of the manifold. There is an isomorphism between the DeRham classes and the Cech classes [10].

Remember that the total magnetic flux through the manifold was determined by the $\{c_{\alpha\beta\gamma}\}$. There several notes of interest. The total magnetic flux through the sphere was determined by conditions on triple overlaps. Quantum mechanics imposes a further condition on the cocycle $\{c_{\alpha\beta\gamma}\}$. The c's must be $2\pi \times$ (integer). This imposes a severe restriction on the cohomology classes. The integers $\mathbf{Z}$ are a subset of the real numbers $\mathbf{R}$. One can define objects $\{n_{\alpha\beta\gamma}\}$ to be integer valued cochains instead of real valued cochains. Since the δ Poincaré lemma does not apply to real valued cochains then it certainly does not apply to the integer valued cochains. Therefore, there will be non-trivial integer valued cohomology. These cohomology classes are called *Cech cohomology classes with integer coefficients* and they will be denoted by $H^p_C(M, \mathbf{Z})$. Quantum mechanics requires that the cocycle $\{c_{\alpha\beta\gamma}/(2\pi)\}$ must be integral. The existence of such a cocycle is determined by whether or not the manifold in question admits integral cocycles in its second Cech cohomology class, i.e., $\mathbf{Z} \subset H^2_C(M, \mathbf{Z})$. The existence of such integral cocycles is determined by the topology of the manifold. The magnetic flux will be quantized if the manifold admits a second cohomology class with integer coefficients that contains the integers.

The situation becomes more interesting when one looks at a two dimensional example. Assume one has a two dimensional non-linear sigma model given as a map ϕ from a two dimensional spacetime S to a manifold M. For simplicity we take S to be $\mathbf{R} \times S^1$. Assume that part of the Lagrangian can be interpreted as the pull back of a two form on M. We will neglect completely the rest of the Lagrangian. Lagrangian will be taken to refer only to the term of possible topological significance. In analogy to the monopole example, the Lagrangian T might not be globally defined. Assume that there is a collection of locally defined two-forms $\{T_\alpha\}$, one two-form for each open set in a good cover of M. Assume that on a non-empty intersection $U_\alpha \cap U_\beta$ the respective Lagrangians differ by the differential of a one form $J_{\alpha\beta}$:

$$T_\alpha - T_\beta = dJ_{\alpha\beta}\,.$$

Note that the collection of Lagrangians defines a zero cocycle and the transition functions define a one cocycle. In the tic-tac-toe box below we have included the Lagrangian and its gauge transformation properties.

Ω^4						
Ω^3						
Ω^2		$\{T_\alpha\}$	$\delta\{T_\alpha\} = \{dJ_{\alpha\beta}\}$			
Ω^1			$\{J_{\alpha\beta}\}$			
Ω^0						
d	$\uparrow$					
δ	$\rightarrow$	C^0	C^1	C^2	C^3	C^4

First we record the consequence of multiple d and δ operations. This is shown in the box below:

$$
\begin{array}{ll|lllll}
\Omega^4 & & 0 & & & & \\
\Omega^3 & & \{dT_\alpha\} & 0 & & & \\
\Omega^2 & & \{T_\alpha\} & \delta\{T_\alpha\} = \{dJ_{\alpha\beta}\} & 0 & & \\
\Omega^1 & & & \{J_{\alpha\beta}\} & \delta\{J\} & 0 & \\
\Omega^0 & & & & & & \\
\hline
d & \uparrow & & & & & \\
\delta & \rightarrow & C^0 & C^1 . & C^2 & C^3 & C^4
\end{array}
$$

One of the pieces of information we have is that δJ is closed, $d\delta J = 0$. This follows from the commutativity of the two operations. The tic-tac-toe box automatically takes this into account. Since δJ is closed and since the cohomology is trivial, there must exist a two cochain K such that J is its differential. This is illustrated in the box below

$$
\begin{array}{ll|lllll}
\Omega^4 & & 0 & & & & \\
\Omega^3 & & \{dT_\alpha\} & 0 & & & \\
\Omega^2 & & \{T_\alpha\} & \delta\{T_\alpha\} = \{dJ_{\alpha\beta}\} & 0 & & \\
\Omega^1 & & & \{J_{\alpha\beta}\} & \delta\{J\} & 0 & \\
\Omega^0 & & & & \{K\} & & \\
\hline
d & \uparrow & & & & & \\
\delta & \rightarrow & C^0 & C^1 & C^2 & C^3 & C^4
\end{array}
$$

Applying the d and δ information to the box above we find:

$$
\begin{array}{ll|lllll}
\Omega^4 & & 0 & & & & \\
\Omega^3 & & \{dT_\alpha\} & 0 & & & \\
\Omega^2 & & \{T_\alpha\} & \delta\{T_\alpha\} = \{dJ_{\alpha\beta}\} & 0 & & \\
\Omega^1 & & & \{J_{\alpha\beta}\} & \delta\{J\} & 0 & \\
\Omega^0 & & & & \{K\} & \delta\{K\} & 0 \\
\hline
d & \uparrow & & & & & \\
\delta & \rightarrow & C^0 & C^1 & C^2 & C^3 & C^4
\end{array}
$$

We learn that δK is a closed three-cocycle. This cocycle is represented by constant cocycle $\{c_{\alpha\beta\gamma\delta}\} = \delta K$. The other piece of information we need to know is that $\{dT_\alpha\}$ defines a closed global differential form $\mathcal{G}$. This is all depicted in the box below.

$$
\begin{array}{lll|lllll}
\Omega^4 & 0 & & 0 & & & & \\
\Omega^3 & \mathcal{G} & & \{dT_\alpha\} & 0 & & & \\
\Omega^2 & & & \{T_\alpha\} & \delta\{T_\alpha\} = \{dJ_{\alpha\beta}\} & 0 & & \\
\Omega^1 & & & & \{J_{\alpha\beta}\} & \delta\{J\} & 0 & \\
\Omega^0 & & & & & \{K\} & \delta\{K\} & 0 \\
\hline
d & \uparrow & & & & & \{c_{\alpha\beta\gamma\delta}\} & 0 \\
\delta & \rightarrow & & C^0 & C^1 & C^2 & C^3 & C^4
\end{array}
$$

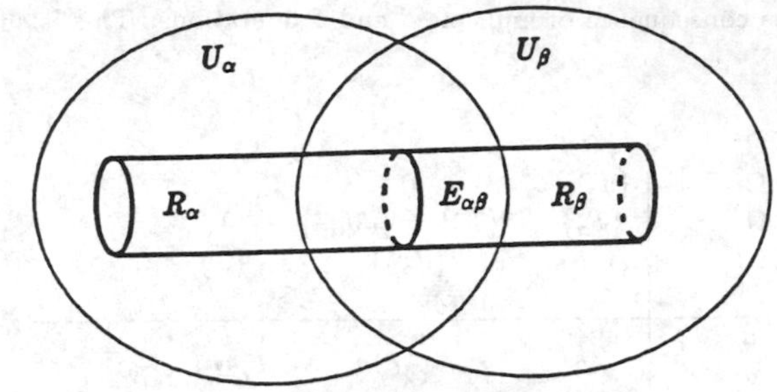

Figure 4: The evolution of a manifold with its spatial topology being a circle. The world sheet lies in two distinct patches. It is subdivided into regions R_α and R_β with the edge being $E_{\alpha\beta}$.

Just as in the electromagnetic case, the Lagrangian and its gauge transformation law determines a closed global differential form and a locally constant cocycle. Is there any significance to the K and c cochains in the above? What is the meaning of the global differential form $\mathcal{G}$? To see the meaning of these quantities on has to go back an see what is the analogue of the Wu-Yang prescription in the two dimensional case.

It is possible to generalize the Wu-Yang construction to this situation. For simplicity, let us assume that the image of spacetime $\phi(S)$ lies entirely in the patches U_α and U_β as depicted in Figure 4. By mimicking the Wu-Yang construction one can show that

$$\int_{R_\alpha} T_\alpha - \int_{E_{\alpha\beta}} J_{\alpha\beta} + \int_{R_\beta} T_\beta$$

is independent of where one chooses the boundary $E_{\alpha\beta}$. This prescription is actually incomplete. We will have to do a further modification to reach a satisfactory answer within the domain of classical field theory.

We have to worry about what happens in triple overlaps. The situation is depicted in Figure 5. One has to see whether the introduction of the triple overlap introduces some $E_{\alpha\beta}$ dependence and a modification of the above is required. The modification is obtained by applying the ideas of Wu and Yang one more time. By using the conditions on the overlaps one can rewrite the previous equation as

$$\int_{R'_\alpha} T_\alpha - \int_{E_{\alpha\gamma}} J_{\alpha\gamma} + \int_{R'_\gamma} T_\gamma - \int_{E_{\gamma\beta}} J_{\gamma\beta} + \int_{R'_\beta} T_\beta$$
$$- \int_{E_{\alpha\beta}} (J_{\alpha\beta} + J_{\beta\gamma} + J_{\gamma\alpha})$$

The form of the above is reminiscent of equation (1). There is an ambiguity in the classical action when one looks at triple overlaps. The above appears to depend on $E_{\alpha\beta}$. Previously we found that the ambiguity was a constant. In the present case we will have to work a little harder.

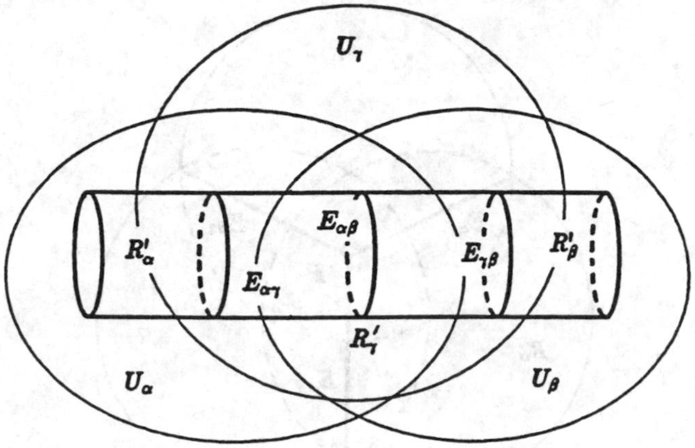

Figure 5: The generalization of Figure 2 to one higher dimension. Note that R_α and R_β have been subdivided into regions R'_α, R'_β and R'_γ. Also note the new edges.

According to the tic-tac-toe box, on the triple overlaps there exist distinct functions $K_{\alpha\beta\gamma}$ such that

$$dK_{\alpha\beta\gamma} = J_{\alpha\beta} + J_{\beta\gamma} + J_{\gamma\alpha}$$

The term involving $E_{\alpha\beta}$ may be rewritten as

$$\int_{E_{\alpha\beta}} dK_{\alpha\beta\gamma} = \int_{\partial E_{\alpha\beta}} K_{\alpha\beta\gamma} = 0$$

This vanishes since $E_{\alpha\beta}$ is boundaryless.

The triple overlaps introduce no ambiguities into the two dimensional field theory. This is unlike the electromagnetic example of Wu and Yang. We will see that a more careful analysis of triple overlaps requires some modifications of the Wu-Yang procedure. We must analyze a new feature of two dimensional field theories which is not present in the one dimensional example. A suitable modification of the Wu-Yang procedure will lead to conditions on quadruple overlaps.

The new feature of the two dimensional field theory is the existence of Y junctions when one subdivides the image of S, see Figure 6. The Wu-Yang prescription can be generalized in a simple manner to incorporate the physics of the Y junctions. The correct way to define

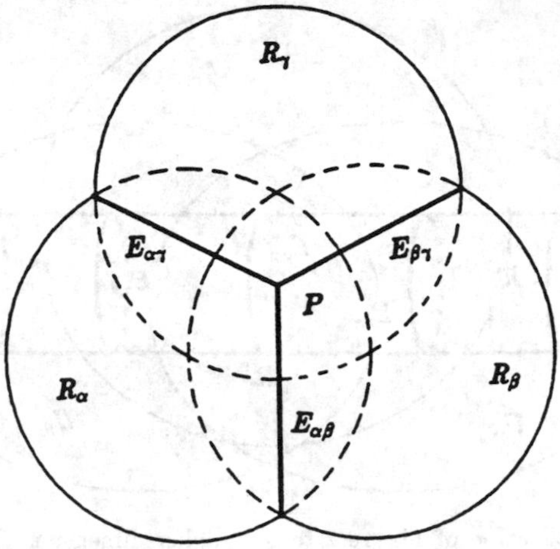

Figure 6: The appearance of Y-junctions when one subdivides a two dimensional integration region into three distinct non-overlapping sets.

the action in the case of Y junctions is

$$\begin{aligned}
&\int_{R_\alpha} T_\alpha - \int_{E_{\alpha\beta}} J_{\alpha\beta} \\
&+ \int_{R_\beta} T_\beta - \int_{E_{\beta\gamma}} J_{\beta\gamma} \\
&+ \int_{R_\gamma} T_\gamma - \int_{E_{\gamma\alpha}} J_{\gamma\alpha} \\
&- K_{\alpha\beta\gamma}(P)
\end{aligned}$$

We have used the notation of Figure 6. One can verify that a small movement of the Y junction leaves the value of the action invariant. This is the modification of the Wu-Yang prescription that is required.

Let us now see what happens when one introduces a fourth patch, U_δ, as in Figure 7 . The above may be rewritten as

$$\begin{aligned}
&\int_{R'_\alpha} T_\alpha + \int_{R'_\beta} T_\beta + \int_{R'_\gamma} T_\gamma + \int_{R'_\delta} T_\delta \\
&- \int_{E_{\alpha\delta}} J_{\alpha\delta} - \int_{E_{\beta\delta}} J_{\beta\delta} - \int_{E_{\gamma\delta}} J_{\gamma\delta} \\
&- K_{\alpha\delta\gamma}(Q_1) - K_{\alpha\beta\delta}(Q_2) - K_{\beta\gamma\delta}(Q_3) \\
&- \Big(K_{\alpha\beta\gamma}(P) + K_{\beta\gamma\delta}(P) + K_{\gamma\delta\alpha}(P) + K_{\delta\alpha\beta}(P)\Big)
\end{aligned}$$

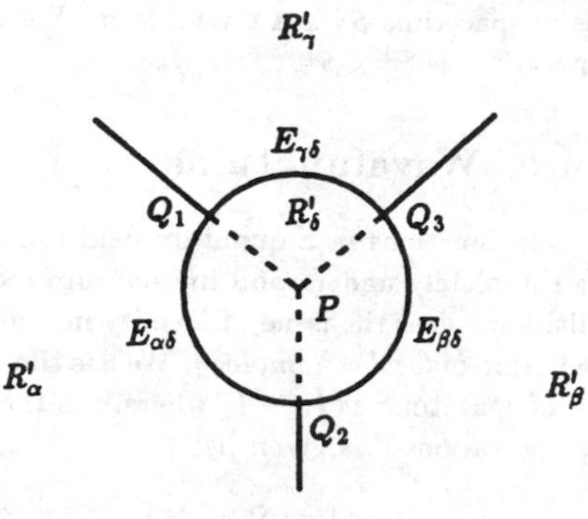

Figure 7: Introduction of a fourth coordinate patch into Figure 6. The R regions have been subdivided into R' regions.

The last line is a constant (independent of P) since $d\delta\{K\} = 0$. We learn that just as in the electromagnetic case the classical action is defined up to an additive constant. A path integral quantization immediately tell us that a consistent quantum theory is only possible if

$$K_{\alpha\beta\gamma}(P) + K_{\beta\gamma\delta}(P) + K_{\gamma\delta\alpha}(P) + K_{\delta\alpha\beta}(P) = 2\pi n_{\alpha\beta\gamma\delta}$$

where the n's are integers. Conditions have to be imposed on quadruple overlaps. Namely, one has to be able to choose a collection of integers $n_{\alpha\beta\gamma\delta}$ on any good cover of the manifold. The three cocycle $\{n_{\alpha\beta\gamma}\}$ is a representative of the third Cech cohomology class of the configurations space: $H^3_C(M, \mathbf{Z})$.

Finally, we mention that there is an analogue of the magnetic field in this problem given by the closed global three form $\mathcal{G}$. This three form is a representative of the third DeRham cohomology class of the manifold. If one calculates the 'flux' by integrating $\mathcal{G}$ over a boundaryless three dimensional region then one discovers that the total flux is given by the sum of $2\pi n_{\alpha\beta\gamma\delta}$ over the patches that intersect the region of interest.

These ideas generalize to higher dimensional field theories. If the dimension of spacetime is d then the *possibility* of a topological Lagrangian with a quantized coupling is determined by whether or not the $(d+1)$ DeRham cohomology class is non-trivial. Remember that there is an isomorphism between the DeRham classes and the Cech classes. It is true that if the $(d+1)$ DeRham cohomology class vanishes then there is no topological quantization. The precise requirements for topological quantization of the Lagrangian require a case by case study. For example, if spacetime is the two sphere S^2 and if the configuration space $M = S^1 \times S^1 \times S^1$ then there is no quantization condition. The reason is subtle.[5] The cohomology of M is the product of the cohomology of the respective circles. Therefore the third cohomology class of M is the product of the one class for each circle. The pullback of

[5]I would like to thank P. Ginsparg and E. Witten for discussions on this point.

each of these one classes to spacetime S^2 is a trivial form. For example, one would reach a different conclusion if spacetime is $S^1 \times S^1$.

4 Classification of Wavefunctions

The classification of wavefunctions in a quantum field theory is not a well understood subject. The problem is completely understood in quantum mechanics. I believe that one of the underlying difficulties involves the issue of locality in a quantum field theory. This is intimately related to the notion of *local cohomology*. We use the standard physics convention of writing the dimension of spacetime as $(n+1)$ where n is the spatial dimensionality.

The space of field configurations $\mathcal{C}$ is given by:

$$\mathcal{C} = \{\varphi : \Sigma \to M\} ,$$

where Σ is the spatial manifold and M is the space where the fields reside, i.e., the target space for the map. In the case of quantum mechanics, a $(0+1)$ dimensional field theory, the space of field configurations is the same as M, the space where the fields reside. Naively, a Schrödinger wavefunction Ψ is a map that assigns to each element $\varphi(\mathbf{x})$ in $\mathcal{C}$ a complex number $\Psi[\varphi(\mathbf{x})]$. More precisely, a wavefunction is a local section of a line bundle over the field configurations $\mathcal{C}$. Since quantum mechanics requires a Hilbert space type of structure, the structure group of the line bundle reduces to $U(1)$. There is a theorem [10] that states that over a sufficiently nice space the line bundles are classified by $H^2_C(\mathcal{C}, \mathbf{Z})$. This may be seen by the following simple argument. Let $\{U_\alpha\}$ be a cover for $\mathcal{C}$. Let $\{\exp(i\xi_{\alpha\beta})\}$ be the transitions functions[6] that define the bundle:

$$\Psi_\alpha = \exp(i\xi_{\alpha\beta})\, \Psi_\beta ,$$

where Ψ_α and Ψ_β are local coordinates on the bundle over the corresponding coordinate patches. Consider what happens as one changes coordinates from patches U_α to U_β to U_γ and back to U_α:

$$\begin{aligned} \Psi_\alpha &= \exp(i\xi_{\alpha\beta})\, \Psi_\beta \\ &= \exp(i\xi_{\alpha\beta})\, \exp(i\xi_{\beta\gamma})\, \Psi_\gamma \\ &= \exp(i\xi_{\alpha\beta})\, \exp(i\xi_{\beta\gamma})\, \exp(i\xi_{\gamma\alpha})\, \Psi_\alpha . \end{aligned}$$

One immediately concludes that

$$\xi_{\alpha\beta} + \xi_{\beta\gamma} + \xi_{\gamma\alpha} = 2\pi n_{\alpha\beta\gamma} ,$$

where the n's are integers. In fact, the $\{n_{\alpha\beta\gamma}\}$ define a two cocycle. In conclusion[7] the transition functions for the line bundle lead to a representative in the second Cech cohomology class $H^2_C(\mathcal{C}, \mathbf{Z})$. If one puts a connection $\mathcal{A}$ on a line bundle over $\mathcal{C}$ then the associated magnetic field $\mathcal{B} = d\mathcal{A}$ when integrated over a two cycle will have a quantized flux which is related to collection of integers in the Cech two cocycle.[8]

[6] I will refer to both ξ and its exponential $\exp(i\xi)$ as the transition function.

[7] This is valid only if the space $\mathcal{C}$ is sufficiently nice.

[8] Mathematically, the above may be sound but it might not necessarily have anything to do with physics.

For example, in the $(0+1)$ dimensional case, the space $\mathcal{C}$ is the same as the target space M. Line bundles in quantum mechanics are characterized by $H^2_{\mathcal{C}}(M,\mathbf{Z})$. The associated integral Cech cocyles represent the quantization of ordinary magnetic flux.

The situation becomes much more interesting in the true field theory case. Note that the transition functions $\exp(i\xi_{\alpha\beta})$ are completely arbitrary. They can be non-local functionals of the fields. From a physical standpoint, this seems to be too strong a requirement. For example, reasonable local changes of variables do not affect the S–matrix but nothing is guaranteed by a non-local change of variables. It is not clear to me whether such non-local transition functions are allowed by nature. This means that $H^2_{\mathcal{C}}(\mathcal{C},\mathbf{Z})$ might not be the relevant object in the classification of the physical wavefunctions [3].

The notion of locality in cohomology theory has arisen in several different ways. There appear to be ways to define *local cohomology* rigorously [13]. We will not worry about these technical details but just discuss the main ideas. Consider an abelian gauge theory in $(3+1)$ dimensions with a left handed Weyl fermion. This theory has the standard chiral anomaly. Since $\pi_5(U(1))=0$, there is no topological obstruction to defining the fermion determinant. There is a physical obstruction that is imposed by locality. Namely, the anomaly cannot be eliminated by the addition of local counter terms to the Lagrangian. A non-local counter term can be used to eliminate the abelian anomaly.

Similar ideas enter in the discussion of the classification of wavefunctions. The relevant object for the classification problem is probably not $H^2_{\mathcal{C}}(\mathcal{C},\mathbf{Z})$ but a "local" version of the second cohomology group. I conjecture that in the type of theories discussed in this paper, the relevant local cohomology is closely related to $H^{n+2}_{\mathcal{C}}(M,\mathbf{Z})$ where n is the spatial dimensionality. My argument is based on an analysis of the gauge transformation properties of the path integral. The path integral is a representation of the time evolution operator $\exp(-itH)$ where H is the Hamiltonian. For simplicity, I will discuss a $(1+1)$ dimensional theory of the type discussed in Section 3. One begins with the initial wave function and one evolves it forward in time by using the path integral to compute the evolution kernel. The discussion of Section 3 explains how to write the the action in such a way that things are well defined. Consider a history where one begins in patch U_β with a wave function Ψ_β. At time t_1 one goes to a patch U_α with wave function Ψ_α, analogous to the situation depicted in Figure 8. The discussion of Section 3 may be interpreted as saying that at time t_1 we are required to make a gauge transformation given by

$$\Psi_\alpha = \exp\left(-i\int_{E_{\alpha\beta}} J_{\alpha\beta}\right)\Psi_\beta\,,$$

where $E_{\alpha\beta}$ is a constant time surface. This situation is is very similar to the quantum mechanical example of Section 2. The only difference has to do with the transition function. In the quantum mechanics case the transition function $\psi_{\alpha\beta}$ was a function of t and $\mathbf{x}$ only. In this case the transition function $\xi_{\alpha\beta}$ is a local functional:

$$\int_{E_{\alpha\beta}} J_{\alpha\beta}\,.$$

This suggests that one has a line bundle over $\mathcal{C}$ with local transition functions. The situation becomes more interesting when one looks at the Y junction case depicted in Figure 9. In

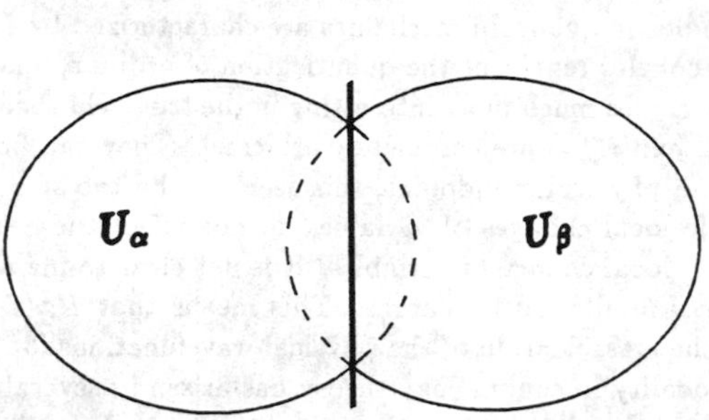

Figure 8: A gauge transformation from one patch to a second patch at time t_1. The solid line denotes an equal time surface.

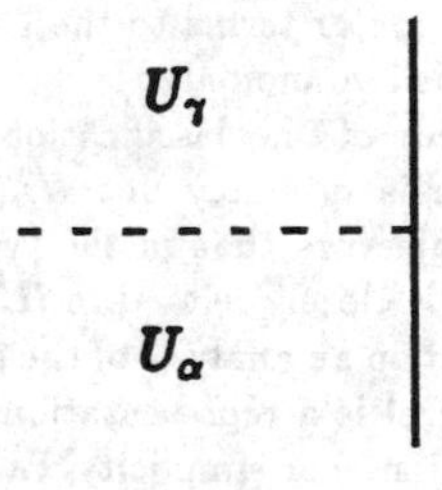

Figure 9: Going from a single patch to a double patch at time t_1. The equal time surface is the solid line. The two "future" patches are separated by the dashed line.

this case the correct transition function at time t_1 is given by:

$$\Psi_{\alpha+\beta} = \exp\left(-i\int_{E_{\alpha\beta}} J_{\alpha\beta}\right) \exp\left(-iK_{\alpha\beta\gamma}(P)\right) \exp\left(-i\int_{E_{\beta\gamma}} J_{\beta\gamma}\right) \Psi_\beta ,$$

where $\Psi_{\alpha+\beta}$ reflects the fact that the wavefunction for $t > t_1$ has to be specified in two coordinate patches. Note that the above is local. If one now looks at sequential changes of patches one discovers the constraint on the third cohomology class of M.

The following interesting question arises. One is constructing a line bundle over C using local transition functions. What is a connection on this line bundle? My guess is that the answer is related to the recent work of Wu and Zee [14]. These authors point out that there is some type of abelian structure in certain intrinsically non-abelian problems.

References

[1] P.A.M. Dirac, "Quantized Singularities in the Electromagnetic Field", *Proc. Royal Soc. London*, A133, 60(1931).

[2] O. Alvarez, "Topological Quantization and Cohomology", Berkeley preprint, to appear in *Commun. Math. Phys.*.

[3] O. Alvarez, unpublished.

[4] S. Deser, R. Jackiw and S. Templeton, "Topologically Massive Gauge Theories", *Ann. Phys.* 140, 372(1982).

[5] S. Deser, R. Jackiw and S. Templeton, "Three Dimensional Massive Gauge Theories", *Phys. Rev. Lett.* 48, 975(1982); J. Schoenfeld, "A Mass Term for Three Dimensional Gauge Fields", *Nucl. Phys.* B185, 157(1981); W. Siegel, "Unextended Superfields in Extended Supersymmetry", *Nucl. Phys.* B156, 135(1979).

[6] E. Witten, "Global Aspects of Current Algebra", *Nucl. Phys*: B223, 422(1983).

[7] J. Wess and B. Zumino, "Consequences of Anomalous Ward Identities", *Phys. Lett.* 37B, 95(1971).

[8] T.T. Wu and C.N. Yang, "Dirac's Monopole without Strings: Classical Lagrangian Theory", *Phys. Rev.* D14, 437(1976).

[9] R.P. Feynman and A.R. Hibbs, *Quantum Mechanics and Path Integrals*, McGraw-Hill, New York, 1965.

[10] R. Bott and L. Tu, *Differential Forms in Algebraic Topology*, Springer-Verlag, New York, 1982.

[11] I.M. Singer and J. Thorpe, *Lecture Notes on Elementary Topology and Geometry*, Springer-Verlag, New York, 1967.

[12] C. Misner, K. Thorne and J.A. Wheeler, *Gravitation*, Freeman, San Francisco, 1970.

[13] L. Bonora and P. Cotta-Ramusino, "Some Remarks on BRS Transformation Anomalies and the Cohomology of the Lie Algebra of the Group of Gauge Transfomations", *Commun. Math. Phys* 87, 589(1983).

[14] Y-S Wu and A. Zee, "Abelian Gauge Structure Inside Non-abelian Gauge Theories", Univesity of Washington preprint 40048-38 P4.

Topological Aspects of Anomalies

Michael Atiyah,
Mathematical Institute, Oxford, England.

1. Introduction

It is quite remarkable that much of the pure mathematics with which I and my colleagues have been involved over the past twenty years has become relevant to present ideas in theoretical physics. I refer, on the mathematical side, to the index theory of elliptic differential operators and the associated parts of topological and differential geometry. In physics these relate to gauge theories of elementary particles (and gravity).

Mathematicians have a natural inclination to generality, pursuing ideas and techniques to their logical conclusion, whereas physicists are constrained by the uniqueness of the physical world. For these reasons it was not surprising that, in the initial stages of the present mathematics/physics interchange, the main difference appeared to be that mathematicians worked with an arbitrary number of dimensions, whereas physicists (with their feet on the ground) stuck to the four dimensions of space-time. But times change and the fashionable dimensions in physics are 10 or 26, whereas mathematicians have discovered surprisingly unique features of 4 dimensions! Moreover, with increasing sophistication, physicists have found uses for all the abstruse generalizations which we mathematicians conceived.

As an introduction to the more detailed and technical talks which will follow, and as illustration of some of the basic ideas involved, I will discuss in elementary terms the simplest relations between topology and the analysis of Dirac operators. This should give the flavour of the subject.

§2. Spectral Flow

In classical applied mathematics and also in the quantum theory of a bosonic particle, Laplace type operators (in 3-space) play a fundamental role. Their essential property is that their Energy levels are positive, or at least bounded below. Thus the spectrum is contained in a half-line.

By contrast, for fermions, we have to deal with Dirac type operators which, as Dirac found, have both positive and negative Energy levels. Thus the spectrum lies on the whole real line, being unbounded in both directions.

The origin of the topological effects associated with fermions lies precisely in the topological difference between the half-line and the whole line. The first case is topologically uninteresting since we can "push the half-line to ∞", whereas in the second case this is not possible since we have $\pm\infty$. Think of pieces of string tied down at $\pm\infty$ and the distinction is clear. Essentially a string with two infinite ends behaves topologically like a circle.

To illustrate these topological effects consider a periodic 1-parameter family of Dirac type operators D_t. For each value of the parameter t the Energy levels $E_n(t)$ (which we assume discrete, by taking space compact) lie on the real axis and are functions of t. As t moves over the period (say $0 \leq t \leq 1$) the energy levels move but, at the end of the period, they must reproduce the original set. However, we need not have $E_n(1) = E_n(0)$: instead we might well have $E_n(1) = E_{n+k}(0)$ for some integer k. This integer represents a shift in the spectrum, as t varies over its period, and it can be viewed as the number of negative Energy levels that have crossed over and become positive. It is called the spectral flow of the family (and was first introduced by G. Lusztig and myself). It is not hard to see that it is a topological invariant of the family D_t: in other words, if we deform D_t continuously into another periodic family D'_t of the same type then D_t and D'_t will have the same spectral flow. Note moreover that, if the Energy levels were bounded below, then we could start enumerating them from the bottom up and the spectral flow would have to be zero. This shows why the spectral flow only turns up for fermions.

As a simple example, take space to have dimension 1 (i.e. a circle) and take

$$(2.1) \quad D_t = -i \frac{d}{dx} + t, \quad x \bmod 2\pi, \quad 0 \leq t \leq 1.$$

The energy levels are clearly given by $E_n(t) = n + t$, so that the spectral flow $k = 1$. Note that the family D_t is periodic in the sense that D_1 and D_0 are gauge-equivalent:

$D_1 = e^{-ix} D_0 e^{ix}$. More generally, for the family D_{kt} (with k an integer) the spectral flow is k and periodicity is given by gauge-transforming with e^{ikx}. This shows that the spectral flow is related to the integer (winding number) describing the components of the group of $U(1)$ gauge transformations on the circle.

In gauge-theories one frequently shifts from the Hamiltonian approach in d-space dimensions to a Euclidean functional-integral approach in $(d+1)$ dimensions. Any basic topological feature of a gauge-theory should persist and be visible, in each approach, in a suitable guise. Let us illustrate this by continuing with our simple example above where $d = 1$. Instead of considering t as a parameter we now interpret it as Euclidean time and introduce the operator $\mathcal{D}$ in (x,t) space given by:

(2.2) $$\mathcal{D} = \frac{\partial}{\partial t} + D_t = \frac{\partial}{\partial t} - i\frac{\partial}{\partial x} + t.$$

This is essentially half the Dirac operator in 2 dimensions (the other half $\mathcal{D}^*$ being the complex conjugate). We consider $\mathcal{D}$ as acting on functions $f(x,t)$ which are periodic in x with period 2π and satisfy

(2.3) $$f(x,t+1) = e^{-ix} f(x,t),$$

i.e. they are periodic in t (with period 1) up to the appropriate gauge transformation. It is then easy to see that the theta-function

(2.4) $$f(x,t) = \sum_n \exp\left(-\frac{(n+t)^2}{2} + inx\right)$$

is (up to a scalar multiple) the <u>unique</u> solution of $\mathscr{D} f = 0$, while $\mathscr{D}^* f = 0$ has no solution (formally we get exponentially growing Fourier coefficients). Thus the <u>index</u> of $\mathscr{D}$, defined as the difference between the number of independent solutions of these two equations, is equal to 1.

The functions $f(x,t)$ satisfying (2.3) (and periodic in x) are sections of a non-trivial complex line-bundle over a 2-dimensional torus. Physically we would say that we are in a gauge sector with non-trivial <u>instanton</u> number, and this (as we have just seen) is related to non-trivial zero modes of the total Dirac operator $\mathscr{D} \oplus \mathscr{D}^*$.

Of course in this 2-dimensional example we have <u>abelian</u> instantons and all the topology arises ultimately from that of the circle. Nevertheless, the general picture as I have presented it, extends naturally to higher dimensions (space-time dimensions and group dimensions being increased simultaneously).

§3. Spaces of Fredholm operators

In §2 I illustrated, with some examples, some topological aspects of Dirac operators. To understand these aspects more thoroughly it is helpful to introduce suitable spaces of abstract operators in Hilbert space. Although differential operators are <u>unbounded</u> we can replace D by $D(1+D^*D)^{-\frac{1}{2}}$ to get <u>bounded</u> operators. Moreover, we are only interested in bounded operators A in Hilbert space for which the equations $Au = 0$ and $A^*v = 0$ have a <u>finite</u> number of independent solutions.

Such operators are called Fredholm operators and the set $\mathfrak{F}$ of all Fredholm operators on Hilbert space has a natural topology (given by the operator norm). Inside $\mathfrak{F}$ we can also consider the subspace $\mathfrak{F}^1$ consisting of self-adjoint Fredholm operators.

The Dirac operator in odd-dimensional (compact) space gives (when rescaled) an operator in $\mathfrak{F}^1$, while half the Dirac operator in even-dimensions gives an operator in $\mathfrak{F}$.

An operator in $\mathfrak{F}$ has an integer index and it is not hard to show that this integer labels the different connected components of $\mathfrak{F}$, or more formally

(3.1) $\pi_0(\mathfrak{F}) \cong Z$.

The space $\mathfrak{F}^1$ has two contractible components $\mathfrak{F}^1_+$, $\mathfrak{F}^1_-$ where $\mathfrak{F}^1_+$ consists of operators which are essentially positive (i.e. whose spectrum on the negative axis consists of only finitely many eigenvalues) while $\mathfrak{F}^1_-$ consists of those which are essentially negative. The rest of $\mathfrak{F}^1$ consists of a component $\mathfrak{F}^1_*$ which is not contractible. Moreover the spectral flow of any periodic 1-parameter family gives an integer which labels the fundamental group, i.e.

(3.2) $\pi_1(\mathfrak{F}^1_*) \cong Z$.

If we consider p-parameter families of Dirac operators then we will naturally encounter topological invariants associated to $\pi_p(\mathfrak{F})$ or $\pi_p(\mathfrak{F}^1_*)$ depending on the parity of the space-dimension. In general higher dimensional homotopy groups of topological spaces are very difficult to compute, so it is remarkable that we have [2]

$$(3.3)\qquad \pi_p(\mathfrak{F}) \cong Z,\quad \pi_p(\mathfrak{F}^1_*) \cong 0 \qquad p \text{ even}$$

$$\pi_p(\mathfrak{F}) \cong 0,\quad \pi_p(\mathfrak{F}^1_*) \cong Z \qquad p \text{ odd}$$

giving a complete generalization of the cases $p = 0,\ 1$ represented by (3.1) and (3.2).

Now there is a well-known space in topology whose homotopy groups behave as in (3.3). This is the large N-limit U of the unitary groups $U(N)$:

$$U = \lim_{N\to\infty} U(N),$$

where the limit is taken with respect to the standard inclusions $U(N) \to U(N+1)$. According to the famous periodicity theorem of Bott [3]:

$$(3.4)\qquad \pi_p(U) \cong Z \qquad p \text{ odd}$$

$$\cong 0 \qquad p \text{ even.}$$

Note that these are statements about $\pi_p(U(N))$ for N large compared to p, in fact

$$(3.5)\qquad \pi_p(U) \cong \pi_p(U(N)) \qquad \text{for} \quad N > p/2.$$

In fact these are consequences of the homotopy equivalence

$$(3.6)\qquad U \sim \Omega^2(U)$$

where, for any space X, $\Omega(X)$ is the space of closed loops on X (with fixed base point).

The results in (3.3) are then consequences of (3.4) and the homotopy equivalences:

(3.7) $\mathfrak{F}^1_* \sim U, \quad \mathfrak{F} \sim \Omega(U).$

Note that (3.6) then implies the equivalences:

(3.8) $\mathfrak{F}^1_* \sim \Omega^2(\mathfrak{F}^1_*), \quad \mathfrak{F} \sim \Omega^2(\mathfrak{F}).$

The 2-fold periodicity expressed by (3.8) lies behind the repetitive pattern in the topological behaviour of Dirac operators as we increase dimensions by 2.

Remark. The inclusion $\mathfrak{F}^1_* \to \mathfrak{F}$ must, by (3.3), induce the 0-map in homotopy and this suggests that $\mathfrak{F}^1_*$ is actually contractible to a point inside $\mathfrak{F}$. Such a contraction is easily constructed by using the linear path connecting A in $\mathfrak{F}^1_*$ to iI (where I is the identity operator). The situation is quite analogous to the inclusion of an equatorial n-sphere in the (n+1)-sphere.

§4. Relation to Anomalies

In §2 I showed how the same topological invariant could arise in different guises, associated in one case to a 1-parameter family of Dirac operators on the circle and in the second to a single Dirac operator on a 2-dimensional torus. In §3 I outlined the general story on topological invariants of such operators (in abstract form). This leads in turn to a systematic generalization to higher-dimensions of the phenomena of §2.

The details differ a little, depending on the parity of the relevant dimensions, but the general idea is always the same. To a p-parameter family of Dirac operators D_t $(t = (t_1,\ldots,t_p))$ on x-space $(x = (x_1,\ldots,x_d))$ one associates the single Dirac operator in $(d+p)$-dimensions

$$\mathcal{D} = D_t + \sum_{j=1}^{p} \gamma_j \frac{\partial}{\partial t_j}$$

where the γ_j are the appropriate matrices, satisfying the usual identities $\gamma_j^2 = -1$, $\gamma_j\gamma_k = -\gamma_k\gamma_j$.

As a concrete illustration take $p = 2$ and $d = 4$ (Euclidean space-time). In 6-dimensions the (half) Dirac operator has an <u>index</u>, associated to an instanton-number and this is essentially the same topological invariant as that which occurs for the 2-parameter family of (half) Dirac operators on S^4. If for simplicity we assume that the (4 dimensional) index of these Dirac operators is zero, then generically the Dirac operator D_t in our family will be invertible except for a finite number of values of t. This finite number (counted with appropriate signs and multiplicities) is the topological invariant of our family. If it is non-zero then the family cannot be deformed to one that is everywhere invertible. This is essentially the <u>anomaly</u> which prevents us defining a guage-invariant complex determinant of the Dirac operator on S^4 (in a background gauge potential). The 2 parameters involved are those of a suitable 2-parameter family of gauge-potentials (see [1] for a more detailed discussion).

If we shift from the Euclidean to the Hamiltonian view-point then we can replace the family above by a 3-parameter family of Dirac operators on S^3, where the third parameter is now time. Since $\pi_3(\mathfrak{F}^1_*) \cong Z$ we again have a topogical invariant. This can be identified with the obstruction to defining the fermionic Fock space in a gauge-invariant manner (only the projectivized Fock space can be so defined). For further details on this interpretation see [4].

So far I have concentrated on the case when we have an integer topological invariant, but there are also physically interesting cases when we have an invariant taking only finitely many values, for example 0 or 1 (mod 2). Such examples arise naturally from reality conditions and the topological theory outlined in §3 extends to the real case, except that the Bott periodicity theorems now involve the dimension modulo 8. Thus the homotopy groups of the "infinite" <u>orthogonal</u> group

$$0 = \lim_{N\to\infty} 0(N)$$

are given by [3]

$p \equiv$	0	1	2	3	4	5	6	7	(mod 8)
$\pi_p(0) =$	Z_2	Z_2	0	Z	0	0	0	Z	

where Z_2 denotes the integers mod 2. Moreover letting $\mathfrak{F}^1(R)$ denote the space of <u>skew-adjoint</u> Fredholm operators on a <u>real</u> Hilbert space, one has a homotopy equivalence

$$\mathfrak{F}^1(R) \sim 0.$$

For example a real skew-adjoint Fredholm operator has a number of zero modes whose parity is a well-defined topological invariant (because other eigenvalues which might degenerate to zero come in complex conjugate pairs). This represents the generator of the group

$$\pi_0(\mathfrak{F}^1(R)) \cong \pi_0(0) \cong Z_2.$$

Mod 2 anomalies associated with such considerations have been studied by Witten [5]. Moreover in this symposium Witten will be reporting on other "global" anomalies, i.e. ones which are essentially discrete and cannot be recovered by infinitesimal (curvature) methods.

REFERENCES

1. M.F. Atiyah, Anomalies and index theory. In Lecture Notes in Physics, vol. 208, Springer-Verlag (1984), 313-322.
2. M.F. Atiyah and I.M. Singer, Index theory for skew-adjoint Fredholm operators, Publ. Math. Institut des Hautes Etudes Sci. 27 (1969), 305-326.
3. R. Bott, The stable homotopy of the classical groups, Ann. of Math. 70 (1959),313-337.
4. G.B. Segal, Faddeev's Anomaly and Gauss's Law, preprint,Oxford.
5. E. Witten, Phys. Lett. 117B (1982), 324.

BLACK HOLES AND QUANTUM MECHANICS

G. 't HOOFT
Institute for Theoretical Physics, University of Utrecht, P.O. Box 80.006, 3508 TA Utrecht, The Netherlands.

ABSTRACT
The equivalence principle in general relativity may have a non-standard form when quantum effects are considered. A theory that may produce the complete spectrum of black holes is outlined.

1. INTRODUCTION

Many attempts are being made to formulate the laws of physics at the Planck length scale. Canonical quantization procedures when applied to Einstein's Lagrangian, reveal fundamental and seemingly uncontrollable space-time fluctuations at distance scales less than the Planck length[1]. It was natural that investigators turned their attention to sophisticated models of gravitation and matter in which the infinities in these fluctuations might cancel out such as "supergravity"[2], "string"[3] and now also "superstring"[4] theories. As yet these theories seem to give relatively little insight into the structure of space-time itself at the Planck length scale.

Gravitating systems are fundamentally unstable against collapse. Classically this is not a great problem: only for very large systems the gravitational force is stronger than the counter forces produced by matter . But in a quantum theory, with huge oscillations near the Planck length the possibility of gravitational collapse cannot be ignored. What we propose is that a healthy theory should not only take into account collapsed chunks of matter but must more likely contain them as essential ingredients. Perhaps all particles can in some sense be viewed as smaller or larger black holes.

Unavoidably our theory must exhibit a "smallest possible length scale"[5]: the smallest possible structure is a particle whose Schwarzschild radius coincides with its Compton wave length. We now notice a situation that reminds one of the familiar "bootstrap" idea; all particles much lighter than the Planck mass are likely to be described reasonably by some Lagrange field theory. All particles much heavier than the Planck mass are black holes with fairly large radii. Their behavior also should follow from field equations - the same Lagrange field theory - with these larger length scales. It is this form of "duality" that interests us: it gives us the impression that quantum gravity should be a completely understandable, finite problem.

But how do the quantum properties of black holes follow from Lagrange field theory? One comfortable result was derived by Hawking[6]: due to vacuum fluctuations near the horizon all heavy black holes must emit particles spontaneously, with a thermal spectrum corresponding to a temperature $T = 1/8\pi M$, where M is the mass of the black hole in natural units. Apparently like most other fundamental particles, black holes are unstable and decay into lighter objects.

This result is extremely powerful since it suggests that no additive conservation law can be exact, with the exception of electric charge conservation, because no chemical potential barring particles such as baryons and leptons from entering a black hole can be accepted, whereas on the other hand the numbers of such particles that a black hole can produce in its decay are limited. Now unfortunately the obtained expressions only produce emission probabilities, not the quantum mechanical amplitudes. The quantum states are represented by density matrices. So it seems that the information produced by this argument is only statistical in nature. Suppose we had a precisely defined Lagrange field theory. Could we then not do better than this?

If the black hole were an ordinary soliton the answer would have been "yes". We would have been able to do calculations such as the ones by Rubakov and Callan[7] on magnetic monopoles. But black holes are not ordinary solitons and some fundamental and tantalizing difficulties prevent us from applying conventional laws of qauntum mechanics.

Hawking had derived his result by relying heavily on the equivalence principle of general relativity: states in Hilbert space were assumed to be well defined in any coordinate system and their inner products were all assumed to be coordinate independent. The difficulty is then that "states" seem to disappear into the horizon of the black hole and in spite of them being all orthogonal to each other they become fundamentally unobservable. One line of thought, as proposed by Hawking, is that pure quantum mechanics is no longer valid at Planck length scales: pure states may undergo transitions towards mixed quantum-mechanical states: the eigenvalues of the density matrix may no longer be constants of motion. This is an extremely important conclusion because it seems to be practically unavoidable whereas it also seems to imply the breakdown of quantum mechanics as we know it at the Planck scale[8].

But how sure are we of the equivalence principle for states in Hilbert space? Could it not be that a coordinate transformation has more subtle effects on Hilbert space if the corresponding observers from a certain moment on can no longer communicate with each other? What if one observer falls right into the system studied by another observer? What is the probability interpretation of a wave function if an observer has a finite chance to become killed by a spacelike singularity?

Of course what we need foremost is a mathematically unique prescription for obtaining the laws of physics for every imaginable system. This "theory" should as much as possible reproduce all known results of ordinary quantum mechanics on the one hand and general relativity on the other. We will be quite content if this "theory" is first formulated in a coordinate-invariant way and then allows us to construct a Hamiltonian suitable to describe anything seen by any observer. But this construction might be dependent on the observer and in particular his "horizon". It could be that the "probabilities" experienced by one observer are not the same as those of another. All is well if the two "classical limits" are as they should be.

We will now make the assumption that the black hole quantum properties[9] somehow follow from Lagrange quantum field theory at the same length scale. We are very well aware of the risk that this may be wrong. Still, we like to know how far one can get. Regrettably, the results to be reported in this paper will be extremely modest.

We will start by making a simplification that caused some confusion for some readers of my previous publication: we first concentrate on the steady state black hole: every now and then something falls in and something else comes out. Nowhere a distinction is made between "primordial" black holes and black holes that have been formed by collapse. It has been argued that Hawking's derivation in particular holds for collapsed black holes and not necessarily for ones eternally in equilibrium. However, if we succeed to describe infalling things in a satisfactory way then one might expect that inclusion of the entire collapse (and the entire evaporation in the end) can naturally be incorporated at a later stage. Our main concern at present will be time scales of order M logM in Planck units, which is much shorter than the black hole's history. As we will see, understanding in- and outgoing things at this scale will be difficult enough, and indeed Hawking's radiation can very well be understood at this time scale.

2. KRUSKAL COORDINATES. BLACK HOLE AT EQUILIBRIUM

In the absence of matter, the metric of a black hole is

$$ds^2 = -\left(1-\frac{2M}{r}\right)dt^2 + \left(1-\frac{2M}{r}\right)^{-1} dr^2 + r^2 d\Omega^2 . \qquad (2.1)$$

The Kruskal coordinates u, v are defined by

$$uv = \left(1-\frac{r}{2M}\right)e^{r/2M} , \qquad (2.2)$$

$$v/u = -e^{t/2M} , \qquad (2.3)$$

and then we have

$$ds^2 = -\frac{32M^3}{r}\, e^{-r/2M}\, du dv + r^2 d\Omega^2 , \qquad (2.4)$$

which is now entirely regular at $r > o$. However (2.2) and (2.3) admit two solutions at every (r,t): we have two universes connected by a "wormhole". The Schwarzschild region, I, is $v > o$, $u < o$. The other regions are indicated in Fig. 1.

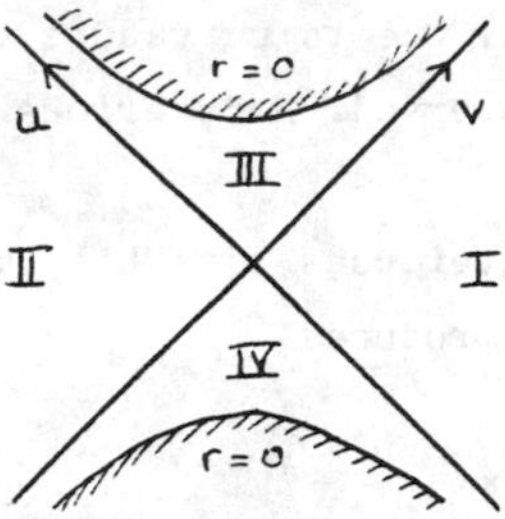

Figure 1

Now the classical picture of a black hole formed by collapse only shows regions I and III, the others being shielded by the imploding matter which accumulates at the past horizon (the u-axis). Similarly, an evaporating black hole (sometimes called a "white hole") only has regions I and IV. In both cases it is convenient to extend analytically the particle content in regions III or IV towards region II, and a black hole in equilibrium is perhaps best described by the entire system I-II-III-IV.

The equivalence theorem should now relate the Hilbert space as needed by an observer in the wormhole ("Kruskal observer") to the one needed to describe the "physical" world I as experienced by an outside observer ("Schwarzschild observer"). Imagine a limited number of soft particles that can be described by the Kruskal observer using standard physics. With "soft" we mean that the energies of these particles are so small that gravitational effects on the metric can be neglected. We have then a reasonable description of an important part of the Hilbert space for the wormhole observer. The evolution of this system is described by a Hamiltonian

$$H = \int \mathcal{H}(\vec{x})d\vec{x} > o, \qquad (2.5)$$

with one ground state

$$H|o\rangle_k = o \qquad (2.6)$$

where k stands for Kruskal. Due to curvature this vacuum is not exactly but only approximately conserved. H describes the evolution in the time coordinate $\tau = u+v$.

Now the outside observer uses t as his time coordinate, and a generator of a boost in t produces

$$\delta v = \frac{v}{2M}\,\delta t, \tag{2.7}$$

$$\delta u = -\frac{u}{2M}\,\delta t, \tag{2.8}$$

so the generator of this boost is

$$h = \frac{1}{2M}\int d\vec{x}\;\rho\mathcal{H}(\vec{x}) \quad ; \quad \rho = v-u. \tag{2.9}$$

We split $h = H_I - H_{II}$:

$$H_I = \frac{1}{2M}\int \rho\mathcal{H}(\vec{x})d\vec{x}\;\Theta(\rho);\; H_{II} = \frac{1}{2M}\int |\rho|\;\mathcal{H}(\vec{x})d\vec{x}\;\Theta(-\rho) \tag{2.10}$$

We have

$$[H_I, H_{II}] = o, \tag{2.11}$$

and we can write the eigenstates of H_I and H_{II} as $|n,m\rangle$ with

$$H_I|n,m\rangle = n|n,m\rangle \quad ; \quad H_{II}|n,m\rangle = m|n,m\rangle. \tag{2.12}$$

Extensive but straightforward calculations show that the "Kruskal vacuum" $|o\rangle_k$ does not coincide with the "Schwarzschild vacuum" $|o,o\rangle$, but instead, we have

$$|o\rangle_k = C\sum_n |n,n\rangle e^{-4\pi Mn}, \tag{2.13}$$

where C is a normalization factor. In these expressions, n is not meant to be an integer but just a shorthand notation for the eigenvalues of the Hamiltonian. Note that we do have

$$h|o\rangle_k = o, \tag{2.14}$$

which is due to Lorentz-invariance of $|o\rangle_k$.

If we consider the equivalence theorem in its usual form and consider all those particles that are trapped into region IV as lost and therefore unobservable then without any doubt the correct prescription for describing the observations of observers in I is to average over the unseen particles. Let $\mathcal{O}$ be an operator built from a field $\phi(\vec{x},t)$ with $\vec{x}$ in region I, then

$$[\mathcal{O},H_{II}] = o \quad , \tag{2.15}$$

$$\mathcal{O}|n,m\rangle = \sum_k \mathcal{O}_{nk}|k,m\rangle \ , \tag{2.16}$$

and

$$\langle\mathcal{O}\rangle = {}_k\langle o|\mathcal{O}|o\rangle_k = C^2 \sum_{n,n'} e^{-4\pi M(n+n')} \langle n',n'|\mathcal{O}|n,n\rangle$$

$$= C^2 \sum_n e^{-8\pi Mn}\mathcal{O}_{nn}. \tag{2.17}$$

We recognize a Boltzmann factor $e^{-\beta n}$ with $\beta = 8\pi M$, corresponding to a temperature

$$T = 1/8\pi M. \tag{2.18}$$

This is Hawking's result in a nutshell. Black holes radiate and the temperature of their thermal radiation is given by (2.18). The only way in which the horizon entered in this calculation is where it acts as a shutter making part of Hilbert space invisible.

As stated in the introduction this result would imply that black holes are profoundly different from elementary particles: they turn pure quantum mechanical states into mixed, thermal, states. Our only hope for a more complete quantum mechanical picture where black holes also show pure transitions, that in principle allow for some effective Hamiltonian is to reformulate the equivalence principle. Let us assume that the location of the horizon has a more profound effect on the interpretation that one should give to a wave function.

A pair of horizons (the u- and the v-axis in Fig. 1.) always separate regions where a boost in t goes in opposite directions with respect to a regular time coordinate such as u+v. As before[10] we speculate that these regions act directly as the spaces of bra states and ket states, respectively. Any "state" as described by a Kruskal observer actually looks like the product of a bra and a ket state to the Schwarzschild observer. More precisely, it looks like an element of his density matrix, ρ:

$$|n,m\rangle \to |n\rangle \langle m| = \rho . \qquad (2.19)$$

Just like any density matrix its evolution is given by the commutator with H_I:

$$\frac{d}{dt}\rho_{nm} = -ih|n,m\rangle = -i(n-m)|n,m\rangle = -i[H_I, |n\rangle \langle m|]$$

$$= -i[H_I, \rho] \qquad (2.20)$$

Now the Kruskal vacuum $|o\rangle_k$ corresponds to the density matrix

$$\rho_{nn'} = C|n\rangle e^{-4\pi Mn} \langle n|\delta_{nn'}, \qquad (2.21)$$

which is a thermal state at temperature

$$T = 1/4\pi M , \qquad (2.22)$$

twice the usual result. The usual result would require not ρ from eq. (2.19) but $\rho\rho^\dagger$ to be the density matrix, from which of course (2.18) follows.

As long as we consider stationary black holes with only soft particles our mapping (2.19) is perfectly acceptable. The Hamiltonian (2.5) may ad libitum be extended to include any kind of interactions including those of curious observers. In the two classical limits we reproduce quantum mechanics and general relativity as required.

The only possible way to settle the question which of the procedures is correct and which of the temperatures (2.18) or (2.22) describe a black hole's radiation spectrum, is to include the effects of "hard" particles. This is also a necessary requirement for understanding the effects of implosion and explosion of black holes. Hard particles are particles whose rest masses may be small, but whose energies are so large that their gravitational effects may not be ignored.

3. HARD PARTICLES

The black holes considered in the previous section were only exactly time-translation-invariant if they were covered by a Kruskal vacuum $|o\rangle_k$ .This is because translations in t correspond to Lorentz-transformations at the origin of the Kruskal coordinate frame and only a vacuum can be Lorentz-invariant. Naturally, $|o\rangle_k$ corresponds to a Schwarzschild density matrix ρwhich is diagonal in the energy-representation.

Any other state will undergo boosts in t as if the Kruskal observer continuously applies Lorentz-transformations to his state, and eventually any "soft" particle will turn into a hard particle. This is why hard particles, particles with enormously large Lorentz γ factors are unavoidable if we want to understand how a system evolves over time scales only slightly larger than (MlogM). Hard particles alter their surrounding space-time metric. Some basic features of their effects on space-time are well-known.

A hard particle in Minkowski space produces a gravitational shock wave[11], sometimes called "impulsive wave", not unlike Cerenkov radiation. Before and behind this shock wave space-time is flat, but the way in which these flat regions are connected at the location of the shock wave produces delta-distributed curvature. Writing

$$u = t-z$$
$$v = t+z \qquad (3.1)$$

we find that a particle moving in the positive z direction with momentum p, at $\tilde{y} = o$, produces a shock wave on the v axis where the two half-spaces are connected after a shift

$$\delta v = -4p\, \ell n(\tilde{y}^2) . \qquad (3.2)$$

Here $\tilde{y}$ is the transverse coordinate. See Fig. 2.

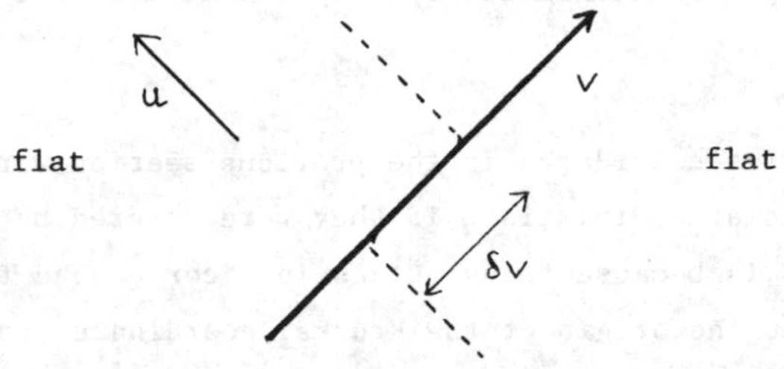

Figure 2

A way to picture this is to choose $g_{\mu\nu} = \eta_{\mu\nu}$ everywhere except at u=o, where all geodesics make a jump δv from past to future.

For us it is interesting to consider now a hard particle on one of the black hole's horizons. It was found that[11] again a displacement of a form similar to (3.2) solves Einstein's equations. In Kruskal's coordinates u,v a hard particle with momentum p again produces a shift δv, with

$$\delta v(\tilde{\Omega}) = pf(\tilde{\Omega},\tilde{\Omega}') , \qquad (3.3)$$

where Ω' is the angle where the particle goes through the horizon and p its momentum. f is given by

$$\Delta f - f = -2\pi\kappa\, \delta(\Theta) , \qquad (3.4)$$

where Θ is the angle between Ω and Ω', Δ the angular Laplacian and κ a dimensionless numerical constant. The solution to (3.4),

$$f = \kappa \sum_{\ell} \frac{\ell+\frac{1}{2}}{\ell(\ell+1)+1} P_{\ell}(\cos\Theta) \ , \qquad (3.5)$$

can be seen to be positive for all Θ .

Because of the shift, the causal structure of space-time is slightly changed. The Penrose diagram for a hard particle coming in along the past horizon is given in Fig. 3.

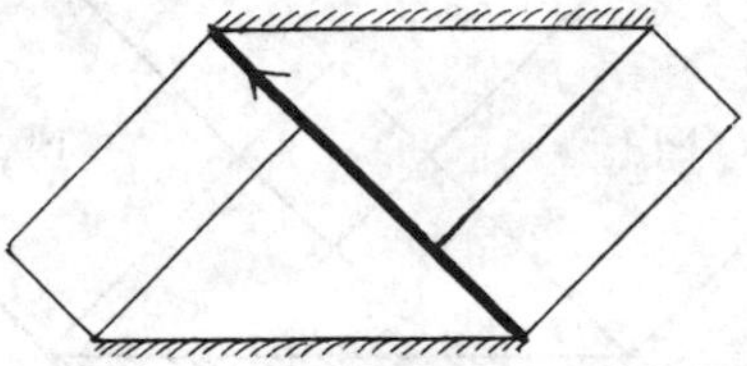

Figure 3

In Fig. 3. the geodesics are defined to go straight through the shock wave but enter into a more or less curved metric.

When two hard particles meet each other from opposite directions the curvature due to the resulting gravitational radiation is not easy to describe. We do need some description of this situation and therefore we introduced a simplification by imposing spherical symmetry. Hard particles are now replaced by spherically symmetric hard shells of matter entering or leaving the black hole. We guessed correctly that then Einstein's equations are also solved by connecting shifted Schwarzschild solutions with different mass parameters[12]. The space-time structure of Fig. 4 results.

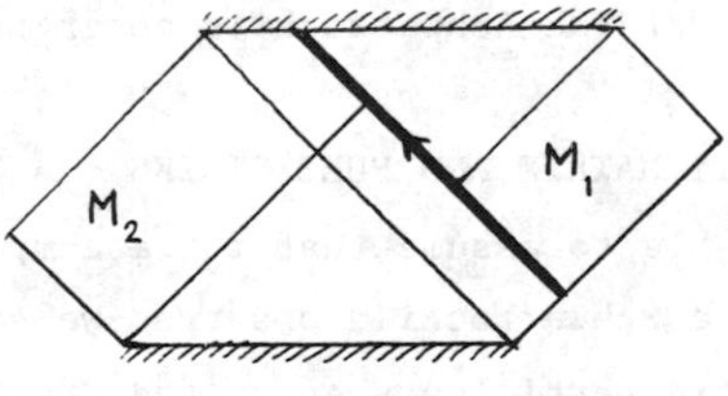

Figure 4

In Fig. 4 matter hits the future singularity at some distance from the past-horizon. In that case $M_1 > M_2$, if we require that the energy content of the shell of matter be positive.

This solution allows us now to combine various shells of ingoing and outgoing matter[12]. One gets the Penrose diagram of Fig. 5.

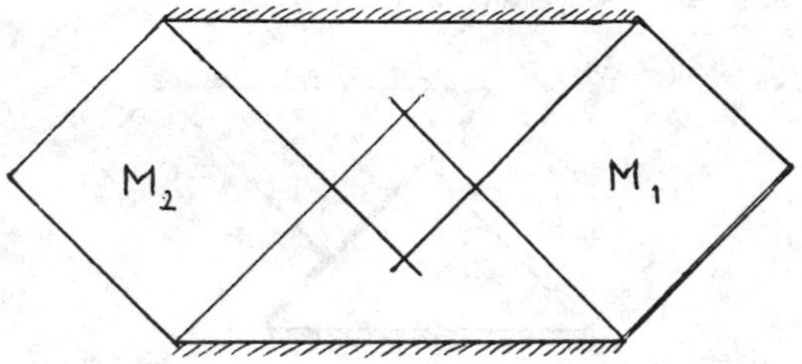

Figure 5

The algebra of the allowed amounts of energy in the shells and the resulting mass parameters M_i is fairly complicated.

An interesting limiting case occurs if one of the internal mass parameters tends to zero. If we require all shell-energies to be positive then such a zero mass region must always connect the future- with the past singularity by an r=o line. This r=o line is the origin of a polar coordinate representation of a flat space and one easily convinces oneself that then no longer any wormhole exists that connects us with another space. Bra- and ket-space are clearly disconnected and indeed we will argue that such a no-bra-space may perhaps be a way to describe a pure state for the Schwarzschild observer.

4. OFF-DIAGONAL DENSITY MATRIX AND PURE STATES - A SPECULATION

It is now reasonable to assume that for a complete description of the Hilbert space for a Schwarzschild observer we need all configurations with hard particles seen by the Kruskal observer. A restriction must be that the metric cannot be distorted so much that any of the Schwarzschild mass parameters close to the singularity become negative, because then the singularity at r=o would become timelike and connect the future with the past singularity. This gives a restriction on the amount of matter acceptable to the Kruskal observer. As stated in the previous sector, the algebra of these requirements is complicated, but perhaps this restriction will be sufficient to cut off an apparent ultraviolet divergence in the spectrum of the Schwarzschild time translation generator h.

In general we will find that the mass-parameter for the black hole in universe I, M_1, differs from M_2 in universe II. We speculate that this could be a direct representation of off-diagonal density matrix elements

$$\sum |M_1,\ldots\rangle \langle M_2,\ldots| \ , \qquad (4.1)$$

where the sum is over the soft particle states. Similarly, if one of the masses tends to zero, we get the matrix

$$\sum |M_1,\ldots\rangle \langle \mu\to o,\ldots| \ . \qquad (4.2)$$

Now if we are indeed allowed to speculate that light black holes behave more and more like ordinary elementary particles then in the vanishing mass limit black holes may occupy a much smaller number of quantum levels than the heavy ones. Thus, in (4.2) only "a few" bra states contribute. Therefore, perhaps, if one of the mass parameters tends to zero we might end up with a "pure state", or more precisely, a one-column density matrix.

Alternatively, consider a Kruskal metric with matter such that one of the center mass parameters tends to zero. Then as stated, the wormhole connecting bra- and ket-space, is closed. Communication between the two worlds becomes negligible and we might expect that the density matrix will tend to factorize:

$$\sum |M_1,\ldots\rangle \langle M_2,\ldots| \to (\sum|M_1,\ldots\rangle)\,(\sum\langle M_2,\ldots|) \ . \qquad (4.3)$$

It becomes the product of two pure states.

We see that these various considerations converge to a description of pure state black holes: there must be exactly enough matter inside the Kruskal frame such that the wormhole disappears and space-time only keeps one asymptotic region (Fig. 6).

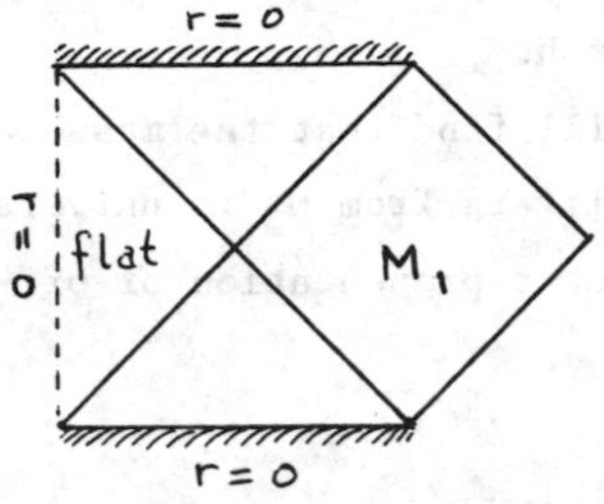

Figure 6

If all matter is mainly distributed along the two horizons this condition corresponds to a selection rule of the form:

$$P^{in}_{tot} \cdot P^{out}_{tot} = C.M^2. \qquad (4.4)$$

where C is a universal constant. Even if one does not wish to go along with our density matrix formulation of the equivalence principle, condition (4.4) with Fig. 6 could be an interesting description of the pure state black hole, and it would be important to be able to derive a radiation temperature directly from this picture. Unfortunately our description now lacks any symmetry under time boosts and therefore there seems to be no easy way to describe the near stationary case of a slowly evaporating black hole.

5. DISCUSSION

A major objection against our density matrix theory for a black hole has been put forward by many critics. It usually amounts to saying that the standard calculation yielding Hawking's temperature $1/8\pi M$ is impeccable and only requires known laws of physics.

Now this is absolutely true if the usual equivalence principle is considered to be a known law of physics. We do claim that the equivalence principle has been used - without general relativity there would be no computable Hawking effect. Somewhere in the line of arguments it was necessary to apply transformations across a horizon. It is here where - perhaps - a different procedure might give different results.

If we were to adopt the density-matrix prescription (and even the author himself is far from certain that it should be adopted) then we can imagine where the usual derivation fails. To see the radiation one has to wait long compared to MlogM after the collapse took place. The only stable matter-metric configuration during such a long time is obtained if from the start the collapsing object were in a mixed state. We suspect that the selection rule (4.4) should be used in the description of the evolution of our pure state beyond times of order MlogM but were unable to implement it.

One might consider another approach to the pure-state black hole. As we argued, when too much matter is allowed as seen in the Kruskal frame, then the r=o singularity becomes timelike. We find solutions of Einstein's equations as sketched in fig. 7a.

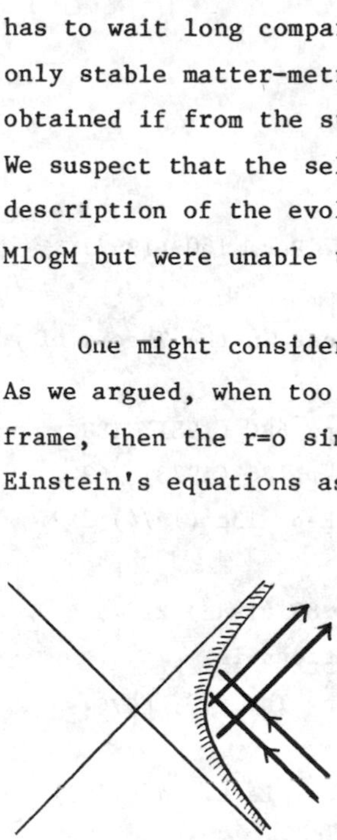

Fig. 7a

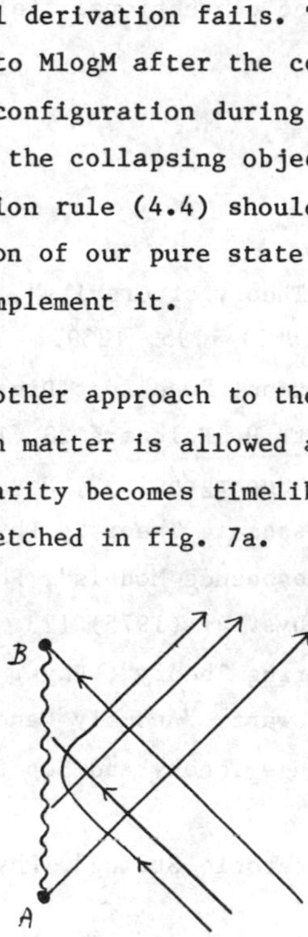

Fig. 7b

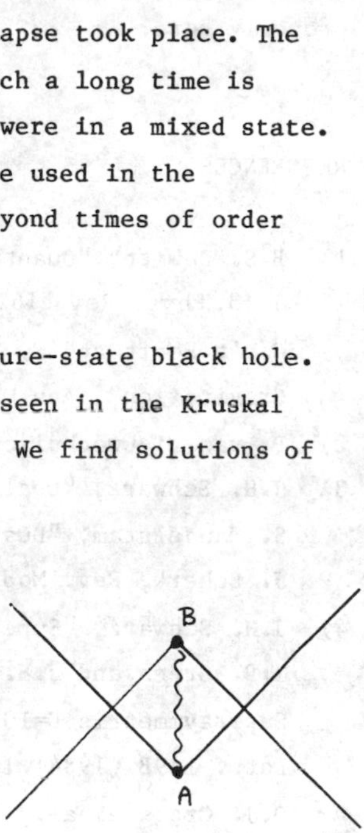

Fig. 7c

A nice aspect of such "solutions" is that they allow a Penrose diagram for the complete history of a black hole including its creation and annihilation (Fig. 7b) using only positive energy matter configurations but at the expense of a naked timelike singularity which corresponds to a negative mass. Before rejecting such a picture we recall that the causal structure here is not unlike that of Feynman diagrams in field theory (Fig. 7c) At point A there is spontaneous creation of positive and negative energy matter. There is no necessary conflict with causality because this fluctuation could be considered as a ubiquitous vacuum fluctuation whose effect only becomes observable because of the annihilation process at B shortly after A. The problem with this picture however is that if the time scales are much longer than the Planck length, the distance scales in Fig. 7b will be considerably shorter than the Planck length so that no conventional field theory will work properly here.

REFERENCES

1) B.S. DeWitt, "Quantum Theory of Gravity", Phys. Rev. 160 (1967) 1113; Phys. Rev. 162 (1967) 1195, 1239.

G. 't Hooft and M. Veltman, "One Loop Divergences in the Theory of Gravitation", Ann. Inst. H. Poincaré 20 (1974) 69.

2) P. van Nieuwenhuizen, "Supergravity", Phys. Rep. 68C (1981) 189.

3) J.H. Schwarz, "Dual Resonance Theory", Phys. Rep. 8c (1973) 269.

S. Mandelstam, "Dual Resonance Models", Phys. Rep. 13c (1974) 259.

J. Scherk, Rev. Mod. Phys. 47 (1975) 123.

4) J.H. Schwarz, "Superstring Theory", Phys. Rep. 89 (1982) 223.

M.B. Green and J.H. Schwarz, "Anomaly Cancellations in Supersymmetric D=10 Gauge Theory and Superstring Theory", Phys. Lett. 149B (1984) 117.

D.J. Gross et al., "Heterotic String", Phys. Rev. Lett. 54 (1985) 502.

5) G. 't Hooft, "Quantum Gravity: a Fundamental Problem and Some Radical Ideas", in "Recent Developments in Gravitation", Cargèse 1978, ed. M. Lévy and S. Deser, Plenum Press, New York and London 1979, p. 323.

T.D. Lee, "Difference Equations as the Basis of Fundamental Physical Theories", Columbia Preprint CU-TP-297 (1984); Proceedings of the International School of Subnuclear Physics. Erice 1983.

6) S.W. Hawking, "Particle Creation by Black Holes", Commun. Math. Phys. 43 (1975) 199.

J.B. Hartle and S.W. Hawking, "Path Integral Derivation of Black Hole Radiance", Phys. Rev. D13 (1976) 2188.

7) V. Rubakov, "Superheavy Magnetic Monopoles and the Decay of the Proton", JETP Lett. 33 (1981) 644; "Adler-Bell-Jackiw Anomaly and Fermion Number breaking in the Presence of a Magnetic Monopole", Nucl. Phys. B203 (1982) 311.

C.G. Callan, "Disappearing Dyons", Phys. Rev. D25 (1982) 2141; "Dyon-Fermion Dynamics", Phys. Rev. D26 (1982) 2058; "Monopole Catalysis of Baryon Decay", Nucl. Phys. B212 (1983) 391.

8) S.W. Hawking, "Breakdown of Predictability in gravitational Collapse", Phys. Rev. D14 (1976) 2460.

9) G. 't Hooft, "On the Quantum Structure of a Black Hole", Nucl. Phys. B (1985), to be published.

10) G. 't Hooft, "Ambiguity of the Equivalence Principle and Hawking's Temperature", J. Geom. and Phys. 1 (1984) 45.

11) T. Dray and G. 't Hooft, "The Gravitational Shock Wave of a Massless Particle", Nucl. Phys. B253 (1985) 173.

12) T.Dray and G. 't Hooft, "The Effect of Spherical Shells of Matter on the Schwarzschild Black Hole", Commun. Math. Physics, in press.

Superstrings*

John H. Schwarz

California Institute of Technology, Pasadena, CA 91125

ABSTRACT

The present status of superstring theory is surveyed. The derivation of the gauge groups SO(32) and $E_8 \times E_8$ is reviewed and the five known superstring theories are described.

Superstring unification is based on the proposition that elementary particles are one-dimensional [1]. As in point-particle theories, we require consistency with relativity and quantum mechanics. Also, interactions must be local to ensure causality and unitarity. The miracle, it seems to me, is that any such theories exist. At the moment there are five of them (aside from two-dimensional theories), but others might yet be found. Ideally, inconsistencies will eventually turn up in all but one of them so that nature can be completely described by the only possible theory. People often ask why we consider strings rather than membranes or higher-dimensional structures. All I can say to this is that the string theories look very attractive, whereas all attempts to construct more complicated schemes have failed. I would be amazed if any such theories were shown to exist. Unfortunately, in contrast to the case of strings, the mathematics is so unwieldy that it is very difficult to display their inconsistencies.

The superstring theories all share a number of common features [2]. First of all, they are formulated in ten dimensions - nine spatial and one time. They are supersymmetric, which implies that they contain one or more consistently coupled gravitinos and that the $D = 10$ Minkowski-space background has super-Poincaré symmetry. Superstring theories have no arbitrary dimensionless parameters in the fundamental equations. Whether such parameters arise in the description of the vacuum is not known. Each of the theories is finite and anomaly-free in perturbation theory to the extent that we have been able to check so far. The central fact that has sustained my enthusiasm for the subject during the past ten years is a simple one: *Apparently, quantum point-particle theories with gravity have nonrenormalizable infinities, whereas quantum string theories require gravity and are finite.*

* Work supported in part by the U.S. Department of Energy under contract DEAC 03-81-ER40050.

Superstring theories exist classically for spacetime dimension 3, 4, 6, or 10, but quantization is known to be possible only in the $D = 10$ case [3]. (This is the analog of the statement that bosonic strings exist classically in any dimension, but quantization singles out 26 dimensions.) There are three possible supersymmetry groups that can arise. The first ($N = 1$) has a conserved supersymmetry charge that transforms under the $D = 10$ Lorentz group as a Majorana-Weyl spinor. Such a spinor has 16 independent real components, corresponding to $N = 4$ on trivial reduction to four dimensions. Theories with $N = 1$ supersymmetry in ten dimensions are necessarily chiral, i.e., left-right asymmetric. There are two possibilities for $N = 2$ theories. The first, called 2A, has two Majorana-Weyl supercharges of opposite chirality. Such a theory is nonchiral. It gives rise to $N = 8$ supersymmetry on trivial reduction to four dimensions. The second $N = 2$ symmetry, called 2B, involves two Majorana-Weyl supercharges of the same chirality. Such a theory is chiral, and it also gives rise to $N = 8$ in four dimensions.

The $N = 2$ theories do not contain a fundamental Yang-Mills symmetry group. The only way in which one could arise would be as a consequence of the compactification of the six extra dimensions. However, standard Kaluza-Klein-type isometries of six compact dimensions are inadequate to account for known gauge symmetries. In string theories one can sometimes generate larger gauge groups than isometry considerations alone would suggest (as we will discuss later), but this trick does not seem to be applicable to the $N = 2$ theories.

In the case of the $N = 1$ theories, a fundamental Yang-Mills gauge group can be introduced. In fact, it has recently been discovered that one *must* be introduced in order to ensure that one-loop quantum corrections do not break gauge invariance, leading to an inconsistent theory. The only groups for which the required anomaly cancellations can be effected are SO(32) and $E_8 \times E_8$ [4]. It is pleasing, of course, to have a fundamental principle that determines the Yang-Mills group (almost) uniquely. It is also encouraging that the ones that are singled out, especially $E_8 \times E_8$, look promising for phenomenology.

The first manifestation of anomalies in ten dimensions arises for hexagon diagrams. In general, the rule for $2n$ dimensions is that the first dangerous diagram is an $n+1$-gon. This is most easily understood from the fact that the anomalous divergence of a Yang-Mills gauge current has the structure

$$\partial \bullet J^a \sim \varepsilon^{\mu_1 \cdots \mu_{2n}} tr(\Lambda^a F_{\mu_1\mu_2} \cdots F_{\mu_{2n-1}\mu_{2n}}) , \tag{1}$$

where the matrices are in the representation of the algebra dictated by the chiral fermions that circulate in the loop. Analogous gravitational anomalies can occur (for n odd) in the divergence of the energy-momentum tensor. The $N = 2$ point-particle supergravity theories in ten dimensions are anomaly-free. In the 2A case this is due to trivial cancellations between contributions of left-handed and right-handed fermions, whereas in the 2B case it is a consequence of highly nontrivial cancellations discovered in ref. [5]. The $N = 1$ theories are even more subtle.

The anomaly cancellation in type I SO(32) superstring theory was discovered by evaluating hexagon loop diagrams in the string theory [6]. A useful way of understanding the result, which I will review briefly here, is in terms of an effective action that corresponds to a low-energy expansion of the string theory [4]. This analysis has the advantage of being applicable to any $N = 1$, $D = 10$ theory. One begins by defining an effective action based on fields for each of the massless modes of the theory, collectively denoted φ_0. It is obtained (in principle) by integrating out all the fields associated with massive string modes, collectively denoted φ_H.

$$e^{iS_{eff}(\varphi_0)} \sim \int D\varphi_H \, e^{iS_{string}(\varphi_0,\varphi_H)} . \tag{2}$$

The effective action S_{eff}, can be expanded in a series of operators of ascending dimension. The leading terms correspond to the point-particle theory for $N = 1$ $D = 10$ super Yang-Mills coupled to supergravity, given in ref. [7]. The higher-dimension terms represent string corrections whose effects are suppressed at low energy (E) by powers of E/M, where M is the characteristic mass scale of the string. A crucial fact is that the theory has anomalies for every Yang-Mills group, unless terms not present in the minimal point-particle theory are taken into account.

The massless fields consist of a super Yang-Mills multiplet and a supergravity multiplet. The super Yang-Mills multiplet contains vector fields A_μ^a and left-handed Majorana-Weyl spinor fields χ_L^a. The index a takes n values corresponding to the generators of the Yang Mills group G ($n = dim\, G$). The supergravity multiplet contains a graviton $g_{\mu\nu}$, a second-rank antisymmetric tensor field $B_{\mu\nu}$, a scalar φ, a left-handed Majorana-Weyl gravitino $\psi_{\mu L}$, and a right-handed Majorana-Weyl spinor λ_R. These fields are all singlets of the gauge group. The chiral spinors χ, ψ, and λ circulating in hexagon (and higher) diagrams give rise to gauge, gravitational, and mixed anomalies.

The analysis of anomalies is facilitated by the use of differential forms. Thus we associate one-forms with the gauge potentials

$$A \equiv A_\mu^a \lambda^a dx^\mu \tag{3a}$$

$$\omega \equiv \omega_\mu dx^\mu . \tag{3b}$$

The matrices λ^a are $n \times n$ matrices in the adjoint representation of the Yang-Mills algebra, i.e., they are the structure constants of the algebra. The spin connection ω_μ is a 10×10 matrix in the fundamental representation of the Lorentz algebra SO(9,1). It is made from the zehnbein in the standard manner (first-order in derivatives). The field-strength two-forms are then given by

$$F \equiv \frac{1}{2} F_{\mu\nu} dx^\mu \wedge dx^\nu = dA + A^2 \tag{4a}$$

$$R \equiv \frac{1}{2} R_{\mu\nu} dx^\mu \wedge dx^\nu = d\omega + \omega^2 , \tag{4b}$$

F is the usual Yang-Mills field strength and R is the Riemann curvature tensor in the zehnbein formalism. Under infinitesimal gauge transformations (with parameters Λ and Θ respectively) one has the usual formulas

$$\delta A = d\Lambda + [A,\Lambda] \tag{5a}$$

$$\delta\omega = d\Theta + [\omega,\Theta] \tag{5b}$$

and

$$\delta F = [F,\Lambda] \tag{6a}$$

$$\delta R = [R,\Theta]\,. \tag{6b}$$

It is also useful to introduce Chern-Simons three-forms

$$\omega_{3Y} = Tr(AF - \frac{1}{3}A^3) \tag{7a}$$

$$\omega_{3L} = tr(\omega R - \frac{1}{3}\omega^3)\,, \tag{7b}$$

which have the properties

$$d\omega_{3Y} = TrF^2 \tag{8a}$$

$$d\omega_{3L} = tr\,R^2 \tag{8b}$$

and

$$\delta\omega_{3Y} = -d\omega_{2Y}^1 \tag{9a}$$

$$\delta\omega_{3L} = -d\omega_{2L}^1\,, \tag{9b}$$

where ω_{2Y}^1 and ω_{2L}^1 are two-forms. The superscript "1" indicates that they are linear in the infinitesimal parameters Λ and Θ, respectively.

The anomalies arising from loops of chiral fermions can be succinctly characterized by a 12-form. This is a purely formal expression from which one can deduce the actual 10-form whose integral is the anomaly by replacing $F \to F + \Lambda$ and $R \to R + \Theta$ and extracting the terms linear in Λ or Θ. The 12-form characterizing all gauge, gravitational, and mixed anomalies due to χ, ψ, and λ loops can be read off from ref. [5]. The result is

$$I_{12} \propto -\frac{1}{15} Tr F^6 - \frac{1}{960} Tr F^2(4 tr R^4 + 5(tr R^2)^2)$$

$$+ \frac{1}{24} Tr F^4 tr R^2 + (\frac{1}{32} + \frac{n - 496}{13,824})(tr R^2)^3$$

$$+ (\frac{1}{8} + \frac{n - 496}{5760}) tr R^2 tr R^4 + (\frac{n - 496}{7560}) tr R^6 . \quad (10)$$

The question then arises whether it is possible for S_{eff} to contain a non-gauge-invariant local interaction term S_c whose gauge variation δS_c cancels the anomaly associated with I_{12}. The result discovered in ref. [4] is that this is only possible if I_{12} factorizes into an expression of the form

$$I_{12} = (tr R^2 + k\, Tr F^2) X_8 . \quad (11)$$

The necessary and sufficient conditions for this to be possible are

$$n = dim\, G = 496 \quad (12)$$

and

$$Tr F^6 = \frac{1}{48} Tr F^4 Tr F^2 - \frac{1}{14,400} (Tr F^2)^3 . \quad (13)$$

In this case one finds that

$$k = -\frac{1}{30} \quad (14)$$

and

$$X_8 = \frac{1}{24} Tr F^4 - \frac{1}{7200} (Tr F^2)^2 - \frac{1}{240} Tr F^2 tr R^2 + \frac{1}{8} tr R^4 + \frac{1}{32} (tr R^2)^2 . \quad (15)$$

When the factorization of I_{12} in eq. (11) takes place the key to the anomaly cancellation is the addition of a term of the form

$$S_c \sim \int B \wedge X_8 \quad (16)$$

where the two-form $B \equiv B_{\mu\nu} dx^\mu \wedge dx^\nu$ has the gauge transformation

$$\delta B = \omega^1_{2L} - \frac{1}{30} \omega^1_{2Y} . \quad (17)$$

This rule is at first sight rather surprising. The potential B transforms under both Yang-Mills and local-Lorentz transformations even though, judging by its indices, one would have expected it to be invariant. The 3-form field strength

$$H = dB + \omega_{3L} - \frac{1}{30}\omega_{3Y} \tag{18}$$

is nonetheless invariant because of eq. (9). The Yang-Mills terms in eqs. (17) and (18) already appear in the minimal theory of ref. [7], but the Lorentz terms are higher-dimension contributions specific to the string effective action. From the point of view of building up S_{eff}, the inclusion of these various terms with appropriate coefficients may appear *ad hoc*. However, they automatically occur in the string theory in just the right way.

Equations (12) and (13) have two solutions: SO(32) and $E_8 \times E_8$. The arithmetic for showing this is straightforward and will not be repeated here. There are additional "trivial" solutions such as $[U(1)]^{496}$ and $E_8 \times [U(1)]^{248}$, but these do not correspond to consistent string theories.

Let us now turn to a description of the various known superstring theories beginning with the type I theory. It has only been defined for SO(n), USp($2n$), and U(n) Yang-Mills groups [8]. As we have seen, the anomaly cancellation can only occur in the SO(32) case. (Green and I are looking at a possible scheme for an $E_8 \times E_8$ type I theory, but it is unlikely that it will succeed.) Type I superstrings include unoriented open and closed strings. The massless open-string modes correspond to the super Yang-Mills multiplet and the massless closed-string modes to the supergravity multiplet. Thus open strings may be regarded as "matter" strings and closed strings as "gravity" strings.

Superstrings can be described by superspace coordinates $x^\mu(\sigma)$ and $\theta^{Aa}(\sigma)$, where the θ's are Grassmann numbers and σ is parameter running along the length of the string. A second-quantized field theory can be formulated in terms of (light-cone-gauge) *functional superfields* that create or destroy an entire string in superspace [9]. In the case of the type I theory there is an open-string field $\Phi[x(\sigma),\theta(\sigma)]$ and a closed-string field $\Psi[x(\sigma),\theta(\sigma)]$. The open-string field Φ has group-theory indices, associated with the ends of the string, and Ψ has no indices.

The type I theory involves two basic interactions. The first is a "Yang-Mills" interaction in which strings break or join as depicted in fig. 1. The same local interaction occurs in the two different con-

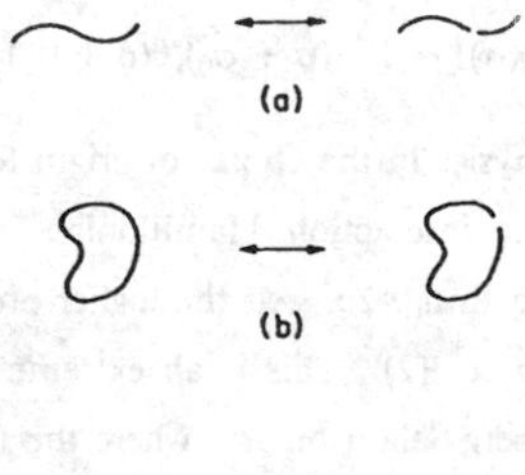

Fig. 1 The two local string interactions of Yang-Mills type.

texts shown in the figure. Given the first one, the second one is required by causality. It can also be deduced from supersymmetry or Lorentz invariance. The second basic interaction is a "gravity" interaction in which strings touch at interior points where they break and rejoin. There are five instances of this interaction in the type I theory depicted in fig. 2. Note that even though strings are spatially extended their interactions are local. Thus superstring field theory is *local field theory.*

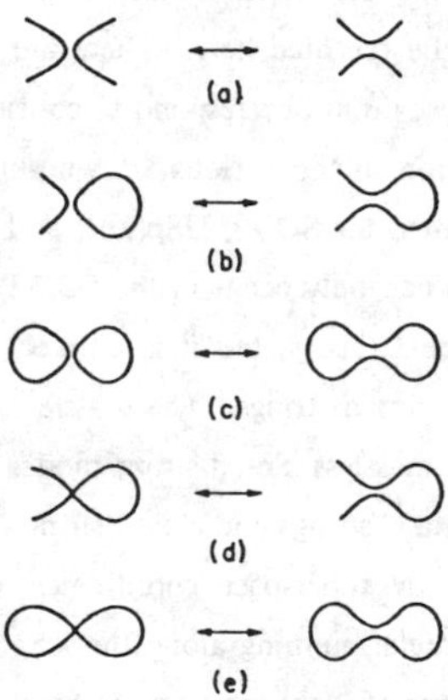

Fig. 2 The five local string interactions of gravity type.

The type II superstring theories are even simpler, consisting of oriented closed strings only. The IIA and IIB theories are distinguished by whether the two Grassmann coordinates $\theta(\sigma)$ and $\tilde{\theta}(\sigma)$, associated with modes that move in opposite directions around the string, are spinors of opposite or same chirality. In either case there is only a single superfield $\Psi[x(\sigma),\theta(\sigma)]$, which has no indices. It is subject to a single constraint

$$\Psi[x(\sigma),\theta(\sigma),\tilde{\theta}(\sigma)] = \Psi[x(\sigma+\sigma_0),\theta(\sigma+\sigma_0),\tilde{\theta}(\sigma+\sigma_0)]\,, \tag{19}$$

expressing the fact that there is no physics in the choice of origin for the parameter σ. This constraint is easy to deal with. Moreover, the interaction Hamiltonian consists of a single Ψ^3 term only, corresponding to the process depicted in fig. 2c. All the higher-order contact terms of S_{eff} arise from integrating out the massive modes in eq. (2). This is an extreme example of a phenomenon already encountered in the case of the Weinberg-Salam theory, where the four-Fermi term is replaced by massive exchanges. In both theories this results in improved ultraviolet behavior. (Supersymmetry also plays a crucial role in canceling infinities for the case of superstrings.)

Shortly after the discovery of SO(32) and $E_8 \times E_8$ it was noted that these groups each have rank 16, which added to $D = 10$ gives 26, the dimension of the old bosonic string theory [10]. This idea is exploited by two new $N = 1$ superstring theories - one for each group [11]. They are oriented closed-string theories that combine the mathematical structure of the $D = 26$ bosonic string theory for right-moving modes with that of $D = 10$ superstrings for left-moving modes. Because of this "cross-breeding," the authors call them "heterotic." The heterotic theories share properties of the type I and type II theories. They have the same $N = 1$ super-Poincaré symmetry as a type I theory, but they have the same topological structure as the type II theories. Namely, the cubic interaction of fig. 2c is the only one. As a result, the unique L-loop Feynman diagram corresponds to a world sheet that is topologically a sphere with L handles, i.e., a closed, oriented 2-manifold of genus L.

The coordinates of heterotic superstrings consist of ten-vectors $x^\mu(\sigma,\tau)$ for left- and right-moving orbital modes, Majorana-Weyl Grassmann coordinates $\theta^a(\sigma-\tau)$ for left-moving moves, and additional right-moving coordinates. The latter coordinates can be described in at least three different equivalent ways. One formulation is in terms of spatial coordinates forming a sixteen torus. The conjugate momenta describe a sixteen-dimensional lattice, which must be self-dual. In each case the lattice can be associated with a weight lattice of a Lie algebra, which is realized as a Yang-Mills gauge symmetry of the theory if the size of the torus is properly adjusted. For example, a cubic lattice would be associated with $[SU(2)]^{16}$. The weight lattice must also be integral and *even*, i.e., denoting lattice sites by sixteen-vectors $\vec{w}_i$,

$$\vec{w}_i \bullet \vec{w}_j \in \begin{cases} \mathbf{Z} & i \neq j \\ 2\mathbf{Z} & i = j \end{cases}. \tag{20}$$

Now it is well-known that there are only two such lattices. One is $\Gamma_8 \times \Gamma_8$, where Γ_8 is the lattice generated by the root vectors of E_8. The other is Γ_{16}, which consists of half the sites of the complete weight lattice of *spin* (32). Γ_{16} is generated by the weight vectors of the adjoint representation plus those of *one* of the spinor representations. Other self-dual lattices, such as the cubic lattice mentioned above, are excluded because they are not even. The Kaluza-Klein isometry of the torus, $[U(1)]^{16}$, corresponds to the Cartan subalgebra.

The heterotic superstring theories incorporate the group theory in a deeper way [12] than the type I theories, where the quantum numbers are simply attached to the ends of open strings. Another difference is that the massive levels involve arbitrarily large representations of the group, i.e. all representations of $E_8 \times E_8$ or $spin(32)/\mathbf{Z}_2$ occur. Also, tree-level gravity processes in the type I theory are generated by one-loop Yang-Mills diagrams, which implies that $\kappa_{10} \propto g_{10}^2$ where κ_{10} is the $D = 10$ gravitational coupling constant and g_{10} is the $D = 10$ Yang-Mills coupling constant. In the heterotic theories, on the other hand, cubic closed-string interactions describe both first-order gravitational and Yang-Mills couplings, so that $\kappa_{10} \propto g_{10}$. Dimensional analysis therefore implies that

$$g_{10}^2 \propto \kappa_{10}\alpha' \qquad (type\ I\ strings) \tag{21a}$$

$$g_{10}^2 \propto \kappa_{10}^2/\alpha' \qquad (heterotic\ strings), \tag{21b}$$

where α' is the Regge-slope parameter (inverse string tension).

If we suppose that six dimensions form a compact space of volume V, then the four-dimensional coupling constants are given by

$$g_4 = g_{10}/\sqrt{V} \tag{22a}$$

$$\kappa_4 = \kappa_{10}/\sqrt{V}\,. \tag{22b}$$

Assuming that g_4 is of order unity and κ_4 is l_{pl}, the Planck length, we find that

$$\sqrt{V}/\alpha' \approx l_{pl} \qquad (type\ I\ strings) \tag{23a}$$

$$\sqrt{\alpha'} \approx l_{pl} \qquad (heterotic\ strings)\,. \tag{23b}$$

Thus, in the heterotic theories the characteristic length scale of strings must be of the order of the Planck length, whereas the condition in the type I theory is not so simple.

Altogether there are five known superstring theories: Type I (with SO(32)), type IIA, type IIB, and heterotic (with SO(32) or $E_8 \times E_8$) that could be finite and anomaly-free. Phenomenologically the $E_8 \times E_8$ theory appears to be the most promising [13]. All observed gauge groups would emerge from one E_8 factor. The other one could play an important role in providing dark matter and breaking symmetries [11, 14-17].

Let me conclude with some questions. Five theories is more than we need; can some of them be ruled out theoretically? Perhaps anomalies that have not yet been calculated could play a role. Supersymmetry anomalies have not yet been analyzed, even at one loop. Gauge and gravitational anomalies have not been calculated beyond one loop. (Is there an Adler-Bardeen theorem for string theories?) Global anomalies have been analyzed by Witten [18]. He found that they do not give additional restrictions at one loop for $D = 10$ Minkowski space, but they might restrict the possibilities for compactification. Nonperturbative effects, although more difficult to analyze, could also be important. The SO(32) heterotic superstring contains a stable massive state (a spinor representation). Perhaps this is indicative of a problem.

Compactification on a manifold with nontrivial fundamental group appears essential for symmetry breaking. However, in the closed-string theories it implies the existence of absolutely stable string states that are wrapped on noncontractible curves. Their consequences need to be investigated.

The next question is an especially important one: What is the fundamental principle that underlies superstring theories? The entire functional superfield ought to have a geometric interpretation, not just the massless modes. This suggests that Riemannian geometry should be regarded only as an approximation valid at distances large compared to $\sqrt{\alpha'}$. Other well-known and important questions are:

- How large are the compact dimensions?
- Why is the cosmological constant zero?
- What are the cosmological implications of strings?
- How do small numbers such as m_W/m_{pl} arise?

I think there is a good chance that progress will be made on some of these questions in the near future.

References

[1] J. Scherk and J. H. Schwarz, Nucl. Phys. B81 (1974) 118.

[2] For reviews see:
J. H. Schwarz, Phys. Reports 89 (1982) 223;
M. B. Green, Surveys in H. E. Physics 3 (1983) 127;
J. H. Schwarz, in "Supersymmetry and Supergravity '84," eds. B. de Wit et al., (World Scientific, 1984) 426.

[3] M. B. Green and J. H. Schwarz, Phys. Lett. 136B (1984) 367.

[4] M. B. Green and J. H. Schwarz, Phys. Lett. 149B (1984) 117.

[5] L. Alvarez-Gaumé and E. Witten, Nucl. Phys. B234 (1983) 269.

[6] M. B. Green and J. H. Schwarz, Caltech preprint CALT-68-1224, to be published in Nucl. Phys. B.

[7] E. Bergshoeff, M. de Roo, B. de Wit, and P. van Nieuwenhuizen, Nucl. Phys. B195 (1982) 97;
G. F. Chapline and N. S. Manton, Phys. Lett. 120B (1983) 105.

[8] J. H. Schwarz in Proc. Johns Hopkins Workshop on Current Problems in Particle Theory 6, (Florence, 1982) 233;
N. Marcus and A. Sagnotti, Phys. Lett. 119B (1982) 97.

[9] M. B. Green and J. H. Schwarz, Nucl. Phys. B243 (1984) 475.

[10] P. Freund, Phys. Lett. 151B (1985) 387.

[11] D. Gross, J. Harvey, E. Martinec, and R. Rohm, Phys. Rev. Lett. 54 (1985) 502 and Princeton Univ. preprint.

[12] I. B. Frenkel and V. G. Kac, Inv. Math. 62 (1980) 23;
P. Goddard and D. Olive, in "Vertex Operators in Mathematics and Physics" eds. T. Lepowsky, S. Mandelstam, and I. M. Singer (Spring-Verlag 1985) 51.

[13] P. Candelas, G. Horowitz, A. Strominger, and E. Witten, Santa Barbara ITP preprint 84-170, to be published in Nucl. Phys. B.

[14] E. Witten, Phys. Lett. 149B (1984) 351.

[15] M. B. Green, J. H. Schwarz, and P. C. West, Caltech preprint CALT-68-1210, to be published in Nucl. Phys. B.

[16] E. W. Kolb, D. Seckel, and M. S. Turner, Fermilab preprint.

[17] M. Dine, R. Rohm, N. Seiberg, and E. Witten, Institute for Advanced Study preprint.

[18] E. Witten, Princeton Univ. preprint.

GLOBAL ANOMALIES IN STRING THEORY

Edward Witten*
Joseph Henry Laboratories
Princeton University
Princeton, New Jersey 08544

Abstract

Various questions involving global anomalies in particle theory and string theory are addressed. It is shown that the question of whether a manifold is a spin manifold is equivalent to a question about global anomalies in the propagation of a point particle. In the superstring case, it is shown that the measure of the heterotic theory has no global anomalies on any Riemann surface. This generalizes known one loop results. Also, a topological condition is derived which restricts the possible choices of Wilson lines for grand unified symmetry breaking. It is argued that the long-term development of global anomalies in string theory will involve eventual study of global anomalies in the determinant of the Dirac-Ramond operator.

---

*Research supported in part by NSF Grant PHY80-19754.

The gravitational interactions of a spin 1/2 particle propagating on a space-time manifold M are consistent only if several conditions are obeyed.* First of all, M must be a spin manifold on which there is no topological obstruction to defining spinors.[1] And if (in 4k+2 dimensions) we wish to discuss spinors of definite chirality, then M must be orientable. These conditions are needed just in order to make sense of the single particle Dirac equation $i\not{D}\psi=0$ (or $i\not{D}(1-\bar{\Gamma})\psi = 0$, in the chiral case; here $\bar{\Gamma} = \Gamma_1\Gamma_2\ldots\Gamma_{4k+2}$ is the chirality operator, the product of the gamma matrices Γ_i).

If we wish to formulate not just the one particle equation but the quantum field theory of spin one half particles on M, some additional conditions arise. It is necessary to be able to define the Dirac determinant $\det i\not{D}$--or, in the chiral case, $\det i\not{D}(\frac{1-\bar{\Gamma}}{2})$. In the chiral case, one encounters an anomaly in perturbation theory in trying to define the determinant.[2] To cancel this anomaly, it is necessary to introduce fields of various spin, perhaps including antisymmetric tensor fields.[3] Even when perturbative anomalies are cancelled the consistency of the theory is still not guaranteed. It is necessary to consider global anomalies. Thus let $f:M\to M$ be a diffeomorphism, not continuously connected to the identity, which leaves fixed the spin structure of M. One must ask whether the Dirac determinant is invariant under f. To answer this question, it is convenient to define the "mapping cylinder" $(M\times S^1)_f$. It is defined as follows: in the Cartesian product $M\times I$ ($I=[0,1]$ is the unit interval) one identifies $(x,0)$ with $(f(x),1)$ for any $x\varepsilon M$. The η invariant of the Dirac operator on $(M\times S^1)_f$ is defined as follows.[5] If λ_i are the Dirac eigenvalues on $(M\times S^1)_f$ then

$$\eta = \lim_{s\to 0} \sum_i \text{sign}\,\lambda_i \exp\text{-}s|\lambda_i| \tag{1}$$

Then it can be shown[4] that the change Δf of the chiral Dirac determinant on M is related to the η invariant on $(M\times S^1)_f$:

---

*Most of the original lecture was devoted to reviewing the derivation of equation (2). As this material has appeared elsewhere,[4] I have chosen in the written version to expand on the concluding portion of the lecture.

$$\Delta_f \ln \det i\not{D}\left(\frac{1-\bar{\Gamma}}{2}\right) = \frac{i\pi\eta}{2}\left((M\times S^1)_f\right) \bmod 2\pi i \qquad (2)$$

Of course, (2) must be summed over all fermion multiplets, and if perturbative anomaly cancellation involved antisymmetric tensor fields, their contribution must be included too, to get the proper formula for the global anomaly. In [4], equation (2) was used to show that ten dimensional supergravity theories (which are of interest because they are the low energy limits of superstring theories) have no global anomalies when formulated on S^{10}. For the future it will be extremely interesting to learn whether these theories have global anomalies when formulated on $S^4\times K$ for various K. Although equation (2) is an appropriate starting point for addressing this question, practicable methods to evaluate this formula for a large class of ten manifolds (and diffeomorphisms) are currently unknown.

Of course, if one finds that the change in the determinant under a diffeomorphism f is not zero, one must be careful in drawing conclusions. Before concluding that the theory is inconsistent, one must make sure that there is a sound physical reason that lack of invariance under f would correspond to inconsistency. In essence, lack of invariance under f leads to inconsistency if upon decompactification from $S^4\times K$ to $R^4\times K$, f has compact support. Lack of invariance under f will then cause the physically relevant Feynmann path integral to vanish.[6] On $S^4\times K$, a "dangerous" f (under which the determinant must be invariant if the theory is to make sense) is one that leaves fixed a copy of K ($p\times K$, where p is the "point at infinity" on S^4). Later, we will discuss the physical meaning of global anomalies in certain cases in which f does not obey this condition.

To recapitulate what I have said so far, in assessing the consistency of the quantum field theory of spin 1/2 particles on a manifold M, there are several steps:

(a) One must make sure that M has a spin structure; and, if chiral fermions are to be considered, one must ask whether M is orientable.

(b) One must ensure the absence of dangerous local and global anomalies in the Dirac determinant.

Of course, merely determining whether a theory is consistent should not satisfy us. We also wish to extract its physical content. I will simply single out one aspect of this:

(c) One would like to determine the symmetries of the quantum field theory, allowing for possible effects of anomalies and other subtleties that might spoil an apparent symmetry.

In these notes I will discuss certain aspects of problems (a), (b), and (c) in field theory, and then discuss the generalization to string theory

While (b) and (c) are manifestly questions that involve anomalies, this is not so for (a). However, as we will now see, the question of whether a manifold admits spinors can be interpreted as a question about global anomalies on the world line of a point particle.

There is an action[7] for a point particle that possesses world line supersymmetry:

$$I = \int d\tau \left[\frac{1}{2} g_{ij}(x(\tau)) \frac{dx^i}{d\tau}\frac{dx^j}{d\tau} + \frac{i}{2}\psi^i(\tau)\left(g_{ij}\frac{d}{d\tau} + \frac{dx^k}{d\tau}\omega_{kij}(x(\tau))\right)\psi^j(\tau)\right] \tag{3}$$

Here x^i are coordinates on M, ω_{kij} is the spin connection of M, and the ψ^i are real anticommuting variables, i being a tangent vector index of M. (In the mathematical sense, the ψ^i take values in the pull-back of the tangent space of M to the line or circle parametrized by τ.) Now, (3) possesses the world-line supersymmetry

$$\delta x^i = i\psi^i\varepsilon$$

$$\delta\psi^i = \frac{dx^i}{d\tau}\varepsilon - i\omega_k{}^i{}_\ell\,\psi^k\psi^\ell\varepsilon \tag{4}$$

where ε is an anticommuting constant. (ε is a scalar under tranformations of M. There is a very different point particle action that possesses space-time supersymmetry.[8]) The conserved quantity corresponding to (4) is $Q = \psi_i \frac{dx^i}{d\tau}$. Upon quantization, the ψ_i obey $\{\psi_i(\tau), \psi_j(\tau)\} = g_{ij}(x(\tau))$, so they are gamma matrices, in effect. The wave functions--on which gamma matrices act--must then be spinor fields on M. As for $\frac{dx^i}{d\tau}$, we note that the canonical momentum is

$$p_i = \frac{\delta I}{\delta(\frac{dx^i}{d\tau})} = g_{ij} \frac{dx^j}{d\tau} + \frac{i}{4} \omega_{ijk} [\psi^j, \psi^k] \tag{5}$$

As is usual in quantum mechanics, canonical quantization corresponds to $p_i = -i \frac{\partial}{\partial x^i}$. (5) can therefore be inverted to give $g_{ij} \frac{dx^j}{d\tau} = -iD_i$, where

$$D_i = \frac{\partial}{\partial x^i} + \frac{1}{4} \omega_{ijk} [\psi^j, \psi^k] \tag{6}$$

is the usual covariant derivative acting on spinors. The conserved charge $Q = \psi_i \frac{dx^i}{d\tau} = -i \psi^i D_i$ is thus the Dirac operator.

This construction seems to make sense for arbitrary M. But if M is not a spin manifold, spinors and Dirac operators cannot be defined on M. We must run into trouble somewhere. How does this happen? One approach to quantization of (4) is path integrals. In this approach, one must define the fermion effective action $\sqrt{\det Y}$ where Y is the "world line Dirac operator"

$$Y = i\left(\frac{d}{d\tau} \delta^i{}_j + \frac{dx^k}{d\tau} \omega_k{}^i{}_j\right) \tag{7}$$

We need the square root of det Y since the ψ^i are real. What we will see is that $\sqrt{\det Y}$ is afflicted with a global anomaly precisely when M is not a spin manifold.

It is convenient to take the world line to be a circle S^1.* Thus, we will study the eigenvalue problem $Y\phi=\lambda\phi$, where Y is defined on a circle, $0 \leq \tau \leq 2\pi$. In essence, $A^i{}_j = \frac{dx^k}{d\tau} \omega_k{}^i{}_j$ is an O(n) gauge field on the circle, n being the dimension of M. The Dirac equation on the circle should require a single gamma matrix Γ obeying $\Gamma^2=1$; for Γ we can pick the 1x1 matrix $\Gamma = 1$. So $Y = i(\frac{d}{d\tau} + A)$ is indeed a one dimensional Dirac operator.

---

*We will use periodic boundary conditions for the fermions, corresponding to calculating $\mathrm{Tr}\, e^{-\beta H} (-1)^F$. Antiperiodic ones would give $\mathrm{Tr}\, e^{-\beta H}$.

In one dimension, the only gauge covariant quantity characterizing the gauge field A is the rotation matrix

$$R = P \exp \int_0^{2\pi} d\tau \ A(\tau) \tag{8}$$

If, say, n=2k, R can always be brought to canonical form, with "rotation angles" $\theta_1 \dots \theta_k$:

$$R = \begin{pmatrix} \cos\theta_1 & \sin\theta_1 & & & & & \\ -\sin\theta_1 & \cos\theta_1 & & & & & \\ & & \cos\theta_2 & \sin\theta_2 & & & \\ & & -\sin\theta_2 & \cos\theta_2 & & & \\ & & & & \ddots & & \\ & & & & & \cos\theta_k & \sin\theta_k \\ & & & & & -\sin\theta_k & \cos\theta_k \end{pmatrix} \tag{9}$$

For given R, A can be gauge transformed into any form that obeys (8). A convenient choice is

$$A = \frac{1}{2\pi} \begin{pmatrix} 0 & \theta_1 & & & & & \\ -\theta_1 & 0 & & & & & \\ & & 0 & \theta_2 & & & \\ & & -\theta_2 & 0 & & & \\ & & & & \ddots & & \\ & & & & & 0 & \theta_k \\ & & & & & -\theta_k & 0 \end{pmatrix} \tag{10}$$

With this choice, the eigenvalues of Y are easily determined. They are $n \pm \frac{\theta_i}{2\pi}$, for arbitrary integer n. Hence formally

$$(\det Y)_0 = \prod_n \prod_i \left(n + \frac{\theta_i}{2\pi}\right)\left(n - \frac{\theta_i}{2\pi}\right) = \prod_{n,i} \left(n^2 - \frac{\theta_i^2}{(2\pi)^2}\right) \tag{11}$$

where the subscript "o" means that the divergent infinite product in (11) needs to be regularized. Noting that the right-hand side of (11) is periodic in each θ_i with a double zero whenever any θ_i is an integer multiple of 2π, we may guess that the proper formula is

$$\det Y = \prod_{i=1}^{k} \sin^2 \theta_i/2 \qquad (12)$$

To derive (12), one may divide (11) by an infinite constant, giving

$$\det Y = \prod_{i=1}^{k} \left(\frac{\theta_i^2}{4} \prod_{n\neq 0} \left(1 - \frac{\theta_i^2}{4\pi^2 n^2}\right)\right) \qquad (13)$$

The convergent product in (13) can be evaluated to give (12).

For the square root of the determinant we have then

$$\sqrt{\det Y} = \prod_{i=1}^{k} \sin \theta_i/2 \qquad (14)$$

However, the sign of (14) is ill-defined, because the θ_i are well-defined only modulo 2π. This is the potential source of a global anomaly.

For a given world line γ, we can just define $\sqrt{\det Y}$ to be positive. For some other world line γ', the sign of $\sqrt{\det Y}$ must be determined by smoothly interpolating from γ to γ' and requiring that $\sqrt{\det Y}$ should vary smoothly. Thus, we find a mapping $\phi: S^1 \times I \to M$, where S^1 is parametrized by the time τ, and I by an auxiliary variable u, $0 \leq u \leq 1$. ϕ is chosen so that $\phi(\tau,0)$ is the curve γ, while $\phi(\tau,1)$ is γ'; thus, as u varies from 0 to 1, $\phi(\tau,u)$ is a one parameter family of curves varying from γ to γ'. Requiring $\sqrt{\det Y}$ to vary smoothly then determines its sign at γ' in terms of the sign chosen at γ.

Thus, at least for curves within a single homotopy class of curves in $\pi_1(M)$, we can determine the sign of $\sqrt{\det Y}$ for all curves in terms of a single overall sign choice. Is there an inconsistency in this procedure? An inconsistency would arise if we find an interpolation $\phi(\tau,u)$ that starts and ends at the <u>same</u> curve γ with the property that (requiring it to vary smoothly with u) $\sqrt{\det Y(u=1)} = -\sqrt{\det Y(u=0)}$.

Mathematically, an interpolation from γ to itself via a one parameter family of curves corresponds to a map

$$\phi: S^1 \times S^1 \to M \qquad (15)$$

Here the first S^1 is parametrized by time τ, and the second by u, $0<u<1$, but now we identify u=1 with u=0. Thus, the first S^1 is mapped into M the same way at u=1 as at u=0. Given such a map, we can define for each u a rotation matrix

$$R(u) = P \exp \int_0^{2\pi} d\tau\ A(\tau;u) \tag{16}$$

As u varies from 0 to 1, R(u) sweeps out a closed curve in the O(n) manifold (R(1) = R(0)). This closed curve defines an element of $\pi_1(O(n)) \cong Z_2$. It is shown in the literature on spin manifolds (for instance, by Hawking and Pope [1]) that M does not admit a spin structure if for some $\phi:S^1\times S^1 \to M$, R(u) is non-zero in $\pi_1(O(n))$. We can now easily see that there is a global anomaly in precisely this situation. The non-zero element of $\pi_1(O(n))$ is related to a 2π rotation, so R(u) is non-trivial in $\pi_1(O(n))$ if (say) one θ_i increases by 2π as u is increased from 0 to 1 and the other θ_j do not change. But (14) is odd under a 2π increase in any of the θ_i. So $\sqrt{\det Y(u=1)} = -\sqrt{\det Y(u=0)}$ precisely when R(u) is non-zero in $\pi_1(O(n))$.

At this point we have shown that studying global anomalies on the world line amounts to asking whether M has a spin structure. Actually, our treatment is complete only when $\pi_1(M) = 0$. We will not attempt here to unravel some further subtleties that arise when $\pi_1(M) \neq 0$.

Concerning the other problems on our list above, we have already discussed those aspects of (b) that we will need for our later discussion of string theory. Therefore, we move on to discuss certain aspects of (c). Readers who are so inclined can skip the following section and jump directly to the remarks on strings.

If we wish to discuss quantum gravity, we are interested in a situation in which the metric g of M is not fixed but is one of the dynamical variables. When we try to define $\sqrt{\det Y}$ for a curve in M, we may regard it as a functional not just of the curve γ but also of the metric along the curve. We ask whether $\sqrt{\det Y}$ is single-valued as a functional of the curve and metric.

In the above discussion, we considered a map $\phi:S^1\times S^1 \to M$, which can be viewed as a one parameter family (u, labeling the second S^1, is the parameter) of maps of S^1 into M--with a <u>fixed</u> metric on M. Instead of taking a fixed metric on M, we could let the metric on M be u dependent--and so consider a one parameter family of maps of S^1 into a one parameter family of space-times. (I will take the liberty of referring to a one parameter family of metrics on M as defining a one parameter family of space-times.) Non-trivial one parameter families of metrics on M are in one to one correspondence with topological classes of diffeomorphisms $f:M \to M$. Thus, let f be such a diffeomorphism and g a metric on M, and suppose g transforms into g^f under f. Then $g(u) = (1-u)g + ug^f$ is a one parameter family of metrics on M. It is intimately connected with the mapping cylinder $E = (M\times S^1)_f$ discussed earlier; one can take the metric of E to be $ds^2 = du^2 + g_{ij}(u)\, dx^i dx^j$.

A one parameter family of maps of S^1 into a one parameter family of space times can be defined as a map $\phi:(S^1\times S^1) \to E$ which is of the special form $\phi(\tau,u) = (x(\tau,u),u)$. A fancier way to consider this is as follows. The mapping cylinder E is a fiber bundle over S^1, the fibration $\beta:E \to S^1$ being defined by $\beta(x,u)=u$. Likewise, $S^1\times S^1$ is a fiber bundle over the second S^1, the fibration $\alpha:S^1\times S^1 \to S^1$ being simply $\alpha(\tau,u)=u$. By a one parameter family of maps of S^1 into a one parameter family of space-times we mean simply a map $\phi:S^1\times S^1 \to E$ such that the diagram

$$\begin{array}{ccc} S^1\times S^1 & \xrightarrow{\ \phi\ } & E \\ & {\scriptstyle\alpha}\searrow \quad \swarrow{\scriptstyle\beta} & \\ & S^1 & \end{array} \tag{17}$$

commutes, in the sense that $\beta\phi = \alpha$.

Physically, this means the following. The map $\phi(\tau,u)$ defines (for each u) a curve in M. As u varies, both the curve and the metric of M vary. But at u=1, the curve and metric are the same as at u=0, up to a diffeomorphism of M. As before, we can calculate $H(u) = \sqrt{\det Y(u)}$ as a function of u. If all is well on heaven and earth, we may expect $H(1) = H(0)$.

If instead $H(1) = -H(0)$, what conclusion should we draw? One might be tempted to conclude that the theory is inconsistent if $H(1) \neq H(0)$ for some choice of E and ϕ. This is far from being the right interpretation. To understand this requires a brief digression.

M is a spin manifold (if the theory under discussion makes sense), so it has one or more spin structures. In studying fermions on M, we choose a spin structure μ.* A diffeomorphism $f:M \to M$ maps μ either into itself or into another spin structure $\tilde{\mu}$. If $f(\mu) = \mu$, μ can be extended to a spin structure on $E = (M \times S^1)_f$. Such an extension is not possible if $f(\mu) \neq \mu$.

What diffeomorphisms $f:M \to M$ are symmetries of our theory? One necessary condition is that $f(\mu) = \mu$. If $f(\mu) \neq \mu$, that means that f changes the boundary conditions obeyed by the fermions, and so is not a symmetry of the theory formulated with spin structure μ.

Returning to the map ϕ in (17), we want to know what it means if $H(1) = -H(0)$ for some ϕ and E. Our previous discussion of global anomalies shows that this means that E is not a spin manifold. This implies that $f(\mu) \neq \mu$ (since, as we just discussed, if $f(\mu) = \mu$, then E inherits a spin structure from the spin structures of M and S^1). But--as we discussed a moment ago--if $f(\mu) \neq \mu$, then f is not a symmetry of the theory with spin structure μ. So this is the interpretation of finding that $H(1) = -H(0)$: it means that the diffeomorphism f is not a symmetry of the theory. There is no paradox in this; a diffeomorphism f that behaves as described here never has compact support in space-time (once time is decompactified). What we have discovered is that global anomalies in a one parameter family of maps into a one parameter family of space-times are one symptom of how a classical symmetry may fail to be a quantum symmetry. What has been described here is a complex way of looking at a relatively simple restriction on diffeomorphisms (a true symmetry f must leave the spin structure fixed), but it will stand us in

---

*As discussed later, choosing a spin structure μ means deciding whether fermions propagate around non-contractible loops with periodic or anti-periodic boundary conditions. The spectrum of elementary particle masses depends on μ. We do not sum over μ. The situation will be completely different later when we consider spin structures on the string world sheet, since the physical role of the world sheet is completely different from that of space-time.

good stead later when we discuss the analogous phenomenon in string theory.

Although somewhat outside our line of development, I would like to pause at this point to discuss a purely mathematical application of the global anomaly in $\sqrt{\det Y}$. Let M be a manifold, and let $\Omega(M)$ be the space of all (oriented, unbased) maps $S^1 \to M$. We wish to ask whether the infinite dimensional manifold $\Omega(M)$ is orientable. To answer this we must find a definition of orientability in the finite dimensional case which makes sense in the infinite dimensional situation.

One notion of orientability for finite dimensional manifolds is that an n dimensional manifold Q is orientable if it admits a real, everywhere non-zero n form (volume element) ε. This notion does not seem to generalize to the infinite dimensional case. For even n, another criterion for orientability is that a manifold Q is orientable if it admits a (real) two form ω which is everywhere nondegenerate. (Nondegeneracy of ω means that at any point $p\varepsilon Q$, for any non-zero tangent vector V^i, $V^i\omega_{ij} \neq 0$. If ω is everywhere nondegenerate, the n form $\varepsilon = \omega^{n/2}$ is everywhere non-zero, so our first criterion for orientability is obeyed.) This notion is rather narrow since even an orientable, even dimensional manifold does not necessarily admit an everywhere nondegenerate two form ω. However, any n dimensional manifold Q admits (if n is even) a two form ω that is nondegenerate except on a subspace of dimension n-1. Introducing a Riemannian metric and raising an index gives a matrix $\omega^i{}_j = g^{ik}\,\omega_{kj}$. It is easy to see that, for any closed loop σ in Q, $\sqrt{\det \omega}$ changes sign in traversing σ if and only if the orientation of Q changes sign in traversing σ. So a finite dimensional manifold Q (of even dimension) is orientable if, picking any two form ω that is smooth and generically nondegenerate, $\sqrt{\det \omega}$ can be defined smoothly throughout Q.

This notion is readily implemented for $\Omega(M)$. Indeed, $Z = iY$ is a real, skew hermitian operator that can be interpreted as a two form on $\Omega(M)$. To see this, we must ask what is a tangent vector at a point γ in $\Omega(M)$. A point γ in $\Omega(M)$ is a loop $x^i(\tau)$ in M. A tangent vector to γ is an infinitesimal displacement $\delta x^i(\tau)$ or $\delta\tilde{x}^i(\tau)$ of this loop. Then the quantity

$$Z(\delta x, \delta\tilde{x}) = \int_0^{2\pi} d\tau\ \delta x^i(\tau)\ \left(g_{ij} \frac{d}{d\tau} + \frac{dx^k}{d\tau}\ \omega_{kij}\right)\ \delta\tilde{x}^j(\tau)$$

is bilinear, and $Z(\delta x, \delta\tilde{x}) = -Z(\delta\tilde{x}, \delta x)$, so Z defines a two form on $\Omega(M)$. We thus can consider $\Omega(M)$ to be orientable if $\sqrt{\det Z}$ is globally definable. We know the criterion for this--M must be a spin manifold. So we conclude that it is reasonable to say that $\Omega(M)$ is orientable if and only if M is a spin manifold.

Returning now to our main theme, we want to discuss--and to implement as far as possible--the steps analogous to (a), (b), and (c) above in the context of string theory. At least some of the steps should be evident:

(a') Analogous to anomalies in the propagation of a single point particle, we must discuss anomalies in the propagation of a single string. While world-line anomalies probe whether M has a spin structure, world-sheet anomalies will probe certain analogous obstacles to consistency of string theory.

(b') Analogous to anomalies in the Dirac determinant which enters the second quantized Dirac field theory, we will have to study anomalies in some generalization of the Dirac determinant that will enter the second quantized string field theory.

(c') After settling questions of consistency, we will want to study more general anomalies that affect the question of which apparent symmetries are actually valid.

As one might expect, the richness of string theory makes all of these questions much more difficult than their field theory analogues. It is possible to give a fairly thorough discussion of (a') and to say something about the other subjects. We will discuss these matters in turn.

First we will discuss (a')--anomalies in the propagation of a single string. This question is most interesting in the heterotic case,[9] since in that case the measure associated with the Euclidean world-sheet integrals is complex. We will discuss global world-sheet anomalies using the covariant, conformal gauge choice discussed in the latter part of the second paper in [9], since the expression given there for the measure is quite convenient for our purposes. The fact that supersymmetry is not manifest in this formalism is irrelevant for our purposes.

Two of the basic ingredients in world-sheet integrals are a Riemann surface Σ (which possesses a conformal structure over which we must integrate) and a map $\phi:\Sigma \to M$ of Σ into the space-time manifold M. Global anomalies always involve a one parameter family of objects of some kind. Global anomalies arise when the function space over which one is integrating is not simply connected, and the effective action does not return to its original value (modulo $2\pi i$) in traversing a non-contractible loop in function space. In string theory, there are several possibilities for which one parameter family of objects one may consider:

(i) One can investigate a one parameter family of Riemann surfaces. This arises if one is given a topologically non-trivial diffeomorphism $h:\Sigma\to\Sigma$. Generically, the metric g of Σ will be transformed into some other metric g^h by h. This leads in the usual way to a one parameter family of metrics on Σ, $g^u = (1-u)g + ug^h$, $0\leq u\leq 1$, which induce a one parameter family of conformal structures on Σ. This family is conveniently studied in terms of the mapping cylinder $(\Sigma\times S^1)_h$.

(ii) Keeping Σ fixed, one can study a one parameter family of maps of Σ into space-time. This amounts to consideration of a map $\phi:\Sigma\times S^1\to M$.

(iii) One can let both Σ and the map into space-time vary. One is then dealing with a one parameter family of maps of a one parameter family of Riemann surfaces into space-time. This amounts to the consideration of a map $\phi:(\Sigma\times S^1)_h\to M$.

In principle, (i) and (ii) are special cases of (iii). ((i) corresponds to the case in which ϕ maps $(\Sigma\times S^1)_h$ to a point, and (ii) to the case h=1.) However, (i) and (ii) are such natural special cases that it is reasonable to single them out. It is (ii) that corresponds most directly to the question which arises--and was discussed above--for a point particle. Neither (i) nor (ii) nor (iii) is vacuous. Anomalies of type (i) were shown in [9] to lead, at the one loop level, to the requirement that the Yang-Mills gauge group be O(32) or $E_8\times E_8$--the same conclusion that follows from consideration of perturbative anomalies in space-time.[3] We will show below that no new information comes from anomalies of type (i) at the multiloop level. As for anomalies of type (ii), they lead to the quantization of the Wess-Zumino interaction, a phenomenon that will be explored elsewhere,[10] and to a restriction on the allowed values of magnetic charge.[11] Anomalies of type (iii) have not been considered before (except for the special cases of type (i) and (ii)); we will see later that they lead to new constraints on allowed compactification.

Considering first (i), let us recall the formula of [9] for the effective world-sheet measure. For heterotic superstrings, there are ten right-moving fermions ψ_i, i=1...10. They come with a spin structure α (one must sum over α^*), and contribute to the measure a factor $(\det_\alpha i\not{D}(\frac{1+\bar{\rho}}{2}))^{10}$. Here $\frac{1+\bar{\rho}}{2}$ is the chirality projection operator, and the notation $\det_\alpha$ is meant to emphasize that the determinant depends on the choice of spin structure α. There is also a Rarita-Schwinger ghost, of the same chirality. It has the same spin structure α, and contributes a factor $(\det_\alpha R(\frac{1+\bar{\rho}}{2}))^{-1}$, where R is the Rarita-Schwinger operator.** Finally, if one realizes the gauge group by fermions, there are two groups of sixteen left-moving fermions with (in general) two different spin structures β and γ. They contribute $(\det_\beta i\not{D}(\frac{1-\bar{\rho}}{2}))^{16} \cdot (\det_\gamma i\not{D}(\frac{1-\bar{\rho}}{2}))^{16}$. For $E_8\times E_8$ gauge group, one sums independently over β and γ; for O(32), they are restricted to obey $\beta=\gamma$. The effective measure is hence

$$S = (\det_\alpha i\not{D}(\tfrac{1+\bar{\rho}}{2}))^{10}\,(\det_\beta i\not{D}(\tfrac{1-\bar{\rho}}{2}))^{16}\,(\det_\gamma i\not{D}(\tfrac{1-\bar{\rho}}{2}))^{16}\,(\det_\alpha R(\tfrac{1+\bar{\rho}}{2}))^{-1} \tag{18}$$

This expression is free of perturbative anomalies, as was noted in [9] (using formulas in [2] to compare the Rarita-Schwinger and Dirac contributions).

---

* Summing over α is a way to project onto the supersymmetric sector of states of definite G parity.

** R is the operator $\psi_\mu \to i\not{D}\psi_\mu$, ψ_μ being a vector-spinor.

Now, we will certainly not try to prove here that the multiloop diagrams are physically acceptable in all respects. We will limit ourselves to the narrower problem of proving that S, in (18), is invariant under any diffeomorphism $h:\Sigma\to\Sigma$. This has already been proved (using explicit formulas for the determinants and standard theorems about theta functions) at the one loop level,[9] so the only novelty is the generalization to higher loops.

S depends on α, β, and γ and on the metric g of Σ. We will prove that $S(\alpha,\beta,\gamma,g) = S(\alpha,\beta,\gamma,g^h)$ if h is any diffeomorphism that leaves fixed α, β, and γ (g^h is the conjugate of g by h). Whether this is so or not is a well-defined question, since one can interpolate continuously from g to g^h. Once it is established that $S(\alpha,\beta,\gamma,g)$ is invariant under any diffeomorphism that leaves fixed α, β, and γ, no new informtion comes from considering a diffeomorphism h that maps α, β, and γ into other spin structures α^h, β^h, and γ^h. One can just define $S(\alpha^h, \beta^h,\gamma^h,g^h) = S(\alpha,\beta,\gamma,g)$. There is no way to test this statement, since as spin structures are discrete, there is no way to interpolate smoothly from α, β, and γ to α^h, β^h, and γ^h. So what really must be done is to prove that $S(\alpha,\beta,\gamma,g) = S(\alpha,\beta,\gamma,g^h)$ if h is such that α, β, and γ are invariant under it.

We first consider the special case $\alpha=\beta=\gamma$. As $\det_\alpha i\not{D}\left(\frac{1+\bar{\rho}}{2}\right) \cdot \det_\alpha i\not{D}\left(\frac{1-\bar{\rho}}{2}\right)$ is real, positive, and anomaly free, S simplifies to

$$\tilde{S} = \left(\det_\alpha i\not{D}\left(\frac{1-\bar{\rho}}{2}\right)\right)^{22} \left(\det_\alpha R\left(\frac{1+\bar{\rho}}{2}\right)\right)^{-1} \tag{19}$$

In view of the basic equation (2) for global anomalies, the change in $\tilde{S}$ under h is

$$\Delta \ln \tilde{S} = \frac{i\pi}{2}\left(22\eta(D) + (\eta(R) - \eta(D))\right) \tag{20}$$

where $\eta(D)$ and $\eta(R)$ are the eta invariants of the Dirac and Rarita-Schwinger operators on the mapping cylinder $Q = (\Sigma\times S^1)_h$.* Now we use

* The appearance of $(\eta_R-\eta_D)$ as the Rarita-Schwinger contribution (rather than η_R as one might have guessed) follows from the fact that a three dimensional vector is a two dimensional vector plus scalar. A similar combination appears in (21) below for the same reason. See [4] for further discussion.

the fact* that the spin cobordism group is trivial in three dimensions, so Q is the boundary of a four dimensional spin manifold B. The Atiyah-Patodi-Singer theorem[5] then asserts that

$$\frac{1}{2}\eta(D) = \text{index}(D) - \int_B \hat{A}(R)$$

$$\frac{1}{2}\eta(R) = (\text{index}(R) - \text{index}(D)) - \int_B (K(R) - \hat{A}(R)) \qquad (21)$$

Here index(D) and index(R) are the Dirac and Rarita-Schwinger index on B (with boundary conditions explained in [5]); $\hat{A}$ and K are the curvature polynomials whose integral over a four manifold <u>without</u> boundary would equal index(R) and index(D). Substituting (21) in (20), we may modulo $2\pi i$ drop index(D) and index(R), since they are even in four dimensions (as explained for instance in [4]), so we get

$$\Delta \ln \tilde{S} = i\pi \int_B (-20\,\hat{A} - K) \bmod 2\pi i \qquad (22)$$

This vanishes because $K = -20\hat{A}$ in four dimensions.**

---

* An oriented manifold has $w_1=0$; if it has a spin structure, then $w_2=0$ in addition. (Here w_k are Stiefel-Whitney classes.) If $w_1=w_2=0$, the tangent bundle is trivial when restricted to the two skeleton, and hence (since $\pi_2(O(N))=0$) it is also trivial when restricted to the three skeleton. Hence $w_3=0$ if $w_1=w_2=0$. Consequently, a three dimensional (oriented) spin manifold has all Stiefel-Whitney classes and all Stiefel-Whitney (or Z_2) characteristic numbers zero. Hence ([12], p. 42) such a manifold (if it has no boundary) bounds an oriented manifold. Except in 8k+1 or 8k+2 dimensions, every spin manifold that bounds an oriented manifold bounds a spin manifold ([12], pp. 46-7). So every three dimensional (closed, oriented) spin manifold is the boundary of a spin manifold.

** $\hat{A}$ corresponds to the term of order x_i^2 in $\prod_{i=1}^{2} \frac{x_i/2}{\sinh x_i/2}$, and K to the term of order x_i^2 in $\prod_{i=1}^{2} \frac{x_i/2}{\sinh x_i/2} \cdot \sum_{j=1}^{2} (2\cosh x_j)$.

We still must consider the possibility that α, β, and γ are not all equal. The correction factor between S and $\tilde{S}$ is

$$U_0 = \left(\frac{\det_\beta i\not{\partial}\left(\frac{1-\bar{\rho}}{2}\right)}{\det_\alpha i\not{\partial}\left(\frac{1-\bar{\rho}}{2}\right)}\right)^{16} \left(\frac{\det_\gamma i\not{\partial}\left(\frac{1-\bar{\rho}}{2}\right)}{\det_\alpha i\not{\partial}\left(\frac{1-\bar{\rho}}{2}\right)}\right)^{16} \tag{23}$$

and we must prove that this is invariant under any diffeomorphism $h:\Sigma\to\Sigma$ that fixes α, β, and γ. Actually, we will prove the stronger statement that

$$U = \left(\frac{\det_\beta i\not{\partial}\left(\frac{1-\bar{\rho}}{2}\right)}{\det_\alpha i\not{\partial}\left(\frac{1-\bar{\rho}}{2}\right)}\right)^{8} \tag{24}$$

is invariant under any diffeomorphism h that fixes α and β. Eight is incidentally the lowest exponent for which this is true, as one loop calculations show.

Since α and β are invariant under h, they both extend to spin structures (which we will also call α and β) on the mapping cylinder $T = (\Sigma\times S^1)_h$. We have two different Dirac operators on T (with spin structures α and β); the two η invariants associated with these two Dirac operators will be called $\eta_\alpha(D)$ and $\eta_\beta(D)$. In view of equation (2), the change in U under a diffeomorphism is

$$\Delta \ell n U = 8\,\frac{i\pi}{2}\left(\eta_\alpha(D) - \eta_\beta(D)\right) \bmod 2\pi i \tag{25}$$

The general theory for calculating differences such as $\eta_\alpha(D)-\eta_\beta(D)$ has been developed by Atiyah, Patodi, and Singer in the last paper in [5]. As we do not wish to calculate $\eta_\alpha(D)-\eta_\beta(D)$, but only to prove that it is an integer multiple of 1/2 (so that (25) vanishes modulo $2\pi i$), a short cut is available. Actually, for <u>any</u> orientable three manifold T (not necessarily a mapping cylinder) and any two spin structures α and β, we will prove

$$8\,\frac{\pi}{2}\left(\eta_\alpha(T) - \eta_\beta(T)\right) = 0 \bmod 2\pi \tag{26}$$

A key to proving this is to understand what is the nature of the difference between two spin structures α and β. When a vector is parallel transported around a closed curve γ in T, it is rotated by a rotation matrix $R_\gamma \in O(3)$. When a spinor (with spin structure α or β) is parallel transported around γ, it returns rotated by a matrix $R_\gamma(\alpha)$ or $R_\gamma(\beta)$ which is a matrix that represents the same R_γ in the spinor representation. Since the spinor representation is double-valued, it is not necessarily so that $R_\gamma(\beta)$ equals $R_\gamma(\alpha)$. In general $R_\gamma(\beta) = (-1)^{n(\gamma)} \cdot R_\gamma(\alpha)$, where $n(\gamma)=\pm 1$ for each γ. The mapping $\gamma \to n(\gamma)$ is a homomorphism $\pi_1(T) \to Z_2$. Given one spin structure α, possible choices of another spin structure β are in one to one correspondence with homomorphisms $\mu:\pi_1 \to Z_2$.

Our goal will be to represent the difference between α and β spin structures as an interaction with an auxiliary SU(2) or O(3) gauge field that will have $F_{ij}{}^a=0$, so it will just enter in modifying the law of parallel transport around closed loops. To this end, think of a mapping $\nu:T \to O(3)$. Any such mapping ν maps a closed curve γ in T into a closed curve $\nu(\gamma)$ in O(3), so it induces a homomorphism $\pi_1(T) \to \pi_1(O(3)) \simeq Z_2$. We want to show that <u>every</u> homomorphism $\mu:\pi_1(T) \to Z_2$ is induced in this way from a mapping $\nu:T \to O(3)$. To this end, pick a triangulation of T.* This means roughly that we realize T as a collection of tetrahedra glued together on their faces. The vertices of the tetrahedra are called 0-simplices S_0, the edges are called 1-simplices S_1, the faces are called 2-simplices S_2, and the interiors are called 3-simplices S_3. The boundary ∂S_q of a q-simplex S_q is topologically a q-1 sphere S^{q-1}. If for some q simplex S_q a mapping $\nu_0:\partial S_q \to O(3)$ has been defined, the obstruction to extending ν_0 over S_q is an element of $\pi_{q-1}(O(3))$.

Now, given a homomorphism $\mu:\pi_1(T) \to \pi_1(O(3)) \simeq Z_2$, we wish to find a mapping $R:T \to O(3)$ which "induces" μ in the manner described in the last paragraph. The strategy is to first define R on 0-simplices, then on 1-simplices, then on 2-simplicies, and finally on 3-simplices. On 0-simplices, one may just take $\nu(x)=1$ for any 0-simplex x. On 1-simplices, the definition of R is determined up to homotopy by μ. (Pick

---

*This is a standard concept in topology; see for instance [13]. A brief exposition was given in [11].

any ordering of the one simplices. Define R first on the "first" one simplex, then on the "second," and finally on the last. At each stage the choice of R is arbitrary unless the 1-simplex which is being added completes a closed loop, in which case μ determines a topological restriction on R which must be obeyed. There never is an inconsistency in obeying these restrictions since μ is a homomorphism of $\pi_1(T)$ into $\pi_1(O(3)) \simeq Z_2$.) Now we try to extend R over two-simplices. The boundary of a two-simplex y is a curve γ. γ is trivial in $\pi_1(T)$ (since it bounds y) so $\mu(\gamma)=0$ in $\pi_1(O(3))$. Hence, having defined R on one simplices to induce the homomorphism μ of fundamental groups, the mapping $R:\gamma\to O(3)$ is topologically trivial for any γ which bounds y and can be extended to $R:y\to O(3)$. Having thus defined R over two simplices, it can always be extended over three simplices, since the obstruction would lie in $\pi_2(O(3))=0$. This completes the proof that every homomorphism $\mu:\pi_1(T)\to Z_2 \simeq \pi_1(O(3))$ is induced by some mapping $R:T\to O(3)$.

Now, we will wish to study the SU(2) gauge field $A_i = R^{-1}\partial_i R$. In integer spin representations of SU(2), this is completely trivial, a pure gauge. In half integer spin representations, R (being double-valued) is not well defined, but $A_i = R^{-1}\partial_i R$ is well-defined. However, in half integer spin representations of SU(2), A_i is trivial only locally, not globally. In such a representation, for any closed curve γ,

$$P \exp \int_\gamma A\cdot dx = (-1)^{n(\gamma)} \tag{27}$$

where $\gamma\to n(\gamma)$ is our homomorphism μ.

Now we wish to pick two representations P and Q of SU(2) with the following properties:

(x) They are real and of the same dimension.

(y) They have the same quadratic Casimir operator.

(z) In P the center of SU(2) is represented by +1, and in Q by -1.

The lowest dimension for which such representations exist is 8. This is why U in (24) will turn out to be single-valued with the exponent 8. The minimal choice is that P should be the $3 \oplus 1 \oplus 1 \oplus 1 \oplus 1 \oplus 1$ of SU(2), while Q is $2 \oplus 2 \oplus 2 \oplus 2$.

To evaluate (25), we must understand the quantities $8\eta_\alpha$ and $8\eta_\beta$. As regards $8\eta_\alpha$, it is the eta invariant for eight spinors with spin structure α. There is no harm in saying they lie in the P representation of SU(2) and interact with the gauge field $A_i = R^{-1}\partial_i R$--since that gauge field is trivial in that representation. So we say

$$8\eta_\alpha = \eta'_{\alpha P} \tag{28}$$

where $\eta_{\alpha P}$ is the eta invariant for a fermion in the P representation of SU(2). The eight fermions interacting with spin structure β, on the other hand, will be treated in a slightly less trivial way. Eight fermions with spin structure β are exactly equivalent to eight fermions in the Q representation of SU(2) with spin structure α--since the not-quite-trivial SU(2) gauge field $A_i = R^{-1}\partial_i R$ has, in the Q representation, the sole effect of flipping the boundary condition, turning spin structure α into β. So

$$8\eta_\beta = \eta_{\alpha Q} \tag{29}$$

Now we will use the Atiyah-Patodi-Singer theorem to evaluate $\eta_{\alpha Q}$ and $\eta_{\alpha P}$ --or at least their difference. Let $W = T\times I$; I is a unit interval with parameter u, $0<u<1$. In contrast to the rather trivial gauge fields we have been discussing, we now consider a highly non-trivial instanton gauge field on W. Let $B_i(x_k,u) = uA_i(x_k)$, $B_u = 0$ (x_k being coordinates for T). This B_i interpolates from 0 at u=0 to A_i at u=1. The Atiyah-Patodi-Singer applied to the manifold W with gauge field B gives

$$\frac{1}{2}\left(\eta_{\alpha P} - 8\eta_\alpha\right) = \text{index}_P(D) - \int_W \hat{A}_P$$

$$\frac{1}{2}\left(\eta_{\alpha Q} - 8\eta_\alpha\right) = \text{index}_Q(D) - \int_W \hat{A}_Q \tag{30}$$

Here $\text{index}_P(D)$ and $\text{index}_Q(D)$ are the index of the Dirac operator on W (with spin structure α) in the P or Q representation. These are even, since P and Q are real. $\hat{A}_P$ and $\hat{A}_Q$ are the curvature polynomials related to the Dirac index in four dimensions; they are equal, since we chose P and Q to have the same quadratic Casimir operator. The left-hand side of (30) involves $\eta_{\alpha P}-8\eta_\alpha$ and $\eta_{\alpha Q}-8\eta_\alpha$ since the boundary of W has two components; the u=1 component contributes $\eta_{\alpha P}$ or $\eta_{\alpha Q}$, while the u=0 component contributes $8\eta_\alpha$. Subtracting the two equations in (30) and using the facts just noted, we learn

$$\eta_{\alpha P} - \eta_{\alpha Q} = 0 \text{ modulo } 4 \tag{31}$$

Equations (28), (29), and (31) imply that $\Delta \ln U$ in (25) is zero. This completes the proof that the measure $S(\alpha,\beta,\gamma;g)$ is invariant under diffeomorphisms tht leave α, β, and γ fixed.

This proof required only very general considerations and few detailed facts about Riemann surfaces. Of course, it leaves open many other questions tied to the consistency of the theory whose resolution may require deeper knowledge of Riemann surfaces. For instance, it is expected from supersymmetry that $\sum_{\alpha,\beta,\gamma} S(\alpha,\beta,\gamma;g) = 0$ but I do not think that this can be proved using only the methods above.

Returning to our list of problems, this completes what we will say here about anomalies involving purely a one parameter family of conformal structures on Σ. We now turn very briefly to discuss anomalies involving mappings into space-time of a fixed Riemann surface Σ. I will not describe any new examples of anomalies (beyond those described in [10] and [11]), but I will comment briefly on the setting for this problem.

As soon as we consider non-trivial maps ϕ of Σ into the space-time M, the spin connection and gauge field in space-time become highly relevant. The spin connection $\omega_i{}^k{}_\ell$ is an O(10) connection on the tangent bundle T of M. Its pull-back to Σ is an O(10) gauge field $a_\alpha{}^k{}_\ell = \frac{\partial x_i}{\partial\sigma^\alpha}\omega_i{}^k{}_\ell$. The factor $\left(\det_\alpha i\not{D}\left(\frac{1+\bar\rho}{2}\right)\right)^{10}$ in (18) becomes replaced by $\det_{\alpha T} i\not{D}\left(\frac{1+\bar\rho}{2}\right)$ where $\det_{\alpha T}$ is the determinant for ten fermions (with spin structure α) interacting with a_α. Henceforth we will abbreviate positive or negative chirality determinants as $\det_\pm$. Likewise we have in spacetime an $E_8\times E_8$ bundle $V = V_1 \oplus V_2$ with the two E_8 gauge fields

$A_{(1)i}$, $A_{(2)i}$. There is no convenient way for E_8 gauge fields to act on 16 fermions. But pragmatically, on the four skeleton of M (all that enters in discussing world-sheet anomalies) the structure group of any E_8 bundle can be reduced to O(16). So for our limited purposes we probably lose little in assuming $A_{(1)i}$ and $A_{(2)i}$ are O(16) gauge fields. Anyway, at present it is the best we can do. Then $A_{(1)}$ and $A_{(2)}$ can be pulled back to gauge fields $B_{(1)\alpha} = \frac{\partial x^i}{\partial\sigma^\alpha} A_{(1)i}$, $B_{(2)\alpha} = \frac{\partial x^i}{\partial\sigma^\alpha} A_{(2)i}$ on Σ. The factors in (18) involving $(\det_\beta)^{16}$ and $(\det_\gamma)^{16}$ become $\det^{(-)}_{\beta V_1}$ and $\det^{(-)}_{\gamma V_2}$. In addition, one more potentially anomalous term must be included in the measure. In space-time there is a two form B_{ij}. Its interaction with the string is $i\int d^2\sigma\, \varepsilon^{\alpha\beta}\, \partial_\alpha x^i\, \partial_\beta x^j\, B_{ij}(x(\sigma))$, which we will abbreviate as $i\int_\Sigma \phi^* B$. ($\phi^* B$ is the pullback of B from M to Σ via ϕ.) So the measure is

$$S = \left(\det^+_{\alpha T}\right)\left(\det^-_{\beta V_1}\right)\left(\det^-_{\gamma V_2}\right)\left(\det^+_\alpha R\right)^{-1} \exp i \int_\Sigma \phi^* B \qquad (32)$$

Now, one difference between the string and the point particle is that in the particle case we only had to consider global anomalies on the world line, but in the case of the string both perturbative and global anomalies on the world sheet must be considered. Indeed, the perturbative anomalies cancel [9] if one considers a trivial map of Σ into space-time. But as soon as one considers a non-trivial map it appears, at first sight, that the anomaly cancellation would be spoiled by so-called sigma model anomalies[14] involving the spin connection and gauge field of space-time. This would indeed be so if we considered only the product of determinants in (32). But the last factor involving B saves the day.[15] Indeed, the sigma model anomaly can be canceled in (32) if one accompanies a gauge and local Lorentz transformation in space-time with

$$\delta B = \mathrm{tr}\,(A d\Lambda) - \mathrm{tr}\,(\omega d\theta) \qquad (33)$$

Here Λ and θ are the parameters of infinitessimal gauge and local Lorentz transformations. This is the same gauge transformation law that cancels anomalies in space-time--a satisfying relation between space-time and world-sheet anomalies.

(33) implies that the gauge invariant field strength H of B obeys not dH=0 but

$$dH = \mathrm{Tr}\, F^2 - \mathrm{tr}\, R^2 \tag{34}$$

This, in turn, has a certain topological interpretation [16]. In de Rham cohomology, dH=0 while $\mathrm{Tr}F^2$ and $\mathrm{tr}R^2$ represent the first Pontryagin classes (with real coefficients) of the $E_8 \times E_8$ bundle V and the tangent bundle T. So (34) implies that the theory is only consistent if T and V are such that

$$P_1(V;R) = P_1(T;R) \tag{35}$$

Here $P_1(\ ;R)$ denotes Pontryagin classes with real coefficients. It is satisfying to see that the world-sheet theory is "aware" of this relation, which also follows from space-time considerations.

Now, Pontryagin classes with real coefficients have a natural generalization--Pontryagin classes $P_1(\ ;Z)$ with integer coefficients. These entered and were explained in [11]. (In that paper, P_1 was sometimes called the second Chern class C_2--which is equivalent for real bundles.) It was found there that magnetic monopoles are not permitted in string theory unless their magnetic charge is such as to not contribute to $P_1(V;Z)$. This result can be unified with (35) if we assume that the actual requirement for consistency of the theory is*

$$P_1(V;Z) = P_1(T;Z) \tag{36}$$

Although I believe that (36) is probably needed in generality for consistency of the theory, it would be beyond the scope of the present notes to try to prove this in full. Many technicalities arise, some of which will be mentioned later. I will limit myself to providing new evidence for (36) by showing that it is required for consistency in a

---

*By $P_1(F;Z)$ for an E_8 bundle F I mean the fourth cohomology class that is the first obstruction to triviality of F. If F is induced from an O(16) bundle $\tilde{F}$ by the embedding $O(16) \subset E_8$, $P_1(F;Z)$ should be taken to mean $P_1(\tilde{F};Z)$.

new physical situation. In the situation I have in mind, little can be learned by considering a one parameter family of maps of a fixed Riemann surface into space-time (corresponding, as was described earlier, to a map $\phi:\Sigma\times S^1\to M$). It will be necessary to consider a one parameter family of maps of a one parameter family of Riemann surfaces into space-time. This corresponds to a map $\phi:T\to M$ where $T = (\Sigma\times S^1)_h$ is a mapping cylinder. Physically, the rationale for considering anomalies in this situation is as follows. If u is a parameter for S^1, then as u is varied, both Σ and its map into M vary. But on returning these to their original values, we require that the amplitude associated with the string propagation should return to <u>its</u> original value.

The situation we wish to consider is that of compactification of the ten dimensional theory on $M^4\times K$, M^4 being four dimensional Minkowski space and K some compact six manifold. We assume that the spin connection of K is embedded in one E_8 factor of the gauge group, breaking $E_8\times E_8$ to $E_6\times E_8$, $O(10)\times U(1)\times E_8$, or $O(10)\times E_8$ depending on whether K has SU(3), U(3), or O(6) holonomy.[17] (Actually, if K has U(3) holonomy, there are several other possibilities for the unbroken group[18].) By itself, this does not introduce any global anomalies, since embedding the spin connection in one E_8 factor gives a vector-like non-linear sigma model on the string world sheet.

If now K is not simply connected, it is possible to introduce grand unified symmetry breaking via Wilson lines. This means that one picks a homomorphism $\pi_1(K)\to G$ of the fundamental group of K into the unbroken group G. This breaks G to the subgroup that commutes with the image of $\pi_1(K)$ in G. The Wilson lines define a flat vector bundle V. What we wish to investigate is whether there are global anomalies associated with the choice of Wilson lines. Global anomalies, being a topological notion, can only detect topological invariants of V. By far the simplest topological invariant of V is its first Pontryagin class, so it is natural to look for global anomalies associated with the Wilson lines via $P_1(V;Z)$.

Rather than trying to be general, we will consider a simple example. Let $K = (S^5/Z_n)\times S^1$. Here S^5/Z_n is the "lens space" consisting of three complex variables (Z_1,Z_2,Z_3) with $|Z_1|^2 + |Z_2|^2 + |Z_3|^2 = 1$

and with (Z_1,Z_2,Z_3) considered equivalent to $(Z_1\alpha,Z_2\alpha,Z_3\alpha)$ where α = exp $22\pi i/n$. Ignoring the S^1 factor, we will consider Wilson lines associated with S^5/Z_n only. As $\pi_1(S^5/Z_n) = Z_n$, we must pick a single Wilson line U obeying $U^n=1$. It always fits into a subgroup $U(8) \subset O(16) \subset E_8$, and in that subgroup it can be written

$$U = \begin{pmatrix} \exp 2\pi i k_1/n & & & \\ & \exp 2\pi i k_2/n & & \\ & & \ddots & \\ & & & \exp 2\pi i k_8/n \end{pmatrix} \tag{37}$$

Actually, we have two such matrices, one for each E_8, and one of them is restricted to commute with the embedded spin connection (requiring $k_6=k_7=k_8$ if K has SU(3) holonomy). We want to calculate global anomalies associated with the choice of U.

A map $\phi:T\to K$ can (since $T=(\Sigma\times S^1)_h$ is three dimensional) only "cover" a three dimensional subspace of K. We will pick this subspace to be the subspace of S^5/Z_n defined by $Z_3=0$. This itself is a lens space $L=S^3/Z_n$.

Now, we want to choose a Riemann surface Σ and a map $h:\Sigma\to\Sigma$ such that we can find a degree one map $\phi:(\Sigma\times S^1)_h\to L$. We will pick Σ to be a torus with periodic coordinates (τ,σ), $0\leq\sigma,\tau\leq 2\pi$. As for h, it will be the map $h(\tau,\sigma) = (\tau+n\sigma,\sigma)$. Thus, $(\Sigma\times S^1)_h$ will consist of triples (τ,σ,u) with $(\tau,\sigma,0)$ identified with $(\tau+n\sigma,\sigma,1)$. As h has been chosen to leave σ invariant, $T = (\Sigma\times S^1)_h$ is actually in this case a fiber bundle over a torus $T_0 = S^1\times S^1$ spanned by σ and u. The fiber S^1 is spanned by τ.

L is also a fiber bundle over a two manifold, in this case a two sphere S^2 with coordinates $\vec{w} = \overset{*}{Z}\vec{\sigma}Z$ (as we set $Z_3=0$ to define L, there are two Z_i; $\vec{\sigma}$ are the standard Pauli matrices). From $\sum_i |Z_i|^2 = 1$ it follows that $\vec{w}^2=1$; the map $\{Z_i\}\to\{w_k\}$ is a fibration $L\to S^2$.

To pick a degree one map $\phi:T\to L$, we begin by picking a degree one map $\phi_0:T_0\to S^2$. There is a simple analytic formula for a degree two map $T_0\to S^2$ given by polar coordinates (w_1 = sin$2\pi u$ cosσ, w_2 = sin$2\pi a$ sinσ, w_3 = cos$2\pi u$). Although there seems to be no simple analytic formula for a degree one map, such a map exists. (Pick a disc D in T_0 and map its boundary and exterior to a single point in S^2. D is thus effectively compactified to a sphere, which has a degree one map onto S^2. This completes the specification of the map $T_0 \to S^2$.) Now, L is an S^1 fiber bundle over S^2, so pulling back this fiber bundle via the map $\phi_0 : T_0 \to S^2$ gives an S^1 fiber bundle over T_0. The total space of this fiber bundle is a three manifold T fibered over T_0. ϕ_0 "lifts" automatically to a degree one map $\phi : T \to L$. Actually T was chosen earlier to be isomorphic to the manifold T just encountered, and ϕ is the desired degree one map $\phi : T \to L$.

Now, we want to calculate the global anomaly associated with the Wilson line U of equation (37). While E_8 can be realized on 16 real fermions, it is convenient, in view of the diagonal form in (37), to think of these as eight complex fermions ψ_a, a = 1...8 and their complex conjugates. A given fermion ψ_a interacts with an Abelian gauge field $A^{(a)}$ in space-time. $A^{(a)}$ is a pure gauge locally but has global holonomy $U = \exp 2\pi i k_a/n$. Now $A^{(a)}$ "pulls-back" to an abelian gauge field $A^{(a)}_\alpha = \frac{\partial x^i}{\partial \sigma^\alpha} A^{(a)}_i$ (here σ^α is τ, σ, or u). $A^{(a)}_\alpha$ is again a pure gauge locally. Its global holonomy can be inferred from that of $A^{(a)}$:

$$\exp i \int_0^{2\pi} d\tau\, A^{(a)}_\tau = \exp 2\pi i k_a/n$$

$$\exp i \int_0^{2\pi} d\sigma\, A^{(a)}_\sigma = \exp i \int_0^{1} du\, A^{(a)}_u = 1 \tag{38}$$

Now we wish to calculate the change in the effective action of the fermion ψ_a between u=0 and u=1. This is the variation under h of

$$X = \frac{\det^-_\beta (A^{(a)})}{\det^-_\beta (0)} \tag{39}$$

Here $\det^-_\beta (A_a)$ is a negative chirality fermion determinant with spin structure β and abelian gauge field $A^{(a)}$; $\det^-_\beta(0)$ is a negative chirality determinant without $A^{(a)}$. X is the factor by which the world sheet measure is corrected by the interaction of ψ_a with $A^{(a)}$. Since the theory was invariant under h at $A^{(a)}=0$, it is the correction factor X that we must study.

By our usual formula (2) (multiplied by a factor of 2 since ψ^a is complex while (2) refers to Majorana-Weyl fermions), the change in X under h is

$$\Delta \ell n X = i\pi \left(\eta_\beta(A^{(a)}) - \eta_\beta(0)\right)_{\mathrm{mod} 2\pi i} \tag{40}$$

where $\eta_\beta\ (A^{(a)}(0))$ and η_β are the η invariants on T with and without $A^{(a)}$.

Now, to evaluate (40), we will pick a manifold B whose boundary is T and use the Atiyah-Patodi-Singer theorem. B is conveniently chosen as follows. The circle S^1 with coordinate τ is the boundary of a disc D with polar coordinates (ρ,τ), $0 \leq \rho \leq 1$, $0 \leq \tau \leq 2\pi$. The S^1 bundle $T \to T_0$ can be extended to a disc bundle $B \to T_0$. (The metric for B may be, for instance, $ds^2 = d\rho^2 + \rho^2\ (d\tau - nud\sigma)^2 + d\sigma^2 + du^2$.) B has boundary T. Actually, B is a spin manifold only if n is even, and we will content ourselves with this case. (The more general case can be studied by using a spin_c structure on B.) Also, the hitherto arbitrary h invariant spin structure β on Σ must be chosen to be extendable over B.

The next step is to extend the U(1) gauge field $A^{(a)}$ on T to a U(1) gauge field (which we will also call $A^{(a)}$) on B. Since $A^{(a)}$ is topologically non-trivial, it is awkward to write an explicit formula for it. But a suitable formula for $F = dA^{(a)}$ is

$$F = \frac{k^{(a)}}{n}\left[d\rho\ (d\tau - nu\ d\sigma) - (1-\rho)\ ndu\ d\sigma\right] \tag{41}$$

This formula has the following key properties:

(1) It is invariant under $u \to u+1$, $\tau \to \tau+n\sigma$, so it actually is defined on B, not just some covering space of B.

(2) $dF = 0$, so locally $F = dA$ for some A.

(3) Restricted to T ($\rho = 1$, $d\rho = 0$), $F = 0$. So the gauge field A associated with F is on T locally a pure gauge. It also has the global holonomy desired for $A^{(a)}$. For instance, $\exp i \int_0^{2\pi} d\tau\, A_\tau^{(a)} = \exp i \int_D F = \exp \frac{2\pi i\ k^{(a)}}{n}$, as desired.

Having found the right gauge field, we can evaluate (40) via the Atiyah-Patodi-Singer theorem. In fact

$$\frac{1}{2}\eta_\beta\,(A^{(a)}) = \text{index}_\beta\,(A^{(a)}) - \int_B \hat{A}\,(A^{(a)})$$

$$\frac{1}{2}\eta_\beta(0) = \text{index}_\beta(0) - \int_B \hat{A}\,(0) \tag{42}$$

Here $\text{index}_\beta\,(A^{(a)})$ and $\text{index}_\beta(0)$ are the Dirac index with and without the gauge field $A^{(a)}$. Also, $\hat{A}(A^a)$ and $\hat{A}(0)$ are the polynomials related to the index theorem, with and without $A^{(a)}$. In fact $A(A^{(a)}) - A(0) = \frac{1}{2(2\pi)^2} F\wedge F$. So we get

$$\Delta\ell nX = -2\pi i \int_B (\hat{A}(A^a) - \hat{A}(0)) = -\frac{2\pi i}{2\cdot(2\pi)^2}\int_B F\wedge F$$

$$= \frac{2\pi i}{2\cdot(2\pi)^2}\int_0^1 d\rho \int_0^{2\pi} d\tau \int_0^{2\pi} d\sigma \int_0^1 du\,\left(\frac{k^{(a)}}{n}\right)^2 n(1-\rho)$$

$$= 2\pi i\,\frac{(k^{(a)})^2}{2n} \bmod 2\pi i \tag{43}$$

The total global anomaly is obtained by summing (43) overall fermion species (a), and vanishes if*

---

*At first sight, it is not clear why Wilson lines are such that $\frac{1}{2}\Sigma k^{(a)2}$ is always an integer. This is paradoxical, since with $\pi_1(K) = Z_n$, we must at most get mod n, not mod 2n, global anomalies. The resolution of the paradox is as follows. With $\pi_1(K) = Z_n$, the only Wilson lines that can be defined are those for which $U^n = 1$ not just in U(8) but also in E_8 when U(8) is embedded in E_8 via $U(8) \subset O(16) \subset E_8$. The key point is that the adjoint of E_8 contains the double-valued spinor of O(16). As a result of this, when n is even, all Wilson lines that can be defined in E_8 have $\Sigma_a k^{(a)}$ even--which always makes $\frac{1}{2}\Sigma k^{(a)2}$ an integer. When n is odd, so that B is not a spin manifold, there are further intricacies which we will not try to unravel.

$$\sum_a \frac{1}{2} k^{(a)2} = 0 \bmod n \tag{44}$$

But as was explained in [11], the contribution of the Wilson lines to $P_1(V;Z)$ is $\frac{1}{2}\sum_a k^{(a)^2} y^2$, where y is the generator of $H^2(K;Z)$. As $\ell y^2=0$ in $H^4(K;Z)$ if and only if $\ell=0 \bmod n$, equation (44) can be regarded as further evidence for the general validity of the requirement (36) that $P_1(V;Z) = P_1(T;Z)$ for consistency.

This calculation raises many questions. First of all, how would one generalize it to establish a universal requirement $P_1(V;Z) = P_1(T;Z)$? As this equation holds rationally because of perturbative anomalies, it is only the torsion piece that we have to worry about. A torsion part of P_1 is necessarily a torsion element of $H^4(K;Z)$, the fourth cohomology group of K with integer coefficients. By the universal coefficients theorem, this is related to a torsion class in $H_3(K;Z)$, the third homology group of K with integer coefficients. Such a class can be represented by an immersed three manifold L. To try to find a global anomaly that forces $P_1(V;Z) = P_1(T;Z)$, one must then look for a Riemann surface Σ, a map $h:\Sigma\to\Sigma$, and a degree one map $\phi:(\Sigma\times S^1)_h\to L$. If this can be found, one can try to repeat the above calculation and find a global anomaly. While I expect that this last step can be pushed through, I will not attempt it here. A more difficult problem arises because, in general, L is such that for any Σ and h there is no degree one map $\phi:(\Sigma\times S^1)_h\to L$. How then can a requirement on P_1 emerge? While I do not know the answer to this question, it is encouraging to note that a similar problem arises in the point particle case. A manifold M fails to be a spin manifold if there is an immersed two manifold N with $w_2(N)=0$. (w_2 is the second Stiefel-Whitney class of M.) Our discussion of global anomalies detected the failure of M to be a spin manifold only if there is some $N\epsilon M$ with a degree one map $S^1\times S^1\to N$ and $w_2(N)\neq 0$. In practice, this means N must be S^2 or $S^1\times S^1$. A more refined treatment of the particle case, exhibiting the fact that the point particle theory is ill defined if there is <u>any</u> $N \epsilon M$ with $w_2(N)\neq 0$, would hopefully generalize to a string theory argument establishing that (irrespective of the topology of L) consistency requires $P_1(V;Z) = P_1(T;Z)$.

This leads to another question. A three manifold L in space-time must be topologically non-trivial (and so non-zero in $H_3(K;Z)$) if a global anomaly is to arise from a degree one map $\phi:(\Sigma\times S^1)_h \to L$. But why must L be a torsion class in $H_3(K;Z)$? If not, L has nothing to do with $H^4(K;Z)$ or P_1. For instance, suppose we compactify not on $K = (S^5/Z_n)\times S^1$ but on $\tilde{K} = (S^3/Z_n) \times S^3$. We could still do the calculation leading to (43), using the subspace $L \doteq S^3/Z_n$ of $\tilde{K}$. But L now has nothing to do with H^4 --and in fact $H^4(K;Z) = 0$. So is not this evidence that the global world sheet anomaly in general can not be interpreted in terms of Pontryagin classes? The answer to this question is rather surprising. If L is not a torsion class in $H_3(K;Z)$, but an element of infinite order, it is always possible to add a Wess-Zumino interaction whose integral over L is non-zero. Adding this term with suitable (fractional) coefficient, it cancels any anomaly associated with fermion determinants on L. This is a curious situation in which a Wess-Zumino interaction is needed for consistency.

Now let us briefly discuss the physical applications of these results. It must be stressed that the anomaly cancellation in (44) can involve a cancellation of a problem in one E_8 against an equal and opposite problem in the second E_8. In fact, it is intriguing to speculate that nature may operate in that way. In that case, Wilson lines carrying out grand unified symmetry breaking in "our" E_8 would define a topologically non-trivial bundle, and grand unified symmetry breaking would be unavoidable (in the sector of the theory based on this bundle) for topological reasons.

This completes what I will say about consistency conditions coming from anomalies on the string world sheet. Although much more remains to be done, it is plausible that a fairly complete picture will emerge in the not too distant future. When these questions are all resolved, we will have merely settled the preliminaries, analogous in the point particle case to making sure that M is a spin manifold. It is necessary then to move on and explore global anomalies in the full-fledged second quantized theory.

In the field theory case, this involves considering anomalies in the determinant of the operator $i\not{D}$. That operator has the following properties. In Minkowski space, its zero modes are the physical, on mass shell states. It flips the chirality, so that in chiral theories it maps physical modes of the right chirality into unphysical modes of the wrong chirality, and vice-versa. Here chirality is measured by an operator $\bar{\Gamma}$ that anticommutes with all the gamma matrices in $\not{D} = \Sigma_i \Gamma^i D_i$.

In string theory, then, we want an operator which (a) generalizes the Dirac operator; (b) vanishes for physical states; (c) anticommutes with some analogue of the chirality operator $\bar{\Gamma}$.

The operator we want is just the operator introduced by Ramond in his original attempt[19] to generalize the Dirac equation to string theory! It is often called the Dirac-Ramond operator. In a modern language, it is the supersymmetry operator on the string world sheet. In the original version, there was a single Dirac-Ramond operator for open strings and two for closed strings. In the heterotic case, there is a single right-moving supercharge on a closed string. Temporarily suppressing the degrees of freedom that carry gauge quantum numbers, the supercharge can be derived from the action with N = 1/2 supersymmetry[20,15]

$$I = \int d^2\sigma \, [g_{ij}(x(\sigma)) \, \partial_+ x^i \, \partial_- x^j + i\psi^i \, (g_{ij} \, \partial_- + \partial_- x^k \, \omega_{kij}) \, \psi^j \tag{45}$$

Here g_{ij} is the metric of space-time, $\partial_\pm = \frac{\partial}{\partial \sigma^\pm}$ where $\sigma^\pm = \frac{1}{\sqrt{2}}(\tau \pm \sigma)$, ψ^j are the fermions of the Ramond-Neveu-Schwarz model, and a possible Wess-Zumino interaction (plus an infinity of possible couplings to massive modes of the string) is being suppressed. The conserved charge is

$$Q = \int_0^{2\pi} d\sigma \, g_{ij} \, \psi^i \left(\frac{\partial x^j}{\partial \tau} + \frac{\partial x^j}{\partial \sigma}\right) = \int_0^{2\pi} d\sigma \, \psi^i \left(-i \frac{D}{Dx^i(\sigma)} + g_{ij} \frac{\partial x^j}{\partial \sigma}\right) \tag{46}$$

The first form is the classical expression, and the second arises from it by canonical quantization, since--much as in our discussion of the point particle--canonical quantization gives $g_{ij} \frac{dx^j}{d\sigma} = -i \frac{D}{Dx^i(\sigma)}$ where $\frac{D}{Dx^i(\sigma)} = \frac{\delta}{\delta x^i(\sigma)} + \omega_{ijk}(x(\sigma)) \, \psi^j(\sigma) \, \psi^k(\sigma)$. Q, which was invented as a generalization of the usual Dirac operator, indeed has many similarities to it. For instance (in a suitable formalism) on mass shell states $|\Lambda\rangle$

are those that obey $Q|\Lambda\rangle = 0$. Also, the analogue of the chirality operator $\bar{\Gamma}$ is the operator $(-1)^F$ (or, in an older language, G parity) which anticommutes with all the $\psi^i(\sigma)$. It certainly obeys $(-1)^F Q = -Q(-1)^F$. Moreover, in superstring theory physical states $|\Lambda\rangle$ obey $(-1)^F|\Lambda\rangle = +|\Lambda\rangle$, while Q maps these to states obeying $(-1)^F|\Lambda\rangle = -|\Lambda\rangle$. Thus the operator Q relevant in superstring theory is a chiral Dirac-Ramond operator, which like the chiral Dirac operator $i\not{D}$ on a finite dimensional manifold maps physical states of positive chirality to unphysical states of negative chirality (and on mass shell states are zero modes of Q or $i\not{D}$).

I would like to make a few remarks aimed at clarifying in what sense Q is a generalization of the finite dimensional Dirac operator. The following remarks may also clarify the last section of [21]. Let M be the space time manifold, and let $\Omega(M)$ be the corresponding loop space. A Riemannian metric $ds^2 = g_{ij}\, dx^i dx^j$ induces a Riemannian metric on $\Omega(M)$ as follows. As we discussed before in our discussion of whether $\Omega(M)$ is orientable, a tangent vector at a point $\gamma\varepsilon\Omega(M)$--$\gamma$ corresponding to a loop $x^i(\sigma)$--is a tangent field δx^i along the loop. The metric on $\Omega(M)$ is defined by saying $\langle\delta x, \delta x\rangle = \int_0^{2\pi} d\sigma\, g_{ij}\,(x(\sigma))\, \delta x^i(\sigma)\, \delta x^j(\sigma)$.

Now, viewing $\Omega(M)$ as an infinite dimensional Riemannian manifold, it is natural to try to define a Dirac operator on $\Omega(M)$ as on a finite dimensional Riemannian manifold. To do so, we need gamma matrices Γ^I, I being a tangent vector index on $\Omega(M)$. But a tangent vector index I on $\Omega(M)$ is really a pair of indices (i,σ)--since a loop $x^i(\sigma)$ in M can be varied at any point σ and in any direction i tangent to M. Gamma matrices Γ^I are thus really fields $\Gamma^i(\sigma)$--and they obey a Clifford algebra $\{\Gamma^i(\sigma), \Gamma^j(\sigma')\} = 2g^{ij}\,\delta(\sigma-\sigma')$. These are the canonical commutation relations for fermions! The Dirac operator on $\Omega(M)$ would then be

$$Q_0 = -i \sum_I \Gamma^I \frac{D}{Dx^I} \tag{47}$$

But in fact $\sum_I$ is a short hand for $\sum_i \int d\sigma$, so

$$Q_0 = -i \int_0^{2\pi} d\sigma\, \psi^i(\sigma) \frac{D}{Dx^{i(\sigma)}} \tag{48}$$

where henceforth we call the gamma matrices by their more familiar name $\psi^i(\sigma)$.

Two things may be noted here. First, Q_0 is almost, but not quite, the Dirac-Ramond operator. The second term in (46) is missing in (48). Second, Q_0 is a formal construction which--even when M is flat and everything can be diagonalized by Fourier transforms--doesn't make sense. As is explained in every book on quantum field theory, the second term in Q is needed to make an operator that makes sense, with a well-defined spectrum, on the infinite dimensional manifold $\Omega(M)$. Adding the second piece to Q may not be sufficient to make a meaningful operator, but it is certainly necessary!

Still, armed with our success in interpreting the first term in Q, we try to find a reasonable interpretation of the second one. Consider then a finite dimensional spin manifold W. On W we have a Dirac operator $i\not{D}$. If in addition a continuous isometry of W is given, generated by a Killing vector field K^i, then a simple generalization of the Dirac operator is $i\not{D}_K = i\not{D} + \Gamma^i K_i$. In fact, $i\not{D}_K$ is not just a simple generalization of the Dirac operator. It is in its own right an operator associated with a rich mathematical theory. It can be used[22] to prove the localization theorem associated with the Atiyah-Singer index theorem. Its analogue for the de Rham complex[21] is related[23] to equivariant cohomology, and its analogue for the $\bar{\partial}$ operator of a complex manifold is related to a system of holomorphic Morse inequalities[24] which so far have not attracted much mathematical attention.

Now, on the loop space of maps $S^1 \to M$, there is a continuous symmetry induced from rotations of the circle. It maps a loop $x^i(\sigma)$ to $x^i(\sigma+\varepsilon)$, for any ε. The infinitesimal form of the transformation is $\delta x^i(\sigma) = \frac{\partial x^i}{\partial \sigma}$. This formula shows that the $(i\sigma)$ component of the associated Killing vector field K^I is just $\delta x^i(\sigma) = \partial x^i/\partial\sigma$. The analogue of $\gamma^i K_i$ on a finite dimensional manifold is thus

$$Q_1 = \sum \Gamma^I K_I = \int_0^{2\pi} d\sigma \; \psi_i(\sigma) \, \frac{\partial x^i}{\partial \sigma} \qquad (49)$$

Q_1 is just the second piece of the Dirac-Ramond operator! The Dirac-

Ramond operator $Q = Q_0+Q_1$ is thus an analogue of the operator $i\not{D}_K$ on a finite dimensional manifold. It is remarkable that unlike $i\not{D}$, $i\not{D}_K$ has a meaningful infinite dimensional analogue.

We now see that $(-1)^F$, which anticommutes with all the gamma matrices $\psi^i(\sigma)$, is really the chirality operator of $\Omega(M)$. As in the finite dimensional case, the chiral Dirac-Ramond operator should make sense only if $\Omega(M)$ is orientable. Is this so? We concluded earlier that $\Omega(M)$ is orientable precisely if M is a spin manifold. Thus, superstring theory should make sense only if space-time is a spin manifold--a satisfactory result. Moving on in the same vein, to define a Dirac-like operator on $\Omega(M)$ should be possible only if $\Omega(M)$ is itself a spin manifold. Is this so? The same sort of reasoning we used to decide if $\Omega(M)$ is orientable would indicate that $\Omega(M)$ is a spin manifold precisely if $w_3(M)$--the third Stiefel-Whitney class of space-time--is zero. Happily, an orientable spin manifold M always has $w_3(M) = 0$.

Now we want to consider a more realistic situation with left-movers as well as right movers along the string. Thus we add to (45) additional terms described in [15] involving left-moving fermions λ^A and preserving N = 1/2 supersymmetry:

$$\Delta I = \int d^2\sigma \, [i\lambda^A(g_{AB}\,\partial_+ + A_{iAB}(x(\sigma))\,\partial_+x^i)\,\lambda^B - \frac{1}{2}F_{ijAB}(x(\sigma))\,\psi^i\psi^j\lambda^A\lambda^B] \tag{50}$$

For any fixed loop $\gamma\in\Omega(M)$, quantization of the λ^A gives an infinite dimensional Hilbert space H_γ. As γ varies, H_γ varies smoothly, giving an infinite dimensional vector bundle X over $\Omega(M)$. In the presence of the λ^A, the Dirac-Ramond operator thus acts not on "ordinary" spinor fields on $\Omega(M)$ but on spinor fields with values in X. The supercharge or Dirac-Ramond operator is still

$$Q = \int_0^{2\pi} d\sigma\, \psi^i(x(\sigma))\left(-i\frac{D}{Dx^i(\sigma)} + g_{ij}\frac{dx^j}{d\sigma}\right) \tag{51}$$

but now the connection in $\frac{D}{Dx^i}$ is modified to include a connection on X. Indeed, by analogy with our previous discussion, canonical quantization of (50) reveals that the covariant derivative is now

$$\frac{D}{Dx^i} = \frac{\delta}{\delta x^i(\sigma)} + \omega_{ijk}\, \psi^j(\sigma)\, \psi^k(\sigma) + A_{iAB}\, \lambda^A(\sigma)\, \lambda^B(\sigma) \qquad (52)$$

Thus, Q is in this case an analogue of $i\not{D}_A + \Gamma\cdot K$ on a finite dimensional manifold, where $i\not{D}_A$ is the Dirac equation acting on spinors with values in some auxiliary vector bundle with connection A.

At this point, one may be tempted to believe that the analogue of $\det i\not{D}$ in field theory is detQ in string theory. For at least one reason, this is not quite right in the case of closed strings. One is required to project onto states that are invariant under translations of σ, $\sigma\to\sigma+c$. Translations of σ are generated by a "momentum" operator P. One must project onto states of P=0. Since [P,Q]=0, Q maps the P=0 subspace of Hilbert space into itself. Let $\tilde{Q}$ be the restriction of Q to the P=0 subspace. I believe that $\det\tilde{Q}$ is the proper string theoretical generalization of $\det i\not{D}$. I will refer to it as the "equivariant determinant" of Q.

An analogous concept can be considered, but does not seem too natural, in field theory. Given a manifold M and a continuous symmetry generated by a Killing vector field K, we could restrict the Dirac operator to act on the K invariant spinor fields and calculate the corresponding equivariant determinant $\det i\tilde{\not{D}}$. Like the ordinary Dirac determinant, the equivariant determinant may be afflicted with anomalies. We may call these equivariant anomalies. Equivariant anomalies may not be a natural concept in field theory, but in the case of perturbative anomalies there is a natural way to calculate them. In fact, the same family index theorem that gives a topological interpretation of ordinary perturbative Dirac anomalies[25] also gives a topological interpretation of equivariant perturbative Dirac anomalies. When coupled with the localization theorem mentioned earlier, it predicts the equivariant anomaly in terms of ordinary anomalies of a suitable Dirac operator defined on the fixed point set of K--the subspace M_0 of M consisting of points invariant under K. By contrast, there is no localization theorem for global equivariant anomalies.[26]

Now, what can we expect to learn from Dirac-Ramond anomalies? I do not believe that perturbative Dirac-Ramond anomalies will teach us much we do not already know. In fact, the localization theorem would relate the perturbative equivariant anomalies on $\Omega(M)$ to anomalies of a suitable operator on $\Omega_0(M)$--the subspace of loops that are invariant under translations of σ. But such loops, obeying $x^i(\sigma) = x^i(\sigma+c)$ for any c, are constant maps $S^1 \to M$. So $\Omega_0(M) \simeq M$, and perturbative equivariant anomalies are related to calculations on M. Thus--while many details of this argument must be worked out--perturbative equivariant anomalies can be (and presumably already have been[2,3]) understood from suitable calculations on the finite dimensional manifold M.

Global equivariant anomalies are another matter, since there is no localization theorem for global equivariant anomalies. There is no telling what secrets may be locked in global equivariant Dirac-Ramond anomalies--or how long it will be before we know enough about string theory to unlock them. Although general arguments[4] show that field theoretic global anomalies could not explain why we do not live in uncompactified ten dimensional space, it is not obvious that this is impossible for Dirac-Ramond global anomalies. It is also possible that some presently known superstring theories may be rendered wholly inconsistent by global Dirac-Ramond anomalies.

A localization argument similar to the one just sketched was used elsewhere[21] to argue that in the supersymmetric nonlinear sigma model in 1+1 dimensions, formulated on S^1, any state with zero energy in lowest order actually has precisely zero energy. (Under special conditions, but not generically, this follows more simply from an index theorem.) This has applications to string theory in proving that states massless in the field theoretic limit are actually massless in string theory. The argument in [21] was carried out for N=1 supersymmetry with periodic fermion boundary conditions in both directions. Superstring theory requires both this and other cases. It is not clear if the argument generalizes to the other cases.

In the field theory case, we discussed one other question about global anomalies on the particle world line. Let $g: M \to M$ be a gauge transformation or diffeomorphism of space-time, and $E = (M \times S^1)_g$ the associated cylinder. We repeat here equation (17) for convenience:

$$\begin{array}{ccc} S^1\times S^1 & \xrightarrow{\ \phi\ } & E \\ & {\scriptstyle\alpha}\searrow \quad \swarrow{\scriptstyle\beta} & \\ & S^1 & \end{array} \qquad (53)$$

Here ϕ is a map that makes the above diagram commute. We found that a global anomaly associated with such a picture means that g is not a symmetry of the quantum theory.

In string theory the analogous picture is

$$\begin{array}{ccc} (\Sigma\times S^1)_h & \xrightarrow{\ \phi\ } & E \\ & {\scriptstyle\alpha}\searrow \quad \swarrow{\scriptstyle\beta} & \\ & S^1 & \end{array} \qquad (54)$$

Here Σ is a Riemann surface, h is a diffeomorphism of Σ, E is again $(M\times S^1)_g$, and we again require $\beta\phi=\alpha$. An anomaly associated with such a picture presumably means, as in field theory, that g is not a valid symmetry.

I will make no effort to investigate this situation systematically, but I cannot resist mentioning one example. Let Λ be the "big" gauge transformation associated with QCD instantons. In QCD, Λ is conserved, and this is a nuisance. It means that the physical world has a quantum number called θ_{QCD} defined by saying $\Lambda|\Omega\rangle = e^{i\theta_{QCD}}|\Omega\rangle$. (Since Λ commutes with all local operators, θ_{QCD} is the same for all states in a given "world".) The appearance of θ_{QCD} makes trouble. It is the origin of the strong CP problem. How much happier we would be if the QCD Hamiltonian did not commute with Λ! There would be no θ_{QCD}, and no strong CP problem.

Let us probe for conservation of Λ in superstring theory. To this end, we take space-time to be $M=S^1\times S^3\times K$, where S^1 is "time," S^3 is "space" on which Λ acts, and K is the Kaluza-Klein space. We then consider the mapping cylinder $E_\Lambda = (M\times S^1)_\Lambda$. (As Λ is a gauge transformation rather than a diffeomorphism, $(M\times S^1)_\Lambda$ is just $M\times S^1$ with a modified $E_8\times E_8$ vector bundle.) Because of the relation of Λ with instantons, and the fact that the instanton field has a non-zero P_1, the equation $P_1(V) = P_1(T)$ needed to avoid anomalies is violated on E_Λ. So there are anomalies (even perturbative ones) in (54), and Λ is not a symmetry. We are thus led to hope that superstring theory will solve the strong CP problem. In fact, the arguments just described seem to be a rather baroque way to understand the appearance of axions in superstring theory.[16] While that can be understood more straightforwardly, the example reassures us that we are interpreting correctly (54), which may have other applications.

I would like to thank M. F. Atiyah, D. Freed, T. Killingback, J. Mather, E. Miller, and I. Singer for discussions.

References

1. R. Geroch, J. Math. Phys. 11 (1970) 343; S.W. Hawking and C.N. Pope, Phys. Lett. 73B (1978) 42.
2. L. Alvarez-Gaumé and E. Witten, Nucl. Phys. B234 (1983) 269.
3. M.B. Green and J.H. Schwarz, Phys. Lett. 149B (1984) 117.
4. E. Witten, "Global Gravitational Anomalies," to appear in Comm. Math. Phys.
5. M.F. Atiyah, V.K. Patodi, I.M. Singer, Proc. Camh. Philos. Soc. 77 (1975) 43, 78 (1975) 405, 79 (1976) 71.
6. E. Witten, Phys. Lett. 117B (1982) 324.
7. L. Brink, S. Deser, B. Zumino, P. Di Vecchia, and P. Howe, Phys. Lett. 64B (1976) 435.
8. L. Brink and J.H. Schwarz, Phys. Lett. 100B (1981) 310.
9. D.J. Gross, J.A. Harvey, E. Martinec, and R. Rohm, Phys. Rev. Lett. 52 (1985) 502, and Princeton preprints (1985).
10. R. Rohm and E. Witten, Princeton preprint, to appear.
11. X.-G. Wen and E. Witten, Princeton preprint (1985).
12. R. Stong, Notes on Cobordism Theory (Princeton University Press, 1968).
13. See for instance E.H. Spanier, Algebraic Topology (McGraw Hill, 1966), Chapter 3.
14. G. Moore and P. Nelson, Phys. Rev. Lett. 53 (1984) 1519; P. di Vecchia, S. Ferrara, and L. Girardello, CERN preprint Th.4026/84 (1984); E. Cohen and C. Gomez, CERN preprint Th.4043/84 (1984).

15. C.G. Callan, Jr., D. Friedan, E. Martince, and M. Perry, Princeton preprint (1985); P. Candelas, G. Horowitz, A. Strominger, and E. Witten, these proceedings; C. Hull and E. Witten, to appear.
16. E. Witten, Phys. Lett. 149B (1984) 351.
17. P. Candelas, G. Horowitz, A. Strominger, and E. Witten, to appear in Nucl. Phys. B.
18. K. Pilch and A. Schellekens, SUNY-Stony Brook preprint (1985).
19. P. Ramond, Phys. Rev. D3 (1971) 2415.
20. W. Siegel, Nucl. Phys. B238 (1984) 307; M. Sakamoto, Phys. Lett. 151B (1985) 115.
21. E. Witten, J. Diff. Geom. 17 (1982) 661.
22. E. Witten, in the Proceedings of the 1983 Shelter Island Conference, ed. N. Khuri et al. (MIT Press, 1985).
23. M.F. Atiyah and R. Bott, Harvard preprint (1983).
24. E. Witten, in Algebraic and Differential Topology - Global Differential Geometry, ed. G.B. Rassias (Teubner-Texte zur Mathematik, Band 70, 1984).
25. M.F. Atiyah and I.M. Singer, Proc. Nat. Acad. Sci. 81 (1984) 2597.
26. M.F. Atiyah and I.M. Singer, private communication.

Fractional Charge and Topological Kinks

J.R. Schrieffer

Institute for Theoretical Physics
University of California
Santa Barbara, California 93106

INTRODUCTION

The existence of stable excitations which carry fractional fermion number was first discovered by R. Jackiw and C. Rebbi[1] (JR) They studied a spinless Dirac field coupled to a ϕ^4 Bose field in $1+1$ dimensions. Taking ϕ to be a static tanh kink they found (1) there is one zero energy fermion state for each kink, (2) the change of fermion number in the vicinity of the kink is either $\pm\frac{1}{2}$ depending upon, (3) whether the zero mode is full or empty. Their proof of fractional charge relies on the charge conjugation symmetry of their model.

The existence of stable fractionally charged excitations in condensed matter systems was discovered by W.P. Su, A.J. Heeger and the author[2] (SSH) in the context of quasi one-dimensional conductors,[3] such as polyacetylene $(CH)_x$. They studied a model in which spin $\frac{1}{2}$ electrons hop along a 1d chain of CH groups whose positions u_n relative to a perfect periodic array is described by a Bose field $\phi_n \equiv (-1)^n u_n$ defined on the lattice. While the fermion and boson fields are coupled linearly, dynamical symmetry breaking occurs in this model, leading to two degenerate but inequivalent vacuua, analogous to ϕ^4 theory. The broken symmetry states $\langle\phi_n\rangle = \pm u_0$ lead to a gap 2Δ in the electron spectrum at the electronic fermi surface, as in a semiconductor. However SSH showed that conventional electron and hole excitations are dynamically unstable with respect to decay into charged solitons $S^{\pm,0}$ and polarons[4,5,6] $P^{\pm}$. While the polaron carries conventional quantum numbers of charge Q and spin s, *i.e.*, $Q = \pm e$, $s = \frac{1}{2}$ as electrons and holes in semiconductors, solitons carry the anomalous quantum numbers $Q = \pm e$, $s = 0$ or $Q = 0$, $s = \frac{1}{2}$ apparently violating Kramer's theorem in that adding a charge $+e$ or $-e$ would require addition of one fermion and hence spin $\frac{1}{2}$.

SSH pointed out that the charge $+e$ of S^+ physically arises from the depletion of one-half of a fermion state from the negative energy sea for each spin orientation when the soliton is created. This missing state count leads to a charge of $\frac{e}{2}$ per spin or $Q = e$. However, since the charge deficit occurs in a spin symmetric fashion, the net spin of the soliton is zero.

For a chain of a finite length, all solutions of the Dirac equation are discrete both before and after S is created so that the missing half state must somehow be compensated. This occurs for simple topological reasons; for example in a ring geometry ϕ_n must be single valued so that a soliton in which $\langle\phi_n\rangle$ goes from $-u_n$ to $+u_n$ must be followed by an antisoliton in which $\langle\phi_n\rangle$ goes from $+u_n$ to $-u_n$. Since the solitons and antisoliton ($\bar{S}$) each deplete the negative energy sea by one-half a state for each spin, the total state deficit per spin is integer as required. Nevertheless, the charges of $S^{\pm}$ and of $\bar{S}^{\mp}$ are concentrated in a region of size $2\xi_0$, where ξ_0 is the soliton half width, of order 14 lattice spacings for $(CH)_x$.

As in the JR model, the soliton in $(CH)_x$ also exhibits a zero energy fermion state[2] for S and for $\bar{S}$ as is required by conservation of states as S and $\bar{S}$ are created. This follows since in the vicinity of S one-half a state is depleted from the negative and from the positive energy seas, leading to a single zero energy mode centered on S. A similar effect occurs at $\bar{S}$. The origin of the various charge and spin states of S or $\bar{S}$ is now clear; if the zero mode occupation number $\nu_0 = 0$, the above depletion gives $Q = +e$ and $S = 0$. If $\nu_0 = 1$, $Q = 0$ and $S = \frac{1}{2}$ while if $\nu_0 = 2$, $Q = -e$ and $S = 0$. The same reasoning applies to $\bar{S}$.

It is clear that the fractional fermion effects discovered by JR and by SSH ultimately arise from a single source, vacuum current flow.[7] In essence, as the Bose field is distorted to form a soliton, the wavefunctions of the negative energy states are distorted such that the decreased amplitude of these states in the vicinity of either S of $\bar{S}$ when summed over all states of $E < 0$ leads to a deficit of one-half state. This deficit occurs despite the fact that the negative energy states remain full and no excitations (electrons or holes) are created. The space and time integral of the divergence of this vacuum current is the soliton charge and up to an integer is totally independent of the shape of the soliton or how it was formed, *i.e.*, it is a topological invariant.

The anomalous properties discussed above have been observed experimentally[8] through infrared and optical absorption, nuclear and electron spin resonance as well as transport experiments on pure and chemically doped quasi one-dimensional conductors.

II. PROOFS OF FRACTIONAL CHARGE

There are many approaches to establish that the charge of fermion number carried by solitons in broken symmetry systems is fractional. For concreteness, we consider the SSH model[2] for $(CH)_x$,

$$H = -t_0 \sum_{n,s} (C^+_{n+1,s} C_{ns} + h.c.) + \sum_n \left\{ \frac{P_n^2}{2M} + \frac{K}{2}(u_n - u_{n+1})^2 \right\}$$
$$- \alpha \sum_{ns} (u_n - u_{n+1})(C^+_{n+1,s} C_{ns} + h.c.) \tag{2.1}$$

where C^+_{ns} creates a π electron on site n with spin orientation s. u_n is the displacement of the nth CH group along the chain direction. The first two terms in H describe free electrons moving as a $1d$ lattice and free phonons (bosons). The last term couples these fields.

The effective potential $V_{\rm eff}(u_1...u_N)$ is given by integrating out the electrons within the adiabatic (one loop) approximation. For one electron per site, *i.e.*, a half filled band, one finds that $V_{\rm eff}$, when expressed as a function of the staggered Bose field

$$\phi_n = (-1)^n u_n, \tag{2.2}$$

exhibits degenerate minima for $\phi_n = u_0$ or $-u_0$ with $V_{\rm eff}$ having a double well form like ϕ^4 theory except for nonlocality on the scale of $\xi_0 = \frac{\hbar v_F}{\pi\Delta}$. Here 2Δ is the electron energy gap and v_F is the fermi velocity $v_F = 2t_0a/\hbar$, where a is the lattice spacing. A soliton is a domain wall separating regions having $\phi_n = +u_0$(A vacuum) and $\phi_n - u_0$(B vacuum).

Alternatively, for a one-third filled band (two-thirds of an electron per site) $V_{\rm eff}$ has three degenerate minima.[9] In this case u_n is conveniently expressed in terms of an amplitude A_n and a phase θ_n as

$$u_n = A_n \cos\left(\frac{2\pi n}{3a} + \theta_n\right). \tag{2.3}$$

Clearly this can be generalized to any filling factor ν by replacing 1/3 by ν in this expression. Physically, the spontaneous symmetry breaking modulates the lattice spacing and the electron density with a spacial period $\ell = a/\nu$, creating a charge density wave (CDW). For ν fractional, the lattice and CDW periods are commensurate with $\frac{1}{\nu}$ distinct degenerate ground states.

The case $\nu = \frac{1}{3}$ illustrates how the allowed charge states of the soliton can be simply determined. Let θ_n in (2.3) initially be zero. If θ_n is increased uniformly in space to $\theta_n = \frac{2\pi}{3}$, the CDW is rigidly translated by a distance $+a$ to another degenerate ground state. The same is true if we further increase θ_n to $\frac{4\pi}{3}$ and finally $\frac{6\pi}{3}$, the total translation being $3a$. If we count the number of electrons δ passing a fixed point on the chain as θ_n (for all n) goes from zero to 2π, we find that $\delta = \frac{2}{3} \times 3 = 2$. Suppose however that θ_n is spacially non-uniform, increasing from 0 to $\frac{2\pi}{3}$ near n_1, $\frac{2\pi}{3}$ to $\frac{4\pi}{4}$ near n_2 and $\frac{4\pi}{3}$ to 2π near n_3, remaining constant for $n < n_1$ and $n > n_3$. Thus, we have three kinks located at n_1, n_2 and n_3, with total charge

$$Q_1 + Q_2 + Q_3 = 2e \tag{2.4}$$

since $-2e$ has been transported to infinity by distortion of θ_n. However, the Hamiltonian is invariant under translations a of the primitive lattice and therefore each soliton must have the same charge,

$$Q = \frac{2e}{3}, \tag{2.5}$$

Other charge states are given by occupying the zero mode with the spin assignments

$$Q = \frac{2e}{3},\ -\frac{e}{3},\ -\frac{4e}{3}$$
$$s = 0,\ \frac{1}{2},\ 0. \tag{2.6}$$

The antisolitons have the charge conjugate assignments

$$\bar{Q} = -\frac{2e}{3},\ +\frac{e}{3},\ +\frac{4e}{3}$$
$$\bar{s} = 0,\ \frac{1}{2},\ 0. \tag{2.7}$$

These assignments are different from quarks regarding spin and to my knowledge these fractionally charged kinks bear no relation to quarks.

Another derivation of soliton charge has been given by Goldstone and Wilczek,[10] who calculate the vacuum current flow as the Bose field is adiabatically distorted to create the soliton.

III. SHARPNESS OF FRACTIONAL CHARGE

The above discussion concerns the question of whether the expectation value of the soliton charge is fractional. This we answered affirmatively for systems we are considering. A separate question is whether a soliton is an eigenstate of the charge operator with fractional eigenvalue, that is,

$$Q_{op}|S\rangle = Q|S\rangle \tag{3.1}$$

where Q_{op} is the total charge operator and Q is fractional.

To establish (3.1), Kivelson and the author[11] studied fluctuations around the expected charge

$$\delta Q^2 = (Q_{op} - \langle Q_{op}\rangle)^2 \tag{3.2}$$

As usual, one must choose Q_{op} with care or unphysical effects can occur. Firstly, one wants to integrate only over the region containing the soliton in question and not an antisoliton, *etc.*, as well.

Secondly, the sampling region must be large compared to the extent of the soliton's charge distribution $\sim 2\xi_0$, of order $30\AA$ for $(CH)_x$. Finally, the cutoff of the sampling region at large distance should be smooth to eliminate charge fluctuations due to the CDW vacuum. These can be accomplished by choosing

$$Q_{op} = \int e^{-(x-x_s)^2/L^2} \rho(x) dx \tag{3.3}$$

with the $s\bar{s}$ spacing first going to infinity, then L going to infinity. In this case, one can prove

$$\langle \delta Q^2 \rangle =) \left(\frac{1}{L}\right) + O(e^{L/\xi_0}) \tag{3.4}$$

However, just as the number of particles in a length L for the free Dirac field fluctuates on the scale of $\left(\frac{1}{L}\right)$, so does the number of negative energy electrons in the sampling region fluctuate as $\left(\frac{1}{L}\right)$, whether or not the soliton is present. Thus, we must subtract off the vacuum fluctuations in the absence of the soliton and obtain the physically relevant quantity

$$\Delta \langle \delta Q^2 \rangle = O(e^{-L/\xi_0}) \tag{3.5}$$

Therefore, as $L \to \infty$, $|S\rangle$, or $|\bar{S}\rangle$ becomes an eigenstate of total charge, with fractional eigenvalue.

Other proofs of this result have been given.[12,13,14]

IV. THE QUANTUM HALL EFFECT

The above discussion emphasized the importance of degenerate vacuua in generating the fractional quantization of quasi particle charge. A somewhat different mechanism is operating in the quantum Hall effect, where fractionally charged quasi particles also appear to exist.

Recent experiments[15] on semiconductor surfaces and heterojunctions (24) show that if a very large magnetic field B is applied normal (z) to a $2d$ gas of electrons, and a current I is applied along x, then an electric field E_y appears along y. The Hall conductivity $\sigma_{xy} = I_x/E_y$ is observed to have plateaus at filling factor ν_n of the Landau levels which is integer and surprisingly non integer as well, *i.e.*, $\nu = n/m$, where m is an odd integer.

R.B. Laughlin[16] has proposed that the electrons enter a condensed phase which behaves as an incompressible fluid, with a gap 2Δ for adding extra quasi particles. Working in the symmetric gauge he finds the quasi particles have charge $\pm\frac{e}{m}$ for a filling factor $\nu = \frac{1}{m}$ and that these objects are pinned to charge impurities for ν near $\frac{1}{m}$. In essence, the quasi particle charge comes about from vacuum flow as for the CDW case, however, the allowed charge states are governed by the Landau level quantization rather than the commensurability energy.

Recently it has been shown[17] how fractionally charge quasi particles $Q = \pm\nu e$ in the quantum Hall effect arise when the electrons are described by a lattice type consensate, analogous to a Wigner lattice. In this approach, cooperative exchange processes play an essential role in stabilizing certain filling factors, $\nu = \frac{1}{m}$.

V. FRACTIONAL STATISTICS

Having discussed the physical origin of fractional fermion number and the sharpness of this quantity, we close with a remark concerning the statistics of such objects. Arovas, *et al.* [18] proved in a straight-forward calculation that the phase $\Delta\gamma$ accumulated when two quasi particles each of charge νe are interchanged is

$$\Delta\gamma = \nu\pi \qquad (5.1)$$

For $\nu = 1$, $\Delta\gamma = \pi$ as required for fermi statistics of electrons. The derivation of (5.1) uses the expression of Barry[19] and Simon[20]

$$\frac{d\gamma(t)}{dt} = i\langle\Psi(t)|\frac{d\Psi}{dt}\rangle \tag{5.2}$$

for the adiabatic approximation to the phase change. As the quasi particles are slowly rotated about their midpoint, a term is picked up in (5.2) which is a time derivative and therefore contributes regardless of how slowly the exchange takes place. For a circle of radius large compared to the size ξ_0 of the quasi particles core, this contribution reduces to (5.1). However, if the circle on which the particles are exchanged is smaller than ξ_0, $\Delta\gamma$ is reduced. With these statistics are one can calculate the properties of a gas of such "anyons."[21]

VI. CONCLUSION

We have given a brief discussion of the origin of fractional charge in several systems. while it appears that this phenomenon is of quantum origin, a simple example shows that fractional charge also occurs classically. For example, let charge e objects reside on lattice sites separated by a distance a. If all the even sites n are occupied from $n = -\infty$to $n = 0$, and the odd sites from $n = 1$ to $n = -\infty$, then there is a "soliton" centered between $n = 0$ and 1. Now move the charge on site 1 to site 2. The soliton is now centered between $n = 2$ and 3. Thus the soliton has moved $2a$ while the charge moves a. We calculate the charge of dipole moment ΔP in two ways, from the soliton point of view and from the particle point of view,

$$\Delta P = Q \cdot 2a = ea \tag{5.3}$$

Therefore, the soliton's charge is $Q = e/2$.

In essence this simple physics is what is going on in all of the above models. As a soliton passes on, it alters the state of the vacuum, producing an effective charge on the soliton which reflects the underlying broken symmetry. The reader is referred to the references below for details concerning these issues.

This work was supported in part by the National Science Foundation under Grant No. DMR82-16285.

REFERENCES

1. R. Jackiw and C. Rebbi, Phys. Rev. D**13** 3398 (1976).

2. W.P. Su, J.R. Schrieffer, and A.J. Heeger, Phys. Rev. Lett. **42**, 1692 (1979); Phys. Rev. B**22**, 2099 (1980).

3. M.J. Rice, Phys. Lett. **71**A, 152 (1979).

4. W.P. Su and J.R. Schrieffer, Proc. Natl. Acad. Sci. **77**, 5626 (1980).

5. D.K. Campbell and A.R. Bishop, Phys. Rev. B**24**, 4859 (1981).

6. S.A. Brazvoskii and N. Kirova, JETP Lett. **33** (1981).

7. R. Jackiw and J.R. Schrieffer, Nucl. Phys. **13**, 253 (1981).

8. International Conference on the Physics and Chemistry of Polymeric Conductors, J. Physique C3 (1983).

9. W.P. Su and J.R. Schrieffer, Phys. Rev. Lett. **46**, 738 (1981).

10. J. Goldstone and F. Wilczek, Phys. Rev. Lett. **47**, 986 (1981).

11. S. Kivelson and J.R. Schrieffer, Phys. Rev. B**25**, 6447 (1982).

12. J.S. Bell and R. Rajaraman, Nucl. Phys. B**220**, 1 (1983).

13. R. Jackiw, A.R. Kerman, I. Klebanov and G. Semenoff, Nucl. Phys. B**225**, 233 (1983).

14. R. Prange, Phys. Rev. B26, 991 (1982).

15. D.D. Tsui, H.L. Störmer and A.C. Gossard, Phys. Rev. Lett. **48**, 1559 (1982).

16. R.B. Laughlin, Phys. Rev. Lett. **50**, 1395 (1983).

17. D. Arovas, C. Kallin, S. Kivelson and J.R. Schrieffer, to be published.

18. D. Arovas, J.R. Schrieffer, and F. Wilczek, Phys. Rev. Lett. **53**, 722 (1984).

19. M.V. Berry, Proc. Roy. Soc. London, Ser. **A392**, 45 (1984).

20. B. Simon, Phys. Rev. Lett. **51**, 2167 (1983).

21. D. Arovas, J.R. Schreiffer, F. Wilczek and A. Zee, Nucl. Phys. B**250**, 117 (1985).

ANOMALIES, COCYCLES AND SCHWINGER TERMS*

Bruno Zumino

Physics Department and
Lawrence Berkeley Laboratory
University of California
Berkeley, CA 94720

ABSTRACT

The properties of cocycles on a gauge group and its Lie algebra and their relationship to gauge anomalies are reviewed. The case of supersymmetric gauge theories is briefly discussed.

* This work was supported in part by the Director, Office of Energy Research, Office of High Energy and Nuclear Physics, Division of High Energy Physics of the U.S. Department of Energy under contract DE-AC03-76-SF0-0098 and in part by the National Science Foundation under research grant PHY-81-18547.

1. INTRODUCTION

In this note I shall review briefly some recent developments in the theory of anomalies as related to differential geometry and topology. I shall describe mostly work with which I have been more or less closely associated and shall follow the point of view which seems to me simplest and most direct. However, the subject can be viewed profitably in different ways which are represented by other lecturers at this conference. For alternative viewpoints and useful references I especially recommend the lectures by Alvarez, Guo, Hou, Jackiw, Singer, Stasheff and Thierry-Mieg contained in this volume.

We are concerned with the study of the cohomology of gauge groups, with the aim of also studying their (infinite dimensional) representations. Not much is known at present about the representations[1)] and I have nothing to say about this. The gauge group cohomology was introduced in physics by Faddeev[2)]. It is related to the cohomology of the gauge Lie algebra[3)], in a way similar to the case of Lie groups and Lie algebras, but with some special features which come from the local properties of gauge groups.

In Section 1 the basic concepts of cochains and cocycles on groups are introduced. This section owes much to a clarifying correspondence with R. Stora. In Section 2, the relation with Lie algebras is described and in Section 3 the special case of gauge groups and gauge Lie algebras is discussed.

2. SYMPLICIAL HOMOGENEOUS AND INHOMOGENEOUS GROUP COHOMOLOGY

In this section we recall, without any attempt at a rigorous description, the basic ideas of group cohomology[4),5)]. We begin with general symplicial cohomology.

Let A_0, A_1, A_2, ... be points of some space $\mathcal{A}$. A real valued function $c_n(A_0,A_1,...A_n)$ will be called an n-cochain. One defines the coboundary operator Δ on cochains by

$$\Delta c_0(A_0) = c_0(A_1) - c_0(A_0) \equiv (\Delta c)_1(A_0,A_1) \quad , \tag{2.1}$$

$$\begin{aligned}\Delta c_1(A_0,A_1) &= c_1(A_1,A_2) - c_1(A_0,A_2) + c_1(A_0,A_1) \\ &\equiv (\Delta c)_1(A_0,A_1,A_2) \quad ,\end{aligned} \tag{2.2}$$

and so on. In general

$$\Delta c_{n-1}(A_0,A_1,\ldots A_{n-1}) = \sum_{k=0}^{n} (-1)^k \, c_{n-1}(A_0,A_1,\ldots \hat{A}_k,\ldots A_n)$$
$$\equiv (\Delta c)_n(A_0,A_1,\ldots A_n) \quad , \tag{2.3}$$

where the caret over A_k indicates that the point A_k must be omitted. It is easy to verify that

$$\Delta^2 = 0 \quad . \tag{2.4}$$

A cochain which satisfies

$$\Delta c = 0 \tag{2.5}$$

is called a cocycle. One can define, in the usual way, equivalence classes, etc.: two cochains which differ by a cocycle are equivalent; a cocycle is equivalent to zero if it can be written as Δc, where c is some cochain.

Now let us assume that a group G can act on the space $\mathcal{A}$. For $A \in \mathcal{A}$,

$$A \rightarrow Ag \in \mathcal{A}, \qquad g \in G. \tag{2.6}$$

Let $g_0,g_1\ldots g_n$ be elements of G and take

$$A_0 = Ag_0,\ A_1 = Ag_1,\ldots\ A_n = Ag_n. \tag{2.7}$$

Define

$$f_n(A;g_0,g_1,\ldots g_n) \equiv c_n(Ag_0,Ag_1,\ldots Ag_n) \quad . \tag{2.8}$$

Clearly

$$\Delta f_0(A;g_0) = \Delta c_0(Ag_0) = c_0(Ag_1) - c_0(Ag_0)$$
$$= f_0(A;g_1) - f_0(A;g_0) \equiv (\Delta f)_1(A;g_0,g_1) \quad , \tag{2.9}$$

$$\Delta f_1(A;g_0,g_1) = f_1(A;g_1,g_2) - f_1(A;g_0,g_1) + f_1(A;g_0,g_1)$$
$$\equiv (\Delta f)_2(A;g_0,g_1,g_2) \quad , \tag{2.10}$$

and so on. In general

$$\Delta f_{n-1}(A;g_0,g_1\ldots g_{n-1}) = \sum_{n=0}^{n} (-1)^k \, f_{n-1}(A;g_0,g_1\ldots \hat{g}_k\ldots g_n)$$
$$\equiv (\Delta f)_n(A;g_0,g_1\ldots g_n) \quad . \tag{2.11}$$

Irrespective of the validity of (2.8) we shall consider functions f_n, with the coboundary operator given by (2.11), and shall call them homogeneous group cochains.

A cochain f_n is called invariant if it satisfies

$$^g f_n = f_n(Ag^{-1};gg_0,gg_1,\ldots gg_n) = f_n(A;g_0,g_1,\ldots g_n) \tag{2.12}$$

(Observe that if f_n is given by (2.8) it is invariant by construction. Vice-versa if the two points A and Ag determine the group element g, invariant functions can be written in the form (2.8).) It is easy to verify that

$$\Delta(^g f) = {}^g(\Delta f) \quad . \tag{2.13}$$

We can always change variables by going over to new group elements $\gamma_0,\gamma_1 \ldots$, such that

$$g_0 = \gamma_0,\; g_1 = \gamma_0\gamma_1,\ldots,\; g_n = \gamma_0\gamma_1\ldots\gamma_n \quad , \tag{2.14}$$

$$f_n(A;g_0,g_1,\ldots g_n) \equiv \tilde{f}_n(A;\gamma_0,\gamma_1,\ldots\gamma_n). \tag{2.15}$$

Let f be invariant and define

$$\phi_n(A;\gamma_1,\gamma_2,\ldots\gamma_n) \equiv \tilde{f}_n(A;1,\gamma_1,\gamma_2,\ldots\gamma_n) \tag{2.16}$$

It follows that

$$\Delta\phi_0(A) = \phi_0(A\gamma) - \phi_0(A) \equiv (\Delta\phi)_1(A;\gamma) \tag{2.17}$$

$$\begin{aligned}\Delta\phi_1(A;\gamma_1) &= \phi_1(A\gamma_1;\gamma_2) - \phi_1(A;\gamma_1\gamma_2) + \phi_1(A;\gamma_1)\\ &\equiv (\Delta\phi)_2(A;\gamma_1,\gamma_2)\end{aligned} \tag{2.18}$$

$$\begin{aligned}\Delta\phi_2(A;\gamma_1,\gamma_2) &= \phi_2(A\gamma_1;\gamma_2,\gamma_3) - \phi_2(A;\gamma_1\gamma_2,\gamma_3) + \phi^2(A;\gamma_1,\gamma_2\gamma_3)\\ &\quad - \phi_2(A;\gamma_1,\gamma_2) \equiv (\Delta\phi)_3(A;\gamma_1,\gamma_2,\gamma_3) \quad , \text{etc.}\end{aligned} \tag{2.19}$$

The functions ϕ_n are called inhomogeneous group cochains. Equation (2.4) is still satisfied, of course.

Inhomogeneous cocycles occur as phases in the projective representations of groups. For instance, if

$$\Psi(A) \underset{\gamma}{\rightarrow} V(\gamma)\Psi(A) = e^{i\phi(A,\gamma)}\Psi(A\gamma) \tag{2.20}$$

is a projective representation, associativity requires that $\phi(A,\gamma)$ be a 1-cocycle

$$\Delta\phi = 0 \quad . \tag{2.21}$$

Similarly, if the group G is represented by matrices $U(A;\gamma)$ with the composition law

$$U(A;\gamma_1\gamma_2) = e^{-i\phi(A;\gamma_1,\gamma_2)}U(A;\gamma_1)U(A\gamma_1;\gamma_2) \quad , \tag{2.22}$$

associativity, i.e.,

$$U(A;\gamma_1(\gamma_2\gamma_3)) = U(A;(\gamma_1\gamma_2)\gamma_3) \quad , \tag{2.23}$$

requires that $\phi(A;\gamma_1,\gamma_2)$ be a 2-cocycle

$$\Delta\phi = 0 \ . \tag{2.24}$$

3. INTEGRAL FORMULAS FOR THE COCYCLES

If we have a closed differential form on the space $\mathcal{A}$ we can construct symplicial cocycles. We denote by δ the exterior differential in $\mathcal{A}$ and let $\omega_n(\delta A,A)$ be a closed n-form

$$\delta\omega_n = 0 \ . \tag{3.1}$$

Then, if V_{n+1} is a symplex of dimension $n + 1$, with $n + 2$ vertices $A_0,A_1,\ldots A_n,A_{n+1}$,

$$0 = \int_{V_{n+1}} \delta\omega_n = \int_{\partial V_{n+1}} \omega_n \ . \tag{3.2}$$

For instance, if V_2 is a triangle of vertices A_0,A_1,A_2, we find

$$\int_{A_0}^{A_1} \omega_1 + \int_{A_1}^{A_2} \omega_1 + \int_{A_2}^{A_0} \omega_1 = 0 \ . \tag{3.3}$$

Defining

$$c_1(A_0,A_1) \equiv \int_{A_0}^{A_1} \omega_1 \quad , \tag{3.4}$$

we see that (3.3) is equivalent to

$$\Delta c_1 = 0 \ . \tag{3.5}$$

Observe that (3.4) depends only on the end points A_0 and A_1 and not on the integration path, at least for small deformations of the path. For higher cocycles the integral does depend on the choice of lower dimensional edges, but in concrete applications there is a natural choice for the path connecting any two points of $\mathcal{A}$. For instance, if $\mathcal{A}$ is a space of connections, one will choose the convex interpolation

$$tA_0 + (1 - t)A_1 \quad , \quad 0 \leqslant t \leqslant 1 \ , \tag{3.6}$$

and, in the case of a face having vertices $A_0, A_1, \ldots A_n$,

$$\begin{aligned} &a_0 A_0 + a_1 A_1 + \ldots + a_n A_n \ , \\ &a_0 + a_1 + \ldots + a_n = 1 \quad , \quad 0 \leqslant a_i \leqslant 1 \ . \end{aligned} \tag{3.7}$$

Homogeneous group cocycles, for a group acting on $\mathcal{A}$, could now be constructed by using (2.8). For instance, if $\mathcal{A}$ is the space of gauge potentials (connections), one could try to construct the homogeneous gauge group cocycles from the cocycles on $\mathcal{A}$. However, it turns out that (2.8) does not give directly the physically interesting gauge group cocycles. Although these can still be extracted from the cocycles on $\mathcal{A}$, the procedure is somewhat awkward. It is much simpler and more convenient to construct directly the group cocycles, as follows.

In order to construct homogeneous group cocycles we use differential forms in group space. Let δ ge the exterior differential on the group, which can be thought of as differentiating with respect to parameters λ upon which the group element depends. Then

$$v = g^{-1}\delta g \tag{3.8}$$

is Lie algebra valued and (since $\delta^2 = 0$), it satisfies

$$\delta v = -g^{-1}\delta g \ g^{-1}\delta g = -v^2 \quad . \tag{3.9}$$

Let

$$\delta A_g = Ag \quad , \tag{3.10}$$

then

$$\delta A_g = A\delta g = Ag \ g^{-1}\delta g = A_g v \tag{3.11}$$

The equations

$$\begin{aligned} &\delta v = -v^2 \\ &\delta A_g = A_g v \end{aligned} \tag{3.12}$$

describe a BRS transformation.

Now let $\alpha_n(v,A_g)$ be a polynomial of degree n in v. α_n is an n-form in group space. If

$$\delta\alpha_n = 0 \quad , \tag{3.13}$$

we can integrate over an n + 1 dimensional symplex in group space

$$0 = \int_{V_{n+1}} \delta\alpha_n = \int_{\partial V_{n+1}} \alpha_n \quad . \tag{3.14}$$

For instance, consider a triangle V_2 in group space having vertices g_0, g_1 and g_2. Now

$$\int_{\partial V_2} = \int_{g_1}^{g_2} - \int_{g_0}^{g_2} + \int_{g_0}^{g_1} \quad . \tag{3.15}$$

If we define

$$\int_{g_0}^{g_1} \alpha_1(v,A_g) = f_1(A;g_0,g_1) \tag{3.16}$$

we see that

$$\Delta f_1 = 0 \tag{3.17}$$

Observe that f_1 is invariant. Indeed

$$\begin{aligned} f_1(Ah;h^{-1}g_0,h^{-1}g_1) &= \int_{h^{-1}g_0}^{h^{-1}g_1} \alpha_1(v,A_{hg}) \\ &= \int_{g_0}^{g_1} \alpha_1(v',A_{g'}) = f(A;g_0,g_1) \quad , \end{aligned} \tag{3.18}$$

where we have performed a change of integration variable

$$g' = hg, \quad v' = (g')^{-1}\delta g' = g^{-1}\delta g = v \quad . \tag{3.19}$$

Again, since α_1 is closed, (3.16) is independent of the path of integration for small deformations of the path. For higher cocycles, however, it is necessary to specify the interpolation points for the lower dimensional edges. Here the exponential parametrization of group elements is a convenient choice.

Since the homogeneous cocycles defined here are invariant they can be used to define inhomogeneous cocycles, as explained in the previous section.

4. GAUGE GROUPS

The gauge group element $g(x,\lambda)$ is a function of the space (or space-time) variables x^m and of additional parameters λ^i. We introduce the two exterior differentiations

$$d = dx^m \frac{\partial}{\partial x^m} \qquad \text{and} \qquad \delta = d\lambda^i \frac{\partial}{\partial x^i} \quad , \tag{4.1}$$

which satisfy

$$d^2 = \delta^2 = d\delta + \delta d = 0 \quad . \tag{4.2}$$

The space A is now the space of vector potentials

$$A = A_m(x)dx^m \tag{4.3}$$

and the group action a gauge transformation

$$A_g \equiv g^{-1}Ag + g^{-1}dg \quad . \tag{4.4}$$

We define again Lie algebra valued 1-forms in group space

$$v = g^{-1}\delta g \quad . \tag{4.5}$$

It is easy to verify that

$$\begin{aligned} \delta v &= -v^2 \quad , \\ \delta A_g &= -dv - vA_g - A_g v \equiv -Dv \quad , \end{aligned} \tag{4.6}$$

where D denotes covariant differentiation. These are the BRS transformations for a gauge group. We also use the field strength

$$F = dA + A^2 \quad , \tag{4.7}$$

which transforms as

$$F_g = dA_g + A_g^2 = g^{-1}Fg \quad , \tag{4.8}$$

$$\delta F_g = F_g v - vF_g \quad . \tag{4.9}$$

They satisfy the Bianchi identities

$$DF_g \equiv dF_g + A_g F_g - F_g A_g = 0 \quad . \tag{4.10}$$

The construction of closed forms in group space proceeds here by use of the so-called "descent equations". In the following we simply write A for A_g and F for F_g. Let

$$P(F_1, F_2, \ldots F_n) \tag{4.11}$$

be a symmetric invariant polynomial of the Lie algebra valued variables $F_1, F_2, \ldots F_n$. Because it is invariant one has

$$\delta P(F,F,\ldots F) = 0 \quad . \tag{4.12}$$

On the other hand, the Bianchi identities imply that

$$dP(F,F,\ldots F) = 0 \quad . \tag{4.13}$$

P(F,F,...F) is a 2n-form in x-space. Actually, one can write

$$P(F,F,\ldots F) = d\omega_{2n-1}(dA,A) \tag{4.14}$$

where

$$\omega_{2n-1} = n\int_0^1 dtP(A,F_t,F_t,\ldots F_t) \quad , \quad F_t = tdA + t^2A^2 \tag{4.15}$$

is the Chern-Simons form.

Applying δ to (4.14) one finds

$$d\delta\omega_{2n-1} = 0 \tag{4.16}$$

and one can actually show that

$$\delta\omega_{2n-1} = -d\omega_{2n-2}{}^1 \quad . \tag{4.17}$$

This procedure can be continued and generates the descent equations

$$\begin{aligned} \delta\omega_{2n-2}{}^1 &= -d\omega_{2n-3}{}^2 \\ \delta\omega_{2n-3}{}^2 &= -d\omega_{2n-4}{}^3 \\ &\ldots \\ \delta\omega_0{}^{2n-1} &= 0 \end{aligned} \tag{4.18}$$

Here $\omega_{2n-k}{}^{k-1}$ is a form of degree 2n - k in x-space and of degree k - 1 in λ-space (group-space). Explicit expressions for these forms are given, for instance, in Refs. 3), 6) and 7).

Integrating with respect to x over a compact manifold, the right-hand sides of Eqs. (4.18) give zero. Therefore, the differential forms in group space

$$\alpha_{k-1} = \int_x \omega_{2n-k}^{k-1} \tag{4.19}$$

are closed

$$\delta\alpha_{k-1} = 0 \quad . \tag{4.20}$$

They can be used to construct homogeneous and inhomogeneous gauge-group cocycles by integrating them over group space as described in the preceding section.

In the case of gauge groups, locality in x plays a very important role. The forms ω_{2n-k}^{k-1} are local in x, in the sense that they are constructed from the gauge potential and its x-derivatives up to a finite order. Although the integrated forms α_{k-1} are simply closed in group space, their densities ω_{2n-k}^{k-1} are not closed. For different values of k they are related locally by the descent equations.

A group cocycle is defined as trivial if it can be obtained by applying the coboundary operator δ to a cochain, in which case it satisfies trivially the cocycle condition, since the square of the coboundary operator is zero. More precisely, the cochain must have a global meaning, i.e., be defined and single-valued everywhere. There is, however, a different concept of triviality which uses the concept of local density. If a cocycle is the x-integral of a local density, we shall call it trivial if it can be obtained by applying the coboundary operator to a cochain which is also the integral of a local density. This leads to the idea of local cohomology, which is the physically relevant one for the case of gauge groups. For instance, the anomaly which is the (2n-2)-dimensional integral

$$\alpha_1 = \int_{\text{space-time}} \omega_{2n-2}^{1} \quad , \tag{4.21}$$

and the anomalous Schwinger term, which is the (2n-3)-dimensional integral

$$\alpha_2 = \int_{\text{space}} \omega_{2n-3}^{2} \quad , \tag{4.22}$$

are non-trivial in the sense of local cohomology. They are local, i.e., they are x-integrals of local densities, and they are not expressible as δ applied to a local expression.

Local cohomology plays a role in the study of gravitational anomalies in $4k - 2$ space-time dimensions. Gravitational anomalies can be expressed as violations of general coordinate invariance or as violations of local Lorentz invariance. The two formulations are equivalent and one can pass from one to the other by adding to the vacuum functional a local "counterterm". In other words, local Lorentz anomalies and general coordinate anomalies differ by a term which can be expressed as the coboundary operator applied to a local function[12)].

The differential forms ω^{k-1}_{2n-k}, which give the densities, are determined by the symmetric invariant polynomial (4.11). The correct polynomial appropriate to a particular physical problem can be found by perturbation theory (or equivalently heat-kernel) methods or, more systematically, by use of the relevant index theorem[8-10)]. We shall not discuss this question here.

5. CONSISTENT AND COVARIANT ANOMALIES

The anomaly α_1 given by (4.19) satisfies

$$\mathcal{s}\alpha_1 = 0 \tag{5.1}$$

which is a compact form of the consistency condition[11)]. On the other hand, α_1 is not gauge invariant, if one transforms the ghost parameter v by the adjoint representation. It is often convenient to give the anomaly in a different form, which is gauge invariant. This is called the covariant anomaly. The relation between the two forms for the anomaly is discussed in Ref. 12) where it is shown that they correspond to different, but physically equivalent, definitions of the current whose covariant divergence they represent. The transformation formulas of Ref. 12) have been given an interesting geometric interpretation in a recent work by Bao and Nair[13)] which we shall now describe briefly.

For simplicity let us give the example of two space-time dimensions. Up to an overall proportionality factor, the consistent anomaly is given by

$$\alpha_1 = \int_X \mathrm{Tr}(vdA) \tag{5.2}$$

while the covariant anomaly is

$$\beta_1 = 2\int_X \mathrm{Tr}(vF), \quad F = dA + A^2, \tag{5.3}$$

and Tr denotes the trace. The difference is

$$\beta_1 - \alpha_1 = \int_X \mathrm{Tr}(v(dA + 2A^2))$$

$$= \int_X \mathrm{Tr}((dv + vA + Av)A) \tag{5.4}$$

$$= -\int_X \mathrm{Tr}((\delta A)A) \quad .$$

This suggests the introduction of a 1-form $\theta(\delta A,A)$ on the space of gauge potentials

$$\theta = -\int_X \mathrm{Tr}(\delta A)A) \quad , \tag{5.5}$$

so that (5.4) can be written

$$\beta_1 - \alpha_1 = \theta(\delta A,A) \quad . \tag{5.6}$$

Applying δ to (5.4) we see that the covariant anomaly satisfies the consistency condition

$$\delta\beta_1 = \omega(\delta A,A) \quad , \tag{5.7}$$

where ω is a 2-form on the space of gauge potentials

$$\omega = -\int_X \mathrm{Tr}(\delta A\ \delta A) \tag{5.8}$$

and satisfies

$$\omega = \delta\theta \ , \ \delta\omega = 0 \quad . \tag{5.9}$$

The form ω can be intepreted as a symplectic 2-form on the infinite dimensional space $\mathcal{A}$ of gauge potentials. Since $\mathcal{A}$ is contractible, ω is not only closed but exact. It is gauge invariant. In two space-time dimensions ω is actually independent of A; it depends only on δA and is non-singular. In higher space-time dimensions ω is proportional to

$$\mathrm{STr}\ \delta A\delta AF^n \tag{5.10}$$

and can vanish, for instance, if $F = 0$. Therefore, the space $\mathcal{A}$ does not acquire a true symplectic structure, only a "presymplectic" structure.

The covariant anomaly β_1 has another interesting property. From (5.3) one sees that ($\delta v = 0$)

$$\delta\beta_1 = 2\int_x \mathrm{Tr}(vD\delta A)$$

$$= 2\int_x \mathrm{Tr}(Dv\delta A) \tag{5.11}$$

$$= -2\int_x \mathrm{Tr}(\mathcal{S}A\delta A) = i_{\mathcal{S}A}\omega$$

The equations (5.6), (5.7), (5.9) and

$$\delta\beta_1 = i_{\mathcal{S}A}\omega \tag{5.12}$$

are valid in any even number of dimensions. Equation (5.12) shows that the covariant anomaly β_1 can be considered as a Hamiltonian generating the gauge transformation flow in $\mathcal{A}$. In more technical language, β_1 is a momentum mapping[14]. However, except in two space-time dimensions, (5.12) does not determine uniquely the Hamiltonian vector $\mathcal{S}A$, because ω is singular.

It is easy to see that (5.7) follows from (5.6), (5.9) and from the equation

$$\mathcal{S}\beta_1(v,A) = \beta_1(v^2,A) \tag{5.13}$$

which expresses the gauge invariance of β_1. One can take the point of view that the 2-form ω is the primary quantity and determines θ, β_1 and α_1 through Eqs. (5.9), (5.12) and (5.6).

Observe that θ and ω are local in x for arbitrary δ, and remain local, of course, when one restricts δ to a gauge orbit, $\delta \to \mathcal{S}$. On the other hand, the anomalies α_1 and β_1 are local, but cannot be extended as local forms on $\mathcal{A}$ for arbitrary δ. However, non-local extensions do exist. For instance, the non-local form on $\mathcal{A}$

$$\int_x \varepsilon^{mn}\partial_m A_n \frac{1}{\mathcal{D}^2}\,\mathcal{D}_1\delta A^1\, d^2x \quad , \quad \mathcal{D}^2 \equiv \mathcal{D}_1\mathcal{D}^1 \tag{5.14}$$

reduces to the local expression (5.2) along a gauge orbit, i.e., for

$$\delta A_1 = \mathcal{D}_1 v \equiv \partial_1 v + A_1 v - vA_1 \quad . \tag{5.15}$$

Similarly

$$\int_x \varepsilon^{mn}F_{mn}\frac{1}{\mathcal{D}^2}\,\mathcal{D}_1\delta A^1\, d^2x \tag{5.16}$$

reduces to (5.3) along a gauge orbit. Similar expressions can be found in higher dimensions. They occur in the work of Atiyah and Singer[8].

Finally, we mention that there is a very simple technique[6),7),12)] for deriving all formulas (4.18), (5.1), (5.6), (5.9) and (5.12) in higher dimensions. One makes use of the identity

$$(d + \mathcal{s} + \delta)(A + v) + (A + v)^2 = dA + \delta A + A^2 = F + \delta A \qquad (5.17)$$

which follows from (4.6) (remember that we write A for A_g) and $\delta v = 0$. We now use the basic Chern formulas (4.14) and (4.15), with the substitutions

$$\begin{aligned} d &\to d + \mathcal{s} + \delta \\ A &\to A + v \\ F &\to F + \delta A \quad . \end{aligned} \qquad (5.18)$$

The identity (5.17) implies that

$$\begin{aligned} &P(F + \delta A, F + \delta A, \dots F + \delta A) = \\ &\quad = (d + \mathcal{s} + \delta)\omega_{2n-1}((d + \mathcal{s} + \delta)(A + v), A + v) \end{aligned} \qquad (5.19)$$

Expanding this formula in powers of $\mathcal{s}$, δ and v and equating powers on the left and right hand sides, one obtains a hierarchy of formulas which contain all desired relations, as well as explicit expressions for all differential forms.

6. SUPERSYMMETRIC GAUGE ANOMALY

It is natural to ask whether the methods described in the previous sections can be generalized to the case of supersymmetric gauge theories. There are three ways of formulating Susy gauge theories in four space-time dimensions[15)]. The first uses a super gauge potential in superspace, with constraints on the super field strength. The second can be derived from the first by solving the constraints and uses a real (hermitean) superfield $V(x,\theta,\bar{\theta})$ such that

$$e^{-V}\,\delta e^{V} \qquad (6.1)$$

belongs to the adjoint representation of the Lie algebra of the gauge group. The third can be derived from the second by going into a non-supersymmetric gauge, the Wess-Zumino gauge (WZ-gauge), in which the lower dimensional component fields contained in the superfield V are transformed to zero and only the physical fields A_μ, λ (gaugino) and D (non-propagating auxiliary field) survive. To each of these formulations there corresponds a way of expressing the Susy gauge anomaly. In the first two formulations Susy will be manifest; in the third it will appear that there is a Susy anomaly. However, this Susy anomaly is actually spurious. It is a consequence of the fact that in the WZ-gauge a Susy transformation consists of the sum of an ordinary linear Susy transformation and of a field-dependent gauge transformation. The latter is necessary to reestablish the WZ-gauge condition, since the WZ-gauge is not preserved by linear Susy transformations (the situation is analogous to the case of Lorentz transformations in QED, when it is formulated in the non-Lorentz invariant Coulomb gauge). A gauge anomaly will therefore induce an apparent Susy anomaly, but this is no indication that Susy is broken.

A considerable amount of work has been done by cohomological methods in all three formulations[16-18)]. The Susy gauge anomaly has also been calculated by the heat-kernel (proper-time) technique in the second formulation[19-22)]. The papers which use manifestly supersymmetric superspace methods contain mostly very complicated calculations. Furthermore, the results are complicated and not very transparent superspace formulas. The reason for this is that it can be shown[23),24)] that the answer must be non-polynomial in V and even in e^V. Furthermore, the answers given in the various papers are usually not the same, although they must be equivalent in the sense that they differ by a (local) cocycle.

On the other hand, the calculation which uses from the beginning the WZ-gauge is relatively simple, and so is the result. We modify slightly the formulation of Ref. 18). One must consider the simultaneous cohomology problem for gauge transformations, Susy transformations and translations. The (odd) coboundary operator δ can be defined as follows:

$$\begin{aligned} \delta A_m &= i\bar{\alpha}\gamma_m\lambda + \mathcal{D}_m v + a\cdot\partial A_m \\ \delta\lambda &= -\frac{1}{2} F_{mn}\gamma^m\gamma^n\alpha + D\gamma_5\alpha - \{v,\lambda\} + a\cdot\partial\lambda \\ \delta D &= i\bar{\alpha}\gamma_5\gamma\cdot\mathcal{D}\lambda + [D,v] + a\cdot\partial D \quad , \end{aligned} \tag{6.2}$$

where λ is a real (Majorana) anticommuting spinor. The Susy parameters α are treated as commuting, while the translation parameters a^m and the gauge parameters v are anticommuting. It is

$$\delta\alpha = 0 \quad , \quad \delta a^m = -\frac{i}{2}\bar{\alpha}\gamma^m\alpha$$

$$\delta v = -v^2 + \frac{i}{2}\bar{\alpha}\gamma^m\alpha A_m + a\cdot\partial v \quad . \tag{6.3}$$

It is easy to check that, with these definitions,

$$\delta^2 = 0 \tag{6.4}$$

One can separate in δ the parts which refer to the various transformations

$$\delta = \delta_v + \delta_\alpha + \delta_a \quad . \tag{6.5}$$

They satisfy

$$\delta_v{}^2 = \delta_a{}^2 = \{\delta_a, \delta_v\} = 0 \tag{6.6}$$

and

$$\delta_\alpha{}^2 + \{\delta_\alpha, \delta_v\} + \{\delta_\alpha, \delta_a\} = 0 \quad . \tag{6.7}$$

The consistency condition for the combined anomalies $G(v,\alpha;A,\lambda)$ is now simply

$$\delta G = 0 \tag{6.8}$$

One can assume absence of the translational anomaly. The solution of (6.8) turns out to be independent of the auxiliary field D. The reader can find it in Ref. 18), but I suggest as an exercise to obtain it in the formulation given here.

The use of the WZ-gauge for the study of the anomaly seems very natural[18)] if one is interested in extended (N > 2) Susy gauge theories or in a Susy gauge theory in higher (more than six) dimensions, for which no satisfactory superfield formulation is known. Unfortunately, the only WZ-gauge formulations known for these theories make use only of the physical propagating fields, with no analogue of the auxiliary field D. As a consequence, the algebra closes only " on the mass shell", i.e., there occur terms on the right-hand side of the commutation relations which vanish only by imposing the classical equations of motion for the spinor fields. It is not clear how to use the cohomological method in this case. What is needed is a better understanding and possibly a geometric interpretation for this kind of algebra. This would also be useful for the formulation of the quantum theory.

REFERENCES

1. See, however, G. Segal, Oxford preprint, 1984; I. Frenkel and I. Singer, in preparation.

2. L.D. Faddeev, Phys. Lett. 145B (1984) 81.

3. B. Zumino, Nucl. Phys. B253 (1985) 477.

4. H. Cartan and S. Eilenberg, Homological Algebra, Princeton University Press, 1956.

5. S. MacLane, Homology, Springer, 1963.

6. R. Stora, in New Developments in Quantum Field Theory, eds M. Lévy and P. Mitter, Plenum, New York, 1977, p. 201; LAPP-TH-94, 1984 (Cargèse lectures 1983).

7. B. Zumino, in Relativity, Groups and Topology II, Les Houches, 1983, eds B.S. DeWitt and R. Stora, North Holland, Amsterdam, 1984, p. 1293; B. Zumino, Y-S Wu and A. Zee, Nucl. Phys. B239 (1984) 477.

8. M.F. Atiyah and I.M. Singer, Proc. Natl. Acad. Sci. USA 81 (1984) 2597.

9. O. Alvarez, I.M. Singer and B. Zumino, Commun. Math. Phys. 96 (1984) 409.

10. L. Alvarez-Gaumé and P. Ginsparg, Nucl. Phys. B243 (1984) 449.

11. J. Wess and B. Zumino, Phys. Lett. 37B (1971) 95.

12. W. Bardeen and B. Zumino, Nucl. Phys. B244 (1984) 421.

13. D. Bao and V.P. Nair, Princeton Institute preprint, 1985.

14. R. Abraham and J.E. Marsden, Foundations of Mechanics, Benjamin/Cummings, Reading, Mass., 1978.

15. J. Wess and J. Bagger, Supersymmetry and Supergravity, Princeton University Press, 1983.

16. L. Bonora, P. Pasti and M. Tonin, Padua preprint DFPD 20/84, to appear in Phys. Lett. B; Padua preprint DFPD 12/85.

17. G. Girardi, R. Grimm and R. Stora, Annecy preprint LAPP-TH-130, to appear in Phys. Lett. B.

18. H. Itoyama, V.P. Nair and Ren H-C, Princeton Institute preprint, 1985.

19. N.K. Nielsen, Nucl. Phys. B244 (1984) 499; Odense University preprint, 1985.

20. E. Guadagnini, K. Konishi and M. Mintchev, Pisa preprint IFUP Th 10/85, 1985.

21. A.W. Fisher, Karlsruhe University preprints, 1985.

22. K. Harada and K. Shizuya, Tohoku University preprint TU/85/280, 1985.

23. O. Piguet and K. Sibold, Nucl. Phys. B247 (1984) 484.

24. S. Ferrara, L. Girardello, O. Piguet and R. Stora, CERN-TH. 4134/85, LAPP-TH-131, 1985.

A CLASS OF TWO-DIMENSIONAL FINITE FIELD THEORIES†

L. Alvarez-Gaumé and P. Ginsparg

Lyman Laboratory of Physics
Harvard University
Cambridge, MA 02138

The supersymmetric non-linear σ-model in one and two dimensions has provided a rather fertile arena for the interplay between geometry, topology, and field theory. These theories in 0+1 dimensions were used to refine the Morse inequalities[1] and rederive the index theorem[2] using elementary methods of quantum mechanics. In the case of 2-dimensional field theories, it is easy to show that the existence of extended supersymmetry implies that the σ-model manifold must be of a restricted type: either Kähler for N=2 [3][4], or hyperkähler for N=4 [4]. These geometrical constraints in turn imply rather striking consequences for the ultraviolet behavior of these models. We will show[5] that N=4 and N=2 supersymmetric σ-models defined on Ricci flat manifolds are finite to all orders of perturbation theory, i.e. that they are (contrary to intuition) conformally invariant field theories. It also turns out that such models defined on locally symmetric spaces are super-renormalizable, having only a one-loop on-shell divergence given by the Ricci tensor.

Part of the motivation for clarifying these issues is provided by recent progress[6] in string theory which suggests that certain 10-dimensional supersymmetric string theories provide a nearly unique framework in which quantum gravity may be consistently defined and unified with other known interactions. Phenomenological applications[7] require that the string theory be defined on a manifold of the form $M_4 \times M_6$, where M_4 is assumed to be a maximally symmetric 4-dimensional space time and M_6 is a compact 6-dimensional internal space (in the Kaluza-Klein sense). Whether string ground states of this form actually exist is intimately connected with the ultraviolet finiteness of 2-dimensional supersymmetric non-linear σ-models, where the 2 spacetime dimensions of the σ-model play the role of the internal coordinates on the string world sheet and the target space M plays the role of the compactified M_6. Ultraviolet finiteness implies that the theory is conformally invariant and this in turn is required for a consistent formulation of the string theory on such backgrounds. The results to be presented here suggest that only internal spaces M_6 which are Ricci flat should be considered, and these are in any event preferred for phenomenological reasons[7].

A modification of the standard supersymmetric σ-model which arises in string theory

† supported in part by NSF contract PHY-82-15249

is the addition of a Wess-Zumino term[8]. The UV analysis of these models is more complicated because the Wess-Zumino term represents a non-vanishing torsion contribution to the standard riemannian connection on M. Explicit one- and two-loop computations show[8][9] that the finiteness conditions for these theories are in accord with one's naive guess: the torsion must be Ricci flattening (i.e. $R_{ij}(\Gamma+T)=0$, where Γ is the Christoffel symbol, and T is the torsion). For Lie groups, it is well known that there is a torsion tensor (essentially the structure constants of the group) which is parallelizing, so that theories on Lie groups with the Wess-Zumino term given by the canonical third cohomology class should be finite. It is likely that this result can be proven using Witten's non-abelian bosonization procedure[10]. The authors of [11] have used the results of [10] to obtain a new formulation of the bosonic string (and, in so doing, change the critical dimension). Demanding completely parallelizing torsion leaves only the seven-sphere and Lie groups whereas requiring only Ricci flattening torsion may leave a larger class of spaces on which the string theory could be formulated. We expect that the methods to be presented here may ultimately be extended to resolve these issues.

Let (M_n, g) be an n-dimensional riemannian manifold with metric g_{ij}. For 2-dimensional spacetimes, an N=1 supersymetric σ-model with scalar fields taking values on M_n is given by the lagrangian[12]

$$\mathcal{L}=\frac{1}{2}g_{ij}(\phi)\partial_\mu\phi^i\partial^\mu\phi^j+\frac{i}{2}g_{ij}\overline{\psi}^i\gamma^\mu D_\mu\psi^j+\frac{1}{12}R_{ijkl}\overline{\psi}^i\psi^k\overline{\psi}^j\psi^l$$
$$D_\mu\psi^i=\partial_\mu\psi^i+\Gamma^i_{jk}\partial_\mu\phi^j\psi^k,\quad \gamma^0=\sigma_2,\ \gamma^1=\sigma_1, \tag{1}$$

where Γ^i_{jk} is the Christoffel connection and R_{ijkl} is the Riemann curvature tensor. The ϕ's are the bosonic fields which represent geometrically a coordinate system on M_n, and the fermions ψ^i are two-component Majorana fermions which behave like vectors under coordinate reparametrizations. The supersymmetry transformation rules for (1) are given by

$$\delta\phi^i=\overline{\epsilon}\psi^i,\quad \delta\psi^i=-i\partial\!\!\!/\phi^i\epsilon-\Gamma^i_{jk}(\overline{\epsilon}\psi^j)\psi^k. \tag{2}$$

Even though (2) looks non-covariant, it can be readily checked that the transformations (2) commute with coordinate reparametrizations. The parameter ϵ is a constant anticommuting two-component Majorana spinor. (1) and (2), despite being called N=1, do not actually correspond to the minimal number of supersymmetries in two dimensions. $N=\frac{1}{2}$ supersymmetric systems can be constructed in terms of Weyl-Majorana fermions and either left- or right-moving scalars. These are the types of supersymmetric systems which appear in the recently constructed heterotic string[13]. Analyzing the UV properties of $N=\frac{1}{2}$ supersymmetric σ-models is more difficult than for N=1, because these models are in principle afflicted with anomalies of two types: the σ-model anomalies described in [14] and the gravitational anomalies described in [15]. These may occur when the theory is coupled to an external two dimensional supergravity multiplet as one is instructed to do in the covariant treatment of strings (see [16] for a review and earlier references). The analysis of $N=\frac{1}{2}$ models is likely to enlighten various quantum features of these theories.

Returning now to the quantum properties of the lagrangian (1), we face two immediate problems. First, we need to find a suitable computational method which permits the computation of the divergences and counterterms appearing at the different loop levels, both on- and off-shell. We will be concerned here only with the on-shell counterterms, because we wish to compute the β-function and identify the sufficient conditions which guarantee conformal invariance. The necessary method is given by the background field expansion (for references to the early literature, see [8][17][18]), which allows an efficient computation of the on-shell divergences for σ-models on general riemannian manifolds. Second, we need to find a supersymmetric regulator. The most efficient way of computing Feynman diagrams containing loops is to use the supersymmetric dimensional regularization scheme known as dimensional reduction (see [19] for details). No ambiguities arise up to three-loop order for either 2- or 4-dimensional theories. The rules of dimensional reduction as they currently stand, however, are not obviously consistent to higher order and this procedure may need some modifications for complete reliability. In any event, a simple power counting argument shows that the divergences expected in (1) are logarithmic, so a single Pauli-Villars superfield should suffice as a regulator for 2-dimensional theories. Our results to follow here tacitly depend on our assumed existence of a supersymmetric regulator.

We shall now detail the form of the background field expansion used in explicit computations. For simplicity, we will present the method for the bosonic model. We start by expanding the field ϕ^i around a solution $\phi_0^i(x)$ to the classical equations of motion

$$0 = D_\mu \partial^\mu \phi_0^i = \partial_\mu \partial^\mu \phi_0^i + \Gamma^i_{jk}\, \partial_\mu \phi_0^j\, \partial^\mu \phi_0^k. \tag{3}$$

Given any field ϕ^i close to ϕ_0^i, we could naively write $\phi^i = \phi_0^i + u^i$, and expand the action around ϕ_0. This procedure however does not manifestly ensure the coordinate reparametrization invariance of the S-matrix and on-shell divergences[20]. In order to overcome this shortcoming of the naive background field expansion, we employ the background field expansion in terms of normal coordinates (for more details, see [17][18][21]) defined as follows. If ϕ^i is close enough to ϕ_0^i, there is a unique geodesic which connects ϕ_0^i to ϕ^i, and reaches ϕ^i in unit proper time. If ξ^i represents the tangent vector to the geodesic at ϕ_0^i, we can parametrize ϕ^i in terms of ξ^i. Since ξ^i is a vector under coordinate changes, the functional Taylor expansion of the action around ϕ_0 will be manifestly coordinate invariant, and the vertices will be functions of the curvature and its covariant derivatives. Letting $\phi^i(\lambda)$ be the geodesic joining ϕ_0 and ϕ ($\phi^i(0) = \phi_0^i$, $\phi^i(1) = \phi^i$), so that $\xi^i = d\phi^i(\lambda)/d\lambda|_{\lambda=0}$ and let $\xi^i(\lambda)$ be the tangent vector at any λ. We find that

$$\begin{aligned} \frac{d\mathcal{L}}{d\lambda} &= \frac{d}{d\lambda}\frac{1}{2} g_{ij}(\phi(\lambda))\,\partial_\mu\phi^i\,\partial^\mu\phi^j = g_{ij}(\phi(\lambda))\,D_\mu\xi^i\,\partial^\mu\phi^j \\ \frac{d^2\mathcal{L}}{d\lambda^2} &= g_{ij}(\phi(\lambda))\,\frac{D}{d\lambda}D_\mu\xi^i\,\partial^\mu\phi^j + g_{ij}(\phi(\lambda))\,D_\mu\xi^i\,D^\mu\xi^j \end{aligned} \tag{4}$$

where $\dfrac{D}{d\lambda}\xi^i = \dfrac{d\xi^i}{d\lambda} + \Gamma^i_{jk}\,\xi^j\xi^k$.

Since ξ^i is the tangent vector to the geodesic, we have $D\xi^i/d\lambda = 0$ and

$$\frac{D}{d\lambda}D_\mu\xi^i = \left[\frac{D}{d\lambda}, D_\mu\right]\xi^i = R^i{}_{jkl}\,\xi^j\xi^k\,\partial_\mu\phi^l.$$

This elegant procedure[21] can now be carried out to arbitrarily high order. Formally, we write

$$\mathcal{L} = g_{ij}(\phi)(\partial_\mu\phi^i + e^D D_\mu e^{-D}\,\xi^i)(\partial^\mu\phi^j + e^D D^\mu e^{-D}\,\xi^j)$$

($D = D/d\lambda$) which gives explicitly

$$\begin{aligned} \frac{D}{d\lambda}D_\mu\xi^i &= R^i{}_{jkl}\,\xi^j\xi^k\,\partial_\mu\phi^l \\ \frac{D^2}{d\lambda^2}D_\mu\xi^i &= \nabla_m R^i{}_{jkl}\,\xi^m\xi^j\xi^k\partial_\mu\phi^l + R^i{}_{jkl}\,\xi^j\xi^k D_\mu\xi^l \\ \frac{D^3}{d\lambda^3}D_\mu\xi^i &= \nabla_m\nabla_n R^i{}_{jkl}\,\xi^m\xi^n\xi^j\xi^k\,\partial_\mu\phi^l + 2\,\nabla_m R^i{}_{jkl}\,\xi^m\xi^j\xi^k\,D_\mu\xi^l \\ &\quad + R^i{}_{jkl}\,\xi^j\xi^k\,R^l{}_{mnp}\,\xi^m\xi^n\,\partial_\mu\phi^p \end{aligned} \tag{5}$$

etc.

(If the manifold is locally symmetric, i.e. $\nabla_i R_{jklm} = 0$, then the expansion simplifies to

$$\begin{aligned} \frac{D^{2n+1}}{d\lambda^{2n+1}}D_\mu\xi^i &= (M^{n+1})^i{}_j\,\partial_\mu\phi^j \\ \frac{D^{2n+2}}{d\lambda^{2n+2}}D_\mu\xi^i &= (M^{n+1})^i{}_j\,D_\mu\xi^j \end{aligned}$$

where $M^i{}_j \equiv R^i{}_{klj}\,\xi^k\xi^l$). To second order in ξ^i, we find from (5)

$$\begin{aligned} \mathcal{L} &= g_{ij}(\phi_0)\,\partial_\mu\phi_0^i\,\partial^\mu\phi_0^j \\ &\quad + \frac{1}{2}R_{iklj}\,\xi^k\xi^l\,\partial_\mu\phi_0^i\,\partial^\mu\phi_0^j + \frac{1}{2}g_{ij}(\phi_0)\,D_\mu\xi^i\,D^\mu\xi^j + O(\xi^3). \end{aligned} \tag{6}$$

The propagator of the quantum field ξ^i is proportional to $g^{ij}(\phi_0)$, and the vertices are simple polynomials in $R^i{}_{jkl}$ and its covariant derivatives. It is straightforward to check that the one-loop divergence is proportional to the Ricci tensor $R_{ij}(\phi_0)$.

The extension of this formalism to the supersymmetric case is carried out by writing (1) in terms of a 2-dimensional real superfield $\Phi^i = \phi^i + \overline{\theta}\psi^i + \frac{1}{2}\overline{\theta}\theta F^i$, where θ is a real two-component constant Majorana spinor, $\overline{\theta} = \theta^T\gamma^0$, and F^i is an auxilliary field. The superspace form of (1) is just the naive extension of the purely bosonic σ-model

$$\mathcal{L} = \frac{1}{4i}\int d^2\theta\, g_{ij}(\Phi)\, \overline{D\Phi^i} D\Phi^j$$
$$D_\alpha \Phi^i = \left(\frac{\partial}{\partial\overline{\theta}^\alpha} - i(\gamma^\mu\theta)_\alpha \frac{\partial}{\partial x^\mu}\right)\Phi^i, \qquad \overline{D}_\alpha = D_\beta \gamma^0_{\beta\alpha} \tag{7}$$

and the supersymmetry transformation rules (2) become

$$\delta\Phi^i = \overline{\epsilon}_\alpha \left(\frac{\partial}{\partial\overline{\theta}_\alpha} + i(\not{\partial}\theta)_\alpha\right)\Phi^i. \tag{8}$$

All the previous formulæ for the bosonic case can now be extended verbatim to the supersymmetric case with the obvious substitutions of superfields for fields, and D_α for ∂_μ (the interested reader will find more details on the superspace Feynman rules for these theories in [18]).

Explicit one- and two-loop computations have been carried out in the bosonic[17] and supersymmetric[18] cases, and several surprises are worth pointing out. First note that the superfield Φ^i has zero canonical dimension, so that the degree of divergence of every vertex is zero. Thus, the renormalization counterterms appear as changes in the metric. Using dimensional regularization, this means that the bare metric can be written as

$$g^B_{ij} = \mu^\epsilon \left[g^R_{ij} + \sum_{\nu=1}^{\infty} \frac{T^{(\nu)}_{ij}(g^R)}{\epsilon^\nu}\right], \tag{9}$$

where $\epsilon = d - 2$ and the $T^{(\nu)}_{ij}$'s are symmetric tensors constructed in terms of curvatures and their covariant derivatives. Using methods similar to those in [22], one arrives at the renormalization group equation[17]

$$\mu\frac{\partial}{\partial\mu} g^R_{ij} = -\beta_{ij}(g^R)$$
$$\beta_{ij}(g^R) = \epsilon g^R_{ij} + \left(1 + \lambda\frac{\partial}{\partial\lambda}\right) T^{(1)}_{ij}(\lambda^{-1}g^R)\Big|_{\lambda=1} \tag{10}$$

together with the generalized pole equations

$$\lim_{\lambda\to1}\left(1 + \lambda\frac{\partial}{\partial\lambda}\right) T^{(\nu+1)}(\lambda^{-1}g^R) =$$
$$\lim_{\substack{\eta\to0\\ \lambda\to1}} \eta^{-1}\left[T^{(\nu)}\left(g^R + \eta\left(1+\lambda\frac{\partial}{\partial\lambda}\right)T^{(1)}(\lambda^{-1}g^R)\right) - T^{(\nu)}(g^R)\right]. \tag{11}$$

We see that the higher order poles are completely determined by the $1/\epsilon$ pole, as in the standard 't Hooft renormalization group pole equations[22]. The renormalization group pole equations describe the motion of the metric in the space of all riemannian metrics as the renormalization scale is changed.

Thus far we have seen that any riemannian manifold yields a 2-dimensional $N=1$ supersymmetric σ-model, and we have seen how its divergences may be calculated, but we will have no further insight into the structure of the possible counterterms until we consider the constraints imposed by extended supersymmetry. Before moving on to this subject, we shall first elaborate some useful features of the formalism already introduced. 1) The on-shell counterterms correspond to metric renormalizations $g_{ij} \to g_{ij} + T_{ij}$, where T_{ij} is constructed in terms of curvatures and covariant derivatives. In order to determine at which loop level a given tensor T_{ij} might appear in perturbation theory, we note that if we make a constant rescaling of the metric $g_{ij} \to \lambda^{-1} g_{ij}$, λ plays the role of a loop counting parameter. Thus $T_{ij}(g)$ will appear at ℓ-loop order if $T_{ij}(\lambda^{-1}g) = \lambda^{\ell-1}T_{ij}(g)$. 2) The background field expansion uses only the fact that the manifold M is riemannian, and nowhere uses any particular local or global properties of M. The only properties which enter are the riemannian structure on M and the Bianchi identities, the latter providing the sufficient integrability conditions for a given connection and curvature to originate from a riemannian metric. This simple fact implies that the tensor counterterms are universal, and that the divergent coefficients do not carry any information about the intrinsic properties of M. More mathematically, we can say that the counterterms are functorially defined on the category of riemannian manifolds. 3) Notice that no counterterm generated can ever be explicitly proportional to the metric tensor g_{ij}. This is because the vertices are only functions of curvatures and their covariant derivatives, and the only way the metric enters is in the definition of propagators for the ξ^i, ξ^j fields, and these only appear in internal lines contracting vertices.

We shall now consider the constraints imposed on M by the requirements of extended supersymmetry, and this will take us into the geometry of Kähler and hyperkähler manifolds. Kähler manifolds first emerged in supersymmetric field theories when Zumino tried to construct the most general form of an $N=1$ supersymmetric lagrangian describing the self-interactions of $N=1$ scalar multiplets in 4-dimensions[3]. This lagrangian can be described as a non-linear σ-model taking values on a Kähler manifold. By standard dimensional reduction from 4- to 2-dimensions, we find that $N=2$ supersymmetry in 2-dimensions requires that the manifold M be Kähler. It is possible to show that this is also sufficient for supersymmetry in 2-dimensions (where there is no need to impose chirality constraints in order to define the scalar multiplet) and moreover that a hyperkähler manifold is necessary and sufficient for $N=3,4$ supersymmetry[4]. We give a brief explanation of these geometrical constraints.

A riemannian manifold (M_n, g) is said to be Kähler if there exists a tensor $f^i{}_j$ (the complex structure) on M which satisfies

$$f^i{}_k f^k{}_j = -\delta^i{}_j \tag{12a}$$

$$g_{ij} f^i{}_k f^j{}_l = g_{kl} \tag{12b}$$

$$\nabla_i f^j{}_k = 0. \tag{12c}$$

Since $f^i{}_j$ is real, $(12a)$ implies that the manifold is even dimensional. $f^i{}_j$ represents geometrically multiplication by i on the tangent space. We can divide the tangent space into the two eigenspaces $T \oplus \overline{T}$, with eigenvalues $\pm i$, where T is the space of holomorphic vectors, and $\overline{T}$ is the space of antiholomorphic vectors. $(12c)$ implies that the complex structure defined by $f^i{}_j$ is integrable, i.e. that the manifold can be covered with complex coordinate patches $(z^\alpha, \bar{z}^\beta)$ with holomorphic transition functions on the overlaps. T is thus generated by $\frac{\partial}{\partial z^\alpha}$, and $\overline{T}$ by $\frac{\partial}{\partial \bar{z}^\alpha}$. In these coordinates, (12) implies that the line element can be written as

$$ds^2 = g_{ij}\, dx^i \otimes dx^j = 2g_{\alpha\bar{\beta}}\, dz^\alpha \otimes d\bar{z}^\beta. \tag{13}$$

The conditions $(12a$–$c)$, giving $\nabla_l (g_{kj} f^k{}_i) = 0$, then moreover require that the Kähler-form J, defined as

$$J = \frac{1}{2} g_{kj} f^k{}_i\, dx^i \wedge dx^j = i g_{\alpha\bar{\beta}}\, dz^\alpha \wedge d\bar{z}^\beta, \tag{14}$$

be closed: $dJ = 0$. This is equivalent to the curl-free conditions

$$\partial_\gamma g_{\alpha\bar{\beta}} = \partial_\alpha g_{\gamma\bar{\beta}} \qquad \partial_{\bar{\gamma}} g_{\alpha\bar{\beta}} = \partial_{\bar{\beta}} g_{\alpha\bar{\gamma}}, \tag{15}$$

which tell us that the metric components $g_{\alpha\bar{\beta}}$ may be written locally as

$$g_{\alpha\bar{\beta}} = \frac{\partial^2}{\partial z^\alpha \partial \bar{z}^\beta} K(z, \bar{z}), \tag{16}$$

where $K(z, \bar{z})$ is known as the Kähler potential. K is unique up to Kähler transformations $K(z, \bar{z}) \to K(z, \bar{z}) + f(z) + \bar{f}(\bar{z})$, where $f(z)$ is a holomorphic function.

On a Kähler manifold, we can consider forms which are p-times holomorphic (contain p dz's) and q times antiholomorphic (q $d\bar{z}$'s), so that the space of r-forms Λ^r splits naturally into $\Lambda^r = \Lambda^{(r,0)} \oplus \Lambda^{(r-1,1)} \oplus \ldots \oplus \Lambda^{(0,r)}$. Similarly, the exterior derivative d and its adjoint $\delta = d^*$ can be split as $d = \partial + \bar{\partial}$, $\delta = \partial^* + \bar{\partial}^*$ $(\partial^* = -{*}\bar{\partial}{*}$, $\bar{\partial}^* = -{*}\partial{*})$, so that $\partial: \Lambda^{p,q} \to \Lambda^{p+1,q}$, $\bar{\partial}: \Lambda^{p,q} \to \Lambda^{p,q+1}$, $\partial^*: \Lambda^{(p,q)} \to \Lambda^{(p-1,q)}$, and $\bar{\partial}^*: \Lambda^{(p,q)} \to \Lambda^{(p,q-1)}$. It also follows (see, for example, [23]) from the covariant constancy of the complex structure that the laplacian on forms satisfies $\Box \equiv d\delta + \delta d = 2(\partial\partial^* + \partial^*\partial) = 2(\bar{\partial}\bar{\partial}^* + \bar{\partial}^*\bar{\partial})$, and that $\partial\bar{\partial}^* + \bar{\partial}^*\partial = \bar{\partial}\partial^* + \partial^*\bar{\partial} = 0$. Since the generators of the cohomology groups are the harmonic forms, we have $H^r = H^{(r,0)} \oplus H^{(r-1,1)} \oplus \ldots \oplus H^{(0,r)}$, where $H^{(p,q)}$ is generated by harmonic forms of type (p,q).

The condition (12*b*) means that the metric is a hermitian tensor with respect to the complex structure $f^i{}_j$. Generally, an arbitrary second rank tensor T_{ij} is hermitian if

$$T_{ij}\, f^i{}_k f^j{}_l = T_{kl}. \tag{17}$$

In complex coordinates, this means that $T_{\alpha\beta} = T_{\bar{\alpha}\bar{\beta}} = 0$, i.e. only the mixed components $T_{\alpha\bar{\beta}}$ and $T_{\bar{\alpha}\beta}$ may be non-zero. A symmetric hermitian tensor T_{ij} is called a Kähler tensor if it satisfies as well the Kähler condition

$$\partial_\lambda T_{\alpha\bar{\beta}} = \partial_\alpha T_{\lambda\bar{\beta}}, \quad \partial_{\bar{\lambda}} T_{\alpha\bar{\beta}} = \partial_{\bar{\beta}} T_{\alpha\bar{\lambda}}. \tag{18}$$

(18) says that if T_{ij} is a symmetric hermitian tensor, then the type (1,1) 2-form

$$\tau = \frac{1}{2} T_{kj} f^k{}_i\, dx^i \wedge dx^j = i T_{\alpha\bar{\beta}}\, dz^\alpha \wedge d\bar{z}^\beta, \tag{19}$$

is closed, $d\tau = 0$, if and only if T_{ij} is Kähler (Note that $T_{kj} f^k{}_i$ is automatically antisymmetric in i and j due to the hermiticity condition (17) and symmetry of T_{kj}). A Kähler tensor thus represents a cohomology class in the Hodge-DeRham group $H^{1,1}(M)$. In particular, for a compact manifold the Kähler form J of (14) always generates a non-trivial element of $H^{1,1}(M)$. This is because for a compact manifold M of complex dimension n, the volume form is expressable as $J^n/n!$ and were this exact, the manifold would have zero volume.

A generic riemannian manifold of real dimension n has holonomy group[24] $SO(n)$. Since $f^i{}_j$ is covariantly constant, for a Kähler manifold of $2n$ real dimensions the holonomy group is reduced to $U(n) \subset SO(2n)$. A hyperkähler manifold further admits three covariantly constant complex structures $f^{(a)i}{}_j$, satisfying

$$f^{(a)i}{}_k f^{(b)k}{}_j + f^{(b)i}{}_k f^{(a)k}{}_j = -2\delta^i{}_j\, \delta^{ab} \tag{20}$$

as required for the N=4 supersymmetry algebra. There are thus three complex coordinate systems $(z,\bar{z})$, $(u,\bar{u})$, $(w,\bar{w})$ adapted to the three complex structures, and the Kähler potential behaves as

$$K(z,\bar{z}) \to K(u,\bar{u}) + f(u) + \bar{f}(\bar{u})$$
$$K(z,\bar{z}) \to K(w,\bar{w}) + f(w) + \bar{f}(\bar{w})$$

when changing from one complex coordinate system to another, i.e. the metric is hermitian with respect to the three complex structures. Covariant constancy of (20) implies that there is a natural quaternionic structure on the tangent space, and the holonomy group for a hyperkähler manifold of $4n$ real dimensions thus reduces to $Sp(n) \subset U(2n) \subset SO(4n)$.

On a Kähler manifold the standard formulæ of riemannian geometry simplify dramatically. For example, the only non-vanishing components of Γ^i_{jk} are $\Gamma^\alpha_{\beta\gamma} = g^{\alpha\bar{\rho}}\partial_\beta g_{\gamma\bar{\rho}}$ and $\Gamma^{\bar{\alpha}}_{\bar{\beta}\bar{\gamma}} = (\Gamma^\alpha_{\beta\gamma})^*$ (which are symmetric in β, γ and $\bar{\beta}, \bar{\gamma}$, respectively, by (15)). The curvature tensor becomes

$$R^\alpha{}_{\beta\bar{\rho}\gamma} = \partial_{\bar{\rho}}\Gamma^\alpha_{\beta\gamma}, \tag{21}$$

and the cyclic and Bianchi identities reduce to

$$R_{\alpha\bar{\beta}\gamma\bar{\delta}} = R_{\gamma\bar{\beta}\alpha\bar{\delta}}, \quad R_{\alpha\bar{\beta}\gamma\bar{\delta}} = R_{\alpha\bar{\delta}\gamma\bar{\beta}} \tag{22a}$$

$$\nabla_\lambda R_{\alpha\bar{\beta}\gamma\bar{\delta}} = \nabla_\alpha R_{\lambda\bar{\beta}\gamma\bar{\delta}}, \quad \nabla_{\bar{\lambda}} R_{\alpha\bar{\beta}\gamma\bar{\delta}} = \nabla_{\bar{\beta}} R_{\alpha\bar{\lambda}\gamma\bar{\delta}}. \tag{22b}$$

It is useful to notice that the only non-vanishing components $R_{\alpha\bar{\beta}\gamma\bar{\delta}}$ of the curvature tensor on a Kähler manifold have two holomorphic and two antiholomorphic indices, and otherwise satisfy the usual symmetries of the Riemann tensor. Finally, the Ricci tensor on a Kähler manifold turns out to take the simple form

$$R_{\alpha\bar{\beta}} = g^{\mu\bar{\lambda}} R_{\bar{\lambda}\mu\alpha\bar{\beta}} = -\partial_\alpha \partial_{\bar{\beta}} \ln\det(g). \tag{23}$$

$R_{\alpha\bar{\beta}}$ is a Kähler tensor, and generates a non-trivial cohomology class in general because in going from a coordinate patch z^α to another z'^α, $\log\det g \to \log\det g + h(z) + \bar{h}(\bar{z})$, where $h(z) = \log\det(\frac{\partial z^\alpha}{\partial z'^\lambda})$. In fact the Ricci form

$$\Sigma = iR_{\alpha\bar{\beta}}\, dz^\alpha \wedge d\bar{z}^\beta, \tag{24}$$

can be shown[25] to represent the first Chern class on any Kähler manifold.

On a hyperkähler manifold, (21)–(23) hold for the different complex structures. We now introduce a formalism better suited to taking advantage of the geometrical features of hyperkähler manifolds (see, for example, [26]). Since the holonomy group of a hyperkähler manifold is $Sp(n) \subset SU(2n) \subset SO(4n)$, we can covariantly split the tangent space as the tensor product of the 2-dimensional representation of $Sp(1)$ and the fundamental $2n$-dimensional representation of $Sp(n)$. Each tangent space index i can then be represented in terms of an $Sp(1)$ index α=1,2 and an $Sp(n)$ index A=1,2n. The interpolation between indices i and (α, A) is then provided by covariantly constant matrices $\sigma^i{}_{\alpha A}$ (this construction is the natural generalization of the familiar decomposition of $SO(4) \supset SU(2) \times SU(2) \approx Sp(1) \times Sp(1)$ in which case the σ's are the usual $\sigma^\mu_{\alpha\dot{\beta}}$ matrices). Taking $\epsilon_{\alpha\beta}$ and ϵ_{AB} to be the fundamental antisymmetric invariant tensors of $Sp(1)$ and $Sp(n)$ respectively, it follows that the metric g_{ij} adapted to these $Sp(1) \times Sp(n)$ frames is simply $g_{ij}\sigma^i_{\alpha A}\sigma^j_{\beta B} = \epsilon_{\alpha\beta}\epsilon_{AB}$. Because of the vanishing $Sp(1)$ holonomy, the connection 1-form becomes $\omega_{\alpha A,\beta B} = \epsilon_{\alpha\beta}\omega_{AB}$, where antisymmetry of ω_{ij} implies the symmetry $\omega_{AB} = \omega_{BA}$. Similarly, the curvature referred to these frames is

$$R_{\alpha A,\beta B,\gamma C,\delta D} = R_{ijkl}\sigma^i_{\alpha A}\sigma^j_{\beta B}\sigma^k_{\gamma C}\sigma^l_{\delta D} = \epsilon_{\alpha\beta}\epsilon_{\gamma\delta}\Omega_{ABCD}, \tag{25}$$

where the usual symmetries of R_{ijkl} imply that Ω_{ABCD} is totally symmetric in A, B, C, and D. The three Kähler structures $f^{(a)i}{}_j$ are given in this language by $f^{(a)k}{}_j g_{ki}\sigma^i_{\alpha A}\sigma^j_{\beta B} = \{\delta_{\alpha\beta}\epsilon_{AB},\ (\tau_1)_{\alpha\beta}\epsilon_{AB},\ (\tau_3)_{\alpha\beta}\epsilon_{AB}\}$ (where τ_1 and τ_3 are the usual 2×2 Pauli matrices). These tensors are manifestly antisymmetric in $\alpha A, \beta B$ and covariantly constant (hence satisfy (12*a*-*c*)), and automatically satisfy the Clifford algebra condition (20).

It follows immediately from the total symmetry of Ω_{ABCD} in (25) that the Ricci tensor vanishes for hyperkähler manifolds. This can also be seen by noting that on a Kähler manifold the curvature 2-form

$$\Omega^\alpha{}_\beta = R^\alpha{}_{\beta\delta\bar\gamma}\, dz^\delta \wedge d\bar z^\gamma \tag{26}$$

is valued in the Lie algebra of $U(2n)$. The trace of the curvature 2-form picks out the $U(1)$ part of the holonomy group and is related to the Ricci form Σ of (24) by

$$\mathrm{tr}\,\Omega = \Omega^\alpha{}_\alpha = R^\alpha{}_{\alpha\delta\bar\gamma}\, dz^\delta \wedge d\bar z^\gamma = R_{\delta\bar\gamma}\, dz^\delta \wedge d\bar z^\gamma = -i\Sigma. \tag{27}$$

It follows that a Kähler manifold has no $U(1)$ holonomy if and only if it is Ricci flat. Now if M is hyperkähler, Ω is valued in the Lie algebra of $Sp(n)$. Since $Sp(n)$ lies entirely within the $SU(2n)$ subgroup of $U(2n)$, its generators are all traceless and we learn that hyperkähler manifolds are automatically Ricci flat. It is easy to show moreover that on hyperkähler manifolds all the odd Chern classes vanish, because the odd Casimir invariants of $Sp(n)$ all vanish.

With our geometrical setup complete, we can now adress the issue of finiteness for σ-models. We have already remarked upon the universality of the divergences generated in perturbation theory for the action (1), and this gives us a powerful means of characterizing the possible infinities which may appear. In order to determine whether the coefficient of a given tensor will be different from zero, we may assume that M is either Kähler or hyperkähler, and determine whether the tensor suitably restricts to a Kähler or hyperkähler tensor. For N=2 supersymmetry, M must be Kähler, and the theory (1) then admits a global, non-chiral $SO(2)$ symmetry

$$\delta\psi^i = \varepsilon f^i{}_j\,\psi^j \tag{28}$$

generated by the complex structure. This global symmetry requires that any counterterms T_{ij} to the metric must be hermitian with respect to the original complex structure,

$T_{ij}f^i{}_k f^j{}_l = T_{kl}$. In terms of coordinates adapted to the complex structure, ψ has components ψ^α and $\psi^{\bar\alpha}$, and invariance under (28) simply corresponds to infinitesimal invariance under the $U(1)$ rotation $\psi^\alpha \to e^{i\varepsilon}\psi^\alpha$, $\psi^{\bar\alpha} \to e^{-i\varepsilon}\psi^{\bar\alpha}$. In these complex coordinates, (1) becomes

$$\mathcal{L} = g_{\alpha\bar\beta}\partial_\mu\phi^\alpha\partial^\mu\bar\phi^\beta + ig_{\alpha\bar\beta}\overline{\psi}^\alpha \not{D}\psi^{\bar\beta} + \frac{1}{4}R_{\alpha\bar\beta\mu\bar\lambda}\overline{\psi}^\alpha\psi^\mu\overline{\psi}^{\bar\beta}\psi^{\bar\lambda}, \tag{29}$$

and counterterms to the metric must take the form of Kähler tensors $T_{\alpha\bar\beta}$. Similarly, for the case of N=4 supersymmetry, the hyperkähler structure gives (1) a full $SU(2)$ symmetry

$$\delta\psi^i = (\varepsilon_1 f^{(1)i}{}_j + \varepsilon_2 f^{(2)i}{}_j + \varepsilon_3 f^{(3)i}{}_j)\psi^j \tag{30}$$

generated by the three complex structures. This corresponds to a global $SU(2)$ rotation in the $Sp(1)$ indices of the tangent space. Invariance under the $SU(2)$ symmetry implies that any counterterm T_{ij} written in symplectic frames becomes $T_{\alpha A,\beta B} = \epsilon_{\alpha\beta}T_{AB}$, where symmetry of T_{ij} gives $T_{AB} = -T_{BA}$. We see that the preservation of N=2 or N=4 supersymmetry depends on having a regulator which preserves the N=1 supersymmetry and the $SO(2)$ or $SU(2)$ global symmetries which exchange the different supercharges.

One might worry that in an arbitrary coordinate system, the $U(1)$ and $SU(2)$ symmetrics are non-linearly realized. In general, symmetries so realized do not necessarily insure manifest invariance of the counterterms[27]. To see that this is not a problem here, notice that the S-matrix of these theories is invariant under coordinate reparametrizations[20]. By choosing an appropriate coordinate system, we can make any two supersymmetries act linearly and homogeneously on the scalar multiplet (ϕ^i, ψ^i, F^i). The arguments of [27] thus do not apply and the counterterms are expected to be invariant under the global $U(1)$ and $SU(2)$ symmetries (we are again only assuming the existence of some regulator which preserves supersymmetry and global non-chiral symmetries).

We now proceed to discuss explicitly the constraints[28] imposed on counterterms by the possibility of higher supersymmetry. Given any counterterm T_{ij}, suppose that M has a Kähler structure. Then the σ-model admits N=2 supersymmetry, and consequently T_{ij} must be a Kähler tensor and the associated two-form τ must be closed (see (18) and (19)). The two types of Kähler tensors are those which are generators of non-trivial classes of $H^{1,1}$, and those which belong to the trivial class. Any tensor of the first type can be written locally in terms of a Kähler potential $T_{\alpha\bar\beta} = \partial_\alpha\partial_{\bar\beta}\Lambda(z,\bar z)$, where Λ is not globally defined. Λ can instead only be defined patchwise, and changes from patch to patch by a Kähler gauge transformation, $\Lambda \to \Lambda + f(z) + \bar f(\bar z)$, where $f(z)$ depends on the holomorphic transition functions between coordinates on the different patches. Kähler tensors in the second class may be written similarly as $T_{\alpha\bar\beta} = \partial_\alpha\partial_{\bar\beta}S(z,\bar z) = \nabla_\alpha\nabla_{\bar\beta}S(z,\bar z)$, but where S is now a globally defined scalar function, invariant from patch to patch. Kähler counterterms generated in $(\ell+1)$-loop order can always be written using the Bianchi identities as $T_{\alpha\bar\beta} = \nabla_\alpha \nabla_{\bar\beta} S$, where S and $T_{\alpha\bar\beta}$ both have conformal weight ℓ. If $T_{\alpha\bar\beta}$ generates a non-trivial cohomology class, then S must change from patch to patch according to $S \to S + f(z) + \bar f(\bar z)$. It is not easy to see why a polynomial in the curvatures with all of its coordinate indices covariantly contracted can be non-invariant under a change of coordinates. In fact, the only way to construct such an S with well-defined conformal weight using only the local tensor constructions available in perturbation theory is in the form $S = \log\det M_{\alpha\bar\beta}$ (a product of logarithms, for example, would not have well-defined conformal weight). Independent of the conformal weight of the tensor $M_{\alpha\bar\beta}$, however, $T_{\alpha\bar\beta} = \nabla_\alpha \nabla_{\bar\beta} S$ then necessarily has zero conformal weight and hence non-trivial generators of cohomology can only appear as tensor counterterms in one-loop order. But we already know that the only counterterm generated in one-loop order is the Ricci tensor $R_{i\bar j}$, so it follows that the only two-index tensor of the first type (i.e. generating non-trivial $H^{1,1}$ cohomology) which appears in σ-model perturbation theory to any order is the Ricci form $\Sigma = iR_{\alpha\bar\beta}\, dz^\alpha \wedge d\bar z^\beta$. All counterterms generated in σ-model perturbation theory beyond one-loop order are of the second type, i.e. cohomologically trivial.

(Although not necessary to our purposes in what follows, we mention that this result is probably related to a much stronger mathematical result, namely that the only generators of cohomology below the top dimension constructible from polynomials in the curvature and its covariant derivatives are identically the generators of the Pontryagin classes in the general riemannian case, and the Chern classes in the Kähler case. To prove this requires a strengthening of Gilkey's lemma, which plays an important role in the heat kernel derivation of the index theorem (for details see [29] which also includes references to the earlier literature). The heat kernel method allows the computation of the index density for an elliptic operator on a manifold as a local function of its curvature, and in principle also its covariant derivatives. Integrating this index density over the manifold then gives an index of the operator in question, universal in the sense that it depends only on topological properties of the manifold. This universality motivates, both from conceptual and practical points of view (to simplify the heat kernel expansions), a characterization of the universal cohomology classes generated by polynomials in the curvature and its covariant derivatives. In [29], it is reported that the only generators of non-trivial cohomology among such polynomials of conformal weight $\ell \le 0$ are the Pontryagin and Chern classes (all having zero conformal weight). This result is easily strengthened to encompass polynomials of arbitrary conformal weight[30], at least for cohomology up to half the dimension of the manifold.)

The result may be made particularly transparent for superfield afficionados by means of a manifestly N=2 invariant superspace formulation[3] of the σ-model (1). In this formulation, a general superfield is a function $\Phi(x, \theta, \overline{\theta})$, where the spacetime coordinates x^μ $(\mu = 1, 2)$ and the constant complex 2-component spinors θ and $\overline{\theta}$ parametrize superspace.

Taylor expanding in θ and $\overline{\theta}$, however, shows Φ to contain too many degrees of freedom to describe a single scalar multiplet, so instead Φ is required to be a chiral superfield by imposing the constraint $\overline{D}_\alpha\Phi = 0$, where $\overline{D}_\alpha$ is the spinor derivative defined in (7) but with θ and $\overline{\theta}$ now taken as independent variables (see [19] for more details). In terms of chiral superfields, the lagrangian can be written

$$\mathcal{L} = \int d^2\theta\, d^2\overline{\theta}\, K(\Phi^i, \overline{\Phi}^j), \tag{31}$$

i.e., entirely in terms of the Kähler potential. The counterterms in this formalism then appear as corrections to the Kähler potential of the original metric. In the one-loop approximation, the effective action is given as the superdeterminant of the quadratic approximation to (31), and its divergent part turns out simply proportional to $\log\det \partial_\alpha\partial_{\overline{\beta}}K$, the Kähler potential for the Ricci tensor. Corrections to K generated in higher loop orders, on the other hand, are proportional only to globally defined scalar curvature polynomials S having non-zero conformal weight with respect to the transformation $K \to \lambda^{-1}K$. This is because, as argued above, $S = \log\det M_{\alpha\overline{\beta}}$ would have zero conformal weight, and an $S = K\cdot P(R)$, with $P(R)$ a curvature polynomial, cannot be generated because this would induce a counterterm of the form $g_{ij}\,P(R)$, earlier argued to be excluded in riemannian perturbation theory. New non-trivial log det's can thus never occur and the induced higher order counterterms $T_{\alpha\overline{\beta}}$ to the metric $g_{\alpha\overline{\beta}} = \partial_\alpha\partial_{\overline{\beta}}K$ are then automatically of the form $\partial_\alpha\partial_{\overline{\beta}}S$, with S globally defined. The only difficulty in carrying out this procedure explicitly is that it is not known at present how to formulate the normal coordinate expansion around a non-trivial background superfield Φ_0^i in a way which preserves the chirality constraint. Using instead a naive background field expansion, the vertices derived from (31) are not necessarily manifestly covariant, although the on-shell counterterms so calculated will of course emerge in covariant form. Modulo this purely technical difficulty of simultaneously manifesting $N{=}2$ supersymmetry and coordinate covariance (which in any event is probably surmountable), the $N{=}2$ superspace formulation thus provides a straightforward and rather intuitive means of understanding the trivial topological structure of counterterms generated beyond one-loop.

We point out that this result also implies that $N{=}2$ σ-models on locally symmetric spaces (for which $\nabla_m R_{ijkl} = 0$) are super-renormalizable. This is because the Kählerity together with the cohomological triviality of the counterterms beyond one-loop forces them to take the form $\nabla_\alpha\nabla_{\overline{\beta}}S$ with S a scalar curvature polynomial. Expanded out, all such terms vanish because they necessarily contain covariant derivatives acting on the curvature tensor, and the only non-vanishing counterterm is hence the one-loop contribution from the Ricci tensor itself. This result could be extended by universality to cover $N{=}1$ models defined on locally symmetric spaces as well by showing that there are no riemannian polynomials constructed purely from the curvature tensor (i.e. without using covariant derivatives) which generically vanish upon restriction to Kähler manifolds.

Kähler tensors of the second type appearing in perturbation theory seem to defy classification since S could naively be expected to be any arbitrary scalar of the appropriate conformal weight constructed from curvatures and covariant derivatives. Tensor structures of the form $\partial_\alpha \partial_{\bar\beta} S(z,\bar z) = \nabla_\alpha \nabla_{\bar\beta} S(z,\bar z)$, however, do not arise naturally in perturbation theory. $\nabla_\alpha \nabla_{\bar\beta} S$ may be rewritten in varioús ways using the Bianchi identities but frequently there is no way of constructing a tensor on a generic riemannian manifold which reduces when restricted to a Kähler manifold to any of these various rewritings without explicitly using the complex structure. Consider for example the case $S = R^2$, $R = g^{ij} R_{ij}$. R has conformal weight $+1$ so $\nabla_\alpha \nabla_{\bar\beta} S$ in this case could be a candidate for a three-loop counterterm

$$\nabla_\alpha \nabla_{\bar\beta} R^2 = 2R\, \nabla_\alpha \nabla_{\bar\beta} R + 2\, \nabla_\alpha R\, \nabla_{\bar\beta} R. \tag{32}$$

A short computation making use of the Kähler condition on $R_{\alpha\bar\beta}$,

$$\begin{aligned}\nabla_\alpha \nabla_{\bar\beta} R &= g^{\mu\bar\lambda} (\nabla_\alpha \nabla_{\bar\beta} + \nabla_{\bar\beta} \nabla_\alpha) R_{\mu\bar\lambda} \\ &= g^{\mu\bar\lambda} (\nabla_\alpha \nabla_{\bar\lambda} R_{\mu\bar\beta} + \nabla_{\bar\beta} \nabla_\mu R_{\alpha\bar\lambda}) \\ &= g^{\mu\bar\lambda} (\nabla_{\bar\lambda} \nabla_\mu R_{\alpha\bar\beta} + \nabla_\mu \nabla_{\bar\lambda} R_{\alpha\bar\beta} + [\nabla_\alpha, \nabla_{\bar\lambda}] R_{\mu\bar\beta} + [\nabla_{\bar\beta}, \nabla_\mu] R_{\alpha\bar\lambda}),\end{aligned}$$

shows that $\nabla_\alpha \nabla_{\bar\beta} R$ is simply the tensor

$$\nabla^k \nabla_k R_{ij} + [\nabla_i, \nabla^k] R_{kj} + [\nabla_j, \nabla^k] R_{ik} \tag{33}$$

in complex coordinates. The tensor $2R\, \nabla_\alpha \nabla_{\bar\beta} R$ can thus be written in a purely riemannian form without using the complex structure $f^i{}_j$. No purely riemannian tensor, on the other hand, can so reduce to the $\nabla_\alpha R\, \nabla_{\bar\beta} R$ term on the right hand side of (32). $\nabla_i R\, \nabla_j R$, for example, is not a hermitian tensor and therefore cannot appear as an on-shell counterterm because it violates the $SO(2)$ global symmetry of N=2 supersymmetry. $\nabla_\alpha R\, \nabla_{\bar\beta} R$ can only be written as $\frac{1}{2}(\delta^k{}_i \delta^l{}_j + f^k{}_i f^l{}_j)\, \nabla_k R\, \nabla_l R$ which will not be generated in perturbation theory due to the absence of the complex structure $f^i{}_j$ in the Feynman rules. This simple argument excludes $\nabla_\alpha \nabla_{\bar\beta} R^2$ from appearing by itself in perturbation theory at three-loop order.

This example suggests a general procedure for obtaining Kähler tensors of conformal weight ℓ which might appear in perturbation theory from those of conformal weight $\ell-1$. If S_{ij} is a Kähler tensor of conformal weight $\ell-1$, then the tensor $\nabla_\alpha \nabla_{\bar\beta}\, g^{ij} S_{ij}$, has conformal weight ℓ, is Kähler, and moreover can be written in riemannian form without mention of the complex structure. Indeed $\nabla_\alpha \nabla_{\bar\beta}\, g^{ij} S_{ij} = \Delta_L S_{\alpha\bar\beta}$ is just minus the Lichnerowicz laplacian acting on $S_{\alpha\bar{\beta}}$ and can be written, using manipulations identical to those preceding (33), in purely riemannian form as

$$-\Delta_L S_{ij} \equiv \nabla^k \nabla_k S_{ij} + [\nabla_i, \nabla^k] S_{kj} + [\nabla_j, \nabla^k] S_{ik} \tag{34}$$

(note that (33) is just a particular case of (34) with $S_{ij} = R_{ij}$). Given a Kähler S_{ij}, there is thus an infinite set of Kähler tensors of the second kind, $(\Delta_L)^{n+1} S_{ij}$, with Kähler potential $(\nabla^k \nabla_k)^n g^{ij} S_{ij}$ and conformal weight $\ell + n$, which may be generated in the riemannian normal coordinate expansion (i.e. with no explicit appearance of $f^i{}_j$). We have indeed been able[31] to pick out diagramatically the coefficient of $(\Delta_L)^{\ell-1} R_{ij}$ in ℓ-loop order and have verified that it is strictly proportional to $1/\epsilon^\ell$ with *no* lower order (i.e. $1/\epsilon^\nu$, $\nu < \ell$) pole contributions. The coefficient moreover checks with that which would be generated uniquely by the renormalization group pole equations from the $1/\epsilon$ pole proportional to R_{ij} which occurs in one-loop order. This result excludes for example any contribution of the form $(\Delta_L)^{\ell-1} R_{ij}$ to the β-function in ℓ-loop order.

Counterterms of the form $(\Delta_L)^{\ell-1} R_{ij}$ are unfortunately not the only possible counterterms which can be written in riemannian form without use of the complex structure. Another class of potential counterterms is given for example by

$$\begin{aligned} M^{kl} \nabla_{(i} \nabla_{j)} N_{kl} - 2M^{kl} \nabla_k \nabla_{(i} N_{j)l} + M^{kl} \nabla_k \nabla_l N_{ij} \\ + \nabla^k M^l{}_{(i} \nabla_{j)} N_{kl} + 2\nabla^k M^l{}_i \nabla_{[k} N_{l]j} \\ + (M \leftrightarrow N), \end{aligned}$$

which reduces to the Kähler tensor $2\nabla_\alpha \nabla_{\bar{\beta}} (M^{\mu\bar{\lambda}} N_{\mu\bar{\lambda}}) = \nabla_\alpha \nabla_{\bar{\beta}} (M^{ij} N_{ij})$ when M_{ij} and N_{ij} are Kähler tensors. Tensors of this form with $M_{ij} = N_{ij} = R_{ij}$ first appear at three-loop order with a non-vanishing $1/\epsilon^3$ coefficient (related to that of $(\Delta_L)^2 R_{ij}$ by the renormalization group pole equations), and vanishing $1/\epsilon^2$ and $1/\epsilon$ coefficients. We have not been able to characterize in general when a Kähler tensor with a given Kähler potential can be written in riemannian form without use of the complex structure but all known examples suggest that it is only possible when the Kähler potential itself decomposes into the product of some number of Kähler tensors similarly so writeable.

Now let us return to the finiteness properties of these models. The case of N=4 supersymmetric σ-models requires a manifold M which is hyperkähler, and moreover the preservation of N=4 supersymmetry in perturbation theory requires that the metric plus induced counterterm T_{ij} preserve the consequent Ricci flatness. Thus, for hyperkähler manifolds it is guaranteed that

$$R_{ij}(g + T) = 0. \tag{35}$$

In the previous section, we argued that Kähler tensors of the first kind, i.e. non-trivial generators of cohomology classes, cannot appear as counterterms in perturbation theory and thus that $T_{\alpha\bar{\beta}} = \partial_\alpha \partial_{\bar{\beta}} S$, where S is a globally defined scalar curvature polynomial. In order to show how this argument works together with the Calabi conjecture to imply the finiteness of Ricci flat σ-models, we now digress momentarily to describe the conjecture and its implications.

Suppose M is a compact complex manifold admitting an infinitely differentiable Kähler metric with Kähler form J and Ricci form Σ. Calabi conjectured[25] that if Σ' is any closed form of type (1,1) cohomologous to Σ, then there exists a unique Kähler metric with associated Kähler form J' cohomologous to J and Ricci form equal to Σ'. Assuming the existence of such a metric, Calabi went on to prove its uniqueness; Yau[32] later provided the proof of its existence. The work of Calabi and Yau in particular establishes that if we have a manifold M whose first Chern class vanishes (so that its Ricci form Σ is automatically cohomologous to zero), then for a given cohomology class of the Kähler form there is a unique metric for which the Ricci tensor vanishes identically. The interpretation of this result is straightforward: the vanishing of the first Chern class represents a condition on the integral of the Ricci form over arbitrary closed 2-surfaces in M, and hence the absence of a global (integrated) obstruction to the existence of a Ricci flat metric. Even in the absence of such a *global* obstruction to removing the $U(1)$ part of the holonomy, there might in principle still be a problem smoothing it away *locally*. Yau's work assures us that this is not the case, i.e. that the absence of a global obstruction insures that there is no local obstruction to removing the $U(1)$ holonomy.

This uniqueness property of the metric for Ricci flat manifolds can now be used to give an immediate proof of finiteness for hyperkähler manifolds (A different proof of the finiteness of N=4 supersymmetric σ-models has been given by Hull[33]). Substituting $T_{\alpha\bar{\beta}} = \partial_\alpha \partial_{\bar{\beta}} S$ in (35) implies that $R_{ij}(g + \partial\bar{\partial}S) = 0$, and then the uniqueness of the Ricci flat metric within a given topological class requires that $\partial_\alpha \partial_{\bar{\beta}} S = 0$ since the original metric g is already Ricci flat. Finiteness thus follows simply from the fact that counterterms from perturbation theory cannot change the topological class of the metric, and hence uniqueness of the Ricci flat metric allows no counterterms at all. The N=4 condition is essential to this argument because otherwise the counterterms would not necessarily have to satisfy (35), i.e. in principle there might occur counterterms which alter the metric structure to have a riemannian connection with non-vanishing $U(1)$ holonomy and uniqueness arguments would no longer apply.

The essential features of this argument can be made more apparent by considering the linearized form of (35)

$$-\frac{1}{2}(\nabla^k \nabla_k T_{ij} - \nabla^k \nabla_i T_{kj} - \nabla^k \nabla_j T_{ik} + \nabla_i \nabla_j T^k{}_k) = 0. \qquad (35)'$$

We first rewrite (35)′ in the form

$$-(\nabla^k \nabla_k T_{ij} + [\nabla_i, \nabla^k] T_{kj} + [\nabla_j, \nabla^k] T_{ik}) \equiv \Delta_L T_{ij} = 0, \qquad (36)$$

having made use of the fact that T_{ij} is Kähler, and hence satisfies $\nabla^k T_{ki} = \frac{1}{2}\nabla_i T^k{}_k$. Since a hyperkähler manifold is in particular Kähler, (36) thus requires that T_{ij} be a zero mode of the Lichnerowicz laplacian of type (1,1), i.e. $\Delta_L T_{\alpha\bar\beta} = 0$. Equivalently, this means that the 2-form $\tau = \frac{1}{2}T_{kj}f^k{}_i\, dx^i \wedge dx^j = iT_{\alpha\bar\beta}\, dz^\alpha \wedge d\bar z^\beta$ is harmonic of type (1,1): $\Box\tau = 0$ (this is because $\Box\tau \equiv (d\delta + \delta d)(\tau_{ij}\, dx^i \wedge dx^j) = (\Delta_L \tau_{ij})\, dx^i \wedge dx^j$). But now we have a contradiction because we have already established that counterterms generated beyond one-loop order are associated with forms which are cohomologically trivial, i.e. exact. By the Hodge decomposition, the only way a form can be both harmonic and exact is by vanishing identically. Thus the conflict between the exactness of any counterterm $T_{\alpha\bar\beta}$ generated beyond one-loop and the linearized condition (36) requiring that it be also harmonic renders supersymmetric σ-models on arbitrary hyperkähler manifolds finite. We note that this argument excludes counterterms from appearing in any order of perturbation theory on any Ricci flat manifold in which a symmetry acts to maintain the Ricci flatness of the metric plus counterterms. Although our argument has been formulated for compact hyperkähler manifolds, we may now appeal to the universality of the coefficient expansion to extend the result to arbitrary hyperkähler manifolds: any counterterm generated on a non-compact hyperkähler manifold is excluded by virtue of having a non-vanishing analog on some compact hyperkähler manifold.

To see how our results fit naturally into the symplectic frame formalism, consider the symmetric tensor counterterm T_{ij} generated in perturbation theory, now written as $T_{\alpha A,\beta B} = T_{\beta B,\alpha A}$. If the $SU(2) \approx Sp(1)$ global symmetry is preserved, preserving the hyperkähler condition, then we must have $T_{\alpha A,\beta B} = \epsilon_{\alpha\beta} T_{AB}$ with $T_{AB} = -T_{BA}$. In these $Sp(n)$ frames, (36) thus becomes

$$\nabla^k \nabla_k T_{AB} - 2\Omega_{CABD} T^{CD} = 0. \tag{37}$$

Antisymmetry of T_{CD} together with the symmetry of Ω_{ABCD} then reduces (37) to $\nabla^k \nabla_k T_{AB} = 0$. Multiplying by T_{AB} and integrating by parts then gives $\nabla_k T_{AB} = 0$, as usual by the positivity of the metric. But if the manifold is irreducible, then the only covariantly constant tensor is ϵ_{AB}, and thus we have that $T_{\alpha A,\beta B} = (\text{const}) \cdot \epsilon_{\alpha\beta}\epsilon_{AB}$, reproducing our result that T_{ij} must be proportional to the metric tensor and thus cannot be generated in perturbation theory (the metric itself, of course, cannot be generated in higher loop perturbation theory because it has conformal weight -1; no polynomial in the curvatures accidentally proportional to the metric could be generated because it would then generate non-trivial cohomology). The integration by parts argument above requires working on either a compact hyperkähler manifold or on a non-compact one with appropriate decay of the curvature at infinity. There are actually known examples of both types. Two infinite classes of irreducible compact hyperkähler manifolds of any real dimension $4n$ are exhibited in [34], and an infinite class of asymptotically locally euclidean non-compact manifolds, comprising the Calabi series of hyperkähler metrics for the cotangent bundle of CP^N (the lowest dimensional example of which corresponds to the Eguchi-Hanson gravitational instanton), is given in [35] (see also [36]). An appeal to universality then establishes the result, as before, for all hyperkähler manifolds (Unless, as pointed out to us by C. Hull, there is some obscure reason for which *all* compact and asymptotically locally euclidean hyperkähler manifolds are so special that some combination of curvature tensors happens to vanish automatically and hence wouldn't necessarily be excluded by the above arguments from appearing as a counterterm on some more general non-compact manifold. We consider this unlikely since among the infinite classes of hyperkähler manifolds mentioned above are some which are irreducible and have no isometries, and should thus be sufficiently generic to eliminate any such accidental degenerate relations among curvature invariants).

Arguing from the finiteness of $N=4$ models to the finiteness of $N=2$ models is difficult since there are tensor counterterms which do not necessarily vanish on Ricci flat Kähler manifolds, but do automatically vanish when restricted to hyperkähler manifolds. Such a generic vanishing is possible since restricting the holonomy group from $SU(2n)$ to $Sp(n)$ reduces the rank of the holonomy group from $2n-1$ to n and hence the curvature 2-form will have fewer independent eigenvalues. In other words, for Ricci flat Kähler manifolds, $\Omega^\alpha{}_\beta$ is valued in the Lie algebra of $SU(n)$ which implies only that $\operatorname{tr}\Omega = 0$. When the manifold is hyperkähler, on the other hand, $\Omega^\alpha{}_\beta$ is valued in the Lie algebra of $Sp(n)$, in which case for example $\operatorname{tr}\Omega^{2p+1} = 0$, and counterterms which could appear for Kähler manifolds may easily be lost on hyperkähler manifolds. The simplest example is the tensor

$$R_{iklj}\, R^k{}_{mnp}\, R^{lmnp} \tag{38}$$

which appears at three-loop order in the bosonic theory but is cancelled by fermions in a supersymmetric theory. To see that this tensor generically vanishes on hyperkähler manifolds, we write it in symplectic frames where it is proportional to $\Omega_{ABCD}\,\Omega^C{}_{EFG}\,\Omega^{DEFG}$. Since the indices E, F, G are contracted with ϵ_{AB}'s, $\Omega^C{}_{EFG}\,\Omega^{DEFG}$ is antisymmetric in C and D. But Ω_{ABCD} is totally symmetric so the original tensor vanishes automatically when restricted to Kähler manifolds. Many other such examples involving arbitrary numbers of curvature tensors and covariant derivatives are easily constructed. The tensor (38) above for example is excluded from appearing in a supersymmetric theory because it is not Kähler, but one can easily construct manifestly Kähler tensors such as

$$\nabla_\alpha \nabla_{\bar\beta}\,(R_{iklj}\, R^k{}_{mnp}\, R^{lmnp}\, R^i{}_{qrs}\, R^{jqrs})$$

which again automatically vanish upon restriction to hyperkähler manifolds. It is unlikely that any such objects can be written in riemannian form without explicit use of the complex structure. But since we have found no way of characterizing in general when this is possible, we cannot argue directly for the finiteness of Ricci flat $N=2$ models from that of $N=4$ models.

Even having such an exhaustive means of identifying and eliminating all possible hermitian counterterms to all orders of perturbation theory, we would still lack a clear understanding of what is so special about these models defined on Ricci flat manifolds. There is an alternative line of argument which relies upon a rather crucial difference between models defined on Ricci flat and arbitrary Kähler manifolds. This difference turns out to be a chiral symmetry whose conservation depends on the Ricci flatness of the Kähler metric. We have already discussed a vectorlike symmetry possessed by any Kähler manifold, namely the global $SO(2)$ rotation generated by the complex structure. This is the $SO(2)$ symmetry that rotates the first supersymmetry into the second. Since it is a vectorlike symmetry, there will be no anomaly in its current conservation equation. In order to exhibit explicitly the form of the chiral symmetries, we recall the form of the different terms in the lagrangian as written in coordinates adapted to the Kähler structure (29). The purely bosonic kinetic term is of no concern here since the bosons are invariant under chiral symmetries. The fermions we shall write using frames adapted to the Kähler structure in the Weyl form $\psi^a_\pm = e^a{}_\alpha \psi^\alpha_\pm$, $\psi^{\bar a}_\pm = e^{\bar a}{}_{\bar\alpha} \psi^{\bar\alpha}_\pm$, $a, \bar a = 1, \ldots, n$ ($n =$ the complex dimension of M, and $\delta_{a\bar b}\, e^a{}_\alpha\, e^{\bar b}{}_{\bar\beta} = g_{\alpha\bar\beta}$). The terms bilinear in the fermions take the form

$$\frac{i}{2}\,\psi^a_+ \overleftrightarrow{D}_+ \psi^{\bar b}_+\,\delta_{a\bar b} + \frac{i}{2}\,\psi^a_- \overleftrightarrow{D}_- \psi^{\bar b}_-\,\delta_{a\bar b}, \tag{39}$$

where

$$D_\pm \psi^a_\pm = \partial_\pm \psi^a_\pm + \omega_i{}^a{}_b\, \partial_\pm \phi^i\, \psi^b_\pm$$

$$\partial_\pm = \frac{\partial}{\partial x^\pm}, \quad x^\pm = \frac{1}{\sqrt{2}}(x^0 \pm x^1),$$

and the quartic fermion term is proportional to

$$R_{a\bar b c\bar d}\, \psi^a_+ \psi^{\bar b}_+ \psi^c_- \psi^{\bar d}_-. \tag{40}$$

(39) and (40) are invariant under the $U(1)_+ \times U(1)_-$ transformations

$$\begin{aligned} \psi^a_+ &\to e^{i\eta}\, \psi^a_+ & \psi^a_- &\to e^{i\eta'}\, \psi^a_- \\ \psi^{\bar a}_+ &\to e^{-i\eta}\, \psi^{\bar a}_+ & \psi^{\bar a}_- &\to e^{-i\eta'}\, \psi^{\bar a}_-. \end{aligned} \tag{41}$$

When $\eta = \eta'$, we have the standard $SO(2)$ (or $U(1)$) vector transformation discussed previously, responsible for preserving the hermiticity of the counterterms. From the riemannian point of view, the existence of this symmetry is what requires the manifold to be Kähler, and the counterterms to be Kähler tensors. The second symmetry, with $\eta = -\eta'$, is an axial symmetry which may be anomalous. Computation of the anomaly is straightforward, because we can consider $\omega^a_{ib}\partial_\mu\phi^i$ as a $U(n)$ gauge field and in two dimensions, only the $U(1)$ subgroup of $U(n)$ induces an anomaly (the remaining $SU(n)$ generators are traceless). Recalling that the $U(1)$ part of the curvature is the Ricci tensor, we deduce the one-loop result

$$\partial_\mu j_5^\mu = \frac{1}{\pi}\epsilon^{\mu\nu}R_{a\bar{b}}\partial_\mu\phi^a\partial_\nu\bar{\phi}^b, \tag{42}$$

where j_5^μ is the current associated with the axial symmetry generated by (41) with $\eta = -\eta'$. To identify the conservation of this axial current with the vanishing of the Ricci tensor, we need an analog of the Adler-Bardeen theorem[37] to show that the vanishing of the anomaly at the one-loop level implies that it does not reappear in any higher order. This requires the existence of a higher covariant derivative regulator which will regulate all diagrams beyond one-loop by virtue of their negative superficial degree of divergence. In a manifest N=2 formalism, we write the chiral superfield $\Phi^a = \phi^a + \theta^A\psi^a_A + \theta^A\theta_A F^a$, $A = 1, 2$, with θ^A a constant complex spinor. We define the axial transformation by $\psi^a_\pm \to e^{\pm i\eta}\psi^a_\pm$, $\theta_\pm \to e^{\pm i\eta}\theta_\pm$ so that both Φ^a and $\overline{\Phi}^a$ are invariant. A higher covariant derivative regulator can be introduced into the superspace action $K(\Phi, \overline{\Phi})$ by substituting $\Phi^a \to (1 + (\hat{D}^A\hat{D}_A)^n/\Lambda^n)\Phi^a$ (n some integer). $\hat{D}_A$ is a supercovariant derivative defined to act on Φ^a by $\hat{D}_A\Phi^a = D_A\Phi^a$, and to act on a vector W^a by

$$\hat{D}_A W^a = D_A W^a + \omega^a_{cb} D_A\Phi^c W^b.$$

This definition ensures the manifest coordinate reparametrization invariance of the regulator. Although this regularization prescription is not practical for doing computations, it does show that if the anomaly does not appear at the one-loop level, it will not appear in any order of perturbation theory. While we expect no difficulties implementing the chirality constraint on the superfields in this formalism, we point out that this regularization can also be implemented in an N=1 formulation of the theory.

We now wish to argue that this axial symmetry on Kähler manifolds can play the role played by N=4 supersymmetry on hyperkähler manifolds, ensuring the Ricci flatness of the metric plus counterterms. Relating the absence of an anomaly in the bare theory to its absence in the renormalized theory requires a two-dimensional version of 't Hooft's anomaly matching conditions[38] for these theories. A proof along the lines of [39] is under consideration[40] to show that Ricci flatness of the renormalized metric implies that the bare metric as well must be Ricci flat, implying in turn that any counterterm $T_{\mu\bar{\lambda}}$ which may appear in any order of perturbation theory must satisfy

$$R_{\alpha\bar{\beta}}(g_{\mu\bar{\lambda}} + T_{\mu\bar{\lambda}}) = 0.$$

The methodology developed earlier here, using the uniqueness of the Ricci flat Kähler metric to exclude any counterterms, then extends directly to a proof of finiteness to all orders of perturbation theory for N=2 models. The relation between the vanishing of the β-function and the vanishing of the axial anomalies is tied together neatly in the supermultiplet containing the trace and conformal anomalies in these theories.

Since we have no such corresponding uniqueness properties for general riemannian metrics, a proof of finiteness for N=1 models must proceed on a different basis. As mentioned in sec. 2, universality places rather severe restrictions on the tensor counterterms generated in perturbation theory: they must reduce to Kähler tensors upon imposing the Kähler condition on the metric. Those which reduce to non-vanishing Kähler tensors are excluded by a proof of finiteness for N=2 models. The only potential difficulty, then, would come from riemannian tensor counterterms which do not vanish on Ricci flat manifolds but would vanish upon imposing the Kähler condition. Few, if any, such terms can appear, however, since the complex structure $f^i{}_j$ is not generated explicitly in perturbation theory, forbidding the construction of any obvious projection operators (It should also be clear that no polynomial in the curvature and covariant derivatives $P^i{}_j$ generated in perturbation theory can be accidentally equal to the complex structure. This is because the form $P_{ij}\, dx^i \wedge dx^j$ would then be proportional to the Kähler form J, contradicting the result that no non-trivial generators of cohomology can be generated in perturbation theory beyond one-loop order). There are, however, tensors such as

$$R_{kl}\, \nabla_{(i}\nabla_{j)}\, R^{kl} - 2R_{kl}\, \nabla_{(i}\, \nabla^k R_{j)}{}^l \tag{43}$$

which are generally non-vanishing on generic riemannian manifolds but which vanish automatically due to the Bianchi identities on Kähler manifolds. (43) is a potential 3-loop counterterm in N=1 models which turns out not to be generated and would of course vanish on Ricci flat manifolds in any event. A proof of finiteness for N=2 models could then be extended to the N=1 case by showing that any potential counterterms lost in going from arbitrary riemannian to Kähler manifolds either are not generated in perturbation theory or, like (43), necessarily vanish on Ricci flat manifolds. Universal dimension independence of the counterterms would then complete the proof.

We wish to mention one final as yet unproven point concerning the β-function for σ-models on non-Ricci flat manifolds. Up to three-loop order it is known that the β-function has only the one-loop contribution

$$\beta_{ij}(g) = \frac{1}{2\pi} R_{ij} + \nabla_i v_j + \nabla_j v_i, \tag{44}$$

where v is a vector absorbable by a coordinate reparametrization. We believe that this result remains true to all orders in perturbation theory (As already mentioned, we have been able to verify that there are no contributions to the β-function of the form $(\Delta_L)^{\ell-1} R_{ij}$ from any order of perturbation theory). Recall that the β-function (10) is given exclusively in terms of the $1/\epsilon$ pole, and that the renormalization group pole equations (11) give the coefficients of the higher order poles in terms of the $1/\epsilon$ poles. Validity of (44) to all orders implies then that even though tensor counterterms on non-Ricci flat manifolds are allowed in $\ell+1$-loop order, they are proportional only to powers of $1/\epsilon^\nu$ with $\nu > 1$. This is equivalent to saying that the tensors $T_{ij}^{(\nu,\ell)}$ with conformal weight ℓ (generated in $\ell+1$ loop order) and coefficent $1/\epsilon^\nu$ are such that $T_{ij}^{(1,\ell)} = 0$ for $\nu = 1$ and all conformal weights $\ell > 0$, and $T_{ij}^{(\nu,\ell)}$ for all $\nu > 1$ are determined by the pole equations exclusively from the $1/\epsilon$ piece $T_{ij}^{(1,0)} = R_{ij}/2\pi$.

References

[1] E. Witten, J. Diff. Geom. 17 (1982) 661;
E. Witten, Holomorphic Morse Inequalities, Princeton preprint (1982).

[2] L. Alvarez-Gaumé, Comm. Math. Phys. 90 (1983) 161, J. Phys. A16 (1983) 4177;
E. Getzler, Comm. Math. Phys. 92 (1983) 163;
D. Friedan and P. Windey, Nucl. Phys. B235 (1984) 395;
B. Zumino, Supersymmetry and the index theorem, Berkeley preprint LBL-17972 (Proc. Shelter Island II Conf. 1983).

[3] B. Zumino, Phys. Lett. 87B (1979) 203.

[4] L. Alvarez-Gaumé and D. Z. Freedman, Comm. Math. Phys. 80 (1981) 443.

[5] L. Alvarez-Gaumé and P. Ginsparg, HUTP-85/A016 (revised).

[6] M. B. Green and J. H. Schwarz, Phys. Lett. 149B (1984) 117;
M. B. Green and J. H. Schwarz, Phys. Lett. 151B (1985) 21.

[7] P. Candelas, G. Horowitz, A. Strominger, and E. Witten, Vacuum Configurations for superstrings, Santa Barbara preprint NSF-ITP-84-170 (1984);
E. Witten, Symmetry breaking patterns in superstring models, Princeton preprint (Feb., 1985).

[8] T. L. Curtright and C. K. Zachos, Phys. Rev. Lett. 53 (1984) 1799;
For a comprehensive list of references and a clarifying discussion, see E. Braaten, T. L. Curtright, and C. K. Zachos, Torsion and Geometrostasis in non-linear sigma models, Florida preprint UFTP-85-01 (1985).

[9] M. Roček, private communication.

[10] E. Witten, Comm. Math. Phys. 92 (1984) 455.

[11] D. Nemeschansky and S. Yankielowicz, Phys. Rev. Lett. 54 (1985) 620;
M. Henneaux and L. Mezincescu, A σ-model interpretation of the Green-Schwarz covariant superstring action, Texas preprint UTTG-26-84 (1984).

[12] D. Z. Freedman and P. K. Townsend, Nucl. Phys. B177 (1981) 282.

[13] D. J. Gross, J. A. Harvey, E. Martinec, and R. Rohm, Phys. Rev. Lett. 54 (1985) 502, and Heterotic string theory I: The free heterotic string, Princeton preprint (1985).

[14] G. Moore and P. Nelson, Phys. Rev. Lett. 53 (1984) 1519.

[15] L. Alvarez-Gaumé and E. Witten, Nucl. Phys. B234 (1984) 269.

[16] J. H. Schwarz, Phys. Rept. 89 (1982) 223.

[17] D. Friedan, Phys. Rev. Lett. 45 (1980) 1057;
D. Friedan, Ph.D. thesis, U. C. Berkeley (unpublished, 1980).

[18] L. Alvarez-Gaumé, D. Z. Freedman, and S. Mukhi, Ann. Phys. 134 (1981) 85.

[19] J. Gates, M. Grisaru, M. Roček, and W. Siegel, *Superspace* (Benjamin, 1983).

[20] J. Honerkamp, F. Krause, and M. Schennert, Nucl. Phys. B69 (1974) 618.

[21] D. Boulware and L. Brown, Ann. Phys. 138 (1982) 392.
[22] G. 't Hooft, Nucl. Phys. B61 (1973) 455.
[23] S. Goldberg, *Curvature and Homology* (Dover Publications, New York, 1982), sec. 5.6.
[24] A. Lichnerowicz, *General Theory of Connections and the Holonomy Group* (Noordhoff, Holland, 1976).
[25] E. Calabi, in *Algebraic Geometry and Topology: a Symposium in Honor of S. Lefschetz* (Princeton Univ. Press, 1957), p. 78.
[26] J. Bagger and E. Witten, Nucl. Phys. B222 (1983) 1.
[27] B. DeWitt and M. T. Grisaru, Phys. Rev. D20 (1979) 2082.
[28] L. Alvarez-Gaumé and D. Z. Freedman, Phys. Rev. D22 (1980) 846.
[29] M. Atiyah, R. Bott, and V. K. Patodi, Inv. Math. 19 (1973) 279.
[30] R. Bott, private communication.
[31] L. Alvarez-Gaumé and P. Ginsparg, unpublished.
[32] S.-T. Yau, Proc. Nat. Acad. Sci. 74 (1977) 1798.
[33] C. M. Hull, Ultraviolet finiteness of supersymmetric non-linear σ-models, IAS preprint (1985).
[34] A. Beauville, J. Diff. Geom. 18 (1983) 755.
[35] E. Calabi, Ann. Scient. Éc. Norm. Sup. 12 (1979) 266.
[36] T. L. Curtright and D. Z. Freedman, Phys. Lett. 90B (1980) 71;
L. Alvarez-Gaumé and D. Z. Freedman, Phys. Lett. 94B (1980) 171.
[37] S. L. Adler and W. A. Bardeen, Phys. Rev. 182 (1969) 1517.
[38] G. 't Hooft, "Naturalness, Chiral Symmetry, and Spontaneous Chiral Symmetry Breaking," in *Recent developments in gauge theories,* ed. G. 't Hooft et al. (Plenum, New York, 1980).
[39] S. Coleman and B. Grossman, Nucl. Phys. B203 (1982) 205.
[40] L. Alvarez-Gaumé, S. Coleman, and P. Ginsparg, in progress.

NEW DIRECTIONS FOR TOPOLOGICAL RESEARCH ON GAUGE THEORIES

R. Jackiw

Center for Theoretical Physics and
Department of Physics
Massachusetts Institute of Technology
Cambridge, Massachusetts 02139 U.S.A.

ABSTRACT

Various research topics arising from chiral anomalies are suggested. It is emphasized that at the center of the topologically and cohomologically intricate anomaly phenomena there is a trivial two-dimensional U(1) structure, which is poorly understood, both physically and mathematically. A possible role for the anomaly in gauge symmetry breaking is indicated.

CONTENTS

My lecture is not on a coherent, completely developed subject; rather, I shall speak about several topics, probably disconnected, and still under investigation.

A. Origin of Chiral Anomalies

Let me begin by recalling the various ways we have of establishing that a chiral anomaly occurs when massless fermions interact with a gauge field. First, there are the original perturbative calculations of Feynman diagrams which show that chiral Ward identities cannot be maintained. These calculations can be performed in momentum space, where the effect arises from momentum routing ambiguities,[1] or in position space, where singularities in the product of fermion bilinears provide the operative mechanism.[2] A second derivation, also known from the beginning, observes that the algebra of chiral generators, when calculated in perturbation theory, fails to close.[3] Later, I shall say more about modern developments in this approach. Third, in the functional integral formulation, the anomaly arises because the fermion measure is not chirally invariant.[4] Fourth, we now have mathematical/ topological and cohomological reasons for understanding that the functional determinant of non-Abelian chiral fermions cannot be defined gauge invariantly.[5]

While all arguments are convincing and striking in the variety of routes they offer to the same goal, they all lack direct physical immediacy; one is still left with the central physical puzzle of the chiral anomaly. This puzzle may be stated in the following way. Consider massless Dirac fermion fields Ψ, in even-dimensional space-time, interacting with an external electromagnetic gauge field A_μ. Dynamics is governed by the Lagrangian,

$$L = \overline{\Psi}(i\not{\partial} - e\not{A})\Psi \tag{1a}$$

which may be decomposed into left and right pieces.

$$\Psi = \Psi_L + \Psi_R$$
$$L = \overline{\Psi}_L(i\not{\partial} - e\not{A})\Psi_L + \overline{\Psi}_R(i\not{\partial} - e\not{A})\Psi_R = L_L + L_R \tag{1b}$$

Why is it in the quantum theory that the separate left and right charges are not conserved, even though there is no apparent interaction between the left and right worlds? A detailed analysis of the second quantized theory gives the answer, but again in terms of a formal rather than physical concept: the Dirac negative energy sea cannot be defined in a gauge invariant way, separately for the left and right portions of the model.[6] This is a consequence of gauge-field configurations that give rise to zero-eigenvalue modes in the Dirac equation in two dimensions lower.[7] For the four-dimensional theory, we observe that the two-dimensional Dirac operator in a constant magnetic field possess zero modes. When the full four-dimensional background gauge field in (1) includes such components, the energy spectrum in the first quantized theory cannot be divided into positive [particle] and negative [antiparticle] states in a gauge invariant manner, separately for the left and right components. It is the insistence on gauge invariance in the second quantized Dirac theory that produces a quantum mechanical coupling between the left and right worlds.

More specifically, the Lagrangian (1) in four dimensions leads to a Hamiltonian problem in three dimensions for determining the modes to be second quantized.

$$Hu_E = [\boldsymbol{\alpha} \cdot (\mathbf{p} - e\mathbf{A}) + eA^0]u_E = E(A)u_E \tag{2}$$

With a background gauge potential chosen so that A_x and A_y produce the constant magnetic field B in the z-direction, A_z constant, and vanishing A^0, the two two-dimensional zero modes cause an energy-momentum dispersion law in (2) of

$$E(A) = p_z - eA_z \tag{3a}$$

for the right-handed fermions, and

$$E(A) = -p_z + eA_z \tag{3b}$$

for the left-handed ones. The zero of each branch cannot be defined in a gauge invariant manner. Moreover, when both branches are included, the ground state [at fixed A_z] of the second quantized theory is defined by "filling" the negative energy levels [at fixed A_z], and leaving the positive levels [at fixed A_z] "empty". However, if A_z is varied abiabatically, empty levels move to positive energies and filled levels move to negative energy [or *vice versa*]. This creates or destroys an amount of charge proportional to $B\delta A_z$ for each chirality, but leaves total charge conserved.

Similarly in a six-dimensional model, the four dimensional instanton produces the zero mode. The two-dimensional Schwinger model[8] realizes this anomaly-producing mechanism trivially, since in two dimensions fewer there is nothing there, and the eigenvalue is obviously zero, while the Hamiltonian problem with vanishing A^0 and constant A^1 obviously possesses eigenvalues of the form (3).[9]

In two dimensions, moreover, we can present the coupling between the left and right worlds very explicitly, because the model is solved.[8] Owing to the two-dimensional identity $i\gamma^\mu\gamma_5 = \varepsilon^{\mu\nu}\gamma_\nu$, one verifies that only one light-cone component of A_μ couples to the right fermions, and the other to the left.

$$L_{(2)} = \overline{\Psi}_L\gamma^-(i\partial_- - eA_-)\Psi_L + \overline{\Psi}_R\gamma^+(i\partial_+ - eA_+)\Psi_R \tag{4}$$

The gauge invariant, effective quantum action is known.

$$-i \ln \det(i\partial\!\!\!/ - eA\!\!\!/) = \frac{e^2}{2\pi} \int A_\mu \left(g^{\mu\nu} - \frac{\partial^\mu \partial^\nu}{\Box}\right) A_\nu \tag{5}$$

$$= -\frac{e^2}{4\pi} \int A_- \frac{\partial_+}{\partial_-} A_- - \frac{e^2}{4\pi} \int A_+ \frac{\partial_-}{\partial_+} A_+ + \frac{e^2}{2\pi} \int A_+ A_-$$

The last contribution, a contact term unambiguously dictated by gauge invariance, puts into evidence the quantum mechanical left-right coupling. Note also that the properly gauge invariant determinant of Dirac fermions is not merely the product of left- and right-handed determinants - gauge invariance can force contact terms that spoil the factorization.

The two-dimensional model may also be viewed as providing the essence for the higher-dimensional anomaly. We begin in 2d + 2 dimensional space-time, and argue as follows: in 2 dimensions lower, *i.e.*, in 2d dimensions, a zero mode may be established with the help of the index theorem. Existence of the zero mode is assured, provided there is a 2d-dimensional anomaly, which in turn requires a zero mode in 2d-2 dimensions, established by the 2d - 2-dimensional index theorem and anomaly, *etc*. Thus, in a very precise way, the two-dimensional Abelian anomaly[10] is at the heart of the entire anomaly phenomenon.

The above is the most "physical" description of chiral anomalies known to me; but still it uses unphysical, formal constructs [Dirac sea, negative energy states].

We have learned much from mathematicians about the topological and cohomological necessity of anomalies,[5] but perhaps physics can, it its turn, advance mathematical concepts by insisting on the fact that the essence of the anomaly lies beyond present topological/cohomological ideas. The latter involve integrated, global quantities, like the Chern-Pontryagin number, yet the anomaly is local. Moreover, anomalies are present even in the absence of obstructions, like in Abelian [U(1)] theories, as in the discussed example which, being two-dimensional, hardly possesses any structure, save the anomaly. The U(1) anomaly, on the other hand, appears to be the heart of the matter, not only for the non-Abelian anomalies, but also for the non-perturbative ones.[11]

Thus, it seems that we are not yet at the end of the physics nor of the mathematics that can emerge from understanding anomalies.

B. Anomalous Gauge Theories

Let us now examine an anomalous theory: right-handed fermions interacting with a gauge field. Apparently, gauge invariance cannot be maintained owing to the anomaly; quantization of the coupled gauge field matter system is problematical. In terms of our earlier discussion, the negative energy chiral anti-fermions cannot be separated gauge invariantly from the positive energy chiral fermions. The nature of the problem has recently been couched in mathematical terms. We consider first the fermion sector, and view the gauge potential, with $A^0 = 0$, as an externally prescribed field - to be quantized later, if possible. Within the fermionic theory, we may construct the unitary operator $U(g) = \exp G_\theta$ that implements the [topologically trivial] gauge transformation $g = e^\theta$. The infinitesimal generator G_θ is $\int d\mathbf{r}\, \theta_a(\mathbf{r})[\delta_a(\mathbf{r}) - i\rho_a(\mathbf{r})]$, where $\delta_a(\mathbf{r}) \equiv -\mathcal{D}_{ab} \cdot \frac{\delta}{\delta \mathbf{A}_b(\mathbf{r})}$ effects an infinitesimal gauge transformation on $\mathbf{A}_a$ and ρ_a, the fermion charge density, performs the same job on the fermion degrees of freedom. The occurence of anomalies in the generators' commutator algebra[3] has led to the suggestion that the operators U give a projective representation for the gauge group,

$$\begin{aligned} g_1 g_2 &= g_{12} \\ U(g_1)U(g_2) &= e^{i2\pi\omega_2(g_1,g_2)}U(g_{12}) \end{aligned} \tag{6}$$

where the 2-cocycle, $2\pi\omega_2$, can be determined by *a priori* arguments when it is cohomologically non-trivial.[12]

While such projective representations of transformation groups are familiar in quantum mechanics, this is the first time they make an appearance in quantized gauge theory. Moreoever, since gauge invariance is conventionally enforced as the first class constraint that U(g) leave physical states invariant [for topologically trivial gauge transformations], we see that owing to the projective composition law the constraint cannot be satisfied. Note, however, that the cocycle occurs even in the cohomologically trivial Abelian theory, for which the original calculation[3] of anomalous commutators was performed. Yet no *a priori* mathematical argument is available to establish existence of the cocycle in the cohomologically trivial case. Here again we have further evidence that the anomaly goes beyond present mathematical ideas.

What to do? The conventional remedy is to adjust fermion content so that the anomaly is absent - *i.e.*, the 2-cocycle vanishes. The principle leads to a physical prediction which is thus far satisfied: the number of leptons must match the number of quarks.[13] Moreover, the same principle has focused attention on the most recent version of the string.[14]

Nevertheless, one may still inquire whether an anomalous theory can yield consistent physics. One suggestion is implicit in Faddeev's[12] work: perhaps gauge invariance in the quantum theory should not be implemented as a first class constraint, but as a higher order one. Thus far, nothing has come from this idea, and it seems to me that further problems abound: the constraints do not properly commute with the electric field, nor do they commute with the Hamiltonian. [However, since the anomalous divergence is itself a total derivative of a gauge non-covariant quantity, one *can* construct a conserved, gauge non-invariant object - but it is unclear that this may be used as a generator.]

An alternative position, recently taken by Rajaraman and me, is to give up the constraints altogether, *i.e.*, abandon gauge invariance and view anomalies as a mechanism for gauge symmetry breaking.[15] The original arguments[13] for cancelling anomalies called attention to two possible pitfalls in our adventurous approach: (1) renormalizability may be lost; (2) unitarity may be lost. We have nothing to say about renormalizability; indeed, we study a finite, two-dimensional model - the chiral Schwinger model - which is anomalous. Owing to the model's simplicity, its spectrum may be analyzed. We find that unitarity *is* preserved; the vector particle acquires a mass, which, however, is not calculable but lies between $\frac{e}{\sqrt{\pi}}$ and infinity; also, there are massless excitations, which appear to be deconfined fermions. Of course, this two-dimensional model is far from reality, and accepting anomalies runs counter to current practice, which as led to the determination of a unique pair of string models. Nevertheless, I find it attractive to speculate that weak interactions, with their deconfined fermions and massive vector mesons, are a remnant of an anomalous chiral gauge theory.

C. 3-Cocycles

I have mentioned field theoretic 2-cocycles - they arise in a projective representation of a transformation group and introduce a phase in the composition law. Familiar also are 1-cocycles: they are phases that occur in the representation operator's action on vectors. For example, the action of Galilean transformations on quantum mechanical wave functions includes a phase, as does the action of gauge transformations on quantum field theoretical wave functionals in gauge theories with topological Chern-Simons terms in the action.[16]

How about 3-cocycles? These have not arisen in the mathematical discussions of representation theory, but several physicists[17] have pointed out that a non-vanishing 3-cocycle, $2\pi\omega_3$, is a measure of non-associativity in the operator algebra of a representation.

$$\big(U(g_1)U(g_2)\big)\, U(g_3) = e^{i2\pi\omega_3(g_1,g_2,g_3)}\, U(g_1)\, \big(U(g_2)U(g_3)\big) \tag{7}$$

An example can be found in the quantum mechanics of a point particle with charge e, moving at $\mathbf{r}$ in an external magnetic field $\mathbf{B}$, which is not necessarily divergence free: $\nabla \cdot \mathbf{B} \neq 0$. The Hamiltonian for this dynamics does not see the magnetic field, because the magnetic field does no work on the charged particle.

$$H = \frac{1}{2} v^2 \tag{8}$$

[We set the mass of the particle to unity.] In order that the Lorentz force law be obtained by commutation with the Hamiltonian, we define

$$[r^i, r^j] = 0, \quad [r^i, v^j] = i\delta^{ij}, \quad [v^i, v^j] = ie\varepsilon^{ijk}B^k \tag{9}$$

and the Lorentz law follows.

$$\begin{aligned} \dot{r}^i &= i[H, r^i] = v^i \\ \dot{v}^i &= i\, H, v^i \;\; = e\varepsilon^{ijk} v^j B^k \end{aligned} \tag{10}$$

Finite translations of $\mathbf{r}$ are represented by

$$U(\mathbf{a}) = e^{i\mathbf{a}\cdot\mathbf{v}} \tag{11}$$

as follows from

$$U(\mathbf{a})\mathbf{r}U^{-1}(\mathbf{a}) = \mathbf{r} + \mathbf{a} \quad . \tag{12}$$

However, these do not represent the translation group faithfully since one finds from (9)

$$U(\mathbf{a}_1)U(\mathbf{a}_2) = e^{-ie\Phi}U(\mathbf{a}_1 + \mathbf{a}_2) \tag{13}$$

where Φ is the flux through the triangle at $\mathbf{r}$ formed from $\mathbf{a}_1$ and $\mathbf{a}_2$; see Figure 1. Moreoever, by considering the triple product $U(\mathbf{a}_1)U(\mathbf{a}_2)U(\mathbf{a}_3)$, associated in the two different ways as in (7), one finds a 3-cocycle, given by -e times the total flux out of the tetrahedron formed at $\mathbf{r}$ from $\mathbf{a}_1$, $\mathbf{a}_2$, and $\mathbf{a}_3$; see Figure 2.

Of course, when $\nabla \cdot \mathbf{B}$ vanishes, the total flux through any closed surface vanishes; there is no 3-cocycle and $\mathbf{v}$ may be realized by linear operators on a Hilbert space: $\mathbf{v} = -i\nabla - e\mathbf{A}$, $\mathbf{B} = \nabla \times \mathbf{A}$.

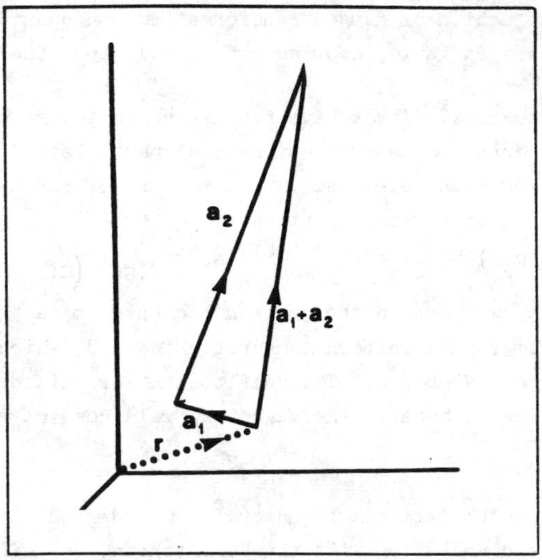

Fig. 1. The triangle at **r** through which the flux Φ is calculated.

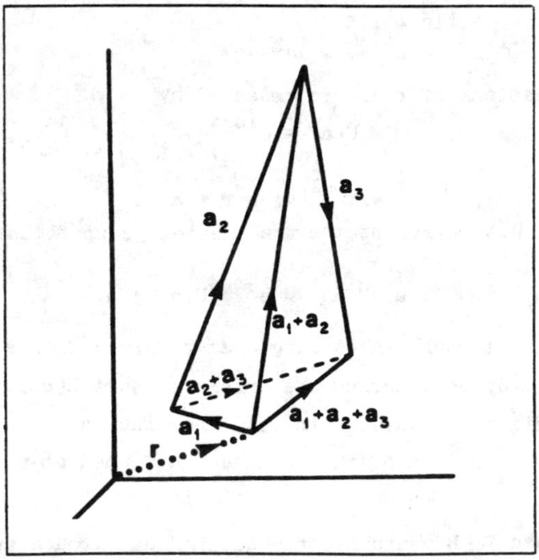

Fig. 2. The tetrahedron at **r** through which the flux determining the 3-cocycle is calculated.

When there are sources, the flux is non-zero, but we may still achieve associativity provided ω_3 is an integer, since then $e^{i2\pi\omega_3} = 1$. This requirement forces: (1) $\nabla \cdot \mathbf{B}$ to consist of localized delta functions, so that the total flux not vary continuously when the $\mathbf{a}_i$'s change; *i.e.*, the sources must be monopoles; (2) since a monopole of strength g produces the cocycle $-4\pi eg$, eg must satisfy the Dirac quantization condition. In this way, removal of the 3-cocycle, which is necessary for conventional quantum mechanics with associative operators on Hilbert space, limits magnetic sources to quantized Dirac monopoles. Other magnetic sources lead to a non-associative algebra.

Finally note that for infinitesimal generators, a non-vanishing 3-cocycle, *i.e.*, non-associativity, implies failure of the Jacobi identity. Indeed, from (9) one deduces that[18]

$$\left[v^1,[v^2,v^3]\right] + \left[v^2,[v^3,v^1]\right] + \left[v^3,[v^1,v^2]\right] = e\nabla \cdot \mathbf{B} \qquad (14)$$

[The triple products are associated in the obvious way.]

D. External U(1) Connections in Field Theory

Is there anything similar in field theory? Violations of the Jacobi identity had been found years ago, but not in gauge group generators, rather in the old U(6) x U(6) current algebra.[19] While it may be interesting to frame this into a coherent mathematical picture, it seems far removed from current interest. However, you may be surprised to hear that an "external magnetic field" of particle mechanics has a sensible analog in gauge field theory.

The aspect of particle dynamics in an external magnetic field that is of interest for the field theoretic generalization, is that the magnetic field is invisible in the Hamiltonian, but reappears in the velocity commutator, as in (8) and (9), *i.e.*, the canonical momentum does not coincide with the velocity.

We have grown accustomed to topological terms contributing to gauge field actions - the θ parameter multiplying the Chern-Pontryagin density in even dimensions, the Chern-Simons term with quantized coefficient in odd dimensions.[16] Since both are topological world scalars, not involving the metric tensor, they do not contribute to the energy-momentum tensor, and the Hamiltonian retains its conventional form.[16]

$$H = \int d\mathbf{r} \left(\frac{1}{2} E^i_a E^i_a + \frac{1}{4} F^{ij}_a F^{ij}_a \right) \tag{15}$$

However, the canonical field momenta, differ from the field "velocities" $-\mathbf{E}_a$, and the difference may be ascribed to an external U(1) field connection. The U(1) field curvature - the analog of the external magnetic field - is determined by the equal-time commutator of the field velocities.

For theories in even-dimensional space-time with a Chern-Pontryagin density, the commutator vanishes - the external field curvature is zero, the connection is flat. This is to be expected, since the topological terms does not affect equations of motion, and the connection is a pure functional gauge. It can be gauged away, and this is the familiar procedure which shifts the vacuum angle from the Lagrangian to the state.[16] In this way, the situation is similar to point vortices on a plane.

The Chern-Simons term in odd-dimensional space-time gives rise to a non-vanishing external field curvature, since it does modify equations of motion. In the three-dimensional theory for example, the equal-time commutator [which lives in two-space] reads

$$i[E^i_a(\mathbf{r}), \ E^j_b(\mathbf{r}')] = \frac{m}{4\pi} \delta_{ab} \varepsilon^{ij} \delta(\mathbf{r} - \mathbf{r}') \qquad m = 0, \pm 1, \ldots \tag{16}$$

The curvature may be described as a constant, functional external U(1) "magnetic" field. That the coefficient is quantized brings out the analogy, once again, between the quantization of Chern-Simons parameters in field theory and the point Dirac monopole.

While this viewpoint towards topological contributions to the gauge field action[20,21] does not produce any new results, it suggests a direction for further investigation. Are there other forms of external U(1) field connections and curvatures that may be added to conventional gauge dynamics?

E. Alternate Gauge Dynamics in Higher Dimensions

In my last topic, I discuss possible generalizations for higher-dimensional gauge-field dynamics. Let us recall that in four dimensions, the Yang-Mills energy momentum tensor may be written in self-dual form.

$$\theta^{\mu\nu} = \mathrm{tr}(F^{\mu\alpha}F^{\nu}_{\ \alpha} + {*F}^{\mu\alpha}{*F}^{\nu}_{\ \alpha}) \tag{17}$$

$$*F^{\mu\nu} = \frac{1}{2}\,\varepsilon^{\mu\nu\alpha\beta}\,F_{\alpha\beta} \tag{18}$$

The energy density is

$$\theta^{00} = \frac{1}{2}\,E^i_a E^i_a + \frac{1}{4}\,F^{ij}_a F^{ij}_a \tag{19}$$

and the potential may also be presented in terms of a derivative of a superpotential - a formula occuring also in supersymmetry models.

$$\theta^{00} = \frac{1}{2}\,E^i_a E^i_a + 32\pi^2 \left(\frac{\delta W(A)}{\delta A^i_a}\right)^2 \tag{20}$$

Here, W(A) is the integrated Chern-Simons 3-form [0-cocycle] whose variation gives $\varepsilon^{ijk}F^{jk}_a$.

The above expression for the energy density is also vacuously true in the two-dimensional theory, where the variation of the Chern-Simons term is constant, but (20) no longer holds in dimensions higher than four. However, we may contemplate a gauge theory in even-dimensional space-time where the energy density is given by (20) rather than (19).[20] For example, in a six-dimensional theory, a variation of the Chern-Simons 5-form is proportional to tr $\varepsilon^{ijklm}T^a F^{jk}F^{lm}$, and the new theory possesses a "potential" quadratic in the field strength.

The proposed modification can be fitted into a covariant energy-momentum tensor. We retain eq. (17) for $\theta^{\mu\nu}$ but replace the definition (18) of the dual by a non-linear formula, which in six dimensions reads,

$$*F^{\mu\nu} \propto \varepsilon^{\mu\nu\alpha\beta\gamma\delta}F_{\alpha\beta}F_{\gamma\delta} \tag{21}$$

and can be obviously generalized to any even-dimensional space-time. Note also that a self-duality equation $*F^{\mu\nu} \propto F^{\mu\nu}$ may be considered. This geometrically attractive model is under further study.

ACKNOWLEDGEMENT

This work is supported in part through funds provided by the U. S. Department of Energy (D.O.E.) under contract #DE-AC02-76ER03069.

REFERENCES

1. H. Fukuda and Y. Miyamoto, *Prog. Theor. Phys.* (Kyoto) **4**, 347 (1949); J. Steinberger, *Phys. Rev.* **76**, 1180 (1949); J. S. Bell and R. Jackiw, *Nuovo Cim.* **60A**, 47 (1969); S. Adler, *Phys. Rev.* **177**, 2426 (1969). Bell and I were directly motivated by Steinberger's calculation, who described it to us over coffee on the CERN patio. Although both the earlier and later papers deal with neutral pion decay, the notion that a symmetry - the chiral symmetry of pion physics - can be broken by quantum effects appears only in the work from the late 1960's, since that symmetry was unknown in the earlier period.

2. J. Schwinger, *Phys. Rev.* **82**, 664 (1951); R. Jackiw and K. Johnson, *Phys. Rev.* **182**, 1459 (1969).

3. Jackiw and Johnson, Ref. 2. These anomalous commutators are sometimes called "Schwinger terms", although this is confusing since Schwinger examined non-canonical contributions to the commutator between time and space components of the current, while here the commutator between time components is under discussion. Anomalies in the time-space component commutators were established earlier by T. Goto and T. Imamura, *Prog. Theor. Phys.* (Kyoto) **14**, 396 (1955) and J. Schwinger, *Phys. Rev. Lett.* **3**, 296 (1959).

4. K. Fujikawa, *Phys. Rev. Lett.* **42**, 1195 (1979).

5. The Abelian anomaly is related to the Atiyah-Singer index theorem; see A. Schwarz, *Phys. Lett.* **67B**, 172 (1977); L. Brown, R. Carlitz and C. Lee, *Phys. Rev. D* **16**, 417 (1977); R. Jackiw and C. Rebbi, *Phys. Rev. D* **16**, 1052 (1977). The non-Abelian anomaly is related to the index theorem in two dimensions higher; see M. Atiyah and I. Singer, *Proc. Natl. Acad. Sci USA* **81**, 2597 (1984); L. Alvarez-Gaumé and P. Ginsparg, *Nucl. Phys.* **B243**, 449 (1984).

6. This argument was developed by many people; I learned it from R. Feynman.

7. Note that the topological arguments in Ref. 5, which establish gauge non-invariance of the chiral fermion determinant, use zero modes in two dimensions higher.

8. J. Schwinger, *Phys. Rev.* **128**, 2425 (1962).

9. For a Hamiltonian analysis of two dimensional models, see N. Manton, *Ann. Phys.* (NY) **159**, 220 (1985).

10. K. Johnson, *Phys. Lett*. **5**, 253 (1963).

11. E. Witten, *Phys. Lett.* **117B**, 324 (1982). The relation between non-perturbative anomalies and the U(1) anomaly was found by J. Goldstone, and is explained by R. Jackiw in *Relativity Groups and Topology II*, B. DeWitt and R. Stora, eds., North-Holland, Amsterdam (1984).

12. L. Faddeev, *Phys. Lett.* **145B**, 81 (1984); L. Faddeev and S. Shatashvili, *Theor. Mat. Fiz.* **60**, 206 (1984) [*Theor. Math. Phys.* **60**, 770 (1984)]; J. Mickelsson, *Comm. Math. Phys.* **97**, 361 (1985); I. Singer (to be published). Further work has been done by I. Frenkel and I. Singer (to be published); S.-Y. Jo, MIT preprint CTP #1236 (1985).

13. D. Gross and R. Jackiw, *Phys. Rev. D* **6**, 447 (1972); C. Bouchiat, J. Iliopolous and Ph. Meyer, *Phys. Lett.* **38B**, 519 (1972).

14. M. Green and J. Schwarz, *Phys. Lett.* **149B**, 117 (1984).

15. R. Jackiw and R. Rajaraman, *Phys. Rev. Lett.* **54**, 1219 (1985).

16. For a review, see Jackiw, Ref. 11.

17. R. Jackiw, *Phys. Rev. Lett.* **54**, 159 (1985); B. Grossman, *Phys. Lett.* **152B**, 92 (1985); B.-Y. and B.-Y. Hou, *Chinese Phys. Lett.* (in press); Y.-S. Wu and A. Zee, *Phys. Lett.* **152B**, 98 (1985). For further discussion see R. Jackiw, *Phys. Lett.* (in press) and *Phys. Rev. Lett.* (in press); J. Mickelsson, *Phys. Rev. Lett.* (in press); B. Grossman, Rockefeller Univer-

sity preprint #RU 85 B110 (1985).

18. H. Lipkin, W. Weisberger and M. Peshkin, *Ann. Phys.* (NY) **53**, 203 (1969). When the three-fold Jacobi identity fails and an algebra is non-associative, one may impose a four-fold identity, the so-called Malcev identity, which requires that $\nabla \cdot \mathbf{B}$ be constant. When this fails, one can impose a five-fold identity, *etc.* For details, see Grossman, Ref. 17; M. Günyadin and B. Zumino, LBL preprint #LBL-19200, UCB-PTH-85/8 (1985).

19. K. Johnson and F. Low, *Prog. Theor. Phys.* (Kyoto) Suppl. **37-38**, 74 (1966). Also, there are hints of 3-cocycles in string theories, see Grossman, Ref. 17.

20. R. Jackiw in E. Fradkin *Festchrift*, A. Hilgar, Bristol (1985) (to be published).

21. Y.-S. Wu and A. Zee, University of Washington preprint #40048-38 P 4 (1984).

22. R. Jackiw, Ref. 20; S. Forte (in preparation).

SYMPOSIUM ON ANOMALIES, GEOMETRY, TOPOLOGY

ANOMALY STRUCTURE I

PAUL GINSPARG

CHAIRMAN

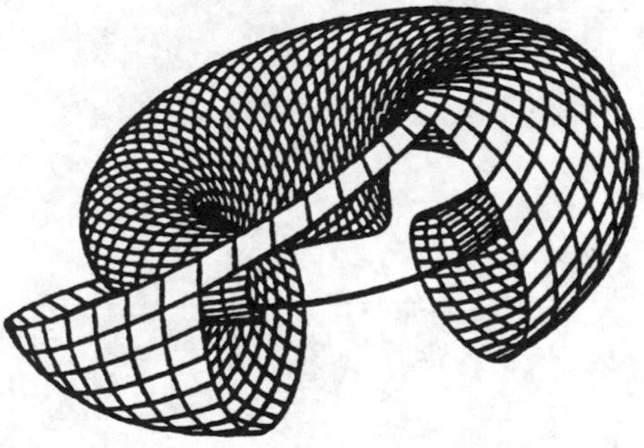

A Physical Interpretation of the 3rd Cocycle in the Group Cohomology of Nonabelian Gauge Theories

Bernard Grossman
The Rockefeller University
1230 York Avenue
New York, New York 10021

The notion of consistency in physics has taken the mathematical form of unitarity, renormalizability and gauge invariance within the context of quantum field theories as well as more general theories. For example, the cancellation of anomalies in gauge currents has been taken as a criterion for a unitary theory. It has been suggested by 't Hooft that anomalies may also place a restriction on symmetry breaking. Quantization conditions can also be considered as consistency conditions. In the case of quantum mechanics, there is a possible non-associativity of the ray representation of the translation of the translating group in the presence of a background magnetic monopole field whose charge has not been quantized according to the Dirac condition. Therefore the lack of consistency is apparent in the appearance of a non-associative

---

Work supported in part under the Department of Energy Contract Grant Number DE-AC02-81ER40033B.

algebra. It is therefore valuable to investigate whether the 3-cocycle in non-abelian gauge theories has a physical interpretation and what consistency requirements it may place on a gauge theory.

In this talk I will offer a physical explanation for the 3-cocycle in nonabelian gauge theories that is based upon a noncommutativity condition familiar to physicists in the guise of the 't Hooft commutation relations for path dependent quantities. This interpretation can be valuable for understanding the dynamics of gauge theories, because the representation that 't Hooft found for these commutation relations depended upon introducing disorder variables creating stringlike singularities as well as the usual order variables, the Wilson loops.

As an interesting historical note, although physicists have only recently discovered an interpretation of a 3-cocycle for group cohomology in quantum mechanics, a 3-cocycle first appeared in the mathematical literature in 1940. It was discovered by Teichmüller in the context of non-commutative Galois theory.

We first review the construction of the non-trivial bundles for a Dirac magnetic monopole. In the same year, 1931, as Dirac discovered his formulation of the magnetic monopole, H. Hopf discovered a non-trivial map from S^3 to S^2. This non-trivial map from a sphere of higher dimension than the sphere which is the image of the map was later discovered to be very much related to the magnetic monopole. The first Chern class classifies the non-trivial U(1) principal bundles over S^2. The Chern number of the bundle determines a winding number which is related to the magnetic charge by the Dirac quantization condition.

One constructs the non-trivial Hopf map by considering S^3 as the set of pairs of complex numbers $(z_1,z_2) \in \mathbb{C}$ such that

$$|z_1|^2 + |z_2|^2 = 1.$$

If one considers an equivalence relation of two such pairs by a common phase $e^{in\theta}$

$$(z_1,z_2) \sim e^{in\theta}\ (z_1,z_2)$$

then the integer n determines a winding number for the map of $S^3 \to S^2$ with a circle sitting in the fiber over every point in S^2. Any two circles are linked n times.

One must choose a connection representing the magnetic monopole compatible with the winding number for the principal bundle. Homotopically, the space R^3 with the magnetic monopole at the origin is like S^2 since there is an incontractible S^2 surrounding the origin. At any given radius, one has an S^2 on which one chooses two coordinates patches. In the upper (lower) hemisphere one chooses a connection $A^{I(II)}$ so that the string singularity is in the lower (upper) hemisphere. The two hemispheres overlap in an equatorial band. The mapping of the equator (coordinatized by ϕ) in the U(1) gauge group has a winding number.

$$A_\phi^{I(II)} = g(\ +(-)1 - \cos\theta)$$

$$A_\phi^{I} - A_\phi^{II} = 2g = -\frac{i}{e}\,U^{-1}\partial_\phi U$$

$$U = \exp\left[2ieg\phi\right]$$

The Dirac quantization condition $eg = n/2$ determines the winding number, n, which must be the same as that for the non-trivial principal bundle.

If one does not impose the Dirac quantization condition, there is a possible obstruction to the composition of open paths or equivalently the translation group in R^3. The gauge invariant translations are generated by the velocity vectors.

$$v_i = -ih \frac{\partial}{\partial x_i} + eA_i$$

Since they do not commute,

$$[v_i, v_j] = -i\hbar e\, F_{ij} ,$$

there is a 2-cochain extension of the algebra of translations. Moreover, since the Jacobi identity is not satisfied,

$$\varepsilon^{ijk}\, [[v_i, v_j],\ v_k] = -i\ e\hbar^2 \vec{\nabla}.\vec{B} \neq 0$$

there is a possible obstruction to the exponentiation to a group determined by the variation of the 2-cochain. This is the 3-cocycle. If one considers the ϕ (equatorial angle for fixed radius) components of the velocity, this should generate a closed loop as a varies from zero to 2π. If eg is not quantized correctly, one must consider the real line covering (open path) of the circle (closed loop). The quantization condition is a consequence of the exact sequence $0 \to Z \to R \to S^1 \to$.

The compatibility condition can be simple stated mathematically in terms of the following diagram, where P is a principal G bundle over the manifold M with $\mathcal{A}$ the space of connections with gauge transformation group $\mathcal{G}$:

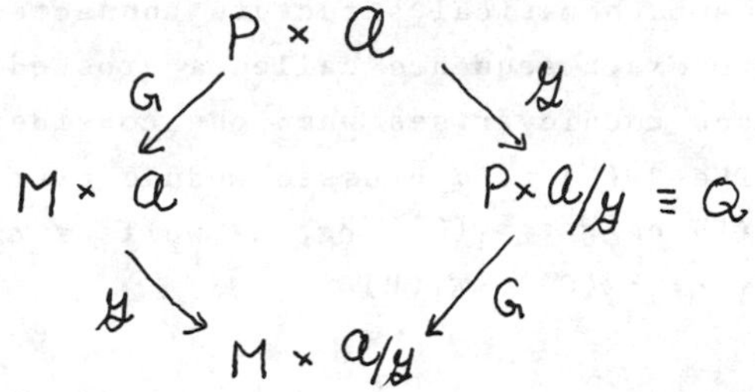

If $M \times \mathcal{A}/\mathcal{G}$ exists, one can then ask whether loops in this space lift to loops in the universal quotient bundle, Q. When the compact Lie group G has a non-trivial center (as in G = SU(N)), there is a possible obstruction to this lifting as determined by the exact sequence.

$$1 \to Z_N \xrightarrow{i} \Omega G \xrightarrow{\alpha} \Omega Q \xrightarrow{\pi} \Omega(M \times \mathcal{A}/\mathcal{G}) \to 1$$

where Z_N is the constant loop at the center of G = SU(N). In general there is a 2-cochain f(C,C') that is determined by the lifting of two loops C, C' by a section S such that πS = identity.

$$S(C)\,S(C') = f(C,C')\,S(C.C')$$

Where . denotes loop composition. This 2-cochain may satisfy an additive 2-cocycle condition as long as the group elements remain within a 1-parameter abelian subgroup of the non-abelian group. However, the 2-cocycle condition does not necessarily lift to a non-abelian condition. If F(C,C') is the lifting of f to ΩG, there is a possible obstruction as determined by the following non-commutativity condition for the path dependent cochains F with β a 3-cocycle:

$$S(C)\,F(C',C'')\,S(C)^{-1}\,F(C,C'.C'')$$

$$= i(\beta\,(C,C',C''))\;\;F(C,C')\,F(C.C',C'')$$

The obstruction is determined by an element of Z_N. Therefore, it appears in the representation when one considers the fundamental or other N-ality nonsinglets.

There is a mathematical structure connected with the above four term exact sequence called a crossed module. The simplest crossed module arises when one considers a principal G bundle P. The $\pi_1(G)$ is a crossed module over $\pi_1(P)$ with an action $p \in \pi_1(P)$ on $g \in \pi_1(G)$, ${}^{p}g$, as well as a homomorphism

$$\alpha: \pi_1(G) \to \pi_1(P)$$

such that

$$\alpha(g)_{g'} = g\, g'\, g^{-1} \qquad g, g' \in \pi_1(G)$$

$$\alpha({}^{p}g) = p\, \alpha(g) p^{-1}$$

In this case, in order to realize the four term exact sequence, $\pi_1(G)$ must be non-abelian with a non-trivial center.

That is why for a U(1) gauge theory, the representation is associative when one uses the Dirac quantization condition for the magnetic monopole. However, if one includes an additional global U(1), like axial U(1) in QED, that does not necessarily commute with the gauged vector U(1), there is a central term and a 3-cocycle.

Returning to the nonabelian gauge theory, the anomaly is an obstruction to restricting a U(N) theory to an SU(N) theory insofar as there is a non-trivial U(1) phase of the determinant of the Dirac operator. If one considers a U(1) extension of an anomalous SU(N) theory where U(1) is mapped N times into a maximal torus of SU(N) (i.e. the U(1) charge is N times the SU(N) charge) then there is the possibility of magnetic monopoles 1/N times the fundamental Dirac charge. The 3rd cocycle detects such monopoles with a non-commutativity condition like 't Hoofts'.

Let $\omega^{i,j}$ be the differential form of the descent series derived from the third Chern class. i indicates the degree of the form with respect to differentiation, d, in space and j, the degree of the form with respect to differentiation, s, on the group. Then $\omega^{i,j}$ determines a j-cocycle for the group cohomology after integration over an i-dimensional space without boundary. Each magnetic monopole has an incontractible two-sphere surrounding it that bounds a three dimensional disc D^3. Therefore, we obtain a 3-cocycle by considering

$$\alpha^3 = \int_{\partial D^3} \omega^{2,3}$$

$$= \int_{D^3} d\omega^{2,3} = - \int_{D^3} s\omega^{3,2}$$

$$\equiv - \delta \int_{D^3} \omega^{3,2}$$

$$\text{so } \delta\alpha^3 = 0$$

We also note that there are additional relations that may appear as a result of lifting higher order loops (N-spheres). For example, there may be an obstruction of lifting a map of $S^2 \to G/H$ to $S^2 \to G$ for G=SU(N), H=U(1) analagous to the obstruction of lifting $S^1 \to G/Z_N$ to $S^1 \to G$. Since these obstructions are determined by non-trivial homotopy, there are quantization conditions with a consequent possible non-associativity or higher order condition placed on the ray representation of the group just as in the quantum mechanics with a background magnetic monopole.

In conclusion note that the extension of the loops in the quotient bundle by loops in the group Ω is related to a possible string theory extension of gauge theories. The central extensions of the loops in the Lie algebra are classified by the Kac-Moody Lie algebras whose representations determine string theories. These exponentiate to a group when the coefficient of the central extension satisfies a quantization condition. This could perhaps be obtained by quantizing the stringlike singularities between magnetic monopoles with 1/N times the usual Dirac charge.

For references and further details see
B. Grossman Phys. Lett. 52B, 93(1985); Rockefeller Univ. preprints RU 85/B/110, 113; also lectures in this conference by O. Alvarez, R. Jackiw, I. Singer, J. Stasheff, B. Zumino, and B.Y. Hou. The mathematics for low dimensional cohomology has been described in
K. Brown, Cohomology of Groups (Springer-Verlag, 1982).

COHOMOLOGY AND ABELIAN GAUGE STRUCTURE IN CONFIGURATION SPACE OF GAUGE FIELDS

Yong-Shi Wu
Department of Physics, University of Utah
Salt Lake City, Utah 84112

ABSTRACT

The topology of configuration space in gauge theories are studied by considering cocycles and U(1) gauge structure on it. The relationship to cohomology of gauge groups and some new applications are also pointed out.

I. Introduction

Recently it turns out[1] that chiral anomalies are related to the cohomology of a gauge orbit $\mathcal{G}$, which is isomorphic to the group of gauge transformations, in the space $\mathcal{A}$ of gauge potentials. An interesting problem is to consider the cohomology of the whole space $\mathcal{A}$ and that of the gauge-orbit space $\mathcal{A}/\mathcal{G}$. Here we are reporting on a recent study[2] of this problem, in which a tower of cocycles in $\mathcal{A}$ are constructed by generalizing the well-known Chern-Weil and Chern-Simons theorems. This construction not only induces (though not directly) the usual Zumino-Faddeev tower of cocycles on a gauge orbit, but also generates nontrivial cocycles in $\mathcal{A}/\mathcal{G}$ by appropriate projection. The Wess-Zumino actions for nonlinear sigma models over a homogeneous space have been explicitly constructed and expressed in terms of the ChernSimons 1-cocycle in the new tower.[2] We expect more applications of the new cocycles will be found.

Another, perhaps more physical way of studying the topology of $\mathcal{A}/\mathcal{G}$ is to consider the so-called gauge potential in potential space induced by topological Lagrangians, as suggested by Zee and myself in ref. 3. Some interesting observations in the study will be reported in this talk too.

Before going on, a few words on notations are in order. We are going to consider cochains in $\mathcal{A}$ which take values in differential forms in space-time variables x. The differentiation with respect to the parameters $t_1, t_2, \cdots$ in $\mathcal{A}$, upon which the potential one-form $A(x; t_1, t_2, \cdots)$ may depend on, by δ. By convention, we assume δ anticommutes with d. In addition we follow the notations and standard terminology of cohomology theory in ref. 1.

II. Cohomology of the Gauge-Potential Space

First let us consider the space, $\mathcal{A}$, of gauge potentials A(x) with a fixed topological number. The n-th Chern character

$$\Omega^0_{2n}(A) = \text{Str } F^n \tag{1}$$

which is a 2n-form in x, can be viewed as a 0-cochain in $\mathcal{A}$. With this interpretation, the well-known Chern-Weil theorem[4]

$$\Omega^0_{2n}(A_1) - \Omega^0_{2n}(A_0) = n \int_0^1 \delta t \ \text{Str}\{A_1 - A_0, F_t^{n-1}\} \tag{2}$$

(where $A_t = tA_1 + (1-t)A_0$, $F_t = dA_t + A_t{}^2$) can be reformulated in the language of cohomology as follows. The coboundary of the Chern-character 0-cochain is an exact form in x:

$$(\Delta\Omega^0_{2n})(A_0, A_1) = d\Omega^1_{2n-1}(A_0, A_1) \tag{3}$$

$$\Omega^1_{2n-1}(A_0, A_1) = n\int_0^1 \text{Str}\{\delta A_t, F_t{}^{n-1}\} \tag{4}$$

where the integral is taken along the straight line connecting A_0 and A_1.

Now think of the (2n-1)-form (in x)Ω^1_{2n-1} as a 1-cochain in $\mathcal{A}$, and call it the Chern-Simons 1-cochain. We observe that eq. (4) has already the structure of the descent equations for cohomology of gauge algebras or gauge groups. So we can play the same trick as used there, namely let Δ act on eq. (4) and, by using $\Delta^2=0$, derive that $d(\Delta\Omega^1_{2n-1})=o$. Locally $\Delta\Omega^1_{2m-1}$ must be exact. Here in fact we are able to prove that $\Delta\Omega^1_{2n-1}$ is globally exact

$$\Delta\Omega^1_{2n-1} = d\Omega^2_{2n-2} \tag{5}$$

$$\Omega^2_{2n-2}(A_o,A_1,A_2) = \frac{n(n-1)}{2} \int_{C_2} \mathrm{Str}\{\delta A_{st},\delta A_{st},F_{st}{}^{n-2}\} \tag{5'}$$

where the integral is over the triangle C_2 $(A_o\ A_1,\ A_2)$ which is represented by

$$A_{st}= sA_2 + tA_1+ (1-s-t)A_o \quad (0\leqslant s,\ t \leqslant 1) \tag{6}$$

Taking $A_o = o$, $A_1 = A(\zeta)$, $A_2 = A(\zeta + \delta\zeta)$ we obtain the Chern-Simons formula.[5]

Going on with the same procedure we obtain

$$\Delta\Omega^k_{2n-1} = d\Omega^{k+1}_{2n-k-1} \quad (o \leqslant k \leqslant n) \tag{7}$$

$$\Omega^k_{2n-k} = \binom{n}{k} \int_{C_k} \mathrm{Str}\ \{(\delta A_{t_1\cdots t_k})^{k}, (F_{t_1\cdots t_k})^{n-k}\} \tag{7'}$$

where C_k is the k-simplex spanned by

$$A_{t_1\cdots t_k}= (1-t_1- \ldots - t_k)\ A_o + t_1A_1 + \cdots + t_kA_k \quad (0 \leqslant t_1, \cdots, t_k \leqslant 1) \tag{8}$$

This tower of descent equations in $\mathcal{O}\!\!\!\!\!\!\mathcal{C}$ terminates at $k = n$: $\Delta\Omega^n_n = 0$.

Now the k-cochain (in $\mathcal{O}\!\!\!\!\!\!\mathcal{C}$) Ω^k_{2n-k} is a (2n-k)-form in x which is globally defined in space-time M. This is because Ω^k_{2n-k} is invariant under a simultaneous gauge transformation of $A_o, \cdots, A_k$:

$$\Omega^k_{2n-k}\ (A_o\ \cdots,\ A_k) = \Omega^k_{2n-k}\ (A^g_o,\ \cdots\ ,\ A^g_k) \tag{9}$$

$$A^g = g(x)^{-1}\ A\ g(x) + g(x)^{-1}dg(x) \tag{9'}$$

Thus Ω^k_{2n-k} is unambiguouslyly defined in the overlap of two or more patches in M when they are needed in the cases corresponding to a nontrivial bundle. When M is compact and of appropriate dimensionality, the integration of Ω^k_{2n-k} over M leads to a k-cocycle in $\mathcal{A}$:

$$\Delta\int_M \Omega^k{}_{2n-k} = 0 \qquad (0 < k < n) \qquad (10)$$

The above contruction can be carried out by starting from any symmetric invariant polynomial of degree n in F (instead of Str F^n) and can be used to define cochains for deformed simplexes (instead of linear simplexes) in $\mathcal{A}$. The deformation of the simplex changes the cochain by an exact form in X and/or a coboundary in $\mathcal{A}$ and, therefore, does not change the cohomology class of the cocycle. Since $\mathcal{A}$ is an affine space, whose topology is trivial, the cocycles we have constructed are all trivial. (This does not imply that they are of no physical interest.)

III. Cohomology of a Gauge-Orbit

A gauge orbit in $\mathcal{A}$ consists of potentials which are the gauge transforms of each other. It is easy to see that a gauge orbit is diffeomorphic to the group , $\mathcal{G}$, of gauge transformations. To restrict the cohomology to one gauge orbit we consider simplexes of which the vertices are all on the same orbit. For them we can write

$$Ao = A \quad , A_1 = A^{g_1} \quad , A_2 = A^{g_1 g_2} \quad , \quad \cdots \qquad (11)$$

where A^g is the gauge-transformed of A by g(x). When both the k- and (k+1)-cochains are in $\mathcal{G}$, the definition of the coboundary operation in $\mathcal{G}$ reduces to that of Faddev's for the cohomology of gauge groups.

When the vertices are all in one connected piece of the orbit, we can directly restrict our construction, eqs. (7) and (7'), to entirely within it by substituting into them only the following simplexes

$$A_{t_1 \cdots t_k} = g(t)^{-1} A_0(t)\, g(t) + g(t)^{-1} dg(t) \qquad (12)$$

where $g(t) = g(x; t_1, \cdots, t_k)$, which lie entirely in one gauge orbit. It can be shown that upon this restriction all cochains constructed above become exact forms in x up to coboundaries, leading to trivial cocycles.

However, we can induce nontrivial cocycles on a gauge orbit as follows. Fix one vertex, say A_0, in the Chern-Simons 1-cochain and then consider it as a 0-cochain in $\mathcal{A}$:

$$\omega^0_{2n-1}(A) \equiv \Omega^1_{2n-1}(A_0, A) \tag{13}$$

The coboundary of this Chern-Simons 0-cochain is an exact form in x when both endpoints are in the one and same gauge orbit, i.e.

$$\begin{aligned}(\Delta\omega^0_{2n-1})(A,A^g) &= -(\Delta\Omega^1_{2n-1})(A_0,A,A^g) + \Omega^1_{2n-1}(A,A^g)\\ &= -d\omega^1_{2n-2}(A,A^g)\end{aligned} \tag{14}$$

Once we have this equation, we can apply the coboundary operation in the same gauge orbit and recover the usual descent equations in the cohomology of the gauge group $\mathcal{G}$:

$$\Delta\omega^k_{2n-1-k} = -d\omega^{l+1}_{2n-2-k} \tag{15}$$

As a by-product we can obtain the expressions of ω^k_{2n-k-1} in terms of the Ω's constructed before. This construction can be carried out in any topologically nontrivial sector of gauge potentials.[6] In the sector with zero topological number one can take the simplest choice $A_0 = 0$.

IV. Čech-DeRhom Cohomology of the Gauge-Orbit Space

The gauge-orbit space, $\mathcal{A}/\mathcal{G}$, is obtained by identifying all potentials on a gauge orbit. It is this space which is considered as the genuine configuration space of a gauge theory and it generally has complicated topology. To consider nontrivial cohomology classes in this space we try to appropriately project our previous construction, Eqs. (7) and (7^1), from $\mathcal{A}$ down to $\mathcal{A}/\mathcal{G}$ as follows. Locally $A(x) \in \mathcal{A}$ can be parameterized by $(a(x), g(x))$ using $A(x) = a(x)^{g(x)}$. Here $a(x)$ represents the gauge orbit which $A(x)$ lies on and can be viewed as local coordinates in a certain patch of $\mathcal{A}/\mathcal{G}$. Substituting this into the integrand of Eq. (7) and extract the part which contains only $\delta a_{t_1 \cdots t_k}$ we obtain the projection of the integrand of Eq. (7) into a patch of $\mathcal{A}/\mathcal{G}$, which is given by the same formula (7^1) with $A_{t_k \cdots t_k}$, $F_{t_1 \cdots t_k}$ replaced by $a_{t_1 \cdots t_k}$ and corresponding field strength.

Unfortunately, the projected differential form obtained in this way is not globally defined on $\mathcal{A}/\mathcal{G}$. But after integration over compact M, two projected forms in two patches of $\mathcal{A}/\mathcal{G}$, which are obtained from one and the same form is given in Eq. (7), differ from each other only by an exact form in t in the overlapping region of the two patches. For example, we have

$$\mathrm{Str}\,\{(\delta a')^k, (f')^{n-k}\} - \mathrm{Str}\,\{(\delta a)^k, f^{n-k}\} = dX + \delta Y \tag{16}$$

where $a' = a^h$ and, when $k = 2$,

$$X = \mathrm{Str}\,\{\delta h h^{-1}, D_a\,(\delta h h^{-1} - 2\delta a)\,,\, f^{n-2}\} \tag{17}$$

$$Y = -\frac{2}{n-1}\,\mathrm{Str}\{\delta h h^{-1}, f^{n-1}\} \tag{17'}$$

when $k = 3$,

$$\begin{aligned} X = {} & -3\,\mathrm{Str}\,\{\delta a, \delta a, \delta h h^{-1}, f^{n-3}\} + 3\,\mathrm{Str}\,\{\delta a, D_a(\delta h h^{-1}), \delta h h^{-1}, f^{n-3}\} \\ & -\mathrm{Str}\,\{\delta h h^{-1}, D_a(\delta h h^{-1}), D_a(\delta h h^{-1})\,, f^{n-3}\} \\ & + \frac{1}{n-2}\,\mathrm{Str}\{\delta h h^{-1}, (\delta h h^{-1})^2, f^{n-2}\} \end{aligned} \tag{18}$$

$$Y = \frac{3}{n-2}\,\mathrm{Str}\{\delta h h^{-1}, D_a(\delta h h^{-1}), f^{n-2}\} - \frac{6}{n-2}\,\mathrm{Str}\{\delta h h^{-1}, \delta a, f^{n-2}\} \tag{18'}$$

Once we have the above result, though we cannot consider DeRham cohomology in this way, it is straightforward to construct the Cech-DeRham double complex and corresponding cohomology in $\mathcal{A}/\mathcal{G}$. For general rules for doing so we refer to O. Alvarez's talk in the same proceeding. The details will be presented elsewhere.

V. Abelian Gauge Structure Inside Non-Abelian Gauge Theories

In quantum mechanics, the coupling of a point particle to a background U(1) potential

$$L_{int} = \int dt \frac{dq^i}{dt} A_i(q(t)) \tag{19}$$

leads to the consequence that the velocity operator $V_i = \dot{q}_i$ is represented by the covariant derivative $-i D_i \equiv -i\partial_i - A_i(q)$. This representation of the velocity operator is of course responsible for profound topological effects such as the Bohm-Aharonov effect and the Dirac quantization of magnetic charge.

Similarly in quantum gauge theory, in the Schrödinger formulation in the Weyl gauge $A_0 = 0$, the topological Lagrangians, such as the $\theta F\tilde{F}$ term in 3 + 1 dimensions or the Chern-Simons term in 2 + 1 dimensions, are always linear in $\dot{A}_i(\vec{x})$. So the inclusion of a topological Lagrangian introduces certain U(1) background fields in the configuration space, which are often topologically nontrivial, reflecting the topology of configuration space.

We have developed in ref. 3 a method using differential forms rather than functional derivatives to calculate the potentials and corresponding field-strengths in both $\mathcal{A}$ and $\mathcal{A}/\mathcal{G}$ which are induced from topological Lagrangians. Our results can be summarized as follows: (1) the θ-term in 3 + 1 dimensions induces a vortex background field in $\mathcal{A}^{(3)}/\mathcal{G}^{(3)}$, which is related to the fact that $\pi_1(\mathcal{A}^{(3)}/\mathcal{G}^{(3)}) = \mathbb{Z}$. The flux of that vortex is just equal to the θ-parameter. Thus the θ-vacuum effect can be identified with a kind of Bohm-Aharonov effect in gauge-orbit space; (2) the topological mass (i.e. Chern-Simons) term in 2 + 1 dimensions leads to a monopole background field in $\mathcal{A}^{(2)}/\mathcal{G}^{(2)}$, which is related to the fact that $\pi_2(\mathcal{A}^{(2)}/\mathcal{G}^{(2)}) = \mathbb{Z}$. The coefficient of this term is related to the monopole strength which should be quantized according to Dirac quantization in order to have a consistent quantum theory. This provides a new understanding of the the quantization of topological mass.[7]

Motivated by the first result, we were led to speculate on a "possible solution of the strong CP problem, namely the space $\mathfrak{A}/\mathfrak{G}$ acts as a superconductor for the background U(1) field in it so that the flux θ is quantized. Unfortunately, we do not know how to implement this idea in the context of quantum gauge theory. Despite this experience, we do hope the new way of looking at topological Lagrangians will shed light on topological effects in QFT.

VI. Applications

The advantage of considering local cohomology of the gauge-potential space is that it provides a unified treatment of topology of both the gauge group $\mathfrak{G}$ and the gauge-orbit space $\mathfrak{A}/\mathfrak{G}$. Many old derivations can be greatly simplified. For cohomology of $\mathfrak{A}$ we have obtained different forms in x which are globally defined even for topologically nontrivial A. And in $\mathfrak{A}$ or in $\mathfrak{A}/\mathfrak{G}$ we have been able to construct more topological quantities which we expect will be found useful in the future.

For example, $\Omega^1_{2n-1}(A_0,A_1)$ have been recently used to explicitly construct the Wess-Zumino Lagrangians in generic nonlinear A-models over G/H with G either gauged or ungauged when G and H satisfy certain conditions.[2] Also the infinitesimal version of Ω^2_{2n-2}, as a 2-form in $\mathfrak{A}$, has been used[8] to define a pre-symplectic structure over $\mathfrak{A}$ and the corresponding momentum-mapping is identified with the covariant anomalies. The consideration of the background U(1) potential also improved our understanding of the effects of topological Lagrangians. We do expect more interesting applications will be coming.

References

1. L. Bonora and P. Cotta-Ramusino, Comm. Math. Phys. 87 (1983) 589; B. Zumino, in Relativity, Groups and Topology II, ed. B.S. DeWitt and R. Stora (North Holland, Amsterdam, 1984); R. Stora, Cargèse Lectures (1983) LAPP-TH-94; B. Zumino, Y.S. Wu and A. Zee, Nucl. Phys. B239 (1984) 477; L.D. Faddeev, Phys. Lett. 145B (1984) 81; B. Zumino, NSF-ITP-84-150 (and references in it and [2]).

2. Y.S. Wu, Phys. Lett. 153B (1985) 70.

3. Y.S. Wu and A. Zee, Seattle preprint 40048-38 P4 (1984).

4. See, e.g., S.S. Chern, Complex Manifolds without Potential Theory, Appendix; 2nd Ed. (Springer, Berlin, 1979).

5. S.S. Chern and J. Simons, Ann. Math. 99 (1974) 48.

6. J. Manes, R. Stora and B. Zumino, Berkeley and LBL preprint (1985).

7. S. Deser, R. Jackiw and S. Templeton, Phys. Rev. Lett. 48 (1982) 975; Ann. Phys. (N.Y.) 140 (1982) 372; Y.S. Wu, Ann. Phys. (N.Y.) 156 (1984) 194.

8. D. Bao and V.P. Nair, IAS (Princeton) preprint (1985).

Note added: Some works similar to Sec. II and III have been independently done by Beijing ITP group and X.C. Song. (See H.Y. Guo in this Proceedings.)

AN INTRODUCTION TO SUPERGRAVITATIONAL ANOMALIES

Laurent BAULIEU

Laboratoire de Physique Théorique et Hautes Energies, Paris.

ABSTRACT

We study the problem of classifying the anomalies which can occur in supergravity theories. Using algebraic methods we come to the conjecture that the structure of the possible anomalous vertices of a given supergravity model is fully determined from the sole knowledge of the boson gauge field sector. Stated with other words, our claim is that no anomaly in the supersymmetry current can exist which is not equivalent to an ABBJ anomaly of the Yang-Mills X Lorentz symmetry of the theory or to an anomaly of the current of a boson p-form gauge field ($p \geqslant 2$). As a consequence, to verify that a given supergravity is anomaly free, it is sufficient to verify the cancellations of the possibly anomalous diagrams with external boson gauge fields.

Université Paris VI
4, Place Jussieu
Tour 16, 1er Etage,
75230 PARIS CEDEX 05

Laboratoire Associé au CNRS (L.A.280)

The study of anomalies which can occur in supergravity is a painfull but necessary step in our understanding of the symmetry of these theories. It is indeed well recognized by now that the existence of anomalies for a given gauge symmetry is deeply rooted in its geometrical structure and goes beyond the level of quantum field theory[1]. The classification of anomalies can also be compared to that of invariant Lagrangians[2]. In supergravity one must consider the possibility of "supergravitational" anomalies, that is to say of anomalies which would be associated with the non conservation of the local supersymmetry current, while not being reducible to the known anomalies of the boson gauge fields of the theory. The cancellation conditions for such new anomalies in the lowest non trivial order of perturbation theory would provide a further criterion for selecting "healthy" supergravity models.

For theories whose gauge fields are of the Yang-Mills type ($A=A_\mu dx^\mu$) and of the p-form type ($B_p = \frac{1}{p+1} B_{\mu_1 \cdots \mu_p} dx^{\mu_1} \cdots dx^{\mu_p}$, $p \geqslant 2$) <u>with no spinorial charges</u>, the problem of classifying the possible anomalous diagrams reduces to a simple algebraïc classification, by now well mastered[2]. Anomalies in n-dimensional space-time are in fact determinable from the d-exact exterior polynomials of rank n+2, functions of the field strengths $F = dA + AA$ and $G_{p+1} = dB_p + R_{p+1}(A, B)$ of A and B, and denoted as $I_{n+2}(F, G)$. R_{p+1} is a (p+1)-form function of A and B such that G_{p+1} satisfies Bianchi identities[2,4]. Note that allthrough this article all products are exterior products and the wedge product symbol $\wedge$ is generally omitted. $d = dx^\mu \frac{\partial}{\partial x^\mu}$ is the exterior derivative. Because I_{n+2} is d- exact, one has

$$I_{n+2}(F,G) = d\,\Delta_{n+1}(A, B, F, G) \qquad (1)$$

where Δ_{n+1} is defined modulo d-exact terms, $\Delta_{n+1} \sim \Delta_{n+1} + d\,K_n(A,B,F,G)$. The so-called "Franco-Russian" formula connects Δ_{n+1}, or equivalently I_{n+2}, with Δ^1_n, the n-form with ghost number 1 which is a possible non spurious obstruction in n dimensions to the Ward identity associated with the BRS symmetry of the system of fields A and B, that is to say the anomaly of the gauge symmetry acting on A and B. One has[2]

$$\begin{aligned} \Delta^1_n &= [\,\Delta_{n+1}(\tilde{A}, \tilde{B}, F, G)]^1_n \\ &= (\,c\,(\delta/\delta A)\big|_{B,F,G} + B^1_{p-1}(\delta/\delta B_p)_{A,F,G})\,\Delta_{n+1}(A, B, F, G) \end{aligned} \qquad (2.a)$$

and Δ^1_n satisfies the anomaly equation

$$\left\{\begin{array}{l} s\,\Gamma^{1\,loop} = \int \Delta^1_n \;,\; \Delta^1_n \neq s\,K^0_n \\ s^2 \;\;= 0 \end{array}\right. \leftrightarrow \left\{\begin{array}{l} s\,\Delta^1_n \;= d\,\Delta^2_{n-1} \\ \Delta^1_n \;\sim\; s\,K^0_n \;+ d\,K^1_{n-1} \end{array}\right. \qquad (2.b)$$

s is the BRS operator of the gauge symmetry, c the Faddeev-Popov ghost of A, B^g_{p-g} $(1 \leq g \leq p)$ the ghost of order g of the p-form gauge field Bp, and we have unified the ghost and classical fields into the generalized forms $\widetilde{A}=A+c$ and $\widetilde{B}_p = B_p + B^1_{p-1}+\ldots+ B^g_{p-g}+\ldots+ B^p_0$. In our notation the upper index of a form is the (additive under exterior product)ghost number, and the lower one is the Lorentz rank. The sum of these two numbers determines the grading of generalized ghost-classical forms. We unify also d and s into the graded exterior derivative $\widetilde{d}=d+s$. The magics of the "Franco-Russian" formula is most simple. The sole trick is that the BRS operator s is consistently defined from the following constraints when they are expanded in ghost number [2)]

$$\begin{array}{l} \widetilde{G}_{p+1} \equiv \widetilde{d}\,\widetilde{B}_p + R_{p+1}(\widetilde{A}, \widetilde{B}, \widetilde{F}, \widetilde{G}) = G_{p+1} \\ \widetilde{F} \;\;\equiv \widetilde{d}\,\widetilde{A} + \frac{1}{2}[\widetilde{A}, \widetilde{A}\,] \;=\; F \end{array} \qquad (3)$$

One has indeed from eq.(3) $I_{n+2}(\widetilde{F},\widetilde{G}\,) = I_{n+2}(F,G)$ and thus $(d+s)\widetilde{\Delta}_{n+1}(\widetilde{A},F,\widetilde{B},G) = d\Delta_{n+1}(A,F,B,G)$, the part with ghost two of which identifies itself with the anomaly equation (2.b), so that the anomaly Δ^1_n is truly given by eq.(2.a). Observe that the components Δ^g_{n+1-g} of $\widetilde{\Delta}_{n+1}$ satisfy too the consistency equations $s\Delta^g_{d+1-g} + d\Delta^{g+1}_{d-g} = 0$, but the meaning of Δ^g_{d+1-g} in field theory is still unclear for $g > 1$.

The anomaly formula (2) remains unchanged when gravity is coupled, but one must include effectively the Lorentz symmetry into the Yang-Mills symmetry of the theory[3,4)]. One has therefore to change A into A $+\omega$ and c into c $+\Omega$ where $\omega = \omega^{ab}_\mu dx^\mu M_{ab}$ is the spin-connection and $\Omega = \Omega^{ab} M_{ab}$ the corresponding Faddeev-Popov ghost. I_{n+2} is now function of F, G and $R=d\omega+\omega\omega$ Note that the field strength of B_p can generally depend on ω through the interaction term R_{p+1} [4)].

This property that the gravitational anomalies reduce in fact to ABBJ anomalies of the Lorentz symmetry relies on the possibility of decoupling the invariance under local diffeomorphisms from the rest of the other internal symmetries among which one includes the local Lorentz symmetry. This decoupling becomes obvious by means of a judicious choice of variables [3,4], and it has been also explicitly verified by direct one-loop diagrammatic computations[5]. These variables are denoted with the "hat" symbol ^ and one has the following correspondence between $\tilde{B}_p$ and $\hat{B}_p$:

$$\hat{A} \equiv (\exp - i_\xi)\tilde{A} = A + \hat{c} \quad , \quad \hat{c} = c - i_\xi A \tag{4}$$

$$\hat{B}_p \equiv (\exp - i_\xi)\tilde{B}_p = \sum_{g=0}^{p} \hat{B}^g_{p-g} \quad , \quad \hat{B}^g_{p-g} = B^g_{p-g} - i_\xi B^{g-1}_{p-g+1} + \dots + (-)^p \frac{\overbrace{i_\xi \cdots i_\xi}^{g} B_p}{g!}$$

Here i_ξ is the contraction orperator along the ghost vector field ξ^μ associated with the diffeomorphisms ($i_\xi Z_{\mu_1 \dots \mu_K} dx^{\mu_1} \dots dx^{\mu_K} \equiv K \xi^{\mu_1} Z_{\mu_1 \dots \mu_K} dx^{\mu_2} \dots dx^{\mu_K}$). One also defines the operator $\hat{s}$ by substracting from the BRS operator s the exterior Lie derivative along ξ^μ, $\hat{s} \equiv s - L_\xi$ with $L_\xi \equiv i_\xi d - d i_\xi$, so that[4]

$$\hat{d} \equiv (\exp - i_\xi)\tilde{d}(\exp i_\xi), \quad \hat{d} = d + \hat{s}, \quad s\xi^\mu = \xi^\alpha \partial_\alpha \xi^\mu \tag{5}$$

and $\hat{d}^2 = 0$ is equivalent to $\tilde{d}^2 = 0$. In curved space the field strengths are $\hat{F} = \hat{d}\hat{A} + \hat{A}\hat{A}$, $\hat{R} = \hat{d}\hat{\omega} + \hat{\omega}\hat{\omega}$ and $\hat{G}_{p+1} = \hat{d}\hat{B}_p + R_{p+1}(\hat{A}, \hat{F}, \hat{B}, \hat{G})$. This system of variables allows one to determine the BRS symmetry in the simplest way, by imposing the horizontality equations $\hat{R} = R$, $\hat{F} = F$, $\hat{G} = G$, and this allows one to still use in curved space the "Franco-Russian" formula to determine the possible anomalies, which explains the above statement for the structure of gravitational anomalies [3,4].

To study the problem of anomalies in supergravity one must solve the consistency equation (2.b) where s is the BRS operator of the full theory and includes therefore local supersymmetry transformations. Since the anomaly equation (2.b) only makes sense when $s^2 = 0$, i.e. when the infinitesimal gauge transformations build a closed system with a Jacobi identity, a completely meaningfull analysis can only be done in those (unfortunately seldom) cases in which the auxiliary field structure is known which allows one to construct s with $s^2 = 0$. By noting, however that an "off-shell" solution to the consistency equation $s\Delta^1_m + d\Delta^2_{m-1} = 0$ implies the existence of an "on-shell" solution (by "on-shell" we mean that the auxiliary fields are eliminated through the equations of motion of an s-invariant action), one can guess and try possible anomaly candidates from an on-shell formulation, but it may happen that these anomaly candidates are no more solutions of the consistency equation, or become spurious, when the auxiliary fields are introduced.

An intriguing question is that of the survival of the "Franco-Russian" formula eqs.(1, 2) in supergravity, that is to say of the possibility of classifying effectively the anomalies in n dimensions from invariant d-exact (n+2)-forms when local supersymmetry is involved. In what follows I will show that the answer to that question is by no mean trivial, and that the link between anomalies and invariants in higher dimensions seems to be broken precisely because of local supersymmetry. I will use as an example the simplest N = 1, n = 4 Poincaré supergravity for which the BRS operator has been recently constructed. Then, by going to the superspace formalism and by displaying the decoupling between the super-diffeomorphisms and the internal symmetries, I will conjecture that no supersymmetry anomaly can exist which cannot be identified with an Adler-Bardeen anomaly of the Yang-Mills $\times$ Lorentz gauge fields, or an anomaly of the current of a boson p-form gauge field of the model.

The n = 4 , N = 1 super Poincaré case.

The complexity of the anomaly problem in supergravity appears already in the simplest case, n = 4 , N = 1. The BRS symmetry of this theory has been determined by Bellon and the author[4], with the auxiliary field structure of Sohnius and West (new minimal system)[6]. The method generalizes that sketched above for boson gauge fields in curved space. The gauge fields are now the Majorana gravitino $\Psi = \Psi_\mu dx^\mu$, the spin-connection $\omega^{ab} = \omega_\mu^{ab} dx^\mu$ the Abelian Chiral gauge field $A = A_\mu \, dx^\mu$ and an uncharged 2-form $B_2 = \frac{1}{2} B_{\mu\nu} dx^\mu_{\wedge} dx^\nu$. Their ghosts are respectively the commuting Majorana spinor χ , Ω^{ab}, c and the primary and secondary ghosts B_1^1 and B_0^2 . They are unified into $\tilde{\Psi} = \Psi + \chi$, $\tilde{\omega} = \omega + \Omega$, $\tilde{A} = A + \mathbf{c}$, $\tilde{B}_2 = B_2 + B_1^1 + B_0^2$. The "hat" quantities are defined as in eq. (4) in view of decoupling the diffeomorphisms from the rest of the supergravity symmetry. In particular $\hat{\chi} = \chi - i_\xi \Psi$. The Vielbein $e^a = e^a_\mu dx^\mu$ acquires a part with ghost number one as in gravity, with $\tilde{e} = e^a + i_\xi e^a$, which is equivalent to $\hat{e}^a = e^a$. As a result of the analysis of ref.(3), the full BRS operator s of the theory is determined uniquely and consistently, i.e. with $s^2 = 0$, from $\hat{e}^a = e^a$ and from the following constraints on the generalized field strengths

$$\hat{T}^a \equiv \hat{d}\, e^a + \hat{\omega}^{ab} e^b + \frac{1}{2} \bar{\hat{\Psi}} \gamma^a \hat{\Psi} = T^a = - \frac{1}{2} G^a_{bc} e^b e^c$$

$$\hat{\rho} \equiv \hat{d}\, \hat{\Psi} + (\hat{\omega} + \hat{A})\, \hat{\Psi} = \rho$$

$$\hat{G}_3 \equiv \hat{d}\,\hat{B}_2 + \frac{1}{2}\,\hat{\bar{\Psi}}\,\gamma^a\hat{\Psi}\,e^a = G_3$$
$$\hat{R}^{ab} \equiv \hat{d}\,\hat{\omega}^{ab} + \hat{\omega}^{ac}\,\hat{\omega}^{cb} = R^{ab} - 2\hat{\bar{\chi}}\,\gamma^{[a}Y^{b]} - \frac{1}{2}\,\hat{\bar{\chi}}\,\gamma^c\,\hat{\chi}\,G_c^{ab}$$
$$\hat{F} \equiv \hat{d}\,\hat{A} = F - \frac{1}{2}\,\hat{\bar{\chi}}\,\gamma^5\gamma^a\,Y_a - \frac{1}{24}\,\hat{\bar{\chi}}\,\gamma^a\,\hat{\chi}\,\epsilon_{abcd}\,G^{bcd} \qquad (6.a)$$

Here $\rho = \frac{1}{2}\rho_{ab}\,e^a e^b$; $G_3 = \frac{1}{6}G_{abc}\,e^a e^b e^c$; $Y_a = \rho_{ab}\,e^b - (G_{abc}\sigma^{bc} + \frac{1}{12}\epsilon_{abcd}\,G^{bcd}\gamma_5)\psi$;
one has also :

$$\hat{d} \equiv d + \hat{s} + i_\varphi, \quad \hat{s} \equiv s - L_\xi, \quad L_\xi = i_\xi d - d\, i_\xi$$
$$\varphi^\mu = \frac{1}{2}\,\hat{\bar{\chi}}\,\gamma^\mu\,\hat{\chi}, \quad \gamma^a = e^a_\mu\,\gamma^\mu \qquad (6.b)$$

One still has that $\hat{d} = (\exp -i_\xi)\,\tilde{d}\,(\exp i_\xi)$, with $\tilde{d} = d + s$, but the novel feature, characteristic of local supersymmetry, is the appearance in the transformation laws of a vectorfield with ghost number 2, $\varphi^\mu = \frac{1}{2}\hat{\bar{\chi}}\gamma^\mu\hat{\chi}$. The use of the "hat" variables has still allowed one to express the symmetry without an explicit dependence in the ghost of diffeomorphisms ξ^μ , but the equation $\hat{T} = T$ determines the (expected) relation between local diffeomorphisms and local supersymmetry

$$s\,\xi^\mu = \xi^\alpha\partial_\alpha\,\xi^\mu + \frac{1}{2}\,\hat{\bar{\chi}}\,\gamma^\mu\,\hat{\chi} \qquad (6.c)$$

The rest of the BRS equations is easy to obtain by expansion of eq.(6.a) in ghost number, but there is no point to display their form here. They can be found in ref. (4).

The striking feature is thus that the BRS symmetry of supergravity can be constructed purely geometrically, that is to say independently of the notion of a Lagrangian or of the Noether method, as resulting from constraints in the space of unified ghost and classical gauge fields, eqs.(6). The difference with the case without local supersymmetry, however, is that the horizontality of field strengths like $\hat{F}$ and $\hat{R}$, which are independent of $\hat{\Psi}$, is distorted by terms proportional to the gravitino ghost χ . This distortion is indeed necessary to enforce the variance of A and ω under local SUSY, which is compulsory because of the relation (6.c) between the diffeomorphisms, under which all fields vary, and the local SUSY transformations. Technically speaking, we have determined these distortion terms in eq.(6.a) by requiring that the constraints on the generalized field strengths be compatible with dimensionality and Bianchi identities. The latter are indeed equivalent to $\hat{d}^2 = 0$, and thus to $\tilde{d}^2 = s^2 = 0$, owing to the identity $\hat{d} = (\exp -i_\xi)\,\tilde{d}\,(\exp i_\xi)$.[4)]

In the BRS symmetry equations (6) each one of the gauge fields has to be considered as a fundamental entity, as gauging part of the full symmetry. The notion of an "auxiliary" field is not contained in the geometry. It is only when one builds a s-invariant action by using eq.(6), such as [4, 6]

$$I_4 = \int \left(\tfrac{1}{4}\epsilon_{abcd}\, e^a e^b R^{cd} + \bar{\psi}\gamma^5\gamma^a \rho\, e^a - 2\,BF + \tfrac{1}{6}(^*G)G \right) \tag{7}$$

that one can interpret B_2 and A as "auxiliary fields", since the equations of motion from I_4 imply that $G_3 = 0$, $F = 0$, and thus that A and B_2 are pure gauges. The symmetry carried by A and B_2 is nevertheless essential since it leads to I_4, in turn equivalent to the on-shell N = 1 , n = 4 supergravity action. Anomalies in the current of A and B_2 would therefore make the supergravity inconsistent, although these fields can be eliminated on-shell at the tree level.

The necessary distortion of the horizontality of certain field strengths in the component formalism turns out to be a great source of complication for the study of the anomaly equation $s\Delta_4^1 + d\Delta_3^2 = 0$. One finds indeed that the link between existing invariant 6 -forms I_6 (F, R, G,...) and an admissible solution Δ_4^1 appears as broken. The only $\hat{d}$-exact 6-forms made from $\hat{F}$, $\hat{R}$, $\hat{G}$, $\hat{T}$, $\hat{e}$, $\hat{\rho}$, are in fact

$$\hat{I}_6 = \hat{F}\hat{F}\hat{F} = \hat{d}\,\hat{\Delta}_5\,, \quad \hat{\Delta}_5 = \hat{A}\hat{F}\hat{F} \tag{8}$$

$$\hat{I}'_6 = \hat{F}\,\mathrm{Tr}(\hat{R}\hat{R}) = \hat{d}\,\Delta'_5\,, \quad \hat{\Delta}'_5 = \hat{A}\,\mathrm{Tr}(\hat{R}\hat{R}) \sim \hat{F}\,\mathrm{Tr}(\hat{\omega}\hat{d}\hat{\omega} + \tfrac{2}{3}\hat{\omega}\hat{\omega}\hat{\omega})$$

By expansion in ghost number one finds that neither $(\hat{\Delta}_5)_4^1$ nor $(\hat{\Delta}'_5)_4^1$ is a solution of the anomaly equation. In fact using the BRS symmetry eqs.(6), one gets

$$\hat{s}\,(\hat{\Delta}_5)_4^1 + d\,(\hat{\Delta}_5)_3^2 = 3\,F_0^2\,F\,F + 3\,F_1^1\,F_1^1\,F \tag{9}$$

$$\hat{s}\,(\hat{\Delta}'_5)_4^1 + d\,(\hat{\Delta}'_5)_3^2 = 2\,F_1^1\,\mathrm{Tr}(R_1^1\,R) + F_0^2\,\mathrm{Tr}(RR) + F\,\mathrm{Tr}(R_1^1\,R_1^1 + 2RR_0^2)$$

Using the form of s, deduced from eq.(6.a) , we have found no possibility of adding $\hat{s}$- or d-exact forms to $(\hat{\Delta}_5)_4^1$ or $(\hat{\Delta}'_5)_4^1$ which would compensate for the R.h.s. of eq.(9), while not obtaining a spurious solution, that is to say a $\hat{s}$- or d-exact term. Notice that the terms which break the equation $\hat{s}\Delta_4^1 + d\Delta_3^2 = 0$ all come from the distortion terms necessary to implement consistently the local supersymmetry in eq.(6). In that sense, local supersymmetry prevents the appearance of an anomaly in the current of the chiral gauge field A_μ . From a physical point of view, this result is rather satisfactory since other systems of auxiliary fields exist which lead to the same on-shell supergravity as the action (7), but which do not include the chiral gauge field A .

By coupling chiral fermions to the supergravity multiplet one might attempt to check the absence of anomalies from the one loop computation of the vertices $\langle \partial^\mu A_\mu, F_{\nu\rho}, F_{\sigma\tau}\rangle$ and $\langle \partial^\mu A_\mu, R^{ab}_{\nu\rho}, R^{ab}_{\sigma\tau}\rangle$ which correspond to Δ_5 and Δ'_5 in eq.(8). Such a computation is however quite tedious, since the coupling between A_μ and $B_{\rho\sigma}$ is non diagonal, as seen in eq.(7), and moreover the full couplings between the chiral fermions and $B_{\mu\nu}$ are needed. The non existence of an anomaly part should result from a cancellation between the anomalous part of the fermion triangle and a vertex related to the A and B interaction. As we shall see the situation is clarified in the superfield formalism.

Superfield approach to the anomaly problem.

In the component formalism, there is no essential difference between the gravitino and the other 1-form gauge fields. One must consider the possibility of having anomalies in the SUSY current, i.e. solutions of the consistency equation $\hat{s}\Delta^1_n + d\Delta^2_{n-1} = 0$ with a dependence on the gravitino ghost $\hat{\chi}$

$$\Delta^1_n = \hat{\chi}\,\Delta_n\,(\text{classical fields}) + \cdots \tag{10}$$

The dots stand for terms proportional to the ghosts $\hat{\Omega}, \hat{c}, \hat{B}^1_1, \ldots$. The point we want to make is that there cannot exist an anomaly with the type (10) which cannot be determined from an anomaly in the current of a boson gauge field. The argument is similar to the one which shows that there is no anomaly proportional to the ghost of the diffeomorphisms which does not correspond to an anomaly in a Yang-Mills field or in a p-form gauge field, but it must be generalized in superspace.

The key observation is that the BRS symmetry of a supergravity can also be derived in superspace from undistorted horizontality conditions within a unified ghost-classical superfield formalism. To be specific, consider again the N=1, n=4 supergravity. In superspace the superfields are the supervielbein $E^A = dz^M E^A_M$, the super spin-connection $\boldsymbol{\omega}^{AB} = dz^M \boldsymbol{\omega}^{AB}_M$, an Abelian 1-form superfield $\mathbf{A} = dz^M \mathbf{A}_M$ and an uncharged super 2-form $\mathbf{B}_2 = \frac{1}{2} dz^M dz^N \mathbf{B}_{MN}$. The ghosts in the superspace are defined as the parts with ghost number 1 of the generalized ghost-classical super-forms :

$$\begin{aligned} \tilde{\omega}^{AB} &= \omega^{AB} + \Omega^{AB} &&= (\exp i_{\xi})\hat{\omega}^{AB} \\ \tilde{A} &= A + C &&= (\exp i_{\xi})\hat{A} \\ \tilde{B}_2 &= B_2 + B^1_1 + B^2_0 &&= (\exp i_{\xi})\hat{B}_2 \\ \tilde{E}^A &= E^A + i_{\xi}E^A &&\Leftrightarrow \hat{E}^A = E^A \end{aligned} \quad (11.a)$$

ξ^M is the superghost for the super-diffeomorphisms. In a superfield expansion ξ^M contains the ghost of the space-time diffeomorphisms ξ^μ and the components $\xi^\alpha, \xi^{\dot\alpha}$ of the Majorana gravitino ghost χ .

The super-space exterior derivative is $d = dz^M \partial_M$ and we define $\tilde{d} = d + s$ from the BRS operator s acting on superfields. The grading of the generalized ghost-classical superforms is clearly defined as the sum of the ghost number and the rank of superforms. The same algebraïc properties as in the component formalism lead us to define $\hat{d}=d+\hat{s}$, $\hat{s}=s-L_{\xi}$, $L_{\xi}=i_{\xi}d-di_{\xi}$. The generalized superfield strengths are

$$\begin{aligned} \hat{R}^{AB} &= \hat{d}\,\hat{\omega}^{AB} + \hat{\omega}^{AC}\hat{\omega}^{CB} \\ \hat{T}^A &= \hat{d}\,E^A + \hat{\omega}^{AB}E^B \\ F &= d\,A \\ G_3 &= d\,B_2 \end{aligned} \quad (11.b)$$

It turns out that s is defined consistently, i.e. with $s^2=0$, from the ghost expansion of the following constraints

$$\hat{E} = E, \quad \hat{T}^A = T^A, \quad \hat{R}^{AB} = R^{AB}, \quad \hat{F} = F, \quad \hat{G}_3 = G_3 \quad (12)$$

One finds in particular $s\xi^M = \xi^N \partial_N \xi^M$ from $\hat{T}=T$ and one can verify that this gives back by a superfield expansion the same definition of $s\xi^\mu$ and $s\chi$, as in eq. (6). This construction of s is algebraïcally identical to that of the BRS symmetry of a system of purely bosonic p-form gauge fields. It is therefore consistent for the same reasons, and one gets that $\hat{s}^2=0 \Leftrightarrow s^2=0$ on all the superfields. Now comes the point to verify that the full superfield expansion of eq.(12) determines also consistently the BRS symmetry operator s in components. If one knows a system of classical superfield constraints, it is in fact possible and meaningful to impose them after the determination of the BRS symmetry in superspace from eq.(12). This procedure is justified because the superfield constraints are compatible with the Bianchi identities, as the BRS constraints (12) are. As an example, using the constraints of Grimm et al.[7], one can verify that eqs.(12) give back eq.(6). As a bonus, using other systems of auxiliary fields, by applying the corresponding superfield constraints in eq.(12), one derives directly the associated BRS symmetry in components. As expected, the ξ^μ and χ dependence of the BRS variations of fields, as determined from eq.(6), is systematically recovered from the superfield expansion of E^A and ξ^M.

If we now study the anomaly equation $s\Delta^1_4 + d\Delta^2_3$ in superspace, one finds from the same algebraïc arguments as for a boson gauge field system in curved space that Δ^1_4 has only a non spurious dependence on Ω, C, B^1_1, but not in ξ^M. By expansion in components, one can therefore only get anomalies which depend on $\hat{\chi}$ in a way which is fully determined from the already known dependence on $\hat{\Omega}$, $\hat{B}^1_1$, $\hat{C}$. It follows that the anomaly cancellation condition for the diagrams with external-legs in $\partial^\mu \omega_\mu^{ab}$, $\partial^\mu A_\mu$ or $\partial^\mu B_{\mu\nu}$ in the N = 1, n = 4 case, which would correspond respectively to solutions Δ^1_4 proportional to $\hat{\Omega}^{ab}$, $\hat{C}$ or $\hat{B}^1_1$, are sufficient to make the theory anomaly free. Our conjecture is that this result holds true for all supergravities, which means that the structure of anomalies is determined from d -exact forms of rank n+2 in superspace, and also that the anomalies in the gravitino current correspond effectively to anomalies in the super -diffeomorphisms, which can be shifted away by mean of redefinitions of super-ghosts.

As a physical application, one can predict that a supergravity model is anomaly free as soon as one has verified the cancellation of the (easy to classify) anomalies in the current of the boson gauge fields of the theory.

The absence of anomaly in the Poincaré N=1 n=4 supergravity can now be understood in a strikingly simple way in superspace. From the system of field strengths (11) and the BRS equations (12), the form of the anomaly is determined as $\Delta_5 = \hbar(\alpha A F F + \beta F\,\mathrm{Tr}(\omega d\omega + \frac{2}{3}\omega\omega\omega))$, where α and β are numbers. If we modify the field strength $\hat{G}_3$ into

$$\hat{G}_3 = \hat{d}\,\hat{B}_2 + \hbar(\alpha\hat{A}\,F + \beta\,\mathrm{Tr}(\hat{\omega}\,\hat{d}\hat{\omega} + \tfrac{2}{3}\hat{\omega}\hat{\omega}\hat{\omega})) \qquad (13)$$

which implies a distortion of order $\hbar$ of the algebra of gauge transformations determined by $\hat{G} = G_3$, we get that the anomaly candidate $\hat{\Delta}_5$ is spurious since

$$\hat{\Delta}_5 = -\,\hat{d}(\hat{B}_2\hat{F}) + \hat{F}\,\hat{G}_3 \qquad (14)$$

Indeed the new BRS equation $\hat{G}=G_3$, together with $\hat{F} = F$, implies that the anomaly candidate $(\Delta_5)^1_4$ equates $(\hat{d}(\hat{B}_2 F))^1_4$ (since $\hat{F}\hat{G}_3=FG_3 \Rightarrow (\hat{F}\hat{G}_3)^1_4 = 0$) and is thus spurious as a $\hat{d}$ exact term. In field theory, this means that the would be anomaly is eliminated by a renormalization of the term $F \wedge B_2$ in the action (7).

REFERENCES

1) See the other contributions to this conference.

2) L. Baulieu, Cargèse Lectures July 1983, LPTHE preprint 84/04;
R. Stora, Cargèse Lectures September 1983;
B. Zumino, Les Houches Lectures July 1983.

3) L. Baulieu, J. Thierry-Mieg, Phys. Lett. 145B (1984) 53;
F. Langouche, T. Shücker, R. Stora, Phys. Lett. 145B (1984) 342.

4) L. Baulieu, M. Bellon, LPTENS preprint 85/05 and 85/09, submitted to Phys. Lett.B and Nucl. Phys.B.

5) B. Bardeen, B. Zumino, to appear in Nucl.Phys.B; see also
L. Alvarez-Gaume, P. Ginsparg, to appear in Annals of Physics and refs. therein.

6) M.F. Sohnius, P.C. West, Phys. Lett. 105B (1981) 353.

7) See G. Girardi, R. Grimm, J. Wess, LAPP preprint and refs. therein.

HOLONOMY ANOMALIES*

JONATHAN BAGGER†
Lyman Laboratory of Physics
Harvard University, Cambridge, Massachusetts, 02138

DENNIS NEMESCHANSKY AND SHIMON YANKIELOWICZ‡
Stanford Linear Accelerator Center
Stanford University, Stanford, California, 94305

Nonlinear sigma models and low-energy effective Lagrangians play an important role in modern particle physics. They were first discussed in the context of chiral dynamics, where they were used to describe the nonlinear interactions of Goldstone bosons. More recently, they have been used to investigate non-perturbative effects in gauge theories, to give a geometrical interpretation to matter couplings in supergravity theories, and even to provide a convenient framework for analyzing the possible compactifications of superstring theories.

In this talk we discuss a new type of anomaly that afflicts certain non-linear sigma models with fermions [1–4]. This anomaly is similar to the ordinary gauge and gravitational anomalies since it reflects a topological obstruction to the reparametrization invariance of the quantum effective action. However, the sigma model anomaly is different in one important respect – it can sometimes be cancelled by a set of local counterterms [3,4]. We will show that these counterterms have a simple topological interpretation, and that the anomaly cancellation requirements can easily be understood by a suitable generalization of 't Hooft's anomaly matching conditions [5].

In the first half of this talk, we construct nonlinear sigma models based on homogeneous spaces G/H. Following Callan, Coleman, Wess and Zumino [6], we add fermions to these models, where the fermions transform in various representations ρ_H of H.

* Work supported by the Department of Energy, contract DE-AC03-76SF00515, and by the National Science Foundation, contract NSF-PHY-82-15249.

† On leave of absence from Stanford Linear Accelerator Center, Stanford University, Stanford, California, 94305.

‡ On leave of absence from the Department of Physics, Tel-Aviv University, Israel.

Anomalies arise when these fermions are chiral. We shall show that these anomalies can sometimes be cancelled by Chern-Simons terms.

In the second half of this talk we consider nonlinear sigma models based on general Riemannian manifolds $\mathcal{M}$. We now take the fermions to live in the tangent space of $\mathcal{M}$. As before, the sigma model anomalies can sometimes be cancelled by appropriate Chern-Simons terms.

Sigma models on homogeneous spaces G/H describe the interactions of the Goldstone bosons that arise by spontaneously breaking a group G down to a subgroup H. The Goldstone bosons can interact with fermions χ^A. The fermions form representations of H, and realize the full G-symmetry nonlinearly [6]. The sigma model Lagrangian is given by

$$\mathcal{L} \;=\; -\,\frac{1}{2}\,g_{ij}(\phi)\,\partial_\mu\phi^i\partial^\mu\phi^j \;-\; \frac{i}{2}\,\overline{\chi}_{LA}\gamma^\mu D_\mu\chi_L{}^A\;, \tag{1}$$

where the covariant derivative $D_\mu\chi^A$ is given by $D_\mu\chi^A = \partial_\mu\chi^A + \partial_\mu\phi^i\,\omega_i{}^A{}_B\chi^B$, and the connection $\partial_\mu\phi^i\,\omega_i{}^A{}_B$ is the pull-back to spacetime of an appropriate connection on G/H.

The most instructive way to think of the manifold G/H is as a *section* of a fiber bundle $\mathcal{E}$, with total space G and fiber H. This section is parametrized by the group element $g = \exp i\phi^i T^i$, where the T^i denote the generators of G that are not in H. In these coordinates, the metric $g_{ij} = \mathrm{Tr}[(g^{-1}\partial_i g)|_K(g^{-1}\partial_j g)|_K]$, where $g^{-1}\partial_i g$ is projected onto $K = G/H$. The fermions χ^A also have a bundle interpretation. They should be thought of as sections of a vector bundle $\mathcal{F}$ associated to $\mathcal{E}$. The fermion connection $\omega_i{}^A{}_B$ is given by the associated H-connection $\omega_i{}^A{}_B = \rho_H[(g^{-1}\partial_i g)|_H]^A{}_B$.

The symmetries of $\mathcal{L}$ are associated with the isometries of the manifold G/H. They are generated by global G-rotations. These transformations rotate points in the bundle $\mathcal{E}$. In particular, they take elements g of G/H into elements kg of $\mathcal{E}$. The transformed elements kg are not necessarily in the section G/H. They must be projected back by field-dependent H-transformations $h(g,k)$, such that $kgh \in G/H$. Under these H-rotations $\omega_i{}^A{}_B$ transforms like a connection. The Lagrangian $\mathcal{L}$ is invariant provided the fermions χ^A transform like tensors, $\chi^A \to \rho_H(h)^A{}_B\chi^B$.

Since the induced H-rotations are local, anomalies arise at the quantum level if the fermions χ^A transform in anomalous representations of H. In four dimensions, the variation of the effective action is given by [7]

$$\delta\Gamma = \frac{1}{24\pi^2}\int d^4x\, \epsilon^{\mu\nu\rho\sigma}\ \mathrm{Tr}\,\epsilon\,\partial_i\left[\omega_j\partial_k\omega_\ell + \frac{1}{2}\omega_j\omega_k\omega_\ell\right] \times\ \partial_\mu\phi^i\partial_\nu\phi^j\partial_\rho\phi^k\partial_\sigma\phi^\ell\,, \qquad (2)$$

where $h = 1+\epsilon$, and the trace is over the fermion representation ρ_H. The anomaly (2) is similar to an ordinary anomaly since it obstructs the invariance of the quantum effective action. In a gauge or gravitational theory, such an obstruction is fatal – unitarity is lost and unphysical degrees of freedom begin to propagate. In a sigma model, the anomaly is more subtle. This is because the gauge fields are composite – they are functions of the scalar fields ϕ^i. Sigma model anomalies do not create any new degrees of freedom. They merely break some of the symmetries and the geometrical interpretation associated with the classical action. For the case at hand, the anomaly breaks all symmetries in G that are not in H.

Sigma models with anomalies are unacceptable for physical reasons. Therefore we would like to know when – if ever – the anomaly can be cancelled. One way to cancel the anomaly is well-known from gauge theories: One simply adds extra spinors so that the fermionic determinant is well-defined. In practical terms, this means that the fermions must transform in an anomaly-free representation of H. In a sigma model, there is a second approach. One can add local counterterms to the effective action in just such a way that the anomaly is cancelled. Both the effective action and the counterterms transform anomalously under H, but the sum remains invariant.

What counterterms must one add to cancel the sigma model anomaly? The answer is obvious: In four dimensions, one simply adds an integral over the five-dimensional Chern-Simons term $\Omega_{ijk\ell m}(\omega)$ [8],

$$
\begin{aligned}
I &= -\,2\pi \int_D d^5y\ \epsilon^{ijk\ell m}\,\Omega_{ijk\ell m}(\omega) \\
&= -\,\frac{1}{120\pi^2}\int_D d^5y\ \epsilon^{ijk\ell m}\ \mathrm{Tr}\left[\omega_i\partial_j\omega_k\partial_\ell\omega_m + \frac{3}{2}\,\omega_i\omega_j\omega_k\partial_\ell\omega_m \right. \\
&\qquad \left. + \frac{3}{5}\,\omega_i\omega_j\omega_k\omega_\ell\omega_m\right] .
\end{aligned}
\tag{3}
$$

The integral I runs over a five-dimensional disk D whose boundary ∂D is the image of spacetime in $\mathcal{E}$ [9]. The variation of I exactly cancels the sigma model anomaly,

$$
\begin{aligned}
\delta I &= -\,\frac{1}{120\pi^2}\int_D d^5y\,\epsilon^{ijk\ell m}\partial_i\ \mathrm{Tr}\left[\epsilon\,\partial_j\left(\omega_k\partial_\ell\omega_m + \frac{1}{2}\,\omega_k\omega_\ell\omega_k\right)\right] \\
&= -\,\frac{1}{24\pi^2}\int d^4x\ \epsilon^{\mu\nu\rho\sigma}\ \mathrm{Tr}\,\epsilon\,\partial_i\left[\omega_j\partial_k\omega_\ell + \frac{1}{2}\,\omega_j\omega_k\omega_\ell\right] \\
&\qquad \times\ \partial_\mu\phi^i\partial_\nu\phi^j\partial_\rho\phi^k\partial_\sigma\phi^\ell .
\end{aligned}
\tag{4}
$$

The coefficient $-1/120\pi^2$ was chosen to cancel the anomaly (2). It is also precisely the right coefficient to ensure that the effective action is independent of D.

The counterterm (3) is written as an integral over a disk D. Lagrangian mechanics, however, requires that an action be written as an integral over spacetime. Equation (3) can be pulled back to an integral over spacetime whenever the Chern-Simons term is closed, $d\Omega = 0$. Then $\Omega = d\alpha$ locally, and

$$
\begin{aligned}
-\,\frac{1}{2\pi}\,I &= \int_D d^5y\ \epsilon^{ijk\ell m}\ \Omega_{ijk\ell m} \\
&= 5\int_{\partial D} d^4y\ \epsilon^{ijk\ell}\ \alpha_{ijk\ell} \\
&= 5\int d^4x\,\epsilon^{\mu\nu\rho\sigma}\ \alpha_{ijk\ell}\,\partial_\mu\phi^i\partial_\nu\phi^j\partial_\rho\phi^k\partial_\sigma\phi^\ell .
\end{aligned}
\tag{5}
$$

It is easy to show that $d\Omega = \mathrm{Tr}\,R^3$, where the curvature $R = d\omega + \omega^2$. We have shown that the sigma model anomaly can be cancelled by local counterterms whenever

$\mathrm{Tr}\, R^3 = 0$. This result can be generalized to any even dimension. In $2n-2$ dimensions, the anomaly is cancelled by the $(2n-1)$-dimensional Chern-Simons term, provided $\mathrm{Tr}\, R^n = 0$.

There are two cases when this condition is automatically satisfied. The first is when $\dim \mathcal{E} \leq 2n-1$. Then $\mathrm{Tr}\, R^n$ automatically vanishes since there are no $2n$-forms on $\mathcal{E}$. The second is when $\mathrm{Tr}\, R^n$ vanishes in any fermionic representation. In two dimensions this happens for symmetric spaces, as can be seen from the commutation relations of the Lie al ebras.

If $\mathrm{Tr}\, R^n \neq 0$, all is not lost, for the connection used to construct the Chern-Simons term is not unique. One can always add a tensor τ to the connection ω. Since τ is a tensor, $\omega' = \omega + \tau$ is a connection, and τ is called torsion. To see how this works, let us restrict ourselves to two dimensions. Instead of the H-connection $\omega = \rho_H[(g^{-1}dg)|_H]$, let us consider the G-connection $\omega' = \rho_G[g^{-1}dg]$. This connection is only defined when the fermion representations ρ_H form G-representations ρ_G. Since $\rho_G[g^{-1}dg] = \rho_G[(g^{-1}dg)|_K] + \rho_G[(g^{-1}dg)|_H]$, we see that the torsion $\tau = \rho_G[(g^{-1}dg)|_K]$. The G-connection clearly satisfies the trace condition since $R' = d\omega' + \omega'^2 = 0$. The corresponding integrated Chern-Simons term takes a very simple form,

$$
\begin{aligned}
I &= -\,2\pi \int_D d^3y\, \epsilon^{ijk}\, \Omega_{ijk} \\
&= \frac{i}{12\pi} \int_D d^3y\, \epsilon^{ijk}\, \mathrm{Tr}\left(\omega'_i \omega'_j \omega'_k\right) .
\end{aligned}
\tag{6}
$$

Its variation is precisely the two-dimensional anomaly,

$$
\begin{aligned}
\delta I &= -\,\frac{i}{12\pi} \int_D d^3y\, \epsilon^{ijk} \partial_i\, \mathrm{Tr}\left(\epsilon\, \partial_j \omega'_k\right) \\
&= -\,\frac{i}{12\pi} \int_D d^3y\, \epsilon^{ijk} \partial_i\, \mathrm{Tr}\left(\epsilon\, \partial_j \omega_k\right) \\
&= -\,\frac{i}{4\pi} \int d^2x\, \epsilon^{\mu\nu}\, \mathrm{Tr}\left(\epsilon\, \partial_i \omega_j\right)\, \partial_\mu \phi^i \partial_\nu \phi^j ,
\end{aligned}
\tag{7}
$$

where we have used the fact that ϵ belongs to H. Therefore (6) cancels the anomaly of the effective action.

In higher dimensions, the G-connection can also be used to cancel the sigma model anomaly. The variation of the Chern-Simons term cancels the anomaly up to local counterterms [4]. These extra counterterms do not appear in two dimensions. The anomaly matching conditions, however, remain unchanged.

Actually, it is not necessary for the fermion representations ρ_H to form complete G-representations ρ_G. All that is necessary is for the two representations to give the *same* anomalous variation of I. A general representation ρ_G of G decomposes into a sum of representations of H. To cancel the anomaly, these representations must include the fermion representations ρ_H. The other representations must be anomaly-free under H.

This condition for anomaly cancellation is precisely the 't Hooft matching condition [6]. It implies that the nonlinear sigma model can be thought of as a low-energy effective Lagrangian corresponding to an underlying preonic theory. The fermions in the underlying theory form representations ρ_G of a global symmetry group G. If G is spontaneously broken to H, the low-energy theory is a nonlinear sigma model on the manifold G/H, with the fermions transforming in representations ρ_H of H. The fermions in the two theories are related by a chiral G-rotation. This change of variables gives rise to a Jacobian that is precisely the Chern-Simons term. Since the preonic theory is globally G-invariant, the H-anomalies of the nonlinear sigma model cancel between the Chern-Simons term and the low-energy fermions [3,4].

If the 't Hooft condition cannot be satisfied, there is no connection ω' such that $\operatorname{Tr} R'^n = 0$. The sigma model anomaly cannot be cancelled, and the nonlinear model does not correspond to any underlying preonic theory. Since the curvature R generates the holonomy group of G/H, we say that such a sigma model suffers from a *holonomy anomaly.*

Within the context of chiral dynamics, it is natural for fermions to transform in representations ρ_H of H. Other choices, of course, are possible. In supersymmetric models, for example, fermions are sections of the tangent bundle $\mathcal{T}$ to $\mathcal{M} = G/H$. More generally, fermions can be sections of vector bundles $\mathcal{U}$ associated to $\mathcal{T}$. In this case the fermions form representations $\rho_{\mathcal{H}}$ of the structure group $\mathcal{H}$ of the tangent bundle $\mathcal{T}$.

If the fermions are to transform in *any* representation of $\mathcal{H}$, it is necessary to introduce an orthonormal frame $e_i{}^a$ on G/H. The orthonormal frame, or vielbein, depends on the coordinates ϕ^i. It gives an orthonormal basis in the tangent space at each point of G/H. The Lagrangian for the sigma model is again given by equation (1). The only difference is that the connection $\omega_i{}^A{}_B$ is valued in the Lie algebra of the structure group $\mathcal{H}$, rather than in the Lie algebra of the isotropy group H. The connection $\omega_i{}^A{}_B$ is just the spin connection in the fermion representation $\rho_{\mathcal{H}}$.

The classical sigma model action is invariant under general coordinate transformations ξ^i, and under local frame rotations L^{ab}. The coordinate transformations are analogous to global G-transformations, and the frame rotations correspond to the compensating H-projections. This can be seen by choosing a frame in which the vielbeins are symmetric in i and a. In this frame, general coordinate transformations must be accompanied by gauge-restoring local frame rotations,

$$\delta e_i{}^a = \partial_i \xi^j e_j{}^a + L^{ab} e_{ib} , \tag{8}$$

where $L^{ab} = \frac{1}{2} e^{ja} e^{kb} (\partial_j \xi_k - \partial_k \xi_j)$. The frame rotation L^{ab} induces field-dependent frame transformations on the spinors χ and on the connection ω. If the fermions are in anomalous representations of $\mathcal{H}$, the effective action is not invariant under diffeomorphisms.

As before, the holonomy anomaly can sometimes be cancelled a Chern-Simons term formed from the connection $\omega_i{}^A{}_B$. If $\operatorname{Tr} R^n = 0$, the Chern-Simons term can be pulled back to spacetime, and Lagrangian mechanics is well-defined. If $\operatorname{Tr} R^n \neq 0$, one must modify the connection by adding torsion.

On a group G one can always find a connection ω' such that $R' = 0$. This follows from the fact that every group manifold is parallelizable. The connection ω' is valued in the Lie algebra of the structure group $\mathcal{G}$ of G. Since G/H can be locally embedded in G, the connection ω' differs from ω by torsion. The connection ω' can be used to cancel the anomaly provided the fermion representations $\rho_{\mathcal{H}}$ can be completed to representations $\rho_{\mathcal{G}}$ of $\mathcal{G}$. This is the appropriate generalization of the 't Hooft matching condition to the present case.

It is now obvious how to cancel the anomaly for a general Riemannian manifold $\mathcal{M}$. As before, the fermions form representations $\rho_{\mathcal{H}}$ of the structure group $\mathcal{H}$ of the tangent bundle $\mathcal{T}$. If the fermions are anomalous, one must add a Chern-Simons term. The Chern-Simons term can be pulled back whenever $\mathrm{Tr}\, R^n = 0$. Otherwise one must modify the connection.

For manifolds $\mathcal{M} = G/H$, we were able to cancel the anomaly using the fact that there is a natural embedding of G/H in G. For a general Riemannian manifold $\mathcal{M}$, the story is almost the same [4]. We now use the fact that $\mathcal{M}$ can be isometrically embedded in a flat space of sufficiently high dimension d. As before, the spin connection ω on $\mathcal{M}$ can be extended to a connection ω' on $\mathbf{R}^d$ if the fermion representations $\rho_{\mathcal{H}}$ can be completed to representations $\rho_{\mathcal{G}}$ of $\mathcal{G} = O(d)$. Since $\mathbf{R}^d$ is flat, $R' = 0$, and the Chern-Simons term built from ω' can be pulled back to spacetime. It cancels the anomaly, up to local counterterms, and the sigma model on $\mathcal{M}$ is well-defined [4].

The purpose of this talk was to give a unified picture of sigma model anomalies. We have shown how the anomalies can be cancelled by Chern-Simons terms built out of appropriate connections ω'. When generalized 't Hooft conditions are satisfied, the Chern-Simons term can be pulled back to an integral over spacetime, and the effective action is well-defined.

---

[1] G. Moore and P. Nelson, Phys. Rev. Lett. 53 (1984) 1519; and Harvard preprint HUTP-84/A076.

[2] E. Cohen and C. Gomez, CERN-TH-4043 (1984); P. DiVecchia, S. Ferrara and L. Girardello, Phys. Lett. 151B (1985) 199.

[3] A. Manohar, G. Moore and P. Nelson, Phys. Lett. 152B (1985) 68.

[4] J. Bagger, D. Nemeschansky and S. Yankielowicz, SLAC-PUB-3588.

[5] C. Callan, S. Coleman, J. Wess and B. Zumino, Phys. Rev. 177 (1969) 2247.

[6] G. 't Hooft, in *Recent Developments in Gauge Theories*, eds. G. 't Hooft *et al.*, (Plenum, New York, 1980).

[7] W. Bardeen, Phys. Rev. 184 (1969) 1848.

[8] S. Chern and J. Simons, Proc. Nat. Acad. Sci. 68 (1971) 791.

[9] E. Witten, Nucl. Phys. B223 (1983) 422.

GENERALIZED CHERN-SIMONS CLASSES, CECH-DE RHAM COMPLEX AND GAUGE GROUP COHOMOLOGIES

Han-ying Guo

Institute of Theoretical Physics, Academia Sinica
P. O. Box 2735, Beijing, China*

and

Institute for Theoretical Physics
State University of New York at Stony Brook
Stony Brook, New York 11794, U.S.A.

In this contribution we shall briefly clarify our recent works on generalized Chern-Simons secondary characteristic classes[1)], relevant cohomologies of gauge groups including Cech-de Rham complex and their applications to cohomological analyses on the structure of anomalies[2)]. We shall also show that the cohomology of gauge groups proposed by Faddeev[3)] and used by Zumino[3)], Song[3)] and others is in fact a particular case of our approach.

As is well known[4)], Chern-Simons secondary polynomials, $Q^{(1)}_{2n-1}(A^0,A^1)$, associated to characteristic polynomials of degree n in the curvature, $P(F^n)$, satisfy the transgression formula

$$P(F^n(A^1)) - P(F^n(A^0)) = dQ^{(1)}_{2n-1}(A^0,A^1), \tag{1}$$

where A's are connection 1-forms, $Q^{(1)}_{2n-1}(A^0,A^1)$ a (2n-1)-form defined by

$$Q^{(1)}_{2n-1}(A^0,A^1) = n\int_0^1 dt\, P\{A^1-A^0, F^{n-1}(A^0 + t(A^1-A^0))\}. \tag{2}$$

It is a remarkable fact[1)] that (1) and (2) can be extended to more generic cases[**)]. Let us define the k-th polynomial $Q^{(k)}_{2n-k}(A^0,\ldots,A^k)$ w.r.t. k+1 ordered connection 1-forms be a (2n-k) form

---

* On leave from Academia Sinica.

**See also Song[3)]. We learn at this Symposium that Y.S. Wu presents similar generalization.

$$Q^{(k)}_{2n-k}(A^0,\ldots,A^k) = (-1)^{\frac{k}{2}(k-1)} \frac{n!}{k!(n-k)!} \int_{\Delta^k} P\{H_0^{\,k}, F^{n-k}(A^0 + \sum_{i=1}^{k} t^i(A^i - A^0))\},$$

$$Q^{(0)}_{2n}(A^0) = P(F^n(A^0)), \tag{3}$$

where $H_0 = \sum_{i=1}^{k} dt^i(A^i - A^0)$, $\Delta^k = \{(t^1,\ldots,t^k) \mid \sum_{i=1}^{k} t^i = 1,\ 0 \le t^i \le 1\}$

is a k-simplex, and introduce an operator, Δ, acting on $Q^{(k)}_{2n-k}$ in the following way

$$(\Delta Q^{(k)}_{2n-k})(A^0,\ldots,A^{k+1}) = \sum_{i=0}^{k+1} (-1)^i Q^{(k)}_{2n-k}(A^0,\ldots,\hat{A}^i,\ldots,A^{k+1}) \tag{4}$$

where the caret denotes omission, then one can prove a generic transgression formula

$$(\Delta Q^{(k)}_{2n-k})(A^0,\ldots,A^{k+1}) = dQ^{(k+1)}_{2n-k-1}(A^0,\ldots,A^{k+1}). \tag{5}$$

As in the case of Chern-Simons secondary classes, $Q^{(k)}_{2n-k}(A^0,\ldots,A^k)$ are globally defined and have topological meaning in their own right. We name them the k-th generalized Chern-Simons secondary classes. In fact, $Q^{(k)}_{2n-k}$ are invariant against gauge transformations $\mathcal{A}$ and each A can be regarded as a representative of an orbit in the connection space $\mathcal{G}$. In this sense, $Q^{(k)}_{2n-k}$ are defined on $\mathcal{A}/\mathcal{G}$ which may have nontrivial topology.

Notice that $\Delta^2 = 0$, i.e. Δ is a coboundary operator as the operator d does. Thus, (5) has profound cohomology meaning. On the one hand, integrals of $Q^{(k)}_{2n-k}$ over a (2n-k)-dimensional manifold M^{2n-k} satisfy

$$(\Delta \int_{M^{2n-k}} Q^{(k)}_{2n-k})(A^0,\ldots,A^{k+1}) = \int_{\partial M^{2n-k}} Q^{(k+1)}_{2n-k-1}(A^0,\ldots A^{k+1}) \tag{6}$$

and present certain gauge group cohomology, H_Δ, which reflects not only the topological property of M^{2n-k} but also that of the gauge group space[2]. On the other hand, (3) and (5) show that $Q^{(k)}_{2n-k}$ form a double complex equipped with two coboundary operators d and Δ. It is easy to show that these two operators can be combined into a single coboundary operator

$$D = \Delta + (-1)^k d, \tag{7}$$

and the combination of $Q^{(k)}_{2n-k}$

$$Q^*_{2r} = Q^{(0)}_{2r} + Q^{(1)}_{2r-1} - Q^{(2)}_{2r-2} + \ldots + (-1)^{[\frac{k}{2}]} Q^{(k)}_{2r-k} + \ldots + (-1)^{[\frac{r}{2}]} Q^{(r)}_{r}, \quad 2r \leq m = \dim M \tag{8}$$

is a cocycle w.r.t. D[5].

In addition to the coboundary operator Δ, there exists another coboundary operator $\bar{\Delta}$ acting on cochains $r^{(k)}$ in the following way

$$(\bar{\Delta} r^{(k)})(A^0, \ldots, A^{k+1}) = \sum_{i=1}^{k+1} (-1)^i r^{(k)}(A^0, \ldots, \hat{A}^i, \ldots A^{k+1}). \tag{9}$$

It is easy to check that

$$\bar{\Delta} r^{(k)} = \Delta r^{(k)} - r^{(k)} \cdot \pi, \quad (\bar{\Delta} r^{(k)}) \cdot \pi = -\Delta(r^{(k)} \cdot \pi) \tag{10}$$

where π is an exclusion operator, π: $(A^0, \ldots, A^k) \to (A^1, \ldots, A^k)$. It has been shown[2] that there exist certain polynomials $\bar{Q}^{(k)}$ consisting of $Q^{(k)}$ to solve the transgression equation for the operator $\bar{\Delta}$

$$(\bar{\Delta} \bar{Q}^{(k)}_{2n-k})(A^0, \ldots, A^{k+1}) = d\bar{Q}^{(k+1)}_{2n-k-1}(A^0, \ldots, A^{k+1}), \quad \bar{Q}^{(0)}_{2n} = Q^{(0)}_{2n} = P(F^n). \tag{11}$$

One set of solutions is

$$\begin{aligned} \bar{Q}^{(k)} &= Q^{(k)} - d^{-1}(\bar{Q}^{(k-1)} \cdot \pi + \Delta(Q^{(k-1)} - \bar{Q}^{(k-1)})) \\ &= Q^{(k)} - d^{-1}(Q^{(k-1)} \cdot \pi + \bar{\Delta}(Q^{(k-1)} - \bar{Q}^{(k-1)})), \quad k = 1,2,\ldots. \end{aligned} \tag{12}$$

where d^{-1} is an antiderivative operator acting only on the closed forms and satisfies $dd^{-1} = 1$, but $d^{-1}d = 1$ mod. exact forms, and in this sense one can make use of Cartan's homotopy operator k[6] to replace d^{-1}. It is plain that $\bar{Q}^{(k)}$-polynomials have also cohomology meaning: their integrals over $(2n-k)$-manifolds without boundaries present elements of cohomology group $H_{\bar{\Delta}}$ w.r.t. the coboundary operator $\bar{\Delta}$, and (12) and (13) form a double complex with two coboundary operators $\bar{\Delta}$ and d as well. This double complex can also be restructed as a single complex w.r.t. the combined coboundary operator

$$\bar{D} = \bar{\Delta} + (-1)^k d , \tag{13}$$

and the combination expression (8) for $\bar{Q}^{(k)}_{2r-k}$ gives rise to

$$\bar{Q}^*_{2r} = \bar{Q}^{(0)}_{2r} + \bar{Q}^{(1)}_{2r-1} - \ldots + (-1)^{[\frac{k}{2}]} Q^{(k)}_{2r-k} + \ldots \qquad 2r \leq m = \dim M, \tag{14}$$

which is a cocycle w.r.t. $\bar{D}$ [5].

Consider a set of such polynomials $\bar{Q}^{(k)}_{2r-k}$ that one connection, say A^0, is zero in an open set U_0. In this case, $\bar{Q}^{(k)}_{2r-k}$ can be regarded as local ones defined on the intersection $\bigsqcup \bigcap_{i=0}^{k-1} U_i$ and depended only on k connections rather than k+1 ones. Redenote A's and $(A^0,\ldots,A^{k-1})$ and $\bar{Q}^{(k)}_{2r-k}$ as $\omega^{(k-1)}_{2r-k}(A^0,\ldots,A^{k-1})$ the transgression equation w.r.t $\bar{\Delta}$ becomes

$$(\Delta\omega^{(k-1)}_{2r-k})(A^0,\ldots,A^k) = d\omega^{(k)}_{2r-k-1}(A^0,\ldots,A^k), \quad \omega^{(-1)}_{2r}(A^0) = P(F^r(A^0)). \tag{15}$$

It is plain that provided we introduce a mapping τ acting on a k-Cech simplex $|\sigma| = \bigcap_{i=0}^{k} U_i$, U_i is the ith open set on which A^i is defined such that $\tau\cdot(U_0,\ldots,U_k) = (A^0,\ldots,A^k)$, (15) can be considered as a Cech-de Rham double complex since

$$(\Delta\omega^{(k-1)}_{2r-k})(A^0,\ldots,A^k) = (\delta_c\, \omega^{(k-1)}_{2r-k}\cdot\tau))(U_0,\ldots,U_k) \tag{16}$$

where δ_c is the Cech coboundary operator[6]. Similarly, we can combine Δ and d to a single coboundary operator $\Delta + (-1)^{k-1}d$ and introduce the combination

$\omega^*_{2r} = \omega^{(-1)}_{2r} + \omega^{(0)}_{2r-1} - \ldots + (-1)^{[\frac{k-1}{2}]} \omega^{(k-1)}_{2r-k} + \ldots$ to be a cocycle w.r.t. $\Delta + (-1)^{k-1}d$.

If we take

$$A^i = A^{g_{1\ldots i}} = g^{-1}_{1\ldots i} A g_{1\ldots i} + g^{-1}_{1\ldots i} dg_{1\ldots i}, \quad g_0 = e, \quad g_{1\ldots i} = g_1 g_2 \cdots g_i \tag{17}$$

and denote $\omega^{(k-1)}_{2r-k}(A^0,\ldots,\hat{A}^i,\ldots,A^k)$ as $\omega^{(k-1)}_{2r-k}(A;g_1,\ldots,g_{ii+1},\ldots g_k)$, then the action of Δ is the same as of δ_F, the coboundary operator in Faddeev's approach, i.e.

$$(\Delta\omega^{(k-1)}_{2r-k})(A^0,\ldots,A^k) = (\delta_F\omega^{(k-1)}_{2r-k})(A;g_1,g_2,\ldots,g_k). \tag{18}$$

It should be emphasized that our approach can also be applied to the cohomological analyses on the structure of anomalies with more than one gauge field. To see this, we start with the abelian anomaly equation in 2n dimensions with both left and right hand gauge field

$$d^*J(U,A_L A_R) = P(F_L^n) - P(F_R^n) \tag{19}$$

where U is such a field that it transforms to $g_L U g_R^{-1}$ under gauge transformations $(g_L,g_R)\in G_L\times G_R$, and its covariant derivative is $DU = dU + A_L U - UA_R$. Taking $({}^U A_L, A_R)$, ${}^U A_L = U^{-1}dU + U^{-1}A_L U$, as (A^0,A^1) and using (3) and (5), we get a general formula for the covariant abelian anomalous current on M^{2n},

$$J(U,A_L,A_R) = -{}^*Q^{(1)}_{2n-1}({}^0A_L,A_R). \tag{20}$$

Taking $({}^U A_L,A_R,0)$ and $(UdU^{-1},A_L,0)$ as (A^0,A^1,A^2), then from (11) and (12), it follows that

$$Q^{(1)}({}^U A_L,A_R) - Q^{(1)}(A_L,0) + d^{-1}Q^{(0)}(A_L) - (A_L \leftrightarrow A_R,\ U \leftrightarrow U^{-1})$$

$$= d(Q^{(2)}({}^U A_L,A_R,0) + Q^{(2)}(A_L,UdU^{-1},0) - d^{-1}Q^{(1)}(UdU^{-1},0)) - (A_L \leftrightarrow A_R, U\leftrightarrow U^{-1}). \tag{21}$$

Thus, under the condition

$$Q^{(1)}_{2n-1}(A_L,0) - d^{-1}Q^{(0)}_{2n}(A_L) = Q^{(1)}_{2n-1}(A_R,0) - d^{-1}Q^{(0)}_{2n}(A_R) \tag{22}$$

the integral of (21) over M^{2n-1} whose boundary $\partial M^{2n-1} = M^{2k-2}$ is the spacetime manifold under consideration

$$\tilde{\Gamma}(U,A_L,A_R) = 2\pi \int_{x\in M^{2n-2}} \{Q^{(2)}_{2n-2}({}^U A_L,A_R,0) - Q^{(2)}_{2n-2}(UdU^{-1},A_L,0) - d^{-1}Q^{(1)}_{2n-1}(UdU^{-1},0)\}$$

$$= 2\pi \int_{M^{2n-1}} Q^{(1)}_{2n-1}({}^U A_L,A_R) \tag{23}$$

gives rise to the gauge invariant Wess-Zumino effective action on M^{2n-2}. The condition (22) is in fact the global version of anomaly free condition in M^{2n-2} which implies that the abelian anomalies in 2n dimensions should be cancelled. Similar analysis can be done for the global form of non-abelian anomalies in M^{2n-2} and other anomalous objects in different dimensions[2).

Finally, we would mention that cohomological analyses either in H_Δ and $H_{\bar{\Delta}}$ or in Cech-de Rham complex can also be made in the relations between anomalous objects of gauge group G and of its reduction subgroup H via the coset space G/H[7) as well as in the cases of gravitational anomalies provided certain invariant polynomial in the curvatures corresponding to the spin complex under consideration is given by Atiyah-Singer index theorems.

Acknowledgements

The author is very grateful to K. C. Chou, B. Y. Hou, S. K. Wang and K. Wu for fruitful collaborations; to S. S. Chern, S. Kobayashi, H. Wu and B. Zumino for helpful discussions during his visiting at UC Berkeley; to W. Bardeen, Y. Nambu and A. White as well as to H. T. Nieh and C. N. Yang for warm hospitality extended to him at the Symposium as well as at the Institute for Theoretical Physics at Stony Brook, respectively.

References

1) H.Y. Guo, K. Wu and S.K. Wang, Comm. Theor. Phys. (Beijing) 4 (1985) 113.

2) H.Y. Guo, B.Y. Hou, S.K. Wang and K. Wu, ibid. 4 (1985) 145; Preprint AS-ITP-84-041, (1984); H.Y. Guo, invited talk given at the Symposium on Yang-Mills gauge theories, Beijing, Dec. 21-23, 1984, to appear in the Proceedings.

3) L.D. Faddeev, Phys. Lett. 145B (1984) 81; B. Zumino, Santa Barbara preprint NSF-ITP-84-150 (1984); X.C. Song, MIT-BNL preprint (1984).

4) S.S. Chern, Complex manifolds without potential theory, Springer (1979).

5) H.Y. Guo and S.K. Wang, Preprint AS-ITP-85-008 (1985).

6) R. Bott and L.W. Tu, Differential forms in algebraic topology, Springer (1982).

7) K.C. Chou, H.Y. Guo and K. Wu, Comm. Theor. Phys. (Beijing) 4 (1985) 91.

SYMPOSIUM ON ANOMALIES, GEOMETRY, TOPOLOGY

ANOMALY STRUCTURE II

PAUL GINSPARG

CHAIRMAN

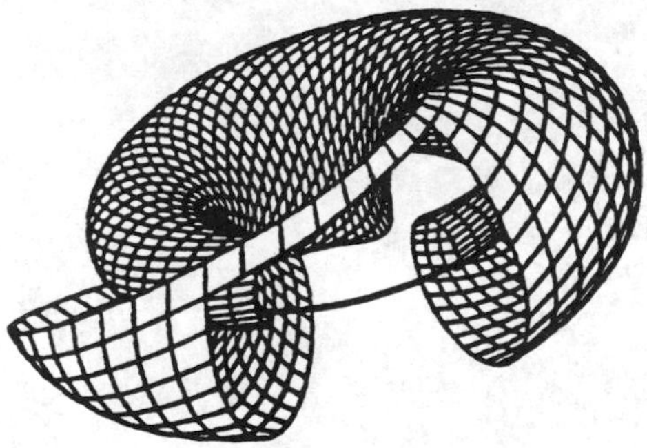

SOME RESULTS ON THE COHOMOLOGY OF

THE BECCHI-ROUET-STORA OPERATOR IN GAUGE THEORY

Claude M. VIALLET

Laboratoire de Physique Théorique et Hautes Energies*
Université de Paris VI
Tour 16, 1er étage, 4 Place Jussieu,
75230 PARIS CEDEX 05 (France)

* Laboratoire Associé au C.N.R.S. (L.A.280)

We know that the consistency conditions [W-Z] for anomalies in quantum gauge theories as well as current algebra appear as cohomological equations for the Becchi-Rouet-Stora operator δ [B-R-S, D , S].

The cohomology of interest is the "local cohomology" of δ , as properly defined in [B-CR] . The problem is to find all solutions of the equation $\delta R=0$, where R is a polynomial function in the gauge and ghost fields and their derivatives, R not being of the form δQ , where Q is a similar polynomial.

We are interested in gauge theory over space time M, and structure group G (compact) accommodated together in some principal fibre bundle P(M,G).

The δ-cohomology is related to the cohomology of the Lie algebra of the group $\mathcal{G}$ of gauge transformations. The operator δ is actually known to be a vertical derivative on the space $\mathfrak{C}$ of connections on P [B-CR] , and the anomaly has been linked with topological properties of the orbit space $\eta = \mathfrak{C}/\mathcal{G}$. [A-S, AG-G] .

However, the purely homotopical arguments suffer some limitations, and it is not clear what part of the topology matters for the cohomology of interest (local cohomology).

For example, there is no identity between $\pi_1(\mathcal{G})$ (and a fortiori $H^1_{deRham}(\mathcal{G})$) and the anomaly, since the first one may vanish while the anomaly is present, nor between $H^2_{de\ Rham}(\eta)$ and the anomaly, since we may increase the dimension of $H^2(\eta)$ by changing the topology of M (i.e. changing the boundary conditions on the fields) and apparently not affect the anomaly. Our argument will be non-homotopical.

Even more: we will work with a trivial bundle P=MxG.

We treat a purely algebraic problem: the cohomology of δ on a certain algebra which we define in paragraph 1.

We first calculate this cohomology on non-integrated polynomial functions of the fields with strong limitations on the number of derivatives of the fields (never more than one) and the actual combinations where they appear (only antisymmetric combinations from their nature as differential forms).

We then use the interplay between δ and the exterior differential d on M, together with the natural bigraduation : bidegree = (degree as form on M, number of ghosts) = (d-degree, δ-degree), to show how to produce solutions of the consistency equations from invariants of the structure group

G, and see how these solutions are unique (or how to climb the so-called "descent" equations). In order to do this we use the notion of δ-cohomology modulo d.

We write down an exact sequence where δ-cohomology-modulo - d groups are sandwiched between δ-cohomology groups which we are able to calculate.

The new results presented here have been obtained in collaboration with M. Dubois-Violette and M. Talon [DV-T-V] .

1. A universal algebra of polynomials.

Consider four copies of the dual $\mathfrak{g}^*$ of the Lie algebra of the group G, with bases A^α, F^α, χ^α, φ^α (α = 1...dim G).

We introduce the free graded-commutative algebra $\mathfrak{A}$ generated by these bases, with the degree assignment 1 for A^α and χ^α, and 2 for F^α and φ^α (α = 1... dim G).

$\mathfrak{A}$ is acted upon by two anticommuting antiderivations d and δ .

These antiderivations will later be sent by an homomorphism of graded algebras respectively onto the exterior differentiation on space-time and the B.R.S. operator.

The action of d and δ is given in terms of the structure constants of $\mathfrak{g}$, i.e. with standard notations :

$$dA = F - \frac{1}{2}[A, A] . \qquad d\chi = \varphi .$$

$$dF = [A , F] . \qquad d\varphi = 0 .$$

$$\delta A = -d\chi - [A,\chi] .$$

$$\delta\chi = -\frac{1}{2}[\chi,\chi] .$$

We will use the natural bidegree. This bidegree is (1,0) for A^α , (2, 0) for F^α , (1, 1) for φ^α and (0, 1) for χ^α , and d and δ are antiderivations of bidegree (1,0) and (0, 1) respectively. The total degree is the sum of the d-degree and the δ-degree.

2. Cohomologies of d, d+δ , and δ on $\mathfrak{A}$.

It is possible to find systems of generators (systems which are homogeneous for the adequate degree) which explicitly show that d and (d+δ) have trivial cohomology on $\mathfrak{A}$ (see [Su]) :

For d it is A^α , dA^α , χ^α , φ^α .

For $d+\delta$ it is A^α, χ^α, $(d+\delta) A^\alpha$, $(d+\delta)\chi^\alpha$ (homogeneous for the total degree).

For δ this does not work since $\delta\chi$ is not algebraically independent of the other generators!

However, A^α, δA^α, χ^α, F^α is a generating system (homogeneous for the bidegree).

The algebra $\mathfrak{A}$ appears to be the product of two algebras, generated respectively by $(A, \delta A)$ and (χ, F). The first one is contractible, and thus the δ-cohomology of $\mathfrak{A}$ reduces to the cohomology of the second one, i.e. : we only have to compute the δ-cohomology of the minimal graded-commutative algebra generated by χ^α and F^α, with $\delta\chi = -\frac{1}{2}[\chi,\chi]$ and $\delta F = -[\chi, F]$. It exactly coincides with the cohomology $H^*(\mathfrak{g}, S\mathfrak{g}^*)$ of the Lie algebra $\mathfrak{g}$ with values in the module of symmetric polynomials on $\mathfrak{g}$. It is known in the case of a reductive algebra [H-S] :

$$H^*(\mathfrak{g}, S\mathfrak{g}^*) = \mathfrak{I}_s(\mathfrak{g}) \times \mathfrak{I}_\wedge(\mathfrak{g}),$$

where $\mathfrak{I}_s$ is the algebra of <u>invariant symmetric polynomials</u> on $\mathfrak{g}$ and $\mathfrak{I}_\wedge$ the algebra of <u>invariant forms</u> on $\mathfrak{g}$. In other words, this cohomology identifies with the algebra generated by $P(F, \ldots, F)$ and $Q(\chi, [\chi,\chi], \ldots, [\chi,\chi])$ where P and Q run over all invariant polynomials on $\mathfrak{g}$.

3. <u>δ-cohomology modulo d. An exact sequence.</u>

Since δ and d anticommute, it is possible to define unambiguously the cohomology groups of δ modulo d.

We denote them by $H^{k,l}(\delta \bmod d)$, where (k,l) is the bidegree. Clearly any representative $Q^{k,l}$ of an element of $H^{k,l}(\delta \bmod d)$ verifies :
$\delta Q^{k,l} + dL^{k-1,l+1} = 0$, where $L^{k-1,l+1}$ is some element in $\mathfrak{A}$ of bidegree $(k-1, l+1)$.

From the canonical injection of $d\mathfrak{A}$ (image of $\mathfrak{A}$ by d) into $\mathfrak{A}$, we have the following short exact sequence:

$$(\mathcal{S}) \qquad 0 \rightarrow (d\mathfrak{A})^{k,*} \xrightarrow{i} \mathfrak{A}^{k,*} \xrightarrow{\pi} C^{k,*}(\delta \bmod d) \rightarrow 0,$$

where $C^{k,*}(\delta \bmod d)$ is the space of δ-cochains modulo d, with d-degree k.

We also have: $H^{k,l}(\delta \bmod d) = H^{k+1,l}(d\mathfrak{A}, \delta)$,
by using the triviality of the d-cohomology of $\mathfrak{A}$.

Thus, from the exact sequence $(\mathcal{S})$, and its connecting homomorphism

∂ , we have a cohomology exact sequence:

$$(\sigma) \cdots \xrightarrow{i^*} H^{k,\ell}(\delta) \xrightarrow{\pi^*} H^{k,\ell}(\delta \bmod d) \xrightarrow{\partial} H^{k-1,\ell+1}(\delta \bmod d) \xrightarrow{i^*} H^{k,\ell+1}(\delta) \xrightarrow{\pi^*} \cdots$$

starting with $0 \to H^{k-1,0}(\delta \bmod d) \xrightarrow{i^*} H^{k\,0}(\delta) \xrightarrow{\pi^*} H^{k\,0}(\delta \bmod d) \xrightarrow{\partial} \ldots$ for $k \geq 2$

$0 \to H^{1,0}(\delta) \xrightarrow{\pi^*} H^{1,0}(\delta \bmod d) \xrightarrow{\partial} H^{0,1}(\delta \bmod d) \xrightarrow{i^*} \ldots$ for $k = 1$.

Remark :

The homomorphism ∂ is precisely what was used to construct the sequence of equations introduced in gauge theories by Dixon [D](see [S]), and sometimes called descent equations. [Some might prefer "tic tac toe" diagrams of common use for spectral sequences, the spectral sequence here being the usual one for the double complex $\mathfrak{A}$].

The homomorphism ∂ has been used to construct solutions of the consistency equations from invariants of the group G, and eventually show the non-vanishing of the anomaly. The exact sequence (σ) tells us where ∂ is injective, surjective, or none, or both, by looking at the steps $H^{k,l}(\delta)$ which we just computed.

4. <u>How to use the universal algebra $\mathfrak{A}$, and in what sense it is universal</u>.

We are interested in solving the equation $\delta R = 0$, where R is an integral over space-time of some polynomial in the fields, of the form of the elements of $\mathfrak{A}$.

We suppose that space-time is a compact manifold without boundary. Setting $R = \int_M r$ leads to the equation $\delta r = dQ$, where r and Q are differential forms on M , d is the exterior differential on M, and δ is the BRS operator. It is clear that the identification ρ of the elements of $\mathfrak{A}$ with forms on M, which sends A (resp. F) onto the usual pull back on M via some section of P of the connection form (resp. curvature form), and d onto the exterior differential on M, is a <u>graded algebra homomorphism</u>. However, ρ is not an isomorphism because M cannot support differential forms of d-degree larger than its dimension n.

It is clear however, that the kernel of ρ is just the subalgebra of $\mathfrak{A}$ of elements of d-degree larger than n. In other words ρ is a linear isomorphism for objects of d-degree smaller than n .

Consequently, all equations $\delta Q^g_k + d\, Q^{g+1}_{k-1} = 0$ <u>for $k \leq n$</u> may very well be solved in $\mathfrak{A}$.

5. How to use the exact sequence. Example of the anomaly in even dimension.

Consider the consistency equation

$$\text{(c)} \qquad \delta Q^1_{2D} + d\, Q^2_{2D-1} \approxeq 0$$

we may consider Q^1_{2D} and Q^2_{2D-1} as elements of $\mathfrak{A}$.

Notice that in $\mathfrak{A}$, $d\, Q^1_{2D}$ need not be zero.

We have :

$$0 \to H^{2D,0}(\delta \bmod d) \to H^{2D-1,0}(\delta) \to H^{2D+1,0}(\delta \bmod d) \xrightarrow{\partial} H^{2D,1}(\delta \bmod d) \to H^{2D+1,1}(\delta)$$

Since $Q^1_{2D} \in H^{2D,1}(\delta \bmod d)$ and $H^{2D-1,1}(\delta) = H^{2D+1,1}(\delta) = 0$, we know there exists $Q^0_{2D+1} \in H^{2D+1,0}(\delta \bmod d) \approx H^{2D+2,0}(d\mathfrak{A}, \delta)$.

Since finally $H^{2D+2,0}(d\mathfrak{A}, \delta) = \mathfrak{I}_D(F,\dots,F)$, we have shown that all solutions of the equation (C) in 2D dimensions come from an invariant of degree D on $\underline{\mathfrak{g}}$.

The general computation of $H^{k,l}(\delta \bmod d)$ can be found in [DV-T-V] .

REFERENCES

[A-S] M.Atiyah, I.Singer, Proc. Nat.Acad. Sci. USA 81 (1984), 2597.

[AG-G] L.Alvarez- Gaumé, P.Ginsparg, Nucl. Phys. B243 (1984), 449.

[B-CR] L.Bonora, P. Cotta-Ramusino, Comm. Math. Phys. 87 (1983), 589.

[B-R-S] C.Becchi, A.Rouet, R.Stora, Ann.Phys. NY 98 (1976), 287.

[D] J.A. Dixon, "Cohomology and Renormalization of Gauge Theories" I, II, III, unpublished.

[DV-T-V] M.Dubois-Violette, M. Talon, C-M.Viallet, "Results on BRS cohomologies in gauge theory", Preprint LPTHE 85-10 (to appear in Physics Letters B);
and "Analysis of the consistency equations in gauge theory", to appear.

[H-S] G. Hochschild, J.P. Serre, Ann. Math.57 , 3 (1953), 591.

[S] R. Stora in "New Developments in Quantum Field Theory and Statistical Mechanics", ed. M. Lévy and P.K. Mitter, Plenum Press (1977).

[Su] D. Sullivan, I.H.E.S. Pub. n°47, (1977), 269.

[W-Z] J.Wess, B.Zumino, Phys. Lett. 37B (1971), 95.

THE DE RHAM BAR CONSTRUCTION AS A SETTING FOR THE ZUMINO, FADE'EV, ETC. DESCENT EQUATIONS

James Stasheff
Mathematics Department, University of North Carolina

Like Molière's bourgeois gentilhomme, I am amazed to discover that I have been doing physics most of my mathematical life, though to paraphrase Phillip Anderson:

> I am amazed at some of the marvelous computations that particle physicists toss off with abandon, though in return they often seem mystified by concepts and techniques I take for granted.

This is especially true with regard to anomalies, many of which look quite familiar to a homotopy theorist; the descent equations are particularly familiar. I'd like to share with you my insights into objects you have rediscovered on your own.

1. Cohomology versus homotopy

With regard to anomalies, it is the cohomology or homotopy of a topological group that is of primary interest, whether a Lie group G, a gauge transformation group $\mathcal{G}$ or the coordinate transformation group of space-time, Diff M.

For any topological group $\mathbb{G}$, we know that $H^*(\mathbb{G};\mathbb{R})$ is the tensor product of an exterior algebra on odd dimensional generators and a polynomial algebra on even dimensional generators. The homotopy groups $\pi_*(\mathbb{G})\otimes\mathbb{R}$ can be identified with the vector space of generators of the algebra $H^*(\mathbb{G};\mathbb{R})$.

If $\mathbb{G}$ is finite dimensional, we have just the exterior algebra. For example, $H^*(SU(N);\mathbb{R}) \approx E(x_3,x_5,\ldots,x_{2N-1})$, the exterior algebra on generators x_{2i-1} of dimension 2i-1.

The relation between cohomology and homotopy is even more clearly expressed from the viewpoint of $\mathbb{R}$-homotopy theory, which regards two simply connected spaces X and Y as equivalent, $X \underset{\mathbb{R}}{\simeq} Y$, if there is a map $f:Y \to X$ inducing an isomorphism of $H^*(\;;\mathbb{R})$ or, equally, of $\pi_*(\;)\otimes\mathbb{R}$. Thus $SU(N) \underset{\mathbb{R}}{\simeq} S^3 \times S^5 \times \ldots S^{2N-1}$, a product of odd dimensional spheres. The homotopy groups see the spheres, cohomology sees the products as well.

WARNING: This viewpoint ignores algebraic torsion information, e.g. $\pi_4(SU(2)) \approx Z/2$, home of the Witten anomaly.

Gauge theory and σ-model theory are both concerned with the space of maps

$$\text{Map }(M,G)$$

for some space or space-time manifold M and Lie group G. For simplicity, let me assume M is compactified Euclidean space, $S^d = R^d \cup \infty$, and restrict to $G^d = \{f:S^d \to G|\infty \to 1\}$.

For d=1, $G^1 = \Omega G = \{\lambda:I \to G|\lambda(0) = \lambda(1) = 1\}$ which we call the space of loops on G.

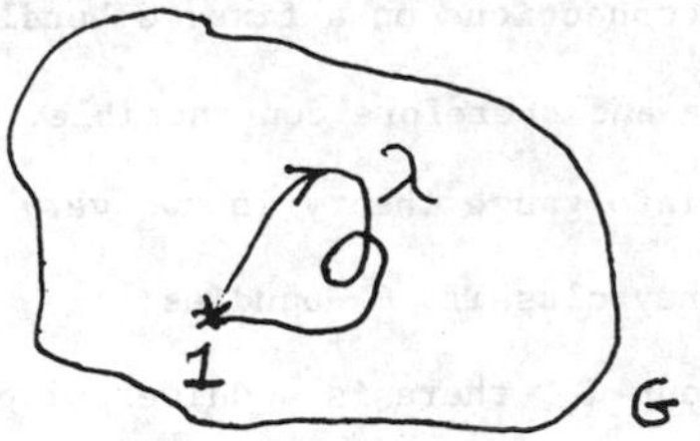

For d > 1, $G^d = \Omega^d G = \Omega(\Omega^{d-1}G) = \Omega\ldots\Omega G$ since the d-parameters of $\mathbb{R}^d$ can be used to parametize the loops on the loops on...

Now algebraic topologists have studied these iterated loop spaces very extensively; I'd like to let you in on some facts I hope you find relevant.

Physicists are becoming used to fibre bundles and principal G-bundles in particular:

A principal (right) G-bundle consists of a map $\pi : P \to B$ and a map $m : P \times \mathbb{G} \to P$ such that

1) π is a fibre bundle with fibre $\mathbb{G}$ i.e. for each $b \in B$, there is an open set U containing b and local coordinates (homeomorphisms)

$$\begin{array}{ccc} \pi^{-1} U & \xrightarrow{h} & U \times \mathbb{G} \\ & \searrow \; \swarrow & \\ & U & \end{array}$$

and 2) m is compatible with right translation in $\mathbb{G}$,

i.e. $\pi(xg) = \pi(x)$ and $h(xg) = h(x)g$ for $x \in P$ and $g \in \mathbb{G}$.

If the space P is contractible, $P \to B = P/\mathbb{G}$ is called universal and $P/\mathbb{G}$ is called a classifying space for $\mathbb{G}$ and often denoted $B\mathbb{G}$.

There are many familiar examples in physics:

1. $G = U(1)$ $\quad P = S^{\infty} \subset \mathbb{C}^{\infty}$ $\quad BU(1) = \mathbb{C}P(\infty)$, complex projective space of infinite dimension,

2. $G = O(n)$ $\quad BO(n) =$ Grassmann manifold of n-planes in $\mathbb{R}^{\infty}$,

3. $G = \mathcal{G}$ $\quad P = \mathcal{A} = \{$connections on a fixed G-bundle over M$\}$ $B\mathcal{G} = \mathcal{A}/\mathcal{G}$, since $\mathcal{A}$ is an affine space and therefore contractible.

Classifying spaces enter into gauge theory in two very important ways. First, as the name reflects, they classify $\mathbb{G}$-bundles:

Theorem. For a topological group $\mathbb{G}$, there is a universal principal $\mathbb{G}$-bundle $E\mathbb{G} \to B\mathbb{G}$ such that any principal $\mathbb{G}$-bundle $P \to B$ over a paracompact base space B is equivalent to the pull back $f^*E\mathbb{G}$ by a map $f : B \to B\mathbb{G}$. The homotopy class of the map f is uniquely determined by $P \to B$.

For a compact Lie group the result is due to Chern and Sun [1949], and Steenrod [1951], while for an arbitrary topological group $\mathbb{G}$ the result is due to Milnor [1956]. We shall give his construction shortly.

Classifying spaces are also important in gauge theory when space-time is Euclidean $\mathbb{R}^d$ because G^d can be recognized as an (iterated) loop space. For any space X, the space of loops ΩX is almost a topological group and $LX = \{\lambda : I \to X | \lambda(0) = *\}$ mapping to X by evaluating $\lambda(1)$ is almost a principal ΩX bundle, enough so for $B\Omega X$ to make sense. The space $B\Omega X$ has the homotopy type of X. On the other hand, $\Omega B\mathbb{G}$ has the homotopy type of $\mathbb{G}$. "Up to homotopy, B and Ω cancel."

These relations imply several homotopy equivalences:

$$BG^d \simeq B\Omega^d G \simeq \Omega^{d-1} G \simeq G^{d-1}$$

but also

$$BG^d \simeq B\Omega^d G \simeq \Omega^d BG.$$

The relation of B and Ω to homotopy groups is very simple:

$$\pi_{n-1}(\Omega\mathbb{G}) \approx \pi_n(\mathbb{G}) \approx \pi_{n+1}(B\mathbb{G}).$$

Cohomology behaves more subtly, but very manageably if we stay with $H^*(\mathbb{G}, \mathbb{R})$, e.g. de Rham cohomology using differential forms. In particular for a simply connected finite dimensional Lie group G, we have

$$H^*(BG) \approx \mathbb{R}[y_1, \ldots, y_k], \text{ degree } y_i = d_i + 1$$

$$H^*(G) \approx E[x_1, \ldots, x_k], \text{ degree } x_i = d_i$$

$$H^*(\Omega G) \approx \mathbb{R}[z_1, \ldots, z_k], \text{ degree } z_i = d_i - 1.$$

Thus to study the cohomology or homotopy groups of A/G, we can use the known results on BG. Indeed the relation can be expressed in terms of $\mathbb{R}$-homotopy equivalence. We have, for example,

$$G = SU(N) \underset{\mathbb{R}}{\simeq} S^3 \times S^5 \times \ldots \times S^{2N-1}$$

$$BSU(N) \underset{\mathbb{R}}{\simeq} \Omega S^5 \times \ldots \times \Omega S^{2N+1}$$

$$\Omega SU(N) \underset{\mathbb{R}}{\simeq} \Omega S^3 \times \ldots \times \Omega S^{2N-1}$$

$$G^d = \Omega^d SU(N) \underset{\mathbb{R}}{\simeq} \Omega S^1 \times \ldots \times \Omega S^{2N-d} \qquad d \text{ odd}$$

$$\underset{\mathbb{R}}{\simeq} S^1 \times \ldots \times S^{2N-d-1} \qquad d \text{ even}$$

which also gives us A/G^d since it is of the homotopy type of $\Omega^{d-1}SU(N) \simeq \Omega^d BSU(N)$.

Remember-these cohomology groups are known. In particular, $H^*(BSU(N);\mathbb{R})$ is generated by the Chern classes c_i for $2 \le i \le N$ and, for this group, $H^*(A/G^d;\mathbb{R})$ is generated by classes that can be denoted $\Omega^d c_i$ for $d/2 \le i \le N$.

WARNING. This is not in general group cohomology which we will see later.

So much we learn from algebraic topology, but physicists want information in terms of differential forms. In particular most of us have some awareness of the Pontrjagin classes for (oriented) O(n)-bundles and the Chern classes for U(n)-bundles since they have such nice expressions in terms of field strength = curvature, namely as invariant polynomials in the matrix entries of the curvature form. Generically, we write this as p(F) where p denotes the polynomial, e.g. $p(F) = Tr(F^k)$.

We assume then a fixed principal G-bundle $P \to M = S^d$ and a fixed connection (=vector potential) A which we regard as a $\mathfrak{g}$ (= Lie algebra of G) -valued 1-form on P. The invariant polynomial p(F) can be regarded as a (closed) form on M or pulled up to P. On P, it is automatically exact (because the universal bundle is contractible); Chern and Simons have shown this by defining a specific form Tp(A) such that $dTp(A) = p(F)$ on P. The formula for Tp is best given by regarding p as a function of k variables

$$\mathfrak{g} \times \mathfrak{g} \times \ldots \times \mathfrak{g} \longrightarrow \mathbb{R}.$$

Thus it makes sense to write

$$Tp(A) = \Sigma a_i p(A, [A,A]^{i-1}, F^{k-i})$$

meaning the first variable is A, the last k-i variables are all F and the remaining ones in between are all [A,A]. For small k, the coefficients a_i are well known in physics:

$$a_i = (-1)^{i-1} k!(k-1)!/2^{i-1}(k+i-1)!(k-i)!$$

In particular the term $a_k \cdot p(A, [A,A]^{k-1})$ restricts to a generator of $H^{2k-1}(G)$ when p represents a Pontrjagin or Chern Class.

In particular, the first Pontrjagin class p_1 is given by $tr\frac{F \wedge F}{2(2\pi)^2}$ and $Tp_1(A)$ by

$$\frac{1}{(2\pi)^2}(A \wedge F - \frac{1}{3} A \wedge [A,A])$$

which is familiar as (a multiple of) the chiral anomaly. Other anomalies, e.g. Wess-Zumino, occur similarly as Chern-Simons forms.

As many of the talks at this conference have emphasized, the Chern-Simons forms, especially for $Tr(F^k)$, occur in gauge theory in the context of descent equations. Some of us in algebraic topology immediately recognized the descent equations as familiar in the computation of BG and therefore not surprising for $\mathcal{B}G$. Notably missing in the physics literature is the appearance of the de Rham bar construction [Dupont, 1978] or, equivalently, Milnor's construction of the universal bundle $EG \to BG$, although its image in $\mathcal{A} \to \mathcal{A}/\mathcal{G}$ can be seen "through a glass darkly."

<u>Milnor's construction for $E\mathbb{G} \to B\mathbb{G}$</u>

For spaces $X_0,\ldots,X_n$ (which can be regarded as sitting disjointly inside some huge (infinite dimensional) linear space), let $X_0{*}X_2{*}\ldots{*}X_n$ denote the set of <u>convex</u> linear combinations of points $x_0,\ldots,x_n$ with $x_i \in X_i$, n=1, the set of oriented line segments $\overline{x_0x_1}$. Formally, we denote a point of $X_0{*}\ldots{*}X_n$ by $[\bar{t},\bar{x}] = [t_0,\ldots,t_n,x_0,\ldots,x_n]$.

Now if all the X_i are duplicates of a single topological space X, denote $X_0{*}\ldots{*}X_{n-1}$ by X^{*n}. If X is a topological group G, let it act on G^{*n} by acting on each g_i simultaneously by (right) translation. The action is free and $X^{*n} \to X^{*n}/G$ is a principle G-fibre bundle. (If we apply this to $G=S^1$, we find $G^{*n} = S^{2n+1}$ and $G^{*n}/G \approx \mathbb{C}P(n)$.)

In the limit, we get $\begin{matrix} EG \\ \downarrow \\ BG \end{matrix}$ with EG contractible; in fact, G^{*n} is contractible within G^{*n+1} by regarding it as corresponding to $(g_1,\ldots,g_n)$ and moving it along the simplex indexed by $(1\ g_1,\ldots,g_n)$.

For the gauge group $\mathcal{G}$, there is a natural map

$$\begin{array}{ccc} E\mathcal{G} & \longrightarrow & \mathcal{A} \\ \downarrow & & \downarrow \\ B\mathcal{G} & \longrightarrow & \mathcal{A}/\mathcal{G} \end{array}$$

if we start with a fixed principal G-bundle $P \to M = S^d$ and choose a connection $A \in \mathcal{A}$, namely,

$$\mathcal{G} \longrightarrow \mathcal{A}$$

$$g \longmapsto A^g$$

$$\mathcal{G}^{*n+1} \longrightarrow \mathcal{A}$$

$$(t_o, \ldots, t_n, g_o, \ldots, g_n) \to \Sigma\, t_i A^{g_i}$$

(To avoid making choices, one could regard the above formulas as defining $\mathcal{A} \times E\mathcal{G} \to \mathcal{A}$.)

Atiyah and Singer [1984] have pointed out that the evaluation map

$$S^d \times \mathcal{A}/\mathcal{G} \to BG$$

is covered by $\frac{P \times \mathcal{A}}{\mathcal{G}} \to EG$. We can extend this to

$$\begin{array}{ccccc} \dfrac{P \times E\mathcal{G}}{\mathcal{G}} & \longrightarrow & \dfrac{P \times \mathcal{A}}{\mathcal{G}} & \longrightarrow & EG \\ \downarrow & & \downarrow & & \downarrow \\ S^d \times B\mathcal{G} & \longrightarrow & S^d \times \mathcal{A}/\mathcal{G} & \longrightarrow & BG \end{array}$$

The Chern-Simons forms are defined as forms on EG. Pulling them back to $P \times EG$ allows them to be analyzed in pieces, illuminating the descent equations.

In general forms on a product $X \times Y$ can be described in terms of forms on X and forms on Y. We denote the Grassmann algebra of all forms on X by $\Lambda^*(X) = \{\Lambda^q(X)\}$. Now q-forms on $P \times EG$ can be approximated by

$$\bigoplus_p \Lambda^q(P \times \Delta^p \times G \times G^p)$$

while those on $\frac{P \times EG}{G}$ can be approximated by

$$\bigoplus_p \Lambda^q(P \times \Delta^p \times G^p).$$

Integration $\int_{\Delta^p}$ over Δ^p brings us to $\bigoplus_p \Lambda^{q-p}(P \times G^p)$ but now the original exterior differential d has been split into two pieces: the exterior derivative d for the space $P \times G^p$ and a "simplicial" coboundary

$$\Delta:\Lambda^{q-p}(P \times G^p) \to \Lambda^{q-p}(P \times G^{p+1})$$

where $\Delta = \Sigma(-1)^i\Delta_i$ and each Δ_i is induced by $P \times G^{p+1} \longrightarrow P \times G^p$ given by

$$(x,g_1,\ldots,g_{p+1}) \longmapsto (x,g_1,\ldots,g_ig_{i+1},\ldots,g_{p+1})$$

except for i=0

$$(x,g_1,\ldots,g_{p+1}) \longmapsto (xg_1,\ldots,g_{p+1})$$

and for i=p+1

$$(x,g_1,\ldots,g_{p+1}) \longmapsto (x,g_1,\ldots,g_p).$$

Just as $d^2=0$, so $\Delta^2=0$ and $d\Delta=\pm\Delta d$ depending on p. Thus $D = \Delta+(-1)^pd$ gives $D^2=0$; we have a "double complex" known as the de Rham bar construction.

The bar construction first occurred in the work of [Eilenberg and MacLane 1945] for $\mathbb{G}$ discrete and was generalized to the chains of a topological group in [Moore 1958]. It was not until the 1970's that the construction was reworked using differential forms [Shulman 1972]; an excellent exposition emphasizing the relation to the Chern-Weil isomorphism is [Dupont, 1978].

If we start with the trivial bundle $S^d \times G$, we can apply $\int_{S^d}$ to reduce further from $\Lambda^{q-p}(S^d \times G \times G^p)$ to $\Lambda^{q-p-d}(G \times G^p)$. Now the cohomology with respect to the total differential is $H^*(\frac{G \times A}{G})$ where the action of G on G is that which regards G as global gauge transformations. This is essentially known; it is the additional information in the pieces of the computation which is of interest. For a class of total dimension q the pieces in $\Lambda^{q-p-d}(G \times G^p)$ form a staircase, part of what Alvarez refers to as a tic-tac-toe pattern.

To see this better let us follow two examples in detail:

Fadéev: Consider TrF^3 for $S^d = S^3$ which is a G-form on

$\frac{S^3 \times G \times EG}{G} = S^3 \times \frac{G \times EG}{G}$. After applying $\int_{S^3}$, the pieces are arrayed

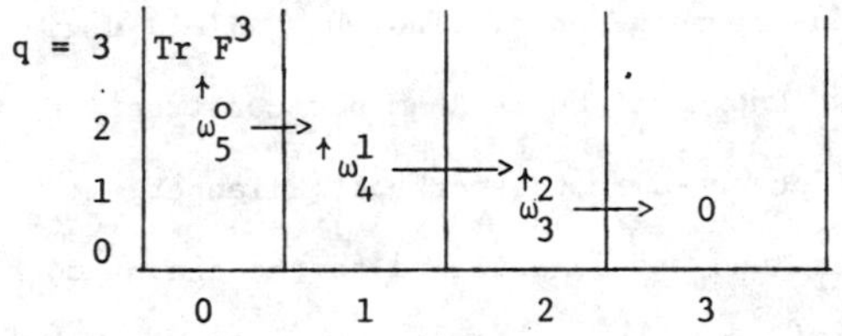

where the arrows $\longrightarrow$, $\uparrow$ correspond to the descent equations and we have used the now standard notation: ω^i_j involves i group variables and is a j-form before integration over S^3. In particular, ω^o_5 is the Chern-Simons for Tp(A) for $p(F) = TrF^3$.

The form ω^2_3 after integration over S^3 is just a real valued function $\alpha_2(g_1,g_2)$ for g_1, $g_2 \in G$. The descent involves choices to turn the corner →↑, i.e. to choose a form with specified exterior derivative. By the use of explicit formulas (as in Zumino or Fade'ev), ω^2_3 will at least be well defined modulo the integers, i.e. $\beta_2 = e^{i\alpha_2}$ is well defined in U(1). The explicit formulas allow us to regard β_2 as having values in Map(A,U(1)), the space of maps of A into U(1). The descent equations of [Fade'ev,] show $\beta_2 : G \times G \to \mathrm{Map}(A,U(1))$ is a continuous group theoretic 2-cocycle, and indeed the group theoretic cohomology class of β_2 is non-trivial.

[Graeme Segal, 1984] interprets this as follows: The sections of $P=S^d \times G \to S^d$ give rise to a Hilbert space of states H_A for each connection A. Together these form a bundle of Hilbert spaces over A/G. It would be nice if this bundle occurred as $H/G \to A/G$ for some bigger Hilbert space H, but the non-trivial class of β_2 is an obstruction to finding such an H (see Segal for details). However, we can assemble the H_A into a single Hilbert space H and construct a group extension

$$\mathrm{Map}(A,U(1)) \to \bar{G} \to G$$

so as to obtain a bundle $H/\bar{G} \to A/\bar{G}$. The anomaly β_2 has indicated its own cure. (This is precisely the infinite dimensional, gauge theoretic analog of Bargman's one-dimensional extension of the Galilean group).

Now what of TrF^4 over S^4? Here I must just speculate-the following makes mathematical sense, but its physical interpretation is obscure.

Again, portray the descent equations:

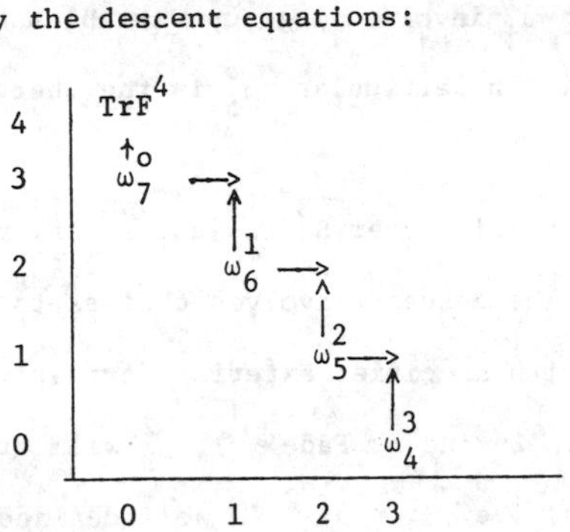

Now ω_5^2, after integration over S^4, takes values in real valued 1-forms on A. The corresponding group theoretic 2-cochain β_2 is a 2-cocycle only if we factor out the exact forms. We can then consider an extension $\bar{G} \to G$ as before, but we would ignore the information in ω_4^3. Alternately we can use β_2 to produce an extension

$$\Lambda^1(A;U(1)) \to \bar{\bar{G}} \to G$$

but since β_2 is not a 2-cocycle, $\bar{\bar{G}}$ will not be a group. If instead of $\Lambda^1(A,U(1))$, we used all of $\Lambda^*(A;U(1))$, then $\bar{\bar{G}}$ would have a homotopy associative multiplication in the sense that $h_1(h_2h_3)$ and $(h_1h_2)h_3$ differ by an exact form depending on h_1,h_2,h_3-this is the content of ω_4^3.

But what has become of the Hilbert space of states? Perhaps it too needs to be described, not in terms of functions, but of differential forms.

Finally notice that these descent equations are universal; after they are set up, they can be pulled back to any particular situation. For example, starting with $P=S^{2n} \times G$, a gauge variation $g: S^1 \to G$ corresponds to $\bar{g}:S^1 \times S^{2n} \to G$ and determines a bundle $\bar{P} \to S^2 \times S^{2n}$ for which

$$\int_{S^2 \times S^{2n}} \mathrm{Tr}F^{n+1} = \int_{S^1 \times S^{2n}} (-1)^{n+1} \frac{(n+1)!n!}{2^n(2n+1)!} \mathrm{tr}(\bar{g}^*\omega)^{2n+1}$$

where ω is the Maurer-Cartan 1-form on G. But this does <u>not</u> require either the Chern-Simons forms nor descent equations.

ANOMALOUS COMMUTATOR OF GAUGE GROUP GENERATORS IN A NON-ABELIAN CHIRAL THEORY

S. Jo
Center for Theoretical Physics
Massachusetts Institute of Technology
Cambridge, Massachusetts 02139 U.S.A.

Abstract Commutators among non-Abelian fermion currents are calculated using the BJL limit. We observe that the gauge dependence of the fermion current with fixed canonical variables should be different from the covariant seagull in order to have correct anomalous commutators.

I. Introduction

We discuss here the chiral fermion theory in the external non-Abelian gauge field. The Lagrangian is $\mathcal{L} = i\bar{\Psi}(\partial\!\!\!/ + A\!\!\!/ P_L)\Psi$, where P_L is the left-handed spinor projection matrix. The gauge group generator $G_a(\vec{x})$ is the sum of two parts

$$G_a(\vec{x}) = G^0_a(\vec{x}) + j^0_a(\vec{x}) \tag{I.1}$$

The first part $G^0_a(\vec{x})$ is the Yang-Mills part, which effects infinitesimal, fixed time gauge transformation on gauge field variables. We assume that $E^i_a(\vec{x})$ in the full theory can be represented by the derivative with respect to the gauge field, $\frac{1}{i}\frac{\delta}{\delta A^a_i(\vec{x})}$ in the external gauge theory. Then

$$G^0_a(\vec{x}) = i D^{ac}_j(\vec{x}) \left(\frac{\delta}{\delta A^c_j(\vec{x})}\right)_C , \quad i\,[G^0_a(\vec{x}), G^0_b(\vec{y})] = f_{abc} G^0_c\, \delta(\vec{x}-\vec{y}) \tag{I.2}$$

The subscript C means that the canonical variables are fixed. The second part $j^0_a(\vec{x})$ is the time component of the fermion source current $j^\mu_a(x)$ defined by

$$j^\mu_a(x) = -\frac{\delta S}{\delta A^a_\mu(x)} , \quad S = \int dx\, \mathcal{L} \tag{I.3}$$

Without the subscript C the variation is with fixed configuration-space variables and their derivatives.

Then the anomalous term $G_{ab}(\vec{x},\vec{y})$ defined by[1]

$$i[G_a(\vec{x}), G_b(\vec{y})] = f_{abc} G_c \delta(\vec{x}-\vec{y}) + G_{ab}(\vec{x},\vec{y}) \qquad (I.4)$$

can be written as

$$G_{ab}(\vec{x},\vec{y}) = J_{ab}(\vec{x},\vec{y}) - \left\{ D_j^{ac}(\vec{x}) \left(\frac{\delta j_b^0(\vec{y})}{\delta A_j^c(\vec{x})} \right)_c - D_j^{bc}(\vec{y}) \left(\frac{\delta j_a^0(\vec{x})}{\delta A_j^c(\vec{y})} \right)_c \right\} \qquad (I.5)$$

where $J_{ab}(\vec{x},\vec{y})$ is defined similarly in $i[j_a^0(\vec{x}), j_b^0(\vec{y})]$.

II. Evaluation of Current-Current Commutator

The BJL limit[2] says

$$\langle i[j_a^0(\vec{x}), j_b^0(\vec{y})] \rangle = \lim_{q_0\to\infty} q_0 \int dt_x\, e^{iq_0(t_x-t)} \langle T\, j_a^0(\vec{x},t_x)\, j_b^0(\vec{y},t) \rangle \qquad (II.1)$$

Naively

$$\langle T j_a^\mu(x) j_b^\nu(y) \rangle = -\frac{\delta^2\, iS_{eff}[A]}{\delta A_\mu^a(x)\, \delta A_\nu^b(y)} \equiv \langle \tilde{T}^* j_a^\mu(x) j_b^\nu(y) \rangle \qquad (II.2)$$

But caution is required here because of the possible difference between the covariant time ordered product and the usual time ordered (step function) product of the two currents. From the path integral formula we obtain

$$\langle \tilde{T}^* j_a^\mu(x)\, j_b^\nu(y) \rangle = \langle T^* j_a^\mu(x) j_b^\nu(y) \rangle + i \left\langle \frac{\delta j_a^\mu(x)}{\delta A_\nu^b(y)} \right\rangle \qquad (II.3)$$

Then the difference, we call it seagull, $\tau_{ab}^{\mu\nu}(x,y)$

$$\langle \tilde{T}^* j_a^\mu(x)\, j_b^\nu(y) \rangle - \langle T\, j_a^\mu(x) j_b^\nu(y) \rangle = \tau_{ab}^{\mu\nu}(x,y) \qquad (II.4)$$

is composed of two parts

$$\tau_{ab}^{\mu\nu}(x,y) = (T^*-T)\, j_a^\mu(x)\, j_b^\nu(y) + i \frac{\delta j_a^\mu(x)}{\delta A_\nu^b(y)} \equiv \sigma_{ab}^{\mu\nu}(x,y) + \tilde{\sigma}_{ab}^{\mu\nu}(x,y) \qquad (II.5)$$

The first part is called covariantizing seagull and the second part covariant seagull. Each of them does not vanish only when x=y and satisfies the symmetry property $\sigma_{ab}^{\mu\nu}(x,y) = \sigma_{ba}^{\nu\mu}(y,x)$. Therefore the total seagull $\tau_{ab}^{\mu\nu}(x,y)$ is a function of δ function and its derivatives which appears as a polynomial of q_0 in momentum space. This implies that

$$\langle [j_a^0(\vec{x}), j_b^0(\vec{y})] \rangle = \lim_{q_0\to\infty} q_0 \int dt_x\, e^{iq_0(t_x-t)} \left(-\frac{\delta^2\, iS_{eff}[A]}{\delta A_0^a(x)\, \delta A_0^b(y)} \right) \qquad (II.6)$$

with any polynomial of q_0 neglected.

In the series expansion of the effective action, we find that only finite number of the lowest order terms contribute to the anomalous term $J_{ab}(\vec{x},\vec{y})$.[3] In 1+1 d, only 2 and 3-point function terms contribute while 3, 4 and 5-point function terms contribute in 1+3 d. The result is

$$J_{ab}(\vec{x},\vec{y}) = -\frac{1}{2\pi}\,\mathrm{tr}\,ab\,\partial_1\delta(\vec{x}-\vec{y}) + \frac{1}{4\pi}\,\mathrm{tr}\,(ab-ba)(A_0+A_1)\delta(\vec{x}-\vec{y}) \; ; \; 1+1\ d$$

$$= -\frac{i}{8\pi^2}\varepsilon^{ijk}\,\mathrm{tr}\,(ab+ba)\partial_i A_j \partial_k \delta(\vec{x}-\vec{y}) \qquad ; \; 1+3\ d$$

$$+\frac{i}{24\pi^2}\varepsilon^{ijk}\,\mathrm{tr}(acdb-abdc)\left\{(\partial_i A^c_j A^d_k - 2A^c_i \partial_j A^d_k)\delta(\vec{x}-\vec{y}) - 3A^c_i(\vec{y})A^d_j(\vec{y})\partial_k\delta(\vec{x}-\vec{y})\right\}$$

$$+\frac{i}{16\pi^2}\varepsilon^{ijk}\left\{\mathrm{tr}(adbc-acbd)\,\partial_i(A^c_j A^d_k) + \mathrm{tr}(ab-ba)A_iA_jA_k - 2\,\mathrm{tr}(aA_ib-bA_ia)A_jA_k\right\}\delta(\vec{x}-\vec{y})$$

III. Gauge Dependence of the Current

In order to fix the gauge dependence of the current we use the previous formula (II.5). $i\,\delta j^\nu_b(y)/\delta A^a_\mu(x) = \tilde{\sigma}^{\mu\nu}_{ab}(x,y)$. The seagull can be evaluated using the Ward identity[4]

$$D^{ac}_\mu(x)\langle T^* j^\mu_c(x)\, j^\nu_b(y)\rangle = i\frac{\delta}{\delta A^b_\nu(y)}\langle D_\mu j^\mu_a(x)\rangle - i f_{abc}\delta(x-y)\langle j^\nu_c\rangle \qquad (\mathrm{III}.1)$$

From this we get

$$\langle D^{ac}_\mu(x)\, T^{\mu\nu}_{ab}(x,y)\rangle = i\frac{\delta}{\delta A^b_\nu(y)}\langle D_\mu j^\mu_a(x)\rangle + i J^\nu_{ab}(\vec{x},\vec{y})\delta(x_0-y_0) \qquad (\mathrm{III}.2)$$

where $J^\nu_{ab}(\vec{x},\vec{y})$ is the anomalous term in the commutator of $j^0_a(\vec{x})$ and $j^\nu_b(\vec{y})$. Solving this equation, we get

$$\sigma^{\mu\nu}_{ab}(x,y) = \frac{i}{2\pi}\,\mathrm{tr}\,ab\left\{\frac{1}{2}(g^{\mu 0}\varepsilon^{\nu 0} + g^{\nu 0}\varepsilon^{\mu 0}) - g^{\mu 0}g^{\nu 0}\right\}\delta(x-y) \; ; \; 1+1\ d$$

$$= \frac{1}{16\pi^2}\,\mathrm{tr}(ab+ba)(\partial_\alpha A_\beta + A_\alpha A_\beta)(g^{\mu 0}\varepsilon^{0\nu\alpha\beta} + g^{\nu 0}\varepsilon^{0\mu\alpha\beta})\delta(x-y) \; ; \; 1+3\ d$$

$$\tilde{\sigma}^{\mu\nu}_{ab}(x,y) = \frac{i}{4\pi}\,\mathrm{tr}\,ab\,g^{\mu\nu}\delta(x-y) \quad ; \quad 1+1\ d$$

$$= -\frac{1}{48\pi^2}\,\mathrm{tr}(ab+ba)\varepsilon^{\mu\nu\alpha\beta}(A_\alpha(x)+A_\alpha(y))\partial_\beta\delta(x-y) + \frac{\varepsilon^{\mu\nu\alpha\beta}}{16\pi^2}\,\mathrm{tr}\,aA_\alpha bA_\beta\,\delta(x-y) \; ; \; 1+3\ d$$

If we assume that $$\left(\frac{\delta j^\nu_b(y)}{\delta A^a_\mu(x)}\right)_C = \frac{\delta j^\nu_b(y)}{\delta A^a_\mu(x)}, \qquad (\mathrm{III}.3)$$

which is natural because canonically the conjugate momentum of ψ is ψ^*, then at fixed time

$$\left(\frac{\delta j^0_b(y)}{\delta A^a_i(x)}\right)_C = -i\,\tilde{\delta}^{i0}_{ab}(x,y) \quad \text{with } \delta(x_0-y_0) \text{ stripped off} \qquad (\text{III}.4)$$

Now we can evaluate $G_{ab}(\vec{x},\vec{y})$ with all of these. We observe that this $G_{ab}(\vec{x},\vec{y})$ is trivial in that a redefinition of the current by adding suitable c-number function (function of external field) to the original one makes the commutator of the redefined generator anomaly free. We also observe that the new current satisfies the gauge covariant divergence anomaly equation.[5]

However this is not what we expected.[6] Therefore we have to abandon the assumption we have made.

IV. Conclusion

If we still assume that $E^i_a(\vec{x})$ can be represented by $\frac{1}{i}\frac{\delta}{\delta A^a_i(\vec{x})}$ then in order to have correct anomaly (up to trivial contribution which can be removed by redefinition of the current) the gauge dependence of the current should be

$$i\left(\frac{\delta j^0_b(y)}{\delta A^a_i(x)}\right)_C = -\frac{i}{4\pi}\,\mathrm{tr}\,ab\;\delta(x-y) \quad ; \quad 1+1\ d \qquad (\text{IV}.1)$$

This expression shows that the conjugate momentum of ψ is not ψ^*. This is because if the conjugate momentum is ψ^*, then $(\delta j^\nu_b(y)/\delta A^a_\mu(x))_C = \delta j^\nu_b(y)/\delta A^a_\mu(x)$ and the latter is a Lorentz covariant second rank tensor, with the correct symmetry property. But there is no way to construct a Lorentz covariant tensor satisfying the symmetry property whose (i0) component given by the above expression.

If we relax the assumption that $E^i_a(\vec{x})$ is represented by $\frac{1}{i}\frac{\delta}{\delta A^a_i(\vec{x})}$ then the Yang-Mills part might have its own anomalous term.

$$i[G^0_a(\vec{x}), G^0_b(\vec{y})] = f_{abc}G^0_c\,\delta(\vec{x}-\vec{y}) + G^0_{ab}(\vec{x},\vec{y}) \qquad (\text{IV}.2)$$

This could be evaluated by considering the full theory in which the gauge field is also quantized. The commutator of $E^i_a(\vec{x})$ and the fermion current which corresponds to the gauge dependence of the current could be obtained directly from the BJL limit.

I am grateful to professor R. Jackiw for suggesting this problem. This work is supported in part through funds provided by the U.S.Department of Energy (D.O.E.) under contract #DE-AC02 -76ER03069.

References

(1) For the cohomological consideration, see J. Mickelsson, Comm. Math. Phys. (in press); L. Faddeev, Phys. Lett. 145B, 81 (1984); L. Faddeev and S. Shatashvili, Theo. Mat. Fiz. 60, 206 (1984); I. Singer, (to be published); B. Zumino, Santa Barbara, preprint NSF-ITP-84-150 (1984). For a review see R. Jackiw in E. Fradkin, Festchrift, (to be published by A. Hilgar, Bristol, U.K., 1985) MIT preprint CTP#1230 (1984).

(2) J. Bjorken, Phys. Rev. 148, 1467 (1966); K. Johnson and F. Low, Prog. Theo. Phys. (Kyoto), Suppl. 37-38, 74 (1966).

(3) For the detail, see S. Jo, MIT preprint CTP#1236 (1985).

(4) D. Gross and R. Jackiw, Nucl. Phys. B14, 269 (1969); for a summary, see R. Jackiw in Lectures on Current Algebra and Its Applications, ed. S. Treiman, R. Jackiw and D. Gross (Princeton University Press, Princeton, NJ, 1972).

(5) N. Paranjape, MIT thesis (1984) (unpublished).

(6) I. Frenkel and I. Singer showed the existence of the non-trivial term. (to be published)

Classical geometrical interpretation of ghost fields and anomalies in Yang-Mills theory and quantum gravity.

Jean THIERRY-MIEG

Lawrence Berkeley Laboratory, California 94720, and
CNRS, Observatoire de Meudon, 92190 France.

To Yuval Ne'eman, on his 60th birthday.

Abstract : The reinterpretation of the BRS equations of Quantum Field Theory as the Maurer Cartan equation of a classical principal fiber bundle leads to a simple gauge invariant classification of the anomalies in Yang Mills theory and gravity.

1 Introduction

The idea that classical Yang-Mills theory [1] should be formulated over a principal fiber bundle, locally the product of space-time by a Lie group, was first expressed by Ikeda and Miyachi [2] in 1956 and later by Lubkin [3] in 1963. It was widely accepted only in 1975 when Wu and Yang [4] showed that this geometrical setting was necessary for a proper understanding of the solitons.

Remarkedly, the same classical geometry controls the quantized theory. I have shown in 1978 [5] that the globally defined Darboux-Maurer-Cartan-Ehresmann (DMCE) structural equations of the principal fiber bundle [6] imply in any given gauge, i.e. over a local section, the Becchi Rouet Stora (BRS) equations of the quantum field theory [7] and hereby control its unitarity and renormalisability [7,8]. The recent finding [9] that the BRS equations also control the algebraic classification of the anomalies greatly increases the interest of this identification.

The aim of my talk is to show that one may identify the anomalies with the secondary characteristic classes of the principal fiber bundle, and hereby obtain their complete classification in a gauge invariant geometrical way.

2 The Darboux-Maurer-Cartan-Ehresmann equation

Let $\mathcal{P}$ denote a differentiable fiber bundle of dimension d+n over a base $\mathcal{B}$ of dimension d. Let Π be the projection map. Let us adorn with a $\tilde{}$ the exterior differential $\tilde{d}$ and any exterior form over $\mathcal{P}$. Let x^μ denote a coordinate system over $\mathcal{B}$. Using the cotangent map Π^*, we can pull back on $\mathcal{P}$ the dx^μ :

$$\tilde{dx}^\mu = \Pi^*(dx^\mu) = \tilde{d}(x^\mu \circ \Pi) \ . \tag{1}$$

Let us now introduce over $\mathcal{P}$ a field of one-forms $\tilde{A}$ valued into a Lie algebra $\mathcal{A}$ of dimension n :

$$\tilde{A} \in \Omega^1(\mathcal{P};\mathcal{A}) \ , \quad \tilde{A} = \tilde{A}^a \lambda_a \ ; \quad \lambda_a \in \mathcal{A} \ , \tag{2}$$

such that the n $\tilde{A}^a$ together with the d $\tilde{dx}^\mu$ define a moving frame (Cartan's repère mobile) over $\mathcal{P}$.

Note that $\tilde{A}$ is a field of one-forms valued into a finite dimensional vector space $\mathcal{A}$, or equivalently a collection of vectors of the infinite dimensional cotangent space ($\mathcal{P}_* = \bigcup \mathcal{P}_{*x}, x \in \mathcal{P}$). As such, $\tilde{A}$ generates an infinite dimensional Grassmann algebra as defined by Berezin [10]. The space of multilocal polynomes in $\tilde{A}$ (Green's functions) is infinite dimensional, whereas the exterior product of $\tilde{A}$ defined over the same point of $\mathcal{P}$ (local operators) are of maximal degree d. In other words, $\tilde{A}$ is not a function on $\mathcal{P}$ valued into a finite Grassmann algebra $\mathcal{A}_*$ but on the contrary a Grassmann field valued in a finite vector space $\mathcal{A}$. A certain confusion was caused by [11] where this distinction was overlooked.

Let us now consider the 2-form of curvature $\tilde{F} = \tilde{d}\tilde{A} + \frac{1}{2}[\tilde{A},\tilde{A}]$. We restrict the geometry by imposing that $\tilde{F}$ should be purely horizontal, i.e. that $\tilde{F}$ can be expressed on the dx^μ only

$$\tilde{F} \ = \ F \ = \ \frac{1}{2} F_{\mu\nu} \, \tilde{dx}^\mu \, \tilde{dx}^\nu \ . \tag{3}$$

This is the celebrated Darboux-Maurer-Cartan-Ehresmann structure equation of the principal fiber bundle [6].

Consider a system of n vector fields on $\mathcal{P}$ dual to $\tilde{A}$:

$$\tilde{D}_a \ \rfloor \ \tilde{A}^b \ = \ \delta^b_a \ , \quad \tilde{D}_a \ \rfloor \ \tilde{dx}^\mu \ = \ 0 \ . \tag{4}$$

The DMCE equation implies that, under Poisson bracket, the n vector fields $\tilde{D}_a$ generate a finite Lie algebra isomorphic to $\mathcal{A}$:

$$[\tilde{D}_a, \tilde{D}_b]_{\rm P.B.} \ = \ \tilde{D}_{[a,b]_\mathcal{A}} \ . \tag{5}$$

Therefore the Lie group G, with Lie algebra $\mathcal{A}$, acts as a transformation group on $\mathcal{P}$. Note however that the structure is only local :

a) $\mathcal{P}$ may admit no global section over $\mathcal{B}$, as usual,

b) $\mathcal{P}$ may admit no global trivialisation map over the group.

Indeed, we have not specified the action of the center of the group. In this respect, $\mathcal{P}$ has a weaker structure than is usually assumed for a principal fiber bundle. We do not know how to resolve this ambiguity or if it plays a role in quantum field theory, but we have to live with it, because the local DMCE equation is the only one preserved by the renormalization.

3 The Becchi-Rouet-Stora equations.

A section Σ , or gauge choice, is a map from an open subset of the base $\mathcal{B}$ into $\mathcal{P}$ not tangent to the fibers. Using the tangent map Σ_*, we can transport forward the vectors ∂_μ tangent to the base onto $\mathcal{P}_*$:

$$(\tilde{\partial}_\mu)_\Sigma \quad = \quad \Sigma_*(\tilde{A}) \tag{6}$$

and pull back the Ehresmann connection $\tilde{A}$ onto the base :

$$A_\Sigma \;=\; \Sigma^*(\tilde{A}) \quad . \tag{7}$$

A_Σ is the Yang-Mills one-form in the gauge Σ . However, $\tilde{A}$ contains more information than A_Σ alone. Given the section Σ , we can complete a coordinate coframe on $\mathcal{P}$ by choosing some coordinates y^i along the fibers such that y^i is zero on Σ , i.e. $\tilde{d}y^i$ is normal to $\tilde{\partial}_\mu$:

$$(\tilde{\partial}_\mu)_\Sigma \rfloor (\tilde{d}y^i)_\Sigma \;=\; 0 \quad , \quad \tilde{\partial}_i \rfloor \tilde{d}x^\mu \;=\; 0 \; . \tag{8}$$

The orientation of the y^i along each fiber is arbitrary, however, if we expand the connection $\tilde{A}$ on this coframe :

$$\tilde{A}^a \;=\; (A^a_\mu)_\Sigma \, \tilde{d}x^\mu \;+\; A^a_b (\tilde{d}y^b)_\Sigma \tag{9}$$

the matrix A^a_b gives at each point the orientation of the coordinate vectors $\tilde{\partial}_a$ with respect to the Killing vectors $\tilde{D}_a$.

We call Faddeev Popov ghost the section dependent object :

$$c \;=\; A^a_b \, (\tilde{d}y^b)_\Sigma \quad . \tag{10}$$

In the same coordinate system, we call Becchi-Rouet-Stora operator the differential :

$$s \;=\; (\tilde{d}y^a) \, \tilde{\partial}_{y^a} \quad . \tag{11}$$

In these notations, the DMCE equation splits into 3 components known as the BRS equations [7] :

$$dA + \frac{1}{2}\,[A,A] = F(A)\ ,\quad sA + dc + [c,A] = 0\ ,\quad sc + \frac{1}{2}\,[c,c] = 0\ . \tag{12}$$

or in a more concise form :

$$\tilde{F}(A+c) = F(A) \tag{13}$$

This equation, that I first proposed in 1978 [5] has been recently nicknamed by Stora the Russian (?) formula.

4 Characteristic classes.

In this section, we wish to find the cohomology classes of $\mathcal{P}$, i.e. the closed exterior forms $\tilde{\omega}$ of degree p modulo exact forms :

$$\tilde{d}\tilde{\omega}(\tilde{A},F) = 0 \quad , \quad \tilde{\omega} \equiv \tilde{\omega} + \tilde{d}\tilde{K}\ . \tag{14}$$

If $p < d$, then the $\tilde{\omega}$ are exterior polynomes in $\tilde{F}$ and represent the primary characteristic classes of the manifold. However, when $p = d + g$, these polynomes vanish since $\tilde{F}$ is horizontal and $\tilde{\omega}$ represents the secondary classes. These forms correspond to the g-cocycles of Zumino [12].

We shall perform the classification intrinsically, without choosing a section, and thus without decomposing $\tilde{A}$ into its gauge and ghost components. In the next section, we shall prove that this geometric problem is equivalent to the classification of the anomalies of Yang Mills theory which may obstruct the gauge invariance, i.e. section independance, of the renormalized action.

We proceed in two steps :

a) we relax the DMCE equation. Then $\tilde{F}$ and $\tilde{A}$ are independent and the cohomology of $\tilde{d}$ on the space of exterior polynomes in $(\tilde{A}\ ,\tilde{F}\ )$ becomes trivial. Then the classification of forms of degree $d+g$ modulo exact forms becomes equivalent to the classification of closed forms I of degree $d+g+1$.

$$\tilde{d}\tilde{\omega}(\tilde{A},\tilde{F}) = \tilde{I}(\tilde{A},\tilde{F}) \tag{15}$$

b) we impose the DMCE equation $\tilde{F} = F$. A polynome in $\tilde{F}$ of degree $\frac{d}{2}$ or higher vanishes as a consequence of the horizontality of F . Observe now that if $u(\tilde{A},\tilde{F}) = \tilde{d}v(\tilde{A},\tilde{F})$, then u is always of higher degree in $\tilde{F}$ than v. Therefore, if v vanishes because of the DMCE condition, u vanishes a fortiori. Reciprocally, if u does not vanish, nor does v.

Thus, when I is annihilated by the DMCE equation but not $\tilde{\omega}$, $\tilde{\omega}$ represents a cohomology class of $\tilde{d}$ on $\mathcal{P}$.

The general solution [13] is the product of q Chern Simons forms Q_{m_i} by a Weyl invariant polynome P_r in F of degree r :

$$\tilde{\omega}(\tilde{A},F) = \prod_{i=1}^{q} Q_{m_i}(\tilde{A},F)\,P_r(F) \ , \quad \tilde{d}Q_{m_j}(\tilde{A},F) = P_{\frac{m_j+1}{2}}(F) \ . \tag{16}$$

The coefficients are subject to the constraints :

$$\sum_{j=1}^{q} m_j + 2r = d+g \ , \quad g \le \sum_{j=1}^{q} m_j \le g + min(m_j) \tag{17}$$

For any value of g such that $d+g$ is odd, there exists a solution with $q=1$. This includes the Deser-Jackiw-Templeton topological mass term in odd dimension and the usual $g=1$ ABJ anomaly in even dimension with its associated $g=2$ Faddeev anomaly in the Hamiltonian formalism. Unusual solutions with $q>1$ occur with $g=1$ only in the presence of two U(1) groups in odd dimension :

$$\tilde{\omega} = \tilde{A}\wedge\tilde{A}'\,P(F,F') \tag{18}$$

With $q=2$, $g=3$, d odd, we note the SU(2).U(1) anomaly :

$$\tilde{\omega} = Tr_{SU(2)}(\tilde{A}^a,\tilde{A}^b,\tilde{A}^c)\,\tilde{A}^{U(1)}\,P_{\frac{d-1}{2}}(F) \tag{19}$$

5 The Wess-Zumino and the descent equations.

Consider a closed non exact form $\tilde{\omega}$ of degree $d+g$:

$$\tilde{d}\tilde{\omega}(\tilde{A},F) = 0 \ , \quad \tilde{\omega} \neq \tilde{d}\tilde{K} \ . \tag{20}$$

If we choose a section Σ and expand $\tilde{\omega}$ in gauge and ghost components :

$$\tilde{\omega}_{d+g} = \sum_{i=0}^{d}\omega_{d-i}^{g+i} \ , \quad \omega_{d-i}^{g+i} = \frac{1}{(g+i)!}(c\frac{\partial}{\partial\tilde{A}})^{g+i}\,\tilde{\omega}(\tilde{A},F)\ |_{\tilde{A}=A} \ . \tag{21}$$

The expansion of $\tilde{\omega}_{d+g}$ starts with ω_d^g since higher horizontal forms vanish identically. If we expand the closure equation, we obtain a set of equations known as *the descent* :

$$s\,\omega_{d-i}^{g+i} + d\omega_{d-i-1}^{g+i+1} = 0 \ . \tag{22}$$

Integrating the $i = 0$ equation over the base and discarding the surface terms, we see that ω_d^g satisfies the dual *Cartan* form of the Wess Zumino consistency condition [9] which defines the possible anomalies :

$$\int s\,\omega_d^g \;=\; 0\;. \tag{23}$$

However, in quantum field theory, the anomaly considered as a quantum correction to the BRS variation of 1pi action [7,8] is a priori a function of A_μ, c, the antighost and the source operators) and (23) could have many more solutions. But recently, I have shown [13] that all Yang-Mills anomalies are of the type (20-22). The proof involves 4 steps :

a) using auxiliary fields, the antighosts and source operators are gauged away (Dixon's problem [9]);

b) the Yang Mills field A_μ is shown, by lengthy Taylor expansions, to contribute as an exterior form $A_\mu\,\tilde{d}x^\mu$ to those anomalies such that $s\omega \neq 0$;

c) the ghost c and Yang Mills form A are combined into $\tilde{A} = A + c$;

d) ω_d^1 is shown to be the first term of the expansion of some $\tilde{d}$ cohomology class $\tilde{\omega}$.

The quantum field theory problem is therefore reduced to the geometric problem studied in the preceeding section and its generic solution is obtained by expanding (16) using the descent equation (22). Steps c) and d) have been established by several authors [14] with similar results (in particular Viallet at this conference).

As we have seen in section 3, the intrinsic geometrical classification formally dispenses of proving b,c,d. Indeed, if the anomaly has an intrinsic meaning, it is not a coordinate artefact and must be globally defined. Therefore it must depend on c and A_μ only through the intrinsic combination $\tilde{A}$ and on d and s only through $\tilde{d}$.

6 Gravitational anomalies.

It is extremely simple to include general relativity in this formalism. One just has to replace the moving frame ($\tilde{A}$, $\tilde{d}x^\mu$) of $\mathcal{P}$ by a Poincaré valued one-form field ($\tilde{\omega}$, $\tilde{e}$) over a 10 dimensional manifold $\mathcal{M}$, the Regge Ne'eman group manifold [15]. $\tilde{\omega}$ denotes a connection form for the Lorentz group, which plays the role of the Yang Mills group, and $\tilde{e}$ is the 'quantized' vierbein. By 'quantized', I mean that in an arbitrary system of coordinates $\tilde{e}$ decompose as a classical vierbein plus ghost field : $\tilde{e}^{\,a} \;=\; e^a_\mu\,\tilde{d}x^\mu \;+\; \eta^a$.η^a is the ghost field of local translations in the tangent space. Equivalently, one may express η^a in terms of a ghost vector field ξ which is the ghost of local diffeomorphisms (Kibble formalism) : $\eta^a \;=\; \xi\,\rfloor\tilde{e}^a$, $\xi \;=\; \xi^\mu\,\partial_\mu$, $\xi^\mu \;=\; \eta^a\,(e^{-1})^\mu_a$.

The generalized DMCE-BRS equations, also known as the rheonomy conditions, state that $\tilde{e}$ ***and all its Lorentz covariant exterior differentials*** can be expanded over $\tilde{e}$ with ***classical*** coefficients.

$$\tilde{e}^a = \delta^a_b\,\tilde{e}^b \ , \quad \tilde{T}^a(\tilde{e},\tilde{\omega}) = \frac{1}{2}\,T^a_{b,c}(e,\omega)\,\tilde{e}^b\,\tilde{e}^c \ , \quad \tilde{R}^{ab}(\tilde{\omega}) = \frac{1}{2}\,R^{ab}_{c,d}(\omega)\,\tilde{e}^c\,\tilde{e}^d \ , \qquad (24)$$

where : $\quad T^a = De^a = de^a + \omega^a_b\,e^b \ , \quad R^{ab} = d\omega^{ab} + \omega^a_e\,\omega^{eb} \quad .$

The system is closed and consistent since : $De = T \ , \quad DT = Re \ , \quad DR = 0$. Considering the dual vector fields $(\tilde{D}_{ab},\, \tilde{D}_a)$, one may easily verify that the $\tilde{D}_{ab}$ represent the Lorentz algebra [15] :

$$[\tilde{D}_{ab},\, \tilde{D}_{cd}] = \tilde{D}_{[ab,cd]} \ . \qquad (25)$$

The difference between $\mathcal{M}$and a principal fiber bundle is that there is no predefined projection map, but the space develops a 'spontaneous fibration' along the $\tilde{D}_{ab}$ directions as a result of the DMCE-BRS equations [16].

The best choice of variables to classify the anomalies is to devellop the $\tilde{\omega}$ themselves on the $\tilde{e}$: $\tilde{\omega} = \omega_a\,\tilde{e}^a + \Omega'$ and to introduce [17] a 'translation covariant' BRS operator s' such that the 'alibi' active translation, or displacement in the tangent space, parametrized by the ghost η^a is compensated for by and 'alias' transformation, a passive relabelling of the coordinates, or displacement along the curved section, induced by a Lie derivative along the ghost vector field ξ associated to η^a : $\quad s' = s - \mathcal{L}_\xi \quad .$ In these variables, $\tilde{e}$ has no ghost ! and the structure equations read [18] :

$$S'\tilde{e}^a = s'\tilde{e}^a + \Omega'^a_b\,\tilde{e}^b = 0 \ , \quad s'\xi = -\frac{1}{2}\,[\xi,\xi] \ , \quad s'\omega = D\Omega' \ , \quad s'\Omega' = -\frac{1}{2}\,[\Omega',\Omega'] \ . \qquad (26)$$

These beautifully simple equations show that the classification of the anomalies of general relativity is reduced to the classification of the anomalies of a Yang Mills theory of the Lorentz group [12,18] since the local cohomology of s and s' are identical : $\int s'\omega^g_d = \int s\omega - d(\xi\,\rfloor\omega) - (\xi\,\rfloor d\omega) = \int s\omega$. Indeed, the second term is exact and the third vanishes since $d\omega$ is a horizontal (d+1) form.

I have developped this presentation of the gauge structure of quantum gravity in several steps. First Regge and Ne'eman [15] analysed the classical theory and obtained the structure equations as equations of motion which Ne'eman and I reinterpreted as BRS equations [16]. Later with Ne'eman and Takasugi [17] we introduced the s' operator and finally with Baulieu [18] we have simplified the equations and classified the anomalies. In this last paper, our proof that all anomalies can be written as exterior forms is incomplete. We were unable to gauge away the BRS closed objects of the form $\phi = \int \xi^\mu\,\partial_\mu\,\Delta\,\sqrt{g}$ where Δ is an arbitrary scalar. This is however possible since Alvarez and Zumino have found that ϕ is s exact : $\phi = -\int s\,\Delta\sqrt{g}\,Log(\sqrt{g})$.

7 Conclusion.

The geometrical formalism reviewed here leads to a clear understanding and a simple classification of the anomalies of Yang Mills theory and general relativity. A straightforward generalization leads to the quantization of antisymmetric tensor gauge fields and it is hoped that the formalism can be extended to supergravity.

It is rewarding to see that the geometrical understanding of the anomalies, the result of a rear guard study by mathematical physicists sometimes considered as futile by the model builders, has finally led to a renewal of unified theories through the discovery of the cancelation of anomalies of d=10, N=1 supergravity when the gauge group is SO(32) (Green and Schwarz [19]) or $E_8 \otimes E_8$ (Thierry-Mieg [20]).

1. C.N.Yang and R.L.Mills, Phys.Rev.96(1954) 191 .

2. M.Ikeda and Y.Miyachi, Prog.Theor.Phys.16(1956) 537.

3. E.Lubkin, Annals Phys. N.Y. 23(1963) 233.

4. T.T.Wu and C.N.Yang, Phys.Rev.D12(1975) 3845-57.

5. J.Thierry-Mieg, Paris sud thesis 1978, J.Math.Phys. 21(1980) 2834, Nuovo Cimento 56A(1980)396.

6. G.Darboux, La théorie des surfaces, Gauthier Villars, Paris 1889; E.Cartan, Bulletin Sc.Math. 34(1910) 1-34 (œuvres vol.3,31,p145); Ch.Ehresmann, c.f. Spivak, Introd.Diff.Geom.,vol.2, chap.8.

7. C.Becchi, A.Rouet and R.Stora, Annals Phys. N.Y. 98(1976) 287, Comm.Math.Phys. 42(1975) 127.

8. B.Lee and J.Zinn-Justin, Phys.Rev.D5(1972) 3121,3137,3155,D7(1973) 1049; T.Kugo and I.Ojima, Prog.Theor.Phy 66(1979).

9. R.Stora, Cargèse lectures 1976; J.Dixon, Harvard peprint HUMTPB76 (1979) unpub.; L.Bonora, P.Cotta-Ramusino and C.Reina, Phys.Rev.Lett.B126(1983) 305; L.Baulieu, Nuclear Phys.B241(1984) 557; R.Stora, Cargèse lectures 1983; B.Zumino, Les Houches lectures 1983.

10. V.A.Berezin, The Method of Second Quantization,Academic Press, N.Y. 1966.

11. J.M.Leinaas and K.Olaussen, Phys.Lett.108B(1982) 199.

12. W.A.Bardeen and B.Zumino, Nuclear Phys.B244(1984) 421; B.Zumino, Nuclear Phys.B253(1985) 477.

13 J.Thierrry-Mieg, Phys.Lett.B147(1984) 430.

14 J.Lott, Phys.Lett.B145(1984) 179, Comm.Math.Phys. 97(1985) 371.

15. E.Cartan, Ann.Ecole normale sup. 40(1923) 325-412 (œuvres vol.3,66,p.669-747); Y.Ne'eman and T.Regge, Rivista Nuovo Cimento 1,5(1978) 1.

16. J.Thierry-Mieg and Y.Ne'eman, Annals Phys. N.Y. 123(1979) 247.

17. Y.Ne'eman, E.Takasugi and J.Thierry-Mieg, Phys.Rev.D22(1980) 2371-79.

18. L.Baulieu and J.Thierry-Mieg, Phys.Lett.B145(1984)53; F.Langouche, T.Schucker and R.Stora, Phys.Lett.B145(342.

19. M.Green and J.Schwarz, Phys.Lett.B149(1984) 117.

20. J.Thierry-Mieg, LBL preprint 18464, oct 84, Phys.Lett.in press.

The Global View of Gauge Group Cocycles

Bo-Yu Hou*

Institute for Theoretical Physics
SUNY at Stony Brook
Stony Brook, New York 11794

The common index characterizes the whole descent equation.

Recently a lot of works show that various nonabelian anomalies are related with topological obstructions to gauge covariance. These obstructions are realized by generators ω^k_{2n-k-1} of cohomology class, (e.g. effective Lag. ω^0_5, anomalous div. ω^1_4, anomalous commutator ω^2_3...). The ω^k_{2n-k-1} are 2n-k-1 forms expressed by polynomials of potential form A and dA and are k-th order in "ghost" v. These ω satisfy the descent eqn. $\delta\omega^k_i = d\omega^{k+1}_{i-1}$. Here, δ is the BRS transformation (i.e. infinitesimal gauge transformation), which is nilpotent $\delta^2 = 0$, hence defines a cohomology sequence ker.δ/imag.δ. Let Ω be the integral of ω^k over k-chain σ_k in group manifold G $\Omega^k_{2n-1-k} = \int_{\sigma_k} \omega^k_{2n-1-k}$, then as shown by Zumino these Ω satisfy another descent eqn. $\Delta\Omega^k_i = d\Omega^{k+1}_{i-1}$, (definition of Δ will be given later).

These notes would emphasize that for topologically nontrivial cases these two descent eqn. are true only locally and globally the whole Δ-d descent may be characterized by a common index z, which is topologically invariant. This descent is a deRham Cech double series. The index z equals also the homotopic cardinality $\pi_k(g^{2n-k-1})$ of gauge transformation group $g^{2n-k-1}_{(x)}$ on compactified 2n-k-1 space x. Finally, this note shows how index z describes the affine space A of sets of potential forms A as a principle bundle $\mathcal{A}(\mathcal{A}/g,g)$ with base $\mathcal{A}/g$, fibre g.

Gauge group K-cochain $\alpha^K(A(x);g_1(x),\ldots g_k(x))$ corresponds to K-simplex chain $\{A_1(x),\ldots,A_k(x)\}$ on the gauge orbit passing A(x), where $A_1 \equiv A$, $A_2 \equiv A_1^{g_1}$, $A_3 \equiv A_2^{g_2},\ldots,A^g = g^{-1}Ag+g^{-1}dg$. Coboundary $\Delta\alpha^k(A(x);g_1(x),\ldots,g_{k+1}(x))$ corresponds to the boundary of K+1 simplex $\partial\{A_1,\ldots,A_{k+1}\}$. Then it is easy to see that corresponding to $\partial^2=0$, we have $\Delta^2=0$. Following Faddeev, we may express α^K by the integral $2\pi\int_{S_{2n-1-k}} \Omega^K_{2n-1-k}(A;g_1,\ldots,g_k)$ over compactified

Permanent address: Northwest Univ. Xian, China

2n-1-k dimensional space, here the 2n-1-k form Ω^k_{2n-1-k} may be derived by descent equations starting from Chern character $C \sim \mathrm{tr}F^n$, $F = dA+A^2$, which is gauge invariant $\Delta C_n=0$, and closed $dC_n=0$. The existence of such descent relies on Poincaré lemma. $dC_n = 0$, exist Ω^0_{2n-1} such that $C_n = d\Omega^0_{2n-1}$ locally. $d(\Delta\Omega^0_{2n-1}) = \Delta(d\Omega^0_{2n-1}) = \Delta C_n = 0$, $\Delta\Omega^0_{2n-1} = d\Omega^1_{2n-2}$ locally. $d(\Delta\Omega^k_{2n-k-1}) = \Delta(d\Omega^k_{2n-k-1}) = \Delta\Delta\Omega^{k-1}_{2n-k}=0$, $\Delta\Omega^k_{2n-k-1}=d\Omega^{k+1}_{2n-k-2}$ locally.

But, Poincaré lemma satisfies globally only if the base manifold is topologically trivial. Thus, the descent equations are valid only locally. We will show: globally, a topologically nontrivial descent is characterized by a common index Z.

$$\Delta\alpha^k = 2\pi Z \text{ for all } K = 0,1,\ldots 2n-1, \text{ with the same } Z \quad Z = \int_{S_{2n}} C_n$$

For example: if $\int_{S_6} C_3 \equiv \int_{S_6} \frac{i}{48\pi}\mathrm{tr}F^3 = Z \neq 0$,

$$\text{then } \int_{S_6} C_3 \neq \int_{S_6} d\Omega^0_5 = 0$$

There is no $\Omega^0_5(A)$, such that $d\Omega^0_5(A) = C_3$ on whole S_6.

We must divide S_6 into two disc $S_6 = \sum_i D_6(i)$, $(i=1,2)$.

Respectively, $F = dA_i + A_i^2$ in $D(i)$, $(A_1 \equiv A \quad A_2 \equiv A^g)$.

$$\text{Thus} \quad z = \int_{S_6} C_3 = \sum_i \int_{D_6(i)} C_3 = \sum_i \int_{D_6(i)} d\Omega^0_5(A_i) = \sum_i \int_{\partial D_6(i)} \Omega^0_5(A_i)$$

$$= \int_{S_5} \Omega^0_5(A_2)-\Omega^0_5(A_1) = \int_{S_5} \Delta\Omega^0_5(A_1,A_2) = \int_{S_5} (g^{-1}dg)^5 = \pi_5(G) = \pi_0(g^5)$$

where: $\pi_5(G)$: winding number of transition function $g(x)$ – map from equator S_5 to Lie group manifold; $\pi_0(g^5)$: the number of disconnected components of gauge group g^5, $g^5 \equiv \{g(x) \mid x\in S^5\}$.

To find Ω^1_4 such that $d\Omega^1_4 = \Delta\Omega^0_5$, we divide S_6 into three discs.

$$S_6 = \sum_i D_6(i) \quad i = 1,2,3$$

$$\partial D_6(i) = S_5(i)$$

$$S_5(i)) = \sum D_5(i,j) = -\sum D_5(i,j)$$

$$\partial D_5(ij) = \varepsilon_{ijk} S_4 \qquad i,j,K = 1,2,3$$

$$Z = \int_{S_6} C^3 = \sum_i \int_{D_6(i)} C^3 = \sum_i \int_{D_6(i)} d\Omega_5^0(A_i) = \sum_i \int_{S_5(i)} \Omega_5^0(A_i) =$$

$$\sum_{i>j} \int_{D_5 i,j)} \Omega_5^0(A_i)) - \Omega_5^0(A_j) = \sum_{i>j} \int_{D_5(k,j)} \Delta\Omega_5^0(A_i,A_j) =$$

$$\sum_{i>j} \int_{D_5(i,j)} d\Omega_4^1(A_i,A_j) = \int_{S_4} \Delta\Omega^1(A_1 d,A_2,A_3) = \pi^1(g^4)$$

$$\Delta\alpha^1(A;g_1,g_2) = 2\pi Z$$

Similarly to define Ω_3^2, such that $d\Omega_3^2 = \Delta\Omega_4^2$, we divided S_6 into 4 discs, so S_4 is divided into D_4, $\partial D_5(1,2) = S_4(1,2) = D_4(1,2,3) + D_4(1,2,4)$ with S_3 as the common boundary of D_4, $\partial D_4(i,j,k) = \varepsilon_{ijk\ell} S_3$.

$$Z = \int_{S_6} C_3 = \sum_{i>j} \int_{D_5(i,j)} d\Omega_4^1(A_i,A_j) = \sum_{i>j>k} \int_{D_4(i,j,k)} \Omega_4^1(A_i,A_j,A_k)$$

$$= \sum_{i>j>k} \int_{D_4(i,j,k)} d\Omega_3^2(A_i,A_j,A_k) = \int_{S_3} \Delta\Omega_3^2(A_1,A_2,A_3,A_4) = \pi_2(g^3)$$

$$\Delta\alpha^2(A;g_1,g_2,g_3) = 2\pi \int_{S_3} \Delta\Omega_3^2(A_1,A_2,A_3,A_4) = 2\pi Z$$

Recurrently, divide S_6 into K+2 discs ($0 \leq K \leq 5$) the common boundary of these discs is S_{5-K}.

$$\int_{S_{5-K}} \Omega_{5-k}^k = Z = \pi_k(g^{5-k})$$

<u>DeRham Cech cohomology</u>. Instead of dividing S_6 exactly into sum of discs, we cover S_6 with union of open sets u_i, $S_6 = \cup u_i$, which constitute a good cover, i.e. all intersection of u_i are either empty or contractible, e.g. 8 open sets with nerve homotopic to the boundaries of a 7-simplex dual to S_6.

Z: De Rham Cech index of d-Δ series

$$
\begin{array}{cccccccc}
C_3 \overset{r}{\rightarrow} C_3 & & & & & & & \\
 & \Omega^0_5 & \Delta\Omega^0_5 & & & & & \\
 & & \Omega^1_4 & \Delta\Omega^1_4 & & & & \\
 & & & \Omega^2_3 & \Delta\Omega^2_3 & & & \\
 & & & & \Omega^3_2 & \Delta\Omega^3_2 & & \\
 & & & & & \Omega^4_1 & \Delta\Omega^4_1 & \\
 & & & & & & \Omega^5_0 & \Delta\Omega^5_0 \\
 & & & & & & & i\uparrow \\
d\uparrow \rightarrow \Delta & & & & & & & C^7(u,R)
\end{array}
$$

r: restriction. i: inclusion. $C^P(U,R)$: constant on intersection of P open sets.

We will show: $\pi_k(g^{5-k})$ <u>depends only on g</u>

For example, when k=0. $\Omega^0_5(A)$ = Chern Simons form, which may be expressed as an integral from $A \rightarrow 0$ in $\mathcal{a}^5$

$$Q^1_5(A,0) \simeq \int_0^1 dt\ \mathrm{tr}(tA\ F_t^2) \ ,$$

It is easy to prove $\int_{S_5} (Q^1_5(A_1,A_2)+Q^1_5(A_2,A_3)+Q^1_5(A_3,A_1)) = 0$

Then

$$\Delta\Omega^0_5(A;g) = \Omega^0_5(A^g) - \Omega^0_5(A) = Q^1_5(A^g,0) - Q^1_5(A,0)$$

$$= Q^1_5(A,gdg^{-1}) - Q^1_5(A,0) = -Q^1_5(gdg^{-1},0) = Q^1_5(g^{-1}dg,0) = \mathrm{tr}(g^{-1}dg)^5$$

More generally we divide Ω into parts $\Omega^k_{5-k}(A_1,\ldots,A_{K+1}) \equiv$

$$\Omega^k_{5-k}(A;g_1,\ldots,g_k) = Q^{k+1}_{5-K}(A_1,\ldots,A_{k+1},0) + R^k_{5-k}(g_1,\ldots,g_k)$$

where

$$Q^k_{2n-k}(A_1,\ldots,A_{k+1}) = (-1)^{k(k+1)/2}\frac{n!}{(n-k)!k!}\int dt_1\ldots dt_{k+1}\,\delta(1-\sum_1^{k+1}t_i)\mathrm{str}(A_t^k F_t^{n-k}),$$

$$A_t = \sum_i^{k+1} t_i A_i\ ,\ F_t = dA_t + A_t^2\ ,\ \sum_i^{k+1} t_i = 1,\ 0 \le t_i \le 1.$$

They satisfy

$$\Delta Q^{k+1}_{2n-k-1}(A_1,\ldots,A_{k+2}) \equiv \sum_i Q^{k+1}_{2n-k-1}(A_1,\ldots,\hat{A}_i,\ldots,A_{k+2})$$

$$= (-1)^k\, d\, Q^{k+2}_{2n-k-2}(A_1,\ldots,A_{k+2})\ (\hat{A}_i : A_i \text{ is excised})$$

Then one can show

$$(\Delta + (-1)^k d)\sum_k R^k_{5-k} = \sum_k Q^{k+1}_{5-k}(g_1^{-1}dg_1,\ (g_1g_2)^{-1}d(g_1g_2),\ldots.$$

$$(g_1\ldots g_1)^{-1}d(g_1\ldots g_k),0)$$

And

$$\pi^k(g^{5-k}) = \int_{S_{5-k}} \Delta\Omega^k_{5-k}(A;g_1,\ldots,g_{k+1})$$

$$= \int_{S_{5-k}} \Delta\Omega^k_{5-k}(0;g_1,\ldots,g_{k+1}) = \int_{S_{5-k}} -Q^{k+1}_{5-k}(g_1^{-1}dg_1,\ldots,(g_1\ldots g_k)^{-1}d(g_1\ldots g_k),0)$$

$$+ \Delta R^k_{5-k}$$

depends on g only.

<u>Bundle</u> $a^{2n-k-1}(a/g,g)$. For example in case of n=3, k=1 we have

$$Z = \pi_1(g^4) = \int_{S_4} \Delta\Omega_4^1 = \int_{S_4} \int_{\partial\sigma_2} \omega_4^1 = \int_{\partial\sigma_2} (\int_{S_4} \omega_4^1) \equiv$$

$$\equiv \int_{\partial\sigma_2} \beta^1 = \int_{\sigma_2} \delta\beta^1$$

where: $\partial\sigma_2 \varepsilon g^4$, $\sigma_2 \varepsilon \alpha^4/g^4$, $\beta^k \equiv \int_{S_i} \omega_i^k$.

Thus the cotangent space of $\alpha^4(\alpha/g,g) \sim \beta^1 \wedge \delta\beta^1$ behaves like a Hopf bundle - "monopole".

More generally this corresponds to the family index

$$\delta\beta = \int_M \hat{A}(M)\mathrm{ch}(F)$$

In this note we have restricted to gauge group cocyles, where the descent series with common index implies that the nontriviality of lower cocycle dictates the nontriviality and existence of higher cocyles.

Now we turn to the case of translation group cocyles, meanwhile the existence of lower cocyle implies the vanishing of higher cocyles. The translation group manifold may be identified to the space time. Then n dimensional subset constitutes the n-chain χ_n, boundaryless chain is called a cycle $\sigma_n, \partial\sigma_n = 0$. The nontrivial cycle are not a boundary of any chain. Cocyles are integrals of closed forms over chains or cycles $\alpha^1 = \int_{\sigma_1} A$, $\alpha^2 = \int_{\sigma_2} F$, $\alpha^3 = \int_{\sigma_3} J$, where: A, F, J are closed 1, 2, 3 forms respectively. We illustrate by examples. One boundary: the pure gauge potential A is exact, $A = d\theta$ globally; correspondingly, σ_1 are 1-boundary always. Topologically nontrivial one cocycle--Dirac string: α^1 equals winding number of σ_1 around the string, the pure gauge A although is closed $dA = 0$, but being the generator of first cohomology, it is not exact globally, i.e. $A = d\theta$ only locally. Two boundary: topologically trivial magnetic field $F = dA$ globally. Nontrivial two cocycle-Dirac monopole: now α^2 equals the pole enlosed by σ_2; strength F is the generator of second cohomology, $F = dA$ only locally, $A \to A + d$ some gauge is defined only up to a gauge. $\int_{S_1} A_{north} - A_{south} = 2\pi Z = \int_{\sigma_2} F$. Similarly, for nontrivial 3-cocyle, $J = dF$ only up to a total differential locally, for

$F \to F + d$(something), the J is unchanged. Also $\int_{S_2} F_N - F_S = 2\pi Z = \int_{\sigma_3} J$. Since now $F \neq dA$, otherwise $J = dF = 0$, there exists no A as the potential. In reality the nonunique F becomes the "potential" two forms, J becomes the three forms "strength". These kinds of quantities occurs in supergravity and superstring, so the interesting nonassociativity and anomalous Jacobi characterizing 3-cocyles may be realized subsequently.

Acknowledgement

I would like to thank ITP Stony Brook and Prof. C. N. Yang for their hospitality. This research was supported in part by the Scientific Foundation of China and the National Science Foundation Grant No. 81-09110A-03.

Reference

M. F. Atiyah, I. M. Singer, R. Jackiw, B. Zumino, H. Y. Guo this proceeding and references in these papers.

ABJ ANOMALY IN SUPERSYMMETRIC GAUGE THEORIES

L. Bonora, P. Pasti and M. Tonin

Dipartimento di Fisica "G. Galilei" - Università degli Studi di Padova

Istituto Nazionale di Fisica Nucleare - Sezione di Padova

Via Marzolo, 8 - 35131 Padova - ITALY

* * *

Recently much attention has been payed to the ABJ or consistent chiral anomaly in supersymmetric Yang-Mills theories (SYMT). In ref. [1] the ABJ anomaly is given implicitly and can be calculated by means of a recursive relation in the prepotential V. Closed expressions for the chiral anomaly in a SYMT, have been obtained in [2] and [3] by explicit calculations of the "heat kernel equation" type. An explicit expression of the ABJ anomaly in terms of superfields has been derived in [4], [5] using an algebraic-cohomological approach. Here we present the approach of ref. [4].

Our notations are those of ref. [4]. $z^M \equiv (x^m, \theta^{\underline{\mu}})$ are the coordinates in the superspace, x^m are the usual space-time coordinates and $\theta^{\underline{\mu}}$ are Grassmann variables $\underline{\mu} \equiv (\mu, \dot{\mu})$, $\mu, \dot{\mu} = 1,2$.

The total differential in the superspace is:

$$d_s = dz^M \frac{\partial}{\partial z^M} = e^A D_A \tag{1}$$

where $e^A = dz^M e_M^A$ are the rigid vielbeins, which satisfy the condition

$$d_s e^A = i e^B e^C \sigma_{CB}^A$$

and σ_{CB}^A is the rigid torsion, whose non vanishing components are $\sigma_{\gamma\dot{\beta}}^a$.

In the following it will useful to split the total differential d_s:

$$d_s = d + \mathcal{D} + T \tag{2}$$

$$d = e^a \frac{\partial}{\partial x^a}, \quad \mathcal{D} = D + \bar{D}, \ D = e^\alpha D_\alpha, \ \bar{D} = e^{\dot{\alpha}} D_{\dot{\alpha}}, \ Te^A = i e^B e^C \sigma_{CB}^A$$

SYMT's are described by a constrained superconnection one form $\varphi(z)$ with values in the Lie algebra G of the gauge group. The constraints are imposed on the curvature two form F. They are

$$\mathcal{F}_{\underline{\alpha}\underline{\beta}} = 0 \tag{3}$$

The constraints (3) are solved by the connection:

$$\varphi_\alpha = e^{-U^\dagger} D_\alpha e^{U^\dagger}, \quad \varphi_{\dot\alpha} = e^{U} D_{\dot\alpha} e^{-U}, \quad \varphi_a = \frac{i}{4}\left(D_\alpha \varphi_{\dot\alpha} + D_{\dot\alpha}\varphi_\alpha + [\varphi_\alpha, \varphi_{\dot\alpha}]_+\right) \tag{4}$$

When the fields U and $U^\dagger$ become the fundamental fields of the theory, a larger gauge invariance arises:

$$e^{U'(z)} = e^{-L(z)} e^{U(z)} e^{\Lambda(z)}, \quad e^{U^{\dagger\prime}(z)} = e^{-\bar\Lambda(z)} e^{U^\dagger(z)} e^{L(z)}$$

$$\bar D \Lambda(z) = D\bar\Lambda(z) = 0 \qquad \Lambda^\dagger(z) = -\bar\Lambda(z) \in \mathcal{G}$$

where L(z) is the usual gauge-matrix and $\Lambda(z)$ represents the additional invariance. Performing suitable field-dependent gauge transformations on the connection φ, we obtain the new connections

$$\omega_\alpha = e^{-V} D_\alpha e^{V}, \quad \omega_{\dot\alpha} = 0, \quad \omega_a = \frac{i}{4}(\sigma_a)^{\alpha\dot\alpha} D_{\dot\alpha}\omega_\alpha \tag{5a}$$

$$\bar\omega_\alpha = 0, \quad \bar\omega_{\dot\alpha} = e^{V} D_{\dot\alpha} e^{-V}, \quad \bar\omega_a = \frac{i}{4}(\sigma_a)^{\alpha\dot\alpha} D_\alpha \bar\omega_{\dot\alpha} \tag{5b}$$

where

$$e^{V} = e^{U^\dagger} e^{U} \tag{6}$$

Under a gauge transformation, $\omega(\bar\omega)$ is affected only by $\Lambda(\bar\Lambda)$.

We denote with c(z), $\gamma(z)$ and $\bar\gamma(z)$ the F.P. ghost superfields associated with the gauge parameters L(z), $\Lambda(z)$ and $\bar\Lambda(z)$ respectively, and with Σ_G^c, Σ_G^γ, $\Sigma_G^{\bar\gamma}$ the coboundary operators associated with the BRST transformations with ghosts c, γ and $\bar\gamma$ respectively. The coboundary operator Σ_G,

$$\Sigma_G = \Sigma_G^c + \Sigma_G^\gamma + \Sigma_G^{\bar\gamma} \tag{7}$$

describes the "total" BRST transformation.

Let us introduce the global F.P. ghost parameters $\varepsilon^A = (0, \varepsilon^\alpha\ \varepsilon^{\dot\alpha})$ associated with rigid supersymmetry. $\varepsilon^{\underline{\alpha}}$ are c-numbers and the functional operator Σ_S defined on superfields integrated over space-time

$$\Sigma_S \int_x \psi(z) = \int_x \varepsilon^A D_A \psi(z) \tag{8}$$

is a coboundary operator, which represents the BRST transformation associated with rigid supersymmetry. Therefore the operator

$$\Sigma_T = \Sigma_G + \Sigma_S \tag{9}$$

is also a coboundary operator, $\Sigma_T^2=0$, and the coupled Ward identities for rigid supersymmetry and gauge transformations is

$$\Sigma_T \Gamma = K(\Delta_G + \Delta_S) + O(K^2) \tag{10}$$

The consistency conditions are:

$$\Sigma_G \Delta_G = 0 \; , \; \Sigma_S \Delta_S = 0$$
$$\Sigma_G \Delta_S + \Sigma_S \Delta_G = 0 \tag{11}$$

Now we look for a non-trivial solution of eqs. (11). To this end we shall use a "generalized transgression formula".

Let us enlarge the superspace by adding a Grassmann variable η and a real variable $y, 0 \leq y \leq 1$. The total differential in this enlarged superspace is

$$d_T = d_s + dy\frac{\partial}{\partial y} + d\eta\frac{\partial}{\partial \eta} = d_s + dy\frac{\partial}{\partial y} + d\eta\,\delta \tag{12}$$

The usual BRST transformation coincides with the "translation" δ along η.

Let $\rho(z)$ be a G-valued superconnection 1-form whose gauge transform is:

$$\rho'(z) = e^{-\mathcal{K}(z)}\rho(z)e^{\mathcal{K}(z)} + e^{-\mathcal{K}(z)} d_s e^{\mathcal{K}(z)}$$

$R(z) = d_s\rho(z) + \rho(z)\rho(z))$ is the corresponding curvature 2-form and $\mathcal{K}(z) \in G$ is the corresponding F.P. ghost superfield. Moreover we consider a G-valued superfield $Z(z)$, which transforms as

$$e^{Z'(z)} = e^{-\mathcal{K}(z)} e^{Z(z)}$$

The three symbols $(\rho, \mathcal{K}, Z)$ represent either $(\varphi, c, U$ or $U^\dagger)$ or $(\omega, \gamma, -U$ or $-V)$ or $(\bar{\omega}, \bar{\gamma}, U^\dagger$ or $V^\dagger)$.

Now let us define in the enlarged superspace the following superconnection:

$$\overset{\eta,y}{\rho}(z,\eta,y) = e^{-H(z,\eta,y)}\rho(z)e^{H(z,\eta,y)} + e^{-H(z,\eta,y)} d_T e^{H(z,\eta,y)} \tag{13}$$

where

$$e^{H(z,\eta,y)} = e^{\eta\mathcal{K}(z)} e^{yZ^{\eta}(z,\eta)} \; , \quad e^{Z^{\eta}(z,\eta)} = e^{-\eta\mathcal{K}(z)} e^{Z(z)} \tag{14}$$

The corresponding curvature is $\overset{\eta,y}{R}(z,\eta,y) = d_T\overset{\eta,y}{\rho}(z,\eta,y) + \overset{\eta,y}{\rho}(z,\eta,y)\,\overset{\eta,y}{\rho}(z,\eta,y)$

If $\overset{\eta,y}{\rho_t} = t\overset{\eta,y}{\rho}$, $\overset{\eta,y}{R_t} = d_T\overset{\eta,y}{\rho_t} + \overset{\eta,y}{\rho_t}\overset{\eta,y}{\rho_t}$ the generalized transgression formula in the enlarged superspace in terms of the enlarged superconnection writes

$$\mathrm{Str}(\overset{\eta,y}{R}, \overset{\eta,y}{R}, \overset{\eta,y}{R}) = 3\, d_T\int_0^1 dt\, \mathrm{Str}(\overset{\eta,y}{\rho}, \overset{\eta,y}{R_t}, \overset{\eta,y}{R_t}) \tag{15}$$

Eq.(15) is the starting point of our analysis and it splits up into several equations.

We note that an m-superform in the enlarged superspace contains at most one factor dy. Therefore, exhibiting the factors dy and $d\eta$, we get

$$\chi(z,\eta,y)=\sum_{\substack{p,q,k\\ p+q+k=m}}(d\eta)^k\,\chi^{k,0}_{p,q}+\sum_{\substack{p,q,k\\ p+q+k=m-1}}(d\eta)^k\,dy\,\chi^{k,1}_{p,q}$$

where $\chi^{k,i}_{p,q}$ contains p space-time vielbeins e and q spinor like vielbeins e^{α}.

First let us consider the sectors $\binom{k,0}{p,q}$ of eq.(15) taken at $\eta=y=0, \rho=\varphi$, $R=\mathcal{F}$, $\kappa=c$. We get

$$\mathrm{Str}(\mathcal{F},\mathcal{F},\mathcal{F})=3\hat{d}_s\int_0^1 dt\,\mathrm{Str}(\hat{\varphi},\hat{\mathcal{F}}_t,\hat{\mathcal{F}}_t)\equiv\hat{d}_s\,Q_5(\varphi,c)\equiv$$
$$\equiv\hat{d}_s\Big(\sum_{\substack{p,q,k\\ p+q+k=5}}(d\eta)^k\,Q^{k,0}_{p,q}(\varphi,c)\Big)\tag{16}$$

where $\hat{d}_s=d_s+d\eta\frac{\partial}{\partial\eta}$, $\hat{\varphi}$ is the superconnection (13) computed for $\eta=0$, $d_T=\hat{d}_s$, $\rho=\varphi$, $\kappa=c$ and $\hat{\mathcal{F}}_t=\hat{d}_s\hat{\varphi}_t+\hat{\varphi}_t\hat{\varphi}_t$

The relevant components of the eq. (16) are those with ghost number 0,1 and 2

$$d\,Q^{0,0}_{3,2}(\varphi)+\mathcal{D}\,Q^{0,0}_{4,1}(\varphi)=[\mathrm{Str}(\mathcal{F},\mathcal{F},\mathcal{F})]_{4,2}\tag{17a}$$
$$d\,Q^{1,0}_{3,2}(c,\varphi)+\mathcal{D}\,Q^{1,0}_{4,0}(\varphi,c)+\delta\,Q^{0,0}_{4,1}(\varphi)=0\tag{17b}$$
$$\delta\,Q^{1,0}_{4,0}(\varphi,c)+d\,Q^{2,0}_{3,0}(\varphi,c)=0\tag{17c}$$

Moreover we have the important identity

$$[\mathrm{Str}(\mathcal{F},\mathcal{F},\mathcal{F})]_{4,2}=\mathcal{D}X^{0,0}_{4,1}\equiv\mathcal{D}\,\frac{i}{24}\,e^f e^c e^b e^a e^\alpha\,\mathrm{Str}(\mathcal{F}_{\alpha a},\mathcal{F}_{\gamma b},(\sigma_c)^{\gamma\dot\gamma}\mathcal{F}_{\dot\gamma f})$$

Let us define

$$\hat{Q}^{0,0}_{4,1}(\varphi)=Q^{0,0}_{4,1}(\varphi)-X^{0,0}_{4,1}(\varphi)\tag{18}$$

and let us apply the operator $(i_\varepsilon)^2$ to eq. (17), the operator i_ε to eq. (17b) and the operator $\int_X(\;)\big|_{\theta=\bar\theta=0}$ to eqs. (17a)-(17c) where i_ε is the interior product of a q-superform w.r.t. the vector field $\varepsilon^M=\varepsilon^A e_A^M$. We get, recalling eq. (8)

$$\Sigma_S \Delta_S(\varphi)=0, \quad \Sigma_G^c \Delta_G(\varphi,c)=0, \quad \Sigma_G^c \Delta_S(\varphi)+\Sigma_S \Delta_G(\varphi,c)=0 \tag{19}$$

where

$$\Delta_S(\varphi)=\int_x \left(i_z \hat{Q}^{0,0}_{4,1}(\varphi)\right)\Big|_{\theta=\bar\theta=0}$$
$$\Delta_G(\varphi,c)=\int_x \left(Q^{1,0}_{4,1}(\varphi,c)\right)\Big|_{\theta=\bar\theta=0} \tag{20}$$

Therefore the quantities $\Delta_G(\varphi,c)$ and $\Delta_S(\varphi)$ are non-trivial solutions of the consistency conditions (11) because Δ_G is a non trivial cocycle of Σ_G^c. If we take eq. (16) at $\rho(z)=\omega(z)(\bar\omega(z))$, $\kappa(z)=\gamma(z)(\bar\gamma(z))$, we obtain as solutions of the eq. (11) the same functionals Δ_G and Δ_S with φ and c replaced by $\omega(\bar\omega)$ and $\gamma(\bar\gamma)$ respectively.

Now we are faced with two problems:

i) $\Delta_T(\varphi)=\Delta_G(\varphi,c)+\Delta_S(\varphi)$, $\Delta_T(\omega)=\Delta_G(\omega,\gamma)+\Delta_S(\omega)$, $\Delta_T(\bar\omega)=\Delta_G(\bar\omega,\bar\gamma)+\Delta_S(\bar\omega)$ are the r.h.s. of eq. (10) when the SYMT is described by the superconnections φ, ω, $\bar\omega$ respectively. The problem is whether these three cocycles are equivalent, i.e. whether they belong to the same cohomology class of Σ_T.;

ii) According to the theorem stated in ref. |7|, $\Delta_S(\varphi)$ must be a trivial cocycle of Σ_S, i.e. $\Delta_S(\varphi)=\Sigma_S C$ for a suitable functional C. If we want an explicit supersymmetric invariant expression for the ABJ anomaly, we must find the explicit form of C and subtract it from the effective action Γ.

These two problems can be solved by using eq. (15) in different sectors.

As to the first question, let us consider eq. (15) taken at $\eta=0$ and with $\rho=\varphi$, $\kappa=c$, $Z=U$, $R=J$ in the sectors $\binom{0,1}{4,1}$ and $\binom{1,1}{4,0}$. Integrating over y and applying the operator $\int_x (\ \ )|_{\theta=\bar\theta=0}$ we get:

$$\Sigma_S C_U = -\Delta_S(\varphi)+\Delta_S(\omega)$$
$$\Sigma_G^c C_U = -\Delta_G(\varphi,c) \tag{21}$$

where C_U is defined by

$$dy\, C_{\mathcal{U}} \equiv \int_x \int_0^1 dy' \int_0^1 dt \left[Str(\rho^{\eta,y'}, R_t^{\eta,y'}, R_t^{\eta,y'}) \right]_{4,0}^{0,1} \Bigg|_{\substack{\eta=0 \\ \rho=\varphi \\ \varkappa=c \\ R_t=\mathcal{F}_t \\ \theta=\bar\theta=0}}$$

Moreover

$$\Sigma_G^{\gamma} C_{\mathcal{U}} = \Delta_G(\omega,\gamma) \qquad \Sigma_G^{\bar\gamma} C_{\mathcal{U}} = 0 \tag{22}$$

Similarly, we obtain

$$\Sigma_G^{c} C_{\mathcal{U}^+} = -\Delta_G(\varphi,c)\,,\quad \Sigma_S C_{\mathcal{U}^+} = -\Delta_S(\varphi) + \Delta_S(\bar\omega) \tag{23}$$
$$\Sigma_G^{\gamma} C_{\mathcal{U}^+} = 0 \qquad \Sigma_G^{\bar\gamma} C_{\mathcal{U}^+} = \Delta_G(\bar\omega,\bar\gamma)\,,\quad C_{\mathcal{U}^+} = (C_{\mathcal{U}})^T$$

From eqs. (22)-(24) it follows that

$$\Delta_T(\varphi) = \Delta_T(\omega) - \Sigma_T C_{\mathcal{U}} = \Delta_T(\bar\omega) - \Sigma_T C_{\mathcal{U}^+} = \Delta_T - \tfrac{1}{2}\Sigma_T(C_{\mathcal{U}} + C_{\mathcal{U}^+}) \tag{24}$$

This method is similar to Bardeen-Zumino's |8|, which allows us to transform gravitational anomalies into Lorentz anomalies and viceversa.

As to the second question we start from eq. (15) taken at $\eta=0$, $\rho=\omega$ $\varkappa=\gamma$, $R=F^{\omega}$, $Z=-V$ and we consider the zero ghost sectors. After a long algebraic calculation we get

$$\hat{Q}_{4,1}^{0,0}(\omega) = -\mathcal{D}Y(\omega) \tag{25}$$

and similarly

$$\hat{Q}_{4,1}^{0,0}(\bar\omega) = -\mathcal{D}\bar{Y}(\bar\omega) \tag{26}$$

that is

$$\Delta_S(\omega) = -\Sigma_S C(\omega)\,,\quad \Delta_S(\bar\omega) = -\Sigma_S \bar{C}(\bar\omega)\,,\quad C(\omega) = \int_x (Y(\omega))\big|_{\theta=\bar\theta=0}$$

Therefore the cocycles

$$\Delta(\omega) = \Delta_T(\omega) + \Sigma_T C(\omega),\quad \Delta(\bar\omega) = \Delta_T(\bar\omega) + \Sigma_T \bar{C}(\bar\omega),\quad \Delta = \Delta_T(\varphi) + \tfrac{1}{2}\Sigma_T(C(\omega) + \bar{C}(\bar\omega))$$

are supersymmetric invariant anomalies which belong to the same cohomological class as $\Delta_T(\omega)$, $\Delta_T(\bar\omega)$, Δ_T, $\Delta_T(\varphi)$. The repeated use of eq. (15) in the sectors with ghost number one at $\eta=0$, $\rho=\omega$, $Z=-V$, $\varkappa=\gamma$ and $\rho=\bar\omega$, $Z=V$, $\varkappa=\bar\gamma$ gives us the following expression for ABJ anomaly.

$$\Delta = \frac{1}{4^4}\int_x \left\{ D^2\bar{D}^2\left[\tfrac{i}{4} Str(\gamma, \bar{D}^{\dot\alpha}\omega^{\beta}, \bar{D}_{\dot\alpha}\omega_{\beta}) + (\sigma^a)^{\alpha\dot\beta}\int_0^1 dy\, P_{a,\alpha\dot\beta}(\gamma^y, \omega^y, V) + h.c.\right]\right\} \tag{27}$$

,

where

$$e^a e^\alpha e^{\dot\alpha} \int_0^1 P_{a\alpha\dot\alpha}(\gamma^y, \omega^y, V) = 6\int_0^1 dt\,(1-t)t \int_0^1 dy\, \mathrm{Str}\Big\{\big(\omega^y, \mathcal{F}_t^{\omega^y}, [\gamma^y, V]\big) - \big(\gamma^y, \mathcal{F}_t^{\omega^y}, [\omega^y, V]\big) + \big(V, \mathcal{F}_t^{\omega^y}, [\omega^y, \gamma^y]\big)\Big\}_{1,2}$$

$$\omega^y = e^{yV}\omega e^{-yV} + e^{yV} d_1 e^{-yV}, \quad \gamma^y = e^{yV}\gamma e^{-yV} + e^{yV}\delta_\gamma e^{-yV}$$

Eq. (27) is our final expression for the chiral anomaly in SYMT.

REFERENCES

[1] O. Piguet and K. Sibold, Nucl. Phys. B247 (1984) 484.

[2] N.K. Nielsen, Nucl. Phys. B244, (1984) 499.

[3] E. Guadagnini, K. Konishi and M. Mintchev, Pisa Preprint IF Pth 10/85.

[4] L. Bonora, P. Pasti and M. Tonin, Padova Preprint DFPD 20/84 and Padova Preprint DFPD 12/85

[5] G. Girardi, R. Grimm and R. Stora, Annecy preprint LAPP-Th 130 (1985)

[6] L. Bonora and M. Tonin, Phys. Lett. B98, (1981), 48.

[7] O. Piguet, M. Schweda and K. Sibold, Nucl. Phys. B174 (1980), 183.

[8] W.A. Bardeen and B. Zumino, Nucl. Phys. B244 (1984), 421.

SYMPOSIUM ON ANOMALIES, GEOMETRY, TOPOLOGY

SUPERSTRINGS I

DAN FRIEDAN

CHAIRMAN

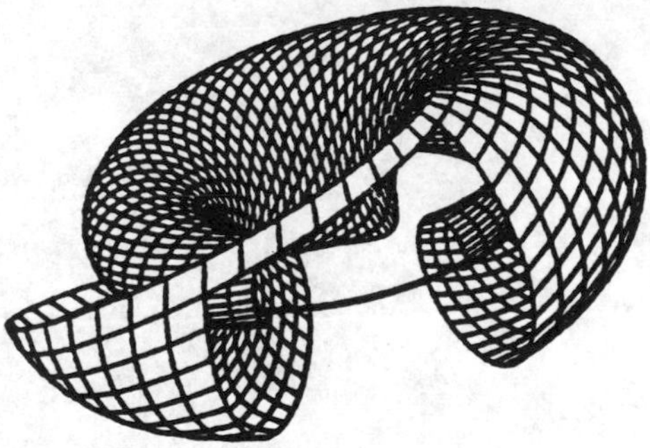

Aspects of Superstring Theory*

Michael B. Green**

California Institute of Technology, Pasadena, CA 91125

Superstring theories may be consistent quantum theories that unify all the forces including gravity with a unifying gauge group that can only be SO(32) or $E_8 \times E_8$. The way in which these groups are deduced by requiring the cancellation of anomalies has been surveyed in this conference and some of the consequent predictions for four-dimensional physics have been described by several people. In this talk I will outline a few other features of superstring theories which have arisen in the course of their development. These will include: I. A discussion of the covariant action that describes the classical dynamics of a superstring in a geometrical manner. II. An outline of light-cone-gauge superstring field theory with an explanation of the absence of higher-order contact interactions in superstring theories. III. A derivation of Yang-Mills field theory as the low-energy limit of the field theory of open superstrings directly from the string-field action.

I. Covariant Action for Free Superstrings [1]

The dynamics of a superstring can be expressed in terms of the ten-dimensional superspace coordinates (which are functions of the parameters of the world-sheet of the string) $x^\mu(\sigma,\tau)$ ($\mu = 0, \cdots, 9$) and one or two ten-dimensional Grassmann spinors $\vartheta^{Ra}(\sigma,\tau)$ (where $a = 1,\ldots,32$ is the spinor index) which satisfy Majorana and Weyl constraints. For type I and type II theories there are two spinors so that $R = 1,2$ whereas for the heterotic string [2] there is only one spinor (and the index R is irrelevant). The action is invariant under global super-Poincaré transformations

$$\delta\vartheta^R = \frac{1}{4} l_{\mu\nu}\gamma^{\mu\nu}\vartheta^R + \varepsilon^R \tag{1}$$

and

* Work supported in part by the U.S. Department of Energy under contract DEAC 03-81-ER40050.

** On leave of absence from Queen Mary College, University of London, U.K. Nuffield Foundation Research Fellow.

$$\delta x^\mu = l^\mu{}_\nu x^\nu + a^\mu + i\bar{\varepsilon}^R \gamma^\mu \vartheta^R \tag{2}$$

where $l^\mu{}_\nu$ are parameters of Lorentz transformations, a^μ are translations and $\varepsilon^R \equiv \varepsilon^{Ra}$ are supersymmetry parameters. For type II theories (which describe oriented closed strings) there are two conserved supercharges and the two spinors ϑ^1 and ϑ^2 can either be chosen to have opposite chirality (resulting in the type IIa theory) or the same chirality (resulting in the chiral type IIb theory). In type I theories (which describe interacting open strings and closed unoriented strings) the open-string boundary conditions break one of the supersymmetries resulting in one conserved (chiral) supercharge.

The spinning string theory (of Ramond [3] and Neveu and Schwarz [4]) was not supersymmetric in ten-dimensional space-time and did not have a geometric formulation. Although the states of the superstring can be viewed in terms of a truncation of the space of states of the spinning string onto a supersymmetric subspace [5], the superstring theory has a considerably more geometric formulation in terms of an action principle that generalizes the Nambu-Goto action [6] to superspace. This action can be written as the sum of two terms [1]

$$S = S_1 + S_2 \tag{3}$$

with

$$S_1 = -\frac{T}{2}\int \sqrt{-g}\, g^{\alpha\beta} \Pi^\mu_\alpha \Pi_{\mu\beta}\, d\sigma\, d\tau \tag{4}$$

where T is the string tension, $g^{\alpha\beta}$ $(\alpha,\beta = 0,1)$ is a two-dimensional metric tensor and Π^μ_α is the obvious generalization of $\partial_\alpha x^\mu$ to superspace

$$\Pi^\mu_\alpha = \partial_\alpha x^\mu - i\bar{\vartheta}^R \gamma^\mu \partial_\alpha \vartheta^R \tag{5}$$

where $\partial_\alpha = (\frac{\partial}{\partial\tau}, \frac{\partial}{\partial\sigma})$ and γ^μ are ten-dimensional Dirac matrices. Π^μ_α is invariant under global supersymmetry transformations (eqs. (1) and (2)) and therefore S_1 is also invariant. Although S_1 is an obvious extension of the familiar Nambu-Goto action it does not seem to be a sensible string action, presumably because it involves interactions (viewed as a two-dimensional field theory in the $\sigma-\tau$ space) which destroy the conformal invariance in the quantum theory. However in [1] we showed that the addition of a new term, S_2, to the action cures this, where

$$S_2 = -iT \int \varepsilon^{\alpha\beta} [\partial_\alpha x^\mu (\bar{\vartheta}^1 \gamma_\mu \partial_\beta \vartheta^1 - \bar{\vartheta}^2 \gamma_\mu \partial_\beta \vartheta^2) - i\bar{\vartheta}^1 \gamma^\mu \partial_\alpha \vartheta^1 \bar{\vartheta}^2 \gamma_\mu \partial_\beta \vartheta^2] . \tag{6}$$

We demonstrated that S_2 is invariant under super-Poincaré transformations. To prove this relies on a Fierz identity, $\gamma^\mu \psi_1 \bar{\psi}_2 \gamma_\mu \psi_3 + perms = 0$, which holds for Majorana spinors in three and four space-time dimensions and Weyl spinors in six dimensions as well as ten-dimensional Majorana-Weyl spinors. As a result a classical superstring action similar to eq. (3) can be written for theories in any of these dimensions although only the $D = 10$ theory has so far been quantized. This leaves open the question of whether the theories in lower dimensions can be quantized by using the procedure advocated by Polyakov [7] for dealing with string theories in less then their critical dimensions. The relative coefficients in S_1 and S_2 are determined uniquely by requiring the total action to possess local fermionic symmetries in the string world-sheet (in addition to the manifest local reparametrization invariance) which allows the choice of the light-cone gauge defined by *

$$\gamma^+ \vartheta^R = 0 \tag{7}$$

and

$$x^+(\sigma, \tau) = x^+ + \frac{p^+}{\pi T} \tau . \tag{8}$$

The latter condition is familiar from the GGRT treatment of the bosonic string theory [8]. Recalling that $(\gamma^+)^2 = 0$, the condition in eq. (7) implies the vanishing of half the Grassmann coordinates. The local fermionic $\sigma - \tau$ symmetry that allows this is given by

$$\delta_\kappa \vartheta^R = 2i\gamma \bullet \Pi_\alpha \kappa^{R\alpha} \qquad \delta_\kappa x^\mu = i\bar{\vartheta}^R \gamma^\mu \delta_\kappa \vartheta^R$$
$$\delta_\kappa(\sqrt{-g}\, g^{\alpha\beta}) = -16\sqrt{-g}\, [P_-^{\alpha\gamma} \bar{\kappa}^{1\beta} \partial_\gamma \vartheta^1 + P_+^{\alpha\gamma} \bar{\kappa}^{2\beta} \partial_\gamma \vartheta^2] \tag{9}$$

where $\kappa^{R\alpha}$ are Grassmann parameters which are two-vectors (with a suppressed ten-dimensional Majorana-Weyl spinor index) and satisfy the (anti) self duality conditions

$$P_+^{\alpha\beta} \kappa_\beta^1 = 0 \tag{10a}$$

$$P_-^{\alpha\beta} \kappa_\beta^2 = 0 \tag{10b}$$

where $P_\pm^{\alpha\beta} = \frac{1}{2}(g^{\alpha\beta} \pm \varepsilon^{\alpha\beta}/\sqrt{-g})$. The invariance of $S = S_1 + S_2$ under the κ transformations uniquely determine the relative coefficients of the two terms.

* The light-cone + and - components of any vector A^μ are defined by $A^\pm = \frac{1}{\sqrt{2}}(A^0 \pm A^9)$.

The term S_1 can be thought of as the action for a non-linear σ-model in which the world sheet is mapped into $N = 2$ $D = 10$ superspace. An interesting observation has been made [9] that the term S_2 also has a geometric meaning as it can be interpreted as a "Wess-Zumino" term. This can be seen by introducing the manifestly super-Poincaré invariant line element

$$\Omega_\alpha^\Gamma \equiv (\partial_\alpha x^\mu - i\bar{\vartheta}^S \gamma^\mu \partial_\alpha \vartheta^S, \partial_\alpha \vartheta^R) \tag{11}$$

where the capital Greek index runs over the values of μ and R. The action S_1 can be written as an integral of a bilinear in Ω_α ($S_1 = -\frac{T}{2}\int \sqrt{-g}\, g^{\alpha\beta}\Omega_\alpha^\Gamma \Omega_\beta^\Gamma$). The term S_2 can be expressed as a three-dimensional integral by formally extending the two-dimensional σ-τ space to three dimensions (in the style of Witten's treatment of Wess-Zumino terms [10])

$$S_2 = \int d^3\xi\, \varepsilon^{\alpha\beta\gamma} \Omega_{\alpha\beta\gamma}^3 \tag{12}$$

where

$$\Omega_{\alpha\beta\gamma}^3 = f_{\Gamma\Delta\Lambda} \Omega_{[\alpha}^\Gamma \Omega_\beta^\Delta \Omega_{\gamma]}^\Lambda \,. \tag{13}$$

The integral in eq. (12) is over any three-dimensional manifold with a boundary which is the two dimensional world-sheet. For Ω^3 to be Lorentz-covariant the non-zero components of $f_{\Gamma\Delta\Lambda}$ must have the form $(\gamma_\mu C^{-1})_{ab}\, a^{RS}$ where C is the charge conjugation matrix and a^{RS} is a symmetric 2×2 matrix. Furthermore, the authors of ref. [9] show that for Ω^3 to be closed (i.e., for it to have vanishing curl) a^{RS} must have the form $a\begin{bmatrix} 1 & \\ & -1 \end{bmatrix}$ where a is a constant. In this case Ω^3 is also exact and can be written in the form $\Omega_{\alpha\beta\gamma}^3 = \partial_{[\alpha}\Omega_{\beta\gamma]}^2$. For a suitable choice of the constant a the integral in eq. (12) over the three-dimensional space with a boundary reduces to the expression (6) for S_2 (where the integrand in eq. (6) is proportional to $\varepsilon^{\alpha\beta}\Omega_{\alpha\beta}$).

The action for the heterotic string may be written down in analogous fashion. In this case the terms S_1 and S_2 are changed by deleting one of the two Grassmann spinors to give $S_1' + S_2'$. The remaining Grassmann spinor reduces, in the light-cone gauge, to a two-dimensional *chiral* spinor (which moves in only one direction, say to the "left"). In addition a new term S_3 must be added to the action which involves 32 fermionic coordinates ψ^I ($I = 1, \cdots, 32$) which are chiral two-dimensional spinors (moving to the "right") carrying the internal symmetry quantum numbers

$$S_3 = \frac{iT}{2}\int d\sigma\, d\tau \quad \bar{\psi}^I \rho \cdot \partial \psi^I \tag{14}$$

where ρ^a are the two-dimensional Dirac matrices. The two different possible internal symmetry groups are obtained by either choosing ψ^I to transform as the defining representation of SO(32) or as two 16's of the SO(16) × SO(16) subgroup of $E_8 \times E_8$. [The internal symmetry can be incorporated by using sixteen bosonic coordinates instead of the 32 fermionic ones. These bosonic coordinates are also two-dimensionally "chiral" which means that each of them is a self-dual two-dimensional scalar.]

Several open questions concerning the covariant formulation are evident.

1) Can the relative coefficient between S_1 and S_2 be determined geometrically? It's value was originally determined to ensure that the theory possessed the local σ–τ supersymmetry that permitted the choice of the light-cone gauge in which it is manifestly free-field theory, and hence conformally invariant. It has been suggested (by Curtright, Mezincescu and Zachos) that the term S_2 corresponds to a torsion term that parallelizes the superspace manifold. This would be similar to the way that the Wess-Zumino term for a non-linear σ model on a group manifold describes a torsion that parallelizes the manifold at a value of the coupling for which the model is conformally invariant [11] (i.e., where the β function vanishes) [10]. For the heterotic string theory the analogy is exact whereas for the type II (or type I) string theories the term S_2 is not exactly the torsion due to the presence of the matrix a^{RS} in eq. (13).

2) The action of eqs. (3), (4) and (6) has never been quantized in a covariant manner. This is obviously desirable to make contact with covariant Feynman rules. The problems stem from the fact that the action of eq. (3) gives rise to canonical phase-space variables which are subject to second-class constraints (as well as first-class ones). The Dirac procedure for defining the quantum brackets leads to terrible quantum ordering problems. Some aspects of this problem are tackled in [12] as well as by Kaku and by Siegel in reports at this meeting.

3) In order to discuss compactified theories there should be a generalization of the covariant action to a curved target space.

II. Superstring Field Theory (in the light-cone gauge)

In the light-cone parametrization defined by eqs. (7) and (8) manifest Lorentz invariance is lost and only the SO(8) subgroup of transformations in the directions transverse to the ± directions is a manifest symmetry. In this formalism the spinors ϑ^{Ra} are not Grassmann coordinates but satisfy the anti-commutation relations, $\{\vartheta^{Ra}(\sigma,\tau),\vartheta^{Sb}(\sigma',\tau)\} = \delta^{ab}\delta^{RS}\delta(\sigma-\sigma')$ and so they are a mixture of "coordinates" and their conjugate "momenta". In order to define fields which are functionals of the string superspace coordinates we must define superspace spinor variables which are

Grassmann-valued (i.e. anticommute). This is possible to achieve by decomposing the SO(8) spinors into spinors of a SU(4) × U(1) subgroup of SO(8) (for details see ref. [13]). The two SO(8) spinors each decompose into a $\bar{4}$ and 4 of SU(4) denoted by $(\vartheta^{\bar{A}}, \lambda^A)$ and $(\tilde{\vartheta}^{\bar{A}}, \tilde{\lambda}^A)$ (where $A, \bar{A} = 1,..4$). The transverse space-time coordinates $x(\sigma,\tau) \equiv x^I(\sigma,\tau)$ ($I = 1,\cdots,8$) form a 6 and 2 singlets of SU(4). λ^A and $\tilde{\lambda}^A$ are "momenta" conjugate to the coordinates $\vartheta^{\bar{A}}$ and $\tilde{\vartheta}^{\bar{A}}$ respectively (i.e. $\lambda^A = \frac{\delta}{\delta\vartheta^{\bar{A}}}$ and $\tilde{\lambda}^A = \frac{\delta}{\delta\tilde{\lambda}^{\bar{A}}}$). I am describing the notation appropriate to the chiral type IIb theory (for the type IIa theory the roles of $\tilde{\vartheta}^{\bar{A}}$ and $\tilde{\lambda}^A$ are interchanged).

Free Fields

String superfields are *functionals* of the light-cone superspace coordinates. I will only discuss open-string fields denoted by

$$\Phi^{ab}_{p^+}[x(\sigma),\vartheta(\sigma),\tilde{\vartheta}(\sigma)]$$

in this lecture although the complete interacting string quantum theory also includes closed-string fields. The light-cone "time," x^+, has been chosen to be zero and the fields are taken to be functions of p^+, the Fourier conjugate variable to x^-.

The super-Poincaré algebra is represented in terms of operators g formed out of the coordinates and the conjugate momenta. It can also be represented at the level of the free field theory by generators, G_2 quadratic in fields

$$G_2 = \int_0^\infty dp^+ \int Dx D\vartheta D\tilde{\vartheta}\, tr(\Phi_{-p^+} g \Phi_{p^+}), \tag{15}$$

(suppressing group theory indices) where the functional integrals involve an infinite product of integrals over each mode of the superspace coordinates. The free-field Hamiltonian, H_2 is obtained by choosing g to be the Hamiltonian operator h, defined by (setting $T = \frac{1}{\pi}$ from now on)

$$h = \int_0^{2\pi|p^+|} \left[sign(p^+)\left[\pi(\frac{\delta}{\delta x^I})^2 + \frac{1}{\pi}(x^{I'})^2\right] - 2i\left[\vartheta^{\bar{A}}\lambda^{A'} + \tilde{\vartheta}^{\bar{A}}\tilde{\lambda}^{A'}\right]\right] \tag{16}$$

(where ' denotes differentiation with respect to σ). The coordinates and momenta x^I, $\frac{\delta}{\delta x^I}$, ϑ, $\tilde{\vartheta}$, $\frac{\delta}{\delta\vartheta}$ and $\frac{\delta}{\delta\tilde{\vartheta}}$ have normal mode expansions in terms of infinite sets of bosonic oscillators modes α^I_n (where $\alpha^I_{-n} \equiv \alpha^{I\dagger}_n$) satisfying $[\alpha^I_n, \alpha^J_n] = m\,\delta_{m+n,0}\delta^{IJ}$ and fermionic modes Q^A_m and $Q^{\bar{A}}_m$ satisfying $\{Q^A_m, Q^{\bar{B}}_n\} = 2p^+\delta^{A\bar{B}}\delta_{m+n,0}$. In terms of these modes h can be written as

$$h = \frac{1}{2p^+}\sum_{-\infty}^{\infty}\left[\alpha^I_{-m}\alpha^I_m + \frac{m}{p^+}Q^{\bar{A}}_{-m}Q^A_m\right] . \tag{17}$$

which is an infinite sum of harmonic oscillator Hamiltonians and their fermionic equivalents.

It is possible to decompose Φ in an infinite series of complete basis functions, comprising sums of products of the infinite set of eigenfunctions of these harmonic oscillators. The coefficient of each of these terms in the sum is a function of ordinary superspace coordinates and is therefore an ordinary superfield, denoted $\varphi^{\{n\}}$ for bosonic fields and $\psi^{\{n\}}$ for fermionic ones (where the superscript $\{n\}$ denotes the occupation numbers of all the modes of the string for the term being considered). These fields are bosonic or fermionic depending on whether there are an even or odd number of Grassmann factors in the corresponding term in the sum. The open-string free-field Hamiltonian can be written in terms of these components as

$$H_2 \sim \int_0^\infty dp^+ \int dx d\vartheta_0 d\tilde{\vartheta}_0 \Big[\sum_{\{n\}}\varphi^{\{n\}}_{-p^+}(-\frac{\delta^2}{\delta x^2} + \frac{N_{\{n\}}}{\alpha'})\varphi^{\{n\}}_{p^+}$$

$$+ \sum_{\{n\}}\psi^{\{n\}}_{-p^+}(-\frac{\delta^2}{\delta x^2} + \frac{N_{\{n\}}}{\alpha'})\frac{1}{p^+}\psi^{\{n\}}_{p^+}\Big] . \tag{18}$$

where ϑ_0 and $\tilde{\vartheta}_0$ are the zero modes of ϑ and $\tilde{\vartheta}$. In eq. (18) $N_{\{n\}}$ is the $(mass)^2$ of the state $\{n\}$ in units of $1/\alpha'$ (where $\alpha' = \frac{1}{2\pi T}$ is the Regge slope parameter). The ground state, denoted by $\{0\}$, is massless, i.e., $N_{\{0\}} = 0$.

Interactions.

Scattering amplitudes for the bosonic string theory can be formulated in a functional approach in terms of sums over all connected world-sheets that are swept out by the incoming and outgoing strings. Presumably, a similarly geometric description of interacting superstrings can be formulated in terms of sums over world-sheets in superspace. For the moment, however, the interactions are only well understood in the light-cone gauge. The interacting light-cone gauge field theory of superstrings generalizes the formalism first developed for the bosonic string in [14].

The full super-Poincaré algebra is realized non-linearly on the fields in the light-cone gauge, a fact which can be used to determine the form of the interactions. An arbitrary generator of the algebra G has an expansion in powers of the coupling constants

$$G = G_2 + gG_3 + \cdots \tag{19}$$

where the suffix indicates the power of the fields so that G_3, for example, is cubic in open-string fields. (The complete theory also includes contributions from terms made of closed-string fields.) Such an expansion is also familiar in the case of ordinary "point" field theories in the light-cone gauge where G_4 is the Yang-Mills contact term and there are an infinite number of contact terms for gravity. The generic form of the cubic generators is

$$G_3 = \int \left(\prod_{r=1}^{3} Dx^{(r)} D\vartheta^{(r)} D\tilde{\vartheta}^{(r)} dp^{+(r)} \right) \Delta(3 - 2 - 1)\, \hat{G}(\sigma = \sigma_I)\, tr(\varphi[1]\varphi[2]\varphi[3])$$

$$+ \textit{perms} \tag{20}$$

where the integral is over the light-cone superspace for each string. The strings 1 and 2 interact at $\tau = 0$ by joining at their endpoints to form string 3. The value of the parameter σ at the joining point on string 3 is σ_I. The factor $\Delta(3 - 2 - 1)$ is a delta functional which imposes the continuity of the superspace coordinates between the incoming strings (#1 and #2) and the outgoing string (#3) at the time of the interaction. There is a *local* operator $\hat{G}(\sigma = \sigma_I)$ made out of products of $\frac{\delta}{\delta x(\sigma_I)}$, $\vartheta(\sigma_I)$, etc. which acts at the interaction point. The detailed form of this operator for the various generators can be found in ref. [13] but will not concern us here.

An important feature of string theories is that there are *no higher-order contact interactions*. Intuitively, this is an obvious consequence of the geometric picture of interactions referred to above.* The situation is reminiscent of the four fermion tree amplitude in the weak interactions as described by the Fermi theory (a nonrenormalizable theory). This is now viewed as a low-energy approximation to the Glashow-Weinberg-Salam theory in which the process is mediated by W or Z boson exchange. In the same manner all the contact terms of supergravity and super-Yang-Mills arise as low-energy effective vertices from superstring theories (where by "low" energy I mean low compared to the Planck scale $\sim 10^{19}\, GeV$). In ref. [13] we gave the following argument, based directly on the closure of the supersymmetry algebra of the interacting field theory, for the absence of string contact interactions. In the notation of [13] a piece of the superalgebra in the light-cone gauge is the relation

* There is a kind of four open-string contact term that arises in light-cone-gauge string theories [14] and contributes to the gravitational interaction between two incoming and two outgoing open strings, but this vanishes in the low energy limit and does not contribute to the Yang-Mills contact interaction.

$$\{Q^{-A}, Q^{-\bar{B}}\} = 2\delta^{A\bar{B}} H \tag{21}$$

where A and $\bar{B}$ denote spinor and anti-spinor labels of SU(4) (in the formalism in which the SO(8) transverse symmetry group is decomposed in terms of an SU(4) × U(1) subgroup). The Q^- operators are components of the supercharges which get interaction corrections so that they have expansions of the same form as in eq. (19).

The explicit expressions for the cubic pieces, Q_3^{-A} and $Q_3^{-\bar{A}}$, can be deduced by substituting these expansions into eq. (21) as well as into the other components of the superalgebra, $\{Q^{-A}, Q^{-B}\} = 0 = \{Q^{-\bar{A}}, Q^{-\bar{B}}\}$, and solving the resulting equations to lowest nontrivial order in g. (The zeroth-order equations involve only the free field expressions, which automatically satisfy the algebra.) The resulting expressions are of the form of eq. (19) with $\widehat{G}$ given by specific fermionic local operators $\widehat{Q}_3^A$ and $\widehat{Q}_3^{\bar{B}}$. To this order eq. (21) also determines H_3. At the next order in g the left-hand side of eq. (21) involves the anticommutator

$$\{Q_3^{-A}, Q_3^{-\bar{B}}\} \tag{22}$$

as well as $\{Q_2^{-A}, Q_4^{-\bar{B}}\} + \{Q_4^{-A}, Q_2^{-\bar{B}}\}$ and the right-hand-side of eq. (21) is proportional to H_4. The easiest way to discuss this anticommutator is to take matrix elements between two incoming states (#1 and #2) and two outgoing states (#3 and #4) of definite p^+. We can then restrict the discussion to terms with an overall group theory factor $tr(\lambda^1\lambda^2\lambda^3\lambda^4)$ (where λ^r is a matrix in the fundamental representation of the gauge group which describes the state of the r'th string). In this manner the terms involving four open strings mentioned in an earlier footnote are excluded since they do not contribute to this particular group theory factor. The anticommutator (22) can be represented (when $p_1^+ > p_4^+ > 0$) by

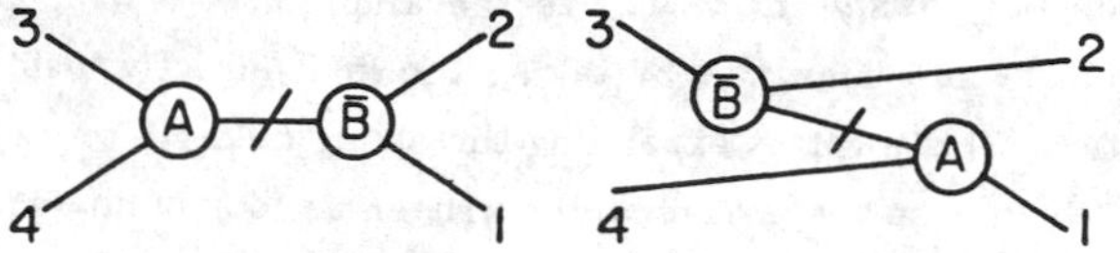

(a) (b)

$+ A \leftrightarrow \bar{B}$

where  denotes a sum over a complete set of intermediate states. The fermionic index associated with the local operator inside each of the supercharges is indicated inside the bubbles. Each of these diagrams describes the simultaneous joining and splitting of the world-sheet at time $x^+ = 0$. This is easiest to see by drawing the world-sheets for the processes (a) and (b) in the parametrization first introduced by Mandelstam in which the width of each string in σ is proportional to the p^+ carried by the string. Both (a) and (b) are represented by the *same* world-sheet diagram.

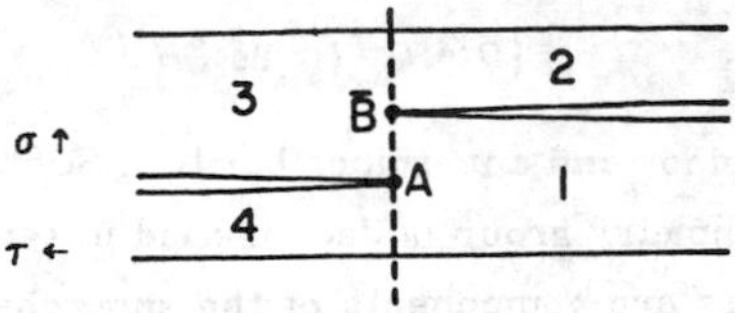

The only difference between (a) and (b) is in the ordering of the fermionic operators ($\hat{Q}_3^A$, $\hat{Q}_3^{\bar{N}}$) at the joining and splitting points. Since these local operators anticommute at different values of σ, the sum $(a) + (b)$vanishes. Hence the anticommutator (22) vanishes and a consistent solution is to take $Q_4^{-A}, Q_4^{-\bar{N}}$ and H_4 to be zero.

This discussion must have a loophole since $\{Q_3^{-A}, Q_3^{-\bar{B}}\}$ is a positive-definite expression and, indeed, when $p_1^+ = p_4^+$ the argument breaks down. The region of this breakdown is in the strictly forward direction (since for other configurations a Lorentz transformation could make $p_1^+ \neq p_4^+$). A careful treatment shows that the anticommutator (22) is proportional to a forward delta function that makes it just like a disconnected piece of the scattering amplitude. This argument generalizes to interactions involving closed strings.

For type II theories (which describe oriented closed strings), and presumably also for the heterotic string, there is just one type of interaction which is cubic in the string fields.

The interpretation of the extra, disconnected, piece in the Hamiltonian, as well as other similar higher- order terms deserves to be studied more systematically.

III. Supersymmetric Yang-Mills Theory from the Superstring Field Theory Action

It is well-known [15] that the open-string scattering amplitudes reduce in the low-energy limit (where all momenta satisfy $|p| \ll \sqrt{T}$) to the amplitudes of (supersymmetric) Yang-Mills theory. I will now show this by taking the limit directly inside the superstring field theory action. This involves expanding the string field Φ into its component point superfields in which case the action can be written as (combining eq. (18) with the cubic interaction and suppressing group theory indices from now on)

$$S = -\int dx^- dx d\vartheta_0 d\bar{\vartheta}_0 \{ \sum_{\{n\}} \frac{1}{2} \varphi_{\{n\}} (-\Box + \frac{N_{\{n\}}}{\alpha'}) \varphi_{\{n\}}$$

$$+ g C_{\{l,m,n\}} \varphi_{\{l\}} \varphi_{\{m\}} \varphi_{\{n\}} + \textit{fermionic superfield terms} \} . \qquad (23)$$

In this expression the interactions are obtained from the form of H_3 deduced in ref. [13]

(and I have written the fields as functions of x^- rather than p^+ in order to simplify notation). I have not included the quartic open-string interaction because it does not contribute in the following argument. Furthermore, the neglect of terms involving closed-string fields would not be consistent if string loop effects were to be included. For our purposes it is sufficient to note that $C_{\{l,m,n\}}$ can be written as

$$C_{\{l,m,n\}} = {}_1\langle \{l\}| \otimes {}_2\langle \{m\}| \otimes {}_3\langle \{n\}|\, H_3\rangle \tag{24}$$

where $|H_3\rangle$ is given by

$$|H_3\rangle = (\underline{\mathbf{P}} - \sum_{r=1}^{3}\sum_{s=1}^{\infty} \frac{N_s^{(r)}\underline{\alpha}_s^{(r)}}{\sqrt{\alpha'}})|V,\alpha'\rangle \tag{25}$$

In eqs. (24) and (25) ${}_r\langle\,|$ is the Fock space state of the rth string, and $|V,\alpha'\rangle$ is a ket vector in the tensor product of the three Fock spaces. The coefficients $N_s^{(r)}$ are known constants and $\underline{\mathbf{P}} = 2p_1^+\underline{p}_2 - 2p_2^+\underline{p}_1$ is symmetric under cyclic permutations of the three strings due to the momentum conservation delta functions which are included in $|V,\alpha'\rangle$.

The factor in parentheses in eq. (25) is a part of $\widehat{G}$ in eq. (20). It is the Fock space expression for a functional derivative $\frac{\delta}{\delta \underline{x}}$ acting at the interaction point σ_I. (The transverse index notation, indicated by the underlining of a vector, is somewhat schematic since it does not distinguish between the 6 and the two 1's of SU(4) but it is adequate for the following argument.) More details of my notation are to be found in ref.[13].

When considering only the open-string sector of the theory (or purely closed-string theories) the limit $|p| \ll \sqrt{T}$ is equivalent to the limit $\alpha' \to 0$. All the dependence on the string tension (or α') has been shown explicitly in eqs. (23) - (25) and an important point is that the $\alpha' \to 0$ limit of $|V,\alpha'\rangle$ is finite (i.e. $|V,0\rangle$ is finite). The limit $\alpha' \to 0$ can then be taken explicitly in the action (ignoring the fermionic terms in eq.(23) for the moment) by rescaling all those fields, $\varphi_{\{n\}}$, which have non-zero $N_{\{n\}}$ in order to remove the factor of $\frac{1}{\alpha'}$ in the mass terms in the action. Define

$$\widehat{\varphi}_{\{n\}} = \sqrt{\frac{N_{\{n\}}}{\alpha'}}\varphi_{\{n\}} \tag{26}$$

when $N_{\{n\}} \neq 0$. The only other factor which looks singular occurs inside $|H_3\rangle$ in eqs. (24) and (25). This only contributes when at least one of the three strings is not in its ground state since the factor of $\frac{1}{\sqrt{\alpha'}}$ is multiplied by $\underline{\alpha}_s^{(r)}$ in eq. (25). But the rescaling of eq. (26) contributes a factor of $\sqrt{\alpha'}$ for each excited string state which makes the limiting interaction terms finite (for terms with only one excited state) or zero (for terms with two or three excited states). Since the cubic interactions involving fermionic superfields in eq.(23) have at least two excited fermionic string states they vanish in the limit, $\alpha' \to 0$. In this limit the action then becomes

$$S \underset{\alpha'\to 0}{\longrightarrow} \int dx^- d\underline{x} d\vartheta_0 d\widetilde{\vartheta}_0 \Big(\frac{1}{2}\varphi_0 \Box \varphi_0 - \sum_{\{n\neq 0\}} \frac{1}{2}\widehat{\varphi}^2_{\{n\}} + g\, C_{000}\varphi_0^3 + g \sum_{\{n\}} \frac{C_{00\{n\}}}{\sqrt{N_{\{n\}}}} \varphi_0^2 \widehat{\varphi}_{\{n\}} + O(\sqrt{\alpha'}) \Big) \tag{27}$$

The fields $\widehat{\varphi}_{\{n\}}$ have no kinetic terms so they appear as auxiliary fields which can be eliminated by integrating them out in the functional integral. This is equivalent to substituting the solutions of their equations of motion back into the action. The result is

$$S \underset{\alpha'\to 0}{\longrightarrow} \int dx^- d\underline{x} d\vartheta_0 d\widetilde{\vartheta}_0 \Big(\frac{1}{2}\varphi_0 \Box \varphi_0 + g C_{000}\varphi_0^3 + g^2 \sum_{\{n\}} \frac{C^2_{00\{n\}}}{N_{\{n\}}} \varphi_0^4 \Big) . \tag{28}$$

Allowing for the suppressed group theory indices the cubic term in eq.(28) is just the usual Yang-Mills coupling in the light-cone gauge. The coefficient C_{000} contains a factor which is linear in transverse momenta as can be seen from eqs. (24) and (25). The quartic term is the Yang-Mills contact term with a coefficient that is independent of the momenta. The evaluation of the coefficient $\sum_{\{n\}} \frac{C^2_{00\{n\}}}{N_{\{n\}}}$ involves essentially the same oscillator algebra as occurred in evaluating the four-particle scattering amplitude in ref. [13]. This is tedious but gives the correct contact term in the end.

The above argument pertains to the low-energy limit of the open-superstring theory at the classical level. When the quantum corrections in the form of open-string loops are taken into account it also becomes necessary to include couplings of open strings to the unoriented closed-string sector.

In the low-energy limit, closed-string on-shell scattering amplitudes with external massless "gravitons" are known to reduce to the amplitudes of conventional (super)gravity point field theories which contain the Einstein-Hilbert action [16,17]. To see this directly from the light-cone gauge string field theory action requires a more subtle analysis than for open strings. In closed-string theories there are two sets of normal modes, corresponding to waves moving in either direction. The cubic term in the Hamiltonian includes a coefficient $C_{\{l,m,n\}}$ similar to the one defined by eq. (24) but with the product of *two* prefactors like the one in eq. (25). In this case there are terms in the action which do not have a finite $\alpha' \to 0$ limit (which occur in the coupling of two $\varphi_{\{0\}}$'s to one massive $\varphi_{\{n\}}$). These terms have to cancel after the integration over the massive modes.

The fact that there are no higher-order contact terms in string theories makes them very different from conventional field theories containing Yang-Mills or gravity at energy scales approaching $\sqrt{T}$ i.e. the Planck scale. Presumably this plays a significant role in ensuring well-behaved quantum properties for superstring loops*

*Even though superstring one-loop amplitudes are known to be finite (for type II theories, the heterotic string and the SO(32) type I theory) the perturbation theory is not necessarily convergent. Indeed, the high energy, fixed momentum transfer one-loop amplitudes are determined by a Regge cut which dominates the tree diagram Regge pole since the Regge pole intercept is two (corresponding to a trajectory containing the graviton).

References

1) M. B. Green and J. H. Schwarz, Phys. Lett. 136B (1984) 367, Nucl. Phys. B243 (1984) 285.
2) D. Gross, J. Harvey, E. Martinec and R. Rohm, Phys. Rev. Lett. 54 (1985) 502.
3) P. Ramond, Phys. Rev. D3 (1971) 2415.
4) A. Neveu and J. H. Schwarz, Nucl. Phys. B31 (1971) 86.
5) F. Gliozzi, J. Scherk and D. I. Olive, Nucl. Phys. B122 (1977) 253.
6) Y. Nambu, Proceedings of Copenhagen Symposium 1970 (unpublished);
T. Goto, Prog. Theor. Phys. 46 (1971) 1560.
7) A. M. Polyakov, Phys. Lett. 103B (1981) 207.
8) P. Goddard, J. Goldstone, C. Rebbi and C.B. Thorn, Nucl. Phys. B56 (1973) 109.
9) M. Henneaux and L. Mezincescu, Phys. Lett. 152B (1985) 340.
10) E. Witten, Nucl. Phys. B223 (1983) 422.
11) T. Curtright and C. Zachos, Phys. Rev. Lett. 53 (1984) 1799.
12) T. Hori and K. Kamimura, Inst. Nucl. Study Univ. Tokyo preprints (1984).
13) M. B. Green and J. H. Schwarz, Nucl. Phys. B243 (1984) 475.
14) S. Mandelstam, Nucl. Phys. B64 (1973) 205, Nucl. Phys. B69 (1974) 77,
M. Kaku and K. Kikkawa, Phys. Rev. D10 (1974) 1110, 1823
J-L. Gervais and B. Sakita, Nucl. Phys. B76 (1974) 209, Nucl. Phys. B90 (1975) 410.
15) J. Scherk, Nucl. Phys. B31 (1971) 222,
A. Neveu and J. Scherk, Nucl. Phys. B36 (1972) 155.
16) T. Yoneya, Nuovo Cimento Lett., 8 (1973) 951, Progr. Theor. Phys., 51 (1974) 1907,
17) J. Scherk and J. H. Schwarz, Nucl. Phys. B81 (1974) 118.

112 CONSTRUCTIONS OF THE BASIC REPRESENTATION OF THE LOOP GROUP OF E_8

Victor G. Kac, Dale H. Peterson

Department of Mathematics, MIT, Cambridge, MA 02139 USA

In this report, we describe a natural family of vertex constructions of the basic representation of the affine Kac-Moody algebra $\hat{\underline{g}}$ associated to a simple finite-dimensional Lie algebra $\underline{g}$ of type A_n, D_n, E_6, E_7 or E_8. Namely, we show that maximal Heisenberg subalgebras of $\hat{\underline{g}}$ are parametrized, up to conjugacy, by conjugacy classes of elements of the Weyl group W of $\underline{g}$. Given $w \in W$, let $\hat{s}_w$ denote the associated Heisenberg subalgebra of $\hat{\underline{g}}$, and let $\tilde{S}_w$ denote the centralizer of $\hat{s}_w$ in the loop group $\tilde{G}$ of the simply-connected group G whose Lie algebra is $\underline{g}$. We show that the basic representation (V,π_0) of $\hat{\underline{g}}$ remain irreducible under the pair $(\hat{s}_w, \tilde{S}_w)$. This leads to a vertex construction of V, so that for $w = 1$ (resp. w = Coxeter element) we recover the homogeneous [2] (resp. principal [10]) realization; for $w = -1$ we recover the construction of [3]. Thus, to each conjugacy class of W we associate canonically a vertex realization of the basic representation of $\hat{\underline{g}}$. In particular, in the case of $\hat{E}_8$ we obtain 112 such constructions.

The homogeneous realization of $\hat{E}_8$ plays an important role in the construction of the heterotic string [5]. We hope that the large variety of constructions of $\hat{E}_8$ provided by this paper could be useful for the treatment of various symmetry breaking patterns.

1. We feel that it is conceptually appropriate to start with the general framework of Kac-Moody Lie algebras.

Let Γ be a finite graph and let Γ_0 be the set of vertices of Γ. Two vertices can be connected by several lines, but we exclude tadpoles. The Cartan matrix of Γ is the $n \times n$-matrix $A = (a_{ij})_{i,j\in\Gamma_0}$ defined as follows: $a_{ii} = 2$, and $-a_{ij} = -a_{ji}$ is the number of lines connecting vertices i and j.

Define the root lattice Q as the lattice on a basis $\{h_i\}_{i\in\Gamma_0}$, with the bilinear form $(h_i|h_j) = a_{ij}$. This is an even integral lattice (i.e. $(h|h)$ is an even integer for $h \in Q$).

Define the <u>Weyl group</u> W as the subgroup of the group of automorphisms of Q generated by the <u>fundamental reflections</u> r_i, $i \in \Gamma_0$, defined by

$$(1.1) \qquad r_i(h_j) = h_j - a_{ji}h_i .$$

The following two types of graphs are relevant to our discussion.

I. <u>Finite-type graphs</u>. These are the Γ with a positive-definite Cartan matrix A , or, equivalently, with a finite Weyl group W . Here is the well-known list of connected finite-type graphs $(|\Gamma_0| = n)$:

Type	Graph Γ	det A
A_n		$n + 1$
D_n		4
E_6	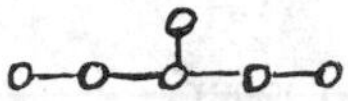	3
E_7		2
E_8		1

It is well-known that every positive-definite even lattice Λ spanned over $\mathbb{Z}$ by elements α with $(\alpha|\alpha) = 2$ is a direct sum of lattices of type A, D or E. Then the discriminant of Λ (= $(\text{vol } \Lambda)^2$ = square of the volume of a fundamental cell) is the product of the corresponding determinants (given by the table).

II. <u>Affine graphs</u>. These are the connected graphs with a positive-semidefinite Cartan matrix A such that $\det A = 0$. They are characterized by having a labelling by (relatively prime) positive integers a_i such that each label equals half of the sum of its neighbors. To each connected finite-type graph Γ, one canonically associates an affine graph $\hat{\Gamma}$ by adding a complementary vertex 0 . The list of affine graphs together with the labels a_i is given below ($|\hat{\Gamma}_0| = n+1$):

$\hat{A}_n$

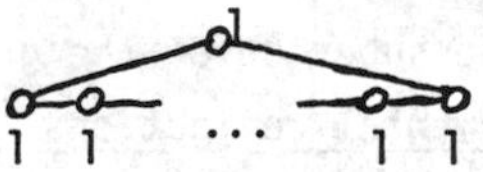

$\hat{D}_n$

$\hat{E}_6$

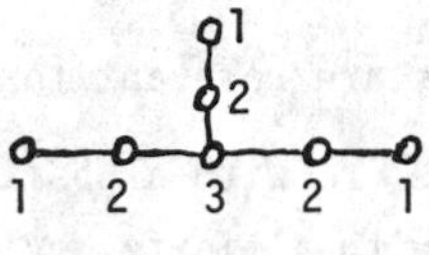

$\hat{E}_7$

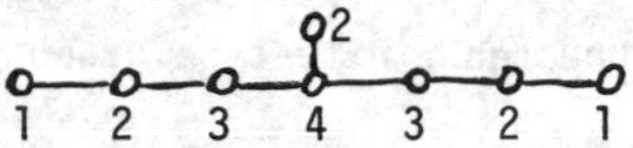

$\hat{E}_8$

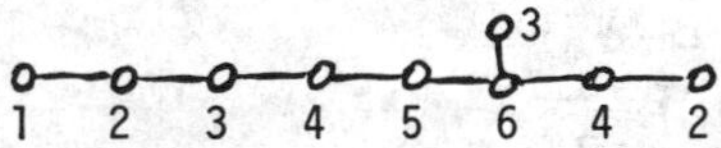

The number $h = \sum_i a_i$ is called the <u>Coxeter number</u>.

2. The <u>Kac-Moody algebra</u> $\underline{g}(\Gamma)$ is the Lie algebra on <u>Chevalley generators</u> e_i, f_i, h_i $(i \in \Gamma_0)$ and the following defining relations:

$$[e_i, f_j] = \delta_{ij} h_i \ ; \ [h_i, h_j] = 0 \ ;$$
$$[h_i, e_j] = a_{ij} e_j \ ; \ [h_i, f_j] = -a_{ij} f_j \ ;$$
$$[\ldots[[e_i, \underbrace{e_j], e_j] \ldots, e_j}_{1-a_{ji} \text{ times}}] = 0 \ ; \ [\ldots[[f_i, \underbrace{f_j], f_j] \ldots, f_j}_{1-a_{ji} \text{ times}}] = 0 \ .$$

An exposition of the theory of Kac-Moody algebras along with some of its many applications to other fields of mathematics may be found in [9]. Here we note only that $\dim \underline{g}(\Gamma) < \infty$ if and only if Γ is of finite type, and $\underline{g}(\Gamma)$ is a simple Lie algebra of type A, D or E if Γ is of that type. (Allowing non-symmetric A, one recovers the algebras of types B, C, G and F as well.)

The commutative subalgebra $\underline{h} = \sum_i \mathbb{C} h_i$ of $\underline{g}(\Gamma)$ is called a <u>Cartan subalgebra</u>; it contains the root lattice Q and the Weyl group W acts on $\underline{h}$ by formula (1.1), preserving Q .

Finally, note that an affine Kac-Moody algebra $\underline{g}(\hat{\Gamma})$ has a 1-dimensional center spanned by the canonical central element $c = \Sigma a_i h_i$.

3. Given a collection of numbers $\overline{\lambda} = \{\lambda_i\}_{i \in \Gamma_0}$, define a highest weight representation $\pi_{\overline{\lambda}}$ of $\underline{g}(\Gamma)$ on a vector space $L(\overline{\lambda})$ as an irreducible represenation which admits a non-zero vector $v_{\overline{\lambda}}$ (heighest weight vector) such that [6]:

(3.1) $\pi_{\overline{\lambda}}(e_i)v_{\overline{\lambda}} = 0$, $\pi_{\overline{\lambda}}(h_i)v_{\overline{\lambda}} = \lambda_i v_{\overline{\lambda}}$; $i \in \Gamma_0$.

This representation is unitary (i.e. it carries a positive-definite Hermitian form such that $\pi_{\overline{\lambda}}(e_i)^* = \pi_{\overline{\lambda}}(f_i)$) if and only if all λ_i are non-negative integers [4], [12]. A unitary representation $L(\overline{\lambda})$ is uniquely determined by its highest weight $\overline{\lambda}$ [9, Proposition 10.4].

Note that in the finite-type case the unitary $L(\overline{\lambda})$ are precisely all finite-dimensional irreducible representations of $\underline{g}(\Gamma)$.

Now let $\underline{g}(\hat{\Gamma})$ be an affine Kac-Moody algebra, and let $L(\overline{\lambda})$ be a highest weight representation. The number $\sum_i a_i \lambda_i$ is called the level of $L(\overline{\lambda})$. It is clear that the level is the eigenvalue of c and that the level of a unitary $L(\overline{\lambda})$ is a non-negative integer, which is zero if and only if $\overline{\lambda} = \overline{0}$, i.e. $L(\overline{\lambda})$ is a trivial 1-dimensional representation. Note that if λ_i is the i-th fundamental representation, i.e. $\lambda_i = 1$, $\lambda_j = 0$ for $j \neq i$, then the level is a_i . It is thus clear from the table that all level 1 represenations of $\underline{g}(\hat{\Gamma})$ are equivalent to π_0 via an isometry of the graph $\hat{\Gamma}$. Thus, $\underline{g}(\hat{\Gamma})$ has a distinguished highest weight representation π_0 , called the basic representation. We will denote the space of this representation by V for short.

4. Here we will explain how to construct the finite-dimensional Lie algebras $\underline{g}(\Gamma)$, where Γ is A_n, D_n or E_n [2]. First, take the root lattice $Q \subset \mathbb{C}^n = \underline{h}$. An explicit construction of it is well known. For example, in the most non-trivial case, E_8 , which is currently of

primary interest to physicists, Q consists of all 8-vectors such that the sum of coordinates is an even integer and either all the coordinates are integers or all the coordinates are half-integers ($\in \frac{1}{2} + \mathbb{Z}$); the bilinear form is standard: $(\alpha|\beta) = \Sigma\, \alpha_i\beta_i$ (see e.g. [15]).

The set of <u>roots</u> of $\underline{g}(\Gamma)$ is

$$\Delta = \{\alpha \in Q\ (\alpha|\alpha) = 2\}\ .$$

In the case of E_8, in the standard basis $\{\varepsilon_i\}$ of $\mathbb{C}^8$ we have:

$$\Delta = \{\pm\varepsilon_i \pm \varepsilon_j \text{ with } i \neq j\ ;\ \tfrac{1}{2}(\pm\varepsilon_1 \pm \dots \pm\varepsilon_8) \text{ with even number of minuses}\}.$$

Then $\underline{g}(\Gamma) = \underline{h} \oplus (\bigoplus_{\alpha\in\Delta} \mathbb{C}\, e_\alpha)$ with the following commutation relations [2]:

$$[\alpha,\beta] = 0 \quad \text{if } \alpha,\beta \in \underline{h}\ ;$$
$$[\alpha,e_\beta] = (\alpha|\beta)e_\beta \quad \text{if } \alpha \in \underline{h}\ ,\ \beta \in \Delta\ ;$$
$$[e_\beta,e_{-\beta}] = -\beta \quad \text{if } \beta \in \Delta\ ;$$
$$[e_\alpha,e_\beta] = 0 \quad \text{if } \alpha,\beta \in \Delta\ , \text{ but } \alpha+\beta \notin \Delta \cup \{0\}\ ;$$
$$[e_\alpha,e_\beta] = \varepsilon(\alpha,\beta)e_{\alpha+\beta} \quad \text{if } \alpha,\beta,\alpha+\beta \in \Delta\ .$$

Here $\varepsilon(\alpha,\beta)$ is a bimultiplicative function on $Q\times Q$ with values in $\{\pm 1\}$ (i.e. $\varepsilon(\alpha+\alpha',\beta) = \varepsilon(\alpha,\beta)\varepsilon(\alpha',\beta)$ and $\varepsilon(\alpha,\beta+\beta') = \varepsilon(\alpha,\beta)\varepsilon(\alpha,\beta')$) satisfying the property:

$$\varepsilon(\alpha,\alpha) = (-1)^{\frac{1}{2}(\alpha|\alpha)}$$

and hence the property $\varepsilon(\alpha,\beta)\varepsilon(\beta,\alpha) = (-1)^{(\alpha|\beta)}$.

5. Now we turn to the construction of affine Lie algebras $\underline{g}(\hat{\Gamma})$, where Γ is a graph of type A, D or E. Normalize the Killing form on the finite-dimensional Lie algebra $\underline{g} = \underline{g}(\Gamma)$ by the condition $(\alpha|\alpha) = 2$ for $\alpha \in \Delta$, as above.

Consider the loop algebra $\tilde{\underline{g}} = \mathbb{C}[t,t^{-1}] \otimes_{\mathbb{C}} \underline{g}$. This is the Lie algebra of <u>loops</u> on $\underline{g}$, i.e., regular rational maps $\mathbb{C}^\times \to \underline{g}$.

Consider the following central extension of $\tilde{\underline{g}}$ by a 1-dimensional center $\mathbb{C}c$:

$$\hat{\underline{g}} = \mathbb{C}[t,t^{-1}] \otimes_{\mathbb{C}} \underline{g} + \mathbb{C}c\ , \tag{5.1}$$

with the commutation relations:

(5.2) $[t^k \otimes a, t^{k'} \otimes a'] = t^{k+k'} \otimes [a,a'] + k\delta_{k,-k'}(a|a')c$.

We identify $\underline{g}$ with the subalgebra $1 \otimes \underline{g}$ of $\hat{\underline{g}}$.

Choosing an orthonormal basis Q^a of $\underline{g}$ so that $[Q^a,Q^b] = f_{abc}Q^c$, we get a basis $Q^a_k = t^k \otimes Q^a$ of $\mathbb{C}[t,t^{-1}] \otimes \underline{g}$ with the following commutation relations familiar to physicists:

$[Q^a_k,Q^b_{k'}] = f_{abc}\ Q^c_{k+k'} + k\delta_{k,-k'}\ \delta_{a,b}\ c$.

To show that $\hat{\underline{g}}$ is the affine Kac-Moody algebra $\underline{g}(\hat{\Gamma})$, choose a set of simple roots $\{\alpha_i\}_{i \in \Gamma_0}$ of $\underline{g}$ and put $e_i = e_{\alpha_i}$ and $f_i = -e_{-\alpha_i}$ for $i \in \Gamma_0$, $e_0 = t \otimes e_{-\theta}$, $f_0 = -t^{-1} \otimes e_\theta$, $h_0 = c-\theta$, where θ is the highest root of $\underline{g}$. Then the elements e_i, f_i, h_i, $i \in \Gamma_0$, satisfy all the relations of Section 2 with (a_{ij}) being the Cartan matrix of the graph $\hat{\Gamma}$. The fact that there are no further relations is less obvious [9, Theorem 9.11].

6. Recall that the <u>Virasoro algebra</u> is a Lie algebra $\underline{d}$ with a basis $\{d_k\ (k \in \mathbb{Z});\ \tilde{c}\}$ and the following commutation relations:

$[d_k,d_r] = (k-r)d_{k+r} + \frac{1}{12}(k^3-k)\ \delta_{k,-r}\ \tilde{c}\ ;\ [\tilde{c},d_k] = 0$.

This Lie algebra acts by derivations of $\hat{\underline{g}}$ by:

$[d_k,P\otimes a + \lambda c] = -t^{k+1}\frac{dp}{dt} \otimes a\ ;\ [\tilde{c},\hat{\underline{g}}] = 0$.

Thus, we get a semidirect sum $\underline{d} \ltimes \hat{\underline{g}}$ of Lie algebras.

Let $(L(\bar{\lambda}),\pi)$ be a unitary highest weight representation of $\hat{\underline{g}}$ of level m . It is a well-known fact which goes back to Sugawara [16] that the representation $\pi_{\bar{\lambda}}$ of $\hat{\underline{g}}$ on $L(\bar{\lambda})$ can be extended uniquely to the whole semidirect sum $\underline{d} \ltimes \hat{\underline{g}}$. The value of the central charge $\tilde{c}$ is then equal to $(\dim \underline{g})m/(m+h)$ (see e.g. [9, Exercises 12.11 and 12.12]). In particular, the eigenvalue of $\pi_0(\tilde{c})$ is n (the rank of $\underline{g}$).

Furthermore, the energy operator $\pi_{\bar{\lambda}}(d_0)$ is diagonalizable, its eigenvalues have finite multiplicities and are non-negative numbers of the form $k + \frac{b}{2(m+h)}$, where b is the eigenvalue of the Casimir of $\underline{g}$ on $\nu_{\bar{\lambda}}$ and $k = 0,1,2,\ldots$. For the basic representation, $b = 0$ and its multiplicity is 1 .

7. Let (L,π) be the direct sum of all unitary highest weight representations $(L(\bar{\lambda}),\pi_{\bar{\lambda}})$ of $\underline{g}$. When restricted to each 3-dimensional subalgebra $\mathbb{C}e_i + \mathbb{C}h_i + \mathbb{C}f_i$, L decomposes into a direct sum of finite-dimensional subrepresentations, and hence can be exponentiated to a representation $\phi_i : SL_2(\mathbb{C}) \to \mathrm{Aut}\, L$. The group $\hat{G}$ generated by all $\phi_i(SL_2(\mathbb{C}))$, $i \in \hat{\Gamma}_0$, is the Kac-Moody group attached to $\hat{\underline{g}}$. The representation of $\hat{G}$ on $L(\bar{\lambda})$ will be also denoted by $\pi_{\bar{\lambda}}$ (and for the fundamental representations by π_i).

The group $\hat{G}$ can be described as follows [12], [13]. Let G be the simply-connected complex Lie group whose Lie algebra is $\underline{g}$. Let $H = \exp \underline{h} \subset G$. Let $\tilde{G}$ be the loop group, i.e. the group of all rational regular maps $\mathbb{C}^\times \to G$ with pointwise multiplication. $\tilde{G}$ may be viewed as the infinite-dimensional group attached to the loop algebra $\tilde{\underline{g}}$. Then $\hat{G}$ is a central extension of $\tilde{G}$ by $\mathbb{C}^\times$. More precisely, $\mathbb{C}^\times$ imbeds into the center of $\hat{G}$ by $\nu : t \to \prod_i \phi_i \begin{pmatrix} t & 0 \\ 0 & t^{-1} \end{pmatrix}^{a_i}$, and $1 \to \mathbb{C}^\times \overset{\nu}{\to} \hat{G} \xrightarrow{\nu_1} \tilde{G} \to 1$ is an exact sequence.

The subgroup of $\hat{G}$ generated by the $\phi_i(SL_2(\mathbb{C}))$ with $i \in \Gamma_0$ is isomorphic to G, and we will identify G with it. Note that ν_1 identifies the subgroup G of $\hat{G}$ in the obvious way with the subgroup of constant loops of G. Note also that the center C of $\hat{G}$ is $\nu(\mathbb{C}^\times)\times(\text{center}(G))$ [13], and that C acts on V by:

$$(7.1) \quad \pi_0(\nu(a)) = a \text{ for } a \in \mathbb{C}^\times ; \quad \pi_0(\text{center}(G)) = 1 .$$

The operators $\pi_{\bar{\lambda}}(g)$, $g \in \hat{G}$, are not of trace class. The situation is fixed as follows. Let $L(\bar{\lambda}) = \bigoplus_k L(\bar{\lambda})_k$ be the eigenspace decomposition with respect to the energy operator $\pi_{\bar{\lambda}}(d_0)$. It is invariant with respect to G since $[\underline{g},d_0] = 0$. We define the character of the representation $\pi_{\bar{\lambda}}$ as follows:

$$(7.2) \quad \mathrm{ch}\, L(\bar{\lambda})(g) = \sum_k (\mathrm{tr}_{L(\bar{\lambda})_k} \pi_{\bar{\lambda}}(g))q^k , \quad g \in G .$$

Thus, to every $g \in G$ we associate a formal power series in $q^{\frac{1}{N}}$, some N (which converges if $|q| < 1$). One knows the Weyl-Kac formula for the

the character $\mathrm{ch}\, L(\bar{\lambda})$ [6] of an arbitrary unitary highest weight representation $\pi_{\bar{\lambda}}$ of $\hat{\underline{g}}$ (and even of any Kac-Moody algebra). For the basic representation (V, π_0), the character formula takes an especially simple form [7]:

$$(7.3) \quad (\mathrm{ch}\, V)(e^h) = \sum_{\gamma \in Q} e^{(\gamma|h)}\, q^{\frac{1}{2}(\gamma|\gamma)}/\phi(q)^n \ , \quad h \in \underline{h} \subset \underline{g} \ .$$

Here $Q \subset \underline{h}$ is the root lattice of $\underline{g}$ and $\phi(q) = \prod_{k=1}^{\infty} (1-q^k)$. Note that the numerator is nothing else but the Riemann theta function, and the denominator is, up to a factor $q^{n/24}$, a power of the Dedekind η-function. In particular, we get the following formula for the partition function $\dim_q V := \Sigma\, (\dim V_k) q^k$ $(= (\mathrm{ch}\, V)(1))$:

$$\dim_q V = \sum_{\gamma \in Q} q^{\frac{1}{2}(\gamma|\gamma)}/\phi(q)^n \ ,$$

a special case of which for $\hat{E}_8$ is [8]

$$q^{-\frac{1}{3}} \dim_q V = \sqrt[3]{j(q)} \ ,$$

where j is the celebrated modular invariant [15].

8. Given a complex algebraic variety X, we denote (as above) by $\tilde{X}$ the <u>loop space</u> of X, the space of all regular rational maps of $\mathbb{C}^\times$ into X. Let $\mathcal{H}$ $(= G/N_G(H)$, where $N_G(H)$ is the normalizer of the Cartan subgroup H) be the variety of all Cartan subalgebras of $\underline{g}$, and let $\tilde{\mathcal{H}}$ be its loop space.

Given a loop $s \in \tilde{\mathcal{H}}$ we define the associated <u>Heisenberg subalgebra</u> of $\tilde{\underline{g}}$:

$$\tilde{s} = \{p \in \tilde{\underline{g}} \mid p(t) \in s(t) \text{ for all } t \in \mathbb{C}^\times\} \ .$$

This is a maximal commutative subalgebra of the loop algebra $\tilde{\underline{g}}$. (The name "Heisenberg" will become clear later.) Regarding s as a vector bundle over $\mathbb{C}^\times$ with fiber $s(t)$ over $t \in \mathbb{C}^\times$, we may view $\tilde{s}$ as a space of sections of the bundle s.

<u>Examples</u>: Taking s to be a map of $\mathbb{C}^\times$ into one point $\underline{h} \in \mathcal{H}$,

we get $\tilde{s} = \tilde{\underline{h}} = \mathbb{C}[t,t^{-1}]\otimes\underline{h} \subset \underline{g}$. This is the homogeneous Heisenberg subalgebra of $\tilde{\underline{g}}$. Another important example, the principal Heisenberg subalgebra of $\tilde{\underline{g}}$, corresponds to the loop s : $t \to$ centralizer in $\underline{g}$ of the element $te_{-\theta} + \sum_{i=1}^{n} e_{\alpha_i}$. In the particular case of $\underline{g} = s\ell_n(\mathbb{C})$ putting

$$s(t) = \text{centralizer of } \begin{pmatrix} 0 & 1 & & 0 \\ & 0 & \ddots & \\ & & \ddots & 1 \\ t & & & 0 \end{pmatrix} ; \; a_{k,m}(t) = t^k \begin{pmatrix} 0 & 1 & & \\ & \ddots & \ddots & \\ & & \ddots & 1 \\ t & & & 0 \end{pmatrix}^m ,$$

the principal Heisenberg subalgebra of $s\tilde{\ell}_n(\mathbb{C})$ is the linear span of the elements $a_{k,m}$ for $m,k \in \mathbb{Z}$, $m \not\equiv 0 \bmod n$.

The homogeneous and principal Heisenberg subalgebras are "responsible" for the homogeneous and principal constructions of the basic representation (V,π_0) of $\hat{\underline{g}}$ ([2], [10]). We shall generalize these constructions to the case of an arbitrary Heisenberg subalgebra $\tilde{s}$.

Similarly, given a loop $s \in \tilde{H}$, we define the associated Heisenberg subgroup of $\tilde{G}$:

$$\tilde{S} = \{g \in \tilde{G} | g(t) \in \exp s(t) \text{ for all } t \in \mathbb{C}^x\}$$

Note that the subgroup $\tilde{S}$ is the centralizer of $\tilde{s}$ in $\tilde{G}$.

9. Fix $w \in W$ and let m be the order of w . Let $\underline{h} = \bigoplus_{j \in \mathbb{Z}/m\mathbb{Z}} \underline{h}_{j/m}$ be the eigenspace decomposition for w , where $\underline{h}_k$ denotes the eigenspace attached to $e^{-2\pi ik}$, so that $\underline{h}_0$ is the fixed point set of w . Let σ be a lifting of w in G , i.e. σ is such that $\mathrm{Ad}\sigma$ leaves $\underline{h}$ invariant and $\mathrm{Ad}\sigma|_{\underline{h}} = w$. There exists $x \in \underline{g}$ (not unique) such that

(9.1) $\sigma = \exp 2\pi i\, x$ and $[x,\underline{h}_0] = 0$.

Given $a \in \underline{g}$, we write $a = \sum_{\lambda} a_\lambda$ as a sum of eigenvectors a_λ of σ with distinct eigenvalues λ . For $k \in \mathbb{C}$ such that $e^{-2\pi ik} = \lambda$, we define the loop $a(k)' \in \tilde{\underline{g}}$ to be $e^{i\phi k}$ Ad(exp $i\phi x)a_\lambda$ at $e^{i\phi}$. It is clear that $a(k)'$ is well-defined. Note also that $\underline{h}(0)' = \underline{h}_0$ and that $\underline{h}(k) \neq 0$ implies that $k \in \frac{1}{m}\mathbb{Z}$.

We put $a(k) = a(k)' + \delta_{k,0}(a|x)c \in \hat{\underline{g}}$. Then we have the following commutation relations:

$$(9.2) \quad [a(k),b(\ell)] = [a,b](k+\ell)+k\delta_{k,-\ell}(a|b)c \quad \text{if} \quad a = a_\lambda, \text{ where } \lambda = \exp(-2\pi ik) .$$

We put:

$$\tilde{s}_w = \bigoplus_{k\in\frac{1}{m}\mathbb{Z}} \underline{h}(k)' ;$$

$$\hat{s}^{\pm}_w = \bigoplus_{k>0} \underline{h}(\pm k) , \quad \hat{s}_w = \hat{s}^-_w + \mathbb{C}c + \hat{s}^+_w .$$

Note that $\tilde{s}_w$ is a commutative subalgebra of $\tilde{\underline{g}}$ and $\hat{s}_w$ is a subalgebra of $\hat{\underline{g}}$ isomorphic to an infinite-dimensional Heisenberg subalgebra. The latter fact is clear by (9.2):

$$(9.3) \quad [h_1(k),h_2(\ell)] = k\delta_{k,-\ell}(h_1|h_2)c \quad \text{if} \quad h_1 \in \underline{h}_k , h_2 \in \underline{h}_\ell .$$

Here k and ℓ run over $\frac{1}{m}\mathbb{Z}$.

For $\alpha \in \underline{h}_0$ and $\beta \in \underline{h}$ such that $\beta - w(\beta) \in \alpha+Q$, define the loop $h(\alpha,\beta)' \in \tilde{G}$ to be $(\exp i\phi x)(\exp i\phi\alpha+2\pi i\beta)(\exp -i\phi x)$ at $e^{i\phi}$, and let $h(\alpha,\beta)$ be a lift of $h(\alpha,\beta)'$ to $\hat{G}$.

We put $\tilde{S}_w = \{h(\alpha,\beta)'\}$; this is a commutative subgroup of $\tilde{G}$. Let $\hat{S}_w = \nu_1^{-1}(\tilde{S}_w)$ be the preimage of $\tilde{S}_w$ in $\hat{G}$. Then the connected component of unity of $\hat{S}_w$ is $\hat{S}^0_w = \exp(\underline{h}_0 + \mathbb{C}c)$.

<u>Proposition</u>. (a) $\tilde{s}_w$ (resp. $\tilde{S}_w$) is the Heisenberg subalgebra of $\tilde{\underline{g}}$ (resp. Heisenberg subgroup of $\tilde{G}$), corresponding to the loop $t \to \text{Ad}(\exp(\log t)x)\ \underline{h}$ of $\tilde{H}$.

(b) The Heisenberg subalgebras $\tilde{s}_w$, corresponding to a set of representatives w of conjugacy classes of W, form a complete non-redundant list of Heisenberg subalgebras of $\tilde{\underline{g}}$ up to conjugacy.

<u>Examples</u>. If $w = 1$, then $\tilde{s}_w = \underline{h}$ is the homogeneous Heisenberg

subalgebra of $\tilde{\underline{g}}$ and $\tilde{S}_w = \tilde{H}$. If $w = r_1 \dots r_n$ is the Coxeter element, then $\tilde{s}_w$ is the principal Heisenberg subalgebra of $\tilde{\underline{g}}$ and $\tilde{S}_w$ is center $(G) \subset \tilde{G}$.

10. Here we introduce the important notion of the <u>defect</u> of $w \in W$. Put

$$M_w = \{\alpha \in \underline{h} \mid \alpha - w(\alpha) \in Q\} ,$$

and define on M_w the following bimultiplicative function:

$$\psi(\alpha,\beta) = \exp 2\pi i(\alpha|\beta - w(\beta)) \quad \text{for } \alpha,\beta \in M_w .$$

One easily shows that ψ is an alternating form (i.e. $\psi(\alpha,\alpha) = 1$). Let M'_w be its radical; note that $M'_w = Q^* + \underline{h}_0$, where Q^* is the dual lattice to Q (the so-called weight lattice). Since ψ is alternating, the order of the finite group $\overline{M}_w = M_w/M'_w$ is a square of a positive integer c_w . We call c_w the <u>defect</u> of w . In other words, c_w^2 is the number of connected components of the group Ad H^w (this uses the exponential map $2\pi i\, M_w \to H^w$).

Here are all possible values of the defect:

A_n : $c_w = 1$; D_n : $c_w = 2^k$, where $k \leq [\frac{n-2}{2}]$;

E_6 : $c_w = 1, 2$ or 3 ; E_7 : $c_w = 1, 2, 3, 4$ or 8 ;

E_8 : $c_w = 1, 2, 3, 4, 5, 6, 8, 9$ or 16.

Let $\underline{h}_0^{\perp}$ be the orthocomplement to $\underline{h}_0$ in $\underline{h}$ and let p denote the orthogonal projection of $\underline{h}$ on $\underline{h}_0$. Let w_* denote the restriction of w to $\underline{h}_0^{\perp}$. We have the following alternative descriptions of the defect c_w :

(10.1) $c_w = (\det(1-w_*))^{\frac{1}{2}} \operatorname{vol} p(Q)/\operatorname{vol} Q$.

(10.2) $c_w = |\operatorname{torsion}(Q/(1-w)Q^*)|^{\frac{1}{2}}$.

An element w of W is called <u>non-degenerate</u> if $\det(1-w) \neq 0$, and is called <u>primitive</u> if $\det(1-w) = \det A$ (note that $\det(1-w)$ is always non-negative and divisible by $\det A$). Note that w is non-degenerate if and only if the group H^w is finite, and w is primitive if and only if H^w is the center of G. Note that $\det A = |Q^*/Q|$.

Remark. One can see from the classification of the conjugacy classes of W [1], that the number of conjugacy classes of primitive elements for A_n, D_n, E_6, E_7, and E_8 is 1, $[\frac{1}{2}n]$, 3, 5 and 9 respectively. This equals the number of orbits on $\hat{\Gamma}_0$ of the group of isometries of $\hat{\Gamma}$, as noted by the second author. We have no explanation of this coincidence. Furthermore, the number of conjugacy classes of non-degenerate elements for A_n, E_6, E_7 and E_8 is 1, 5, 12 and 30 respectively, and the total number of conjugacy classes is $p(n+1)$, 25, 60 and 112 respectively. Note also that the Coxeter element is primitive (and for A_n this is the only primitive conjugacy class).

The discussions of Sections 9 and 10 are linked by the following crucial formula

(10.3) $h(0,\alpha)h(0,\beta) = h(0,\beta)h(0,\alpha)\psi(\alpha,\beta)$,

the proof of which is omitted.

11. Now we can state, and give a sketch of the proof of, the central result of this paper.

Irreducibility Theorem. The basic representation (V,π_0) of an affine Kac-Moody algebra $\hat{\underline{g}}$ of type $\hat{A}_n$, $\hat{D}_n$, $\hat{E}_6$, $\hat{E}_7$ or $\hat{E}_8$ remains irreducible when restricted to the pair $(\hat{s}_w,\hat{S}_w)$ for any $w \in W$.

Outline of the proof. First, we pick a "good" lifting $\sigma = \exp 2\pi i x$ of w, as described in [8, Section 4]. Apart from (9.1), it has the properties that $(x|\underline{h}) = 0$ and all eigenvalues of $\operatorname{ad} x$ are in $\frac{1}{2m}\mathbb{Z}$ and are of absolute value ≤ 1. Put

$$d' = d_0 + x \in \underline{d} \dotplus \hat{\underline{g}} .$$

We have the following useful formulas:

(11.1) $[d',a(k)] = -ka(k)$,

(11.2) $\operatorname{Ad}(h(\beta,\gamma))d' = d' + \beta(0) + \frac{1}{2}|\beta|^2 c$,

(11.3) $\operatorname{Ad}(h(\beta,\gamma))a(k) = e^{2\pi i(\alpha|\gamma)}a(k+(\alpha|\beta)) + \delta_{k,0}(a|\beta)c$,

if $\alpha \in \Delta \cup \{0\}$ and $a \in \underline{g}_\alpha$.

Let V_k denote the eigenspace of $\pi_0(d')$ with the eigenvalue k. Then $V = \bigoplus_{k\geq 0} V_k$ (where k runs over $\frac{1}{2m}\mathbb{Z}_+$). Given a graded subspace U of V, we put $\dim_q U = \sum_{k\geq 0} \dim(U\cap V_k)q^k$.

Let $V^+ = \{v \in V | \pi_0(\hat{s}^+)v = 0\}$. Then an algebraic analogue of the Stone-von Neumann theorem (see e.g. [9, Lemma 14.4]) shows that the theorem holds if V^+ is an irreducible $\hat{S}_w$-module, and that

(11.4) $\dim_q V = (\dim_q V^+) \prod_{j=1}^{\infty} (1-q^{j/m})^{-\dim \underline{h}_{j/m}}$.

Let $V^{++} = \{v \in V^+ | \pi_0(\underline{h}_0)v = 0\}$, and let $\tilde{S}_0 = \{h(0,\beta)'\} \subset \tilde{S}_w$, $\hat{S}_0 = \nu_1^{-1}(\tilde{S}_0)$. Then (11.2) and (11.3) show that the theorem holds if V^{++} is an irreducible $\hat{S}_0$-module, and that

(11.5) $\dim_q V^+ = (\dim_q V^{++}) \sum_{\alpha\in p(Q)} q^{\frac{1}{2}|\alpha|^2}$.

Finally, the commutation relation (10.3) and a Stone-von Neumann theorem for projective representations of finite abelian groups shows that V^{++} is an irreducible $\hat{S}_0$-module if $\dim V^{++} = c_w$.

We give two methods for showing that $\dim V^{++} = c_w$, both of which depend on the transformation properties of modular forms. Let $q = e^{-2\pi T}$, where $T > 0$.

The first method depends on special character formulas for V. The value of the character ch V at σ may be computed by the following simple formula, entirely in terms of the action of w on $\underline{h}$ [8, eq. (6)]:

(11.6) $(\mathrm{ch}\ V)(\sigma) = \sum_{\gamma\in Q^w} q^{\frac{1}{2}|\gamma|^2} / \prod_{j=1}^{\infty} \det_{\underline{h}}(1-q^j w)$.

It is easy to see that, after replacing V by the sum of all level 1 representations of $\hat{\underline{g}}$ and Q by Q^*, formula (11.6) still holds; we denote the resulting formula by (11.6').

Now replace T by $1/T$ in (11.6'). Then, according to [11, Proposition 4.11], (11.6') is transformed into

(11.7) $\dim_q V = c_w \sum_{\gamma\in p(Q)} q^{\frac{1}{2}|\gamma|^2} / \prod_{j=1}^{\infty} (1-q^{j/m})^{\dim \underline{h}_{j/m}}$.

Comparing (11.4), (11.5) and (11.7), we get $\dim_q V^{++} = c_w$, proving the theorem.

Following [14], cf. [11, p. 223], the second method depends on the asymptotics of characters and modular forms. We have asymptotically, as $T \downarrow 0$,

$$\dim_q V \sim e^{\pi n/12T}/\mathrm{vol}(Q)$$

$$\prod_{j=1}^{\infty} (1-q^{j/m})^{-\dim \underline{h}_{j/m}} \sim T^{\frac{1}{2}\dim \underline{h}_0}\, e^{\pi n/12T}/\det(1-w_*)^{\frac{1}{2}}$$

$$\sum_{\alpha\in p(Q)} q^{\frac{1}{2}|\alpha|^2} \sim T^{-\frac{1}{2}\dim \underline{h}_0}/\mathrm{vol}(p(Q)) .$$

Comparing these with (10.1), (11.4) and (11.5), we get $\dim_q V^{++} \sim c_w$, so that $\dim V^{++} = c_w$, proving the theorem again.

Since $V_0^{++} \subset V^{++}$ and V^{++} is an irreducible $\hat{S}_0$-module, we get:

(11.8) $V^{++} = V_0$.

(11.9) $\dim V^{++} = c_w$.

Remark. By a remark in Section 3, it is clear that the Irreducibility Theorem holds for all level 1 representations as well.

12. In this section, we will establish a commutator formula for the $h(\alpha,\beta)$, generalizing formula (10.3).

Take $\tau \in \mathbb{C}$, write $z = e^{\tau}$. We interpret z^k to mean $e^{k\tau}$ and $\log z$ to mean τ. For $b \in \underline{g}$, define the generating function

$$X_b(z) = \sum_k z^{-k}\, b(k) .$$

Here and further on k runs over the set $\{k \in \mathbb{C} | e^{-2\pi ik}$ is an eigenvalue of $\mathrm{Ad}\sigma\}$; if $b \in \underline{h}$, we can assume k to be in $\frac{1}{m}\mathbb{Z}$. In what follows, we are making calculations in the basic representation (V,π_0) of $\hat{\underline{g}}$.

We have the following commutation relations, which follow from (9.2) and (11.3) respectively:

(12.1) $z^{-k}[a(k),X_b(z)] = X_{[a,b]}(z) + k(a|b)c$, if $a = a_\lambda$,

where $\lambda = \exp - 2\pi ik$.

(12.2) $\mathrm{Ad}(h(\beta,\gamma))X_a(z) = e^{2\pi i(\alpha|\gamma)}z^{(\alpha|\beta)}X_a(z) + (a|\beta)c$

if $\alpha \in \Delta \cup \{0\}$ and $a \in \underline{g}_\alpha$.

For $\alpha \in \Delta$ and $a \in \underline{g}_\alpha$ put $E_\alpha^\pm(z) = \sum_{\pm k>0} -\frac{1}{k} z^{-k}\, \alpha(k)$ (here $k \in \frac{1}{m}\mathbb{Z}$), and put $T_a(z) = (\exp -E_\alpha^-(z))X_a(z)(\exp -E_\alpha^+(z))$. Then we have:

(12.3) $[\hat{s}_w, T_a(z)] = 0$,

(12.4) $h(\beta,\gamma)T_a(z)h(\beta,\gamma)^{-1} = e^{2\pi i(\alpha|\gamma)}z^{(\alpha|\beta)}T_a(z)$.

Furthermore, given $\lambda \in \underline{h}_0$, put $V_\lambda^+ = \{v \in V^+ | \pi_0(h(0))v = (\lambda|h)v$ for all $h \in \underline{h}\}$. Then, for $v \in V_\lambda^+$, we have

(12.5) $T_a(z)v = z^{(\lambda|\alpha)+\frac{1}{2}|p(\alpha)|^2}\, a(-(\lambda|\alpha)-\frac{1}{2}|p(\alpha)|^2)v$.

For $\alpha,\beta \in Q$, define constants $B_{\alpha,\beta}$ and $C_{\alpha,\beta}$ by:

$$B_{\alpha,\beta} = m^{-(\alpha|\beta)} \prod_{r=1}^{m-1} (1-e^{2\pi i r/m})^{(w^r(\alpha)|\beta)} ,$$

$$C_{\alpha,\beta} = (-1)^{(\alpha|\beta)}\, B_{\beta,\alpha}/B_{\alpha,\beta} = \prod_{r=1}^{m} (-e^{2\pi i r/m})^{(\alpha|w^r(\beta))} .$$

Then we have, for $a \in \underline{g}_\alpha$, $b \in \underline{g}_\beta$:

(12.6) $B_{\alpha,\beta}\, T_a(z)\, T_b(z) = T_{[a,b]}(z)$ if $(\alpha|\beta) = -1$;

(12.7) $B_{\alpha,\beta}\, T_a(z)\, T_b(z) = (a|b)$ if $(\alpha|\beta) = -2$;

(12.8) $T_a(z)T_b(z') = C_{\alpha,\beta}(z/z')^{(p(\alpha)|p(\beta))}T_b(z')T_a(z)$.

Comparing (12.4) with (12.8) allows us to identify $T_a(z)$, up to a multiplicative scalar, with an element of $\pi_0(\hat{S})$:

(12.9) $T_a(z) \in \mathbb{C}^\times \pi_0(h(\beta,\gamma))$,

where $\beta = -p(\alpha)$, and

$$\gamma = (\frac{m}{2} + \frac{1}{2\pi i}\log z)p(\alpha) - \frac{1}{m}\sum_{r=1}^{m-1} r w^r(\alpha)$$
$$= (1-w_*)^{-1}(\alpha - p(\alpha)) + (\frac{1}{2} + \frac{1}{2\pi i}\log z)p(\alpha) .$$

Comparing (12.7) and (12.8), we obtain the following important commutator formula, which is valid in $\hat{G}$:

(12.10) $h(\alpha,\beta)h(\alpha',\beta') = (\exp 2\pi i\, Dc)h(\alpha',\beta')h(\alpha,\beta)$,
where $D = \frac{1}{2}(\alpha|\alpha') + (\alpha|\beta') - (\alpha'|\beta) + (\beta|\beta'-w(\beta'))$.

The following two formulas are useful:

(12.11) $T_{(\mathrm{Ad}\sigma)a}(z) = T_a(e^{2\pi i}z)$.

(Recall that $T_a(z)$ actually depends on $\log z$.)

(12.12) $T_a(z') = T_a(z)\exp((\log(z'/z))(\alpha(0)+\frac{1}{2}|p(\alpha)|^2c))$ if $a \in \underline{g}_\alpha$.

We have obtained the following formula:

(12.13) $\sum_k z^{-k}\, \pi_0(e_\alpha(k)) =$

$$=: \exp \sum_{k\in\frac{1}{m}\mathbb{Z}\setminus\{0\}} -\frac{1}{k} z^{-k}\,\pi_0(\alpha(k)) : T_{e_\alpha}(z)\ , \quad \alpha \in \Delta\ .$$

Here : : denotes the normal ordering, so that

$$:\exp \sum_{k\neq 0} -\frac{1}{k}z^{-k}\pi_0(\alpha(k)) := (\exp \sum_{k>0} \frac{1}{k}z^{k}\pi_0(\alpha(-k)))(\exp \sum_{k>0} -\frac{1}{k}z^{-k}\pi_0(\alpha(k)))\ ,$$

and $T_{e_\alpha}(z)$ is given, up to multiplicative factor, by (12.9). Since $c, e_\alpha(k)$ and $\alpha(k)$ for $\alpha \in \Delta$ and all k , span $\hat{\underline{g}}$, formula (12.13) describes the basic representation (V,π_0) of $\hat{\underline{g}}$ in terms of the operators $\pi_0(\alpha(k))$ and $\pi_0(h(\beta,\gamma))$.

One also easily finds formulas for the representation of the Virasoro algebra in terms of operators $\pi_0(h(k))$, $h \in \underline{h}$. Choose a basis $\{u_i\}$ of $\underline{h}$ and let $\{u^i\}$ be the dual basis, i.e. $(u_i|u^j) = \delta_{ij}$. Define the "twisted" Virasoro operators $D_j = d_j + x(j)'$, $j \in \mathbb{Z}$. Then

(12.14) $\pi_0(D_j) = \frac{1}{2} \sum_{k\in\frac{1}{m}\mathbb{Z}} \sum_{i=1}^{n} :\pi_0(u_i(-k))\pi_0(u^i(k+j)):$.

13. Fix $w \in W$. The Irreducibility Theorem and the commutation relations

(9.3), (11.3) and (12.10) allow one to associate to w a vertex construction of the basic representation (V,π_0) described below.

We have $w^m = 1$ for some positive m. Given $k \in \frac{1}{m}\mathbb{Z}$, let $\hat{k}$ stand for the element $k \bmod \mathbb{Z}$ of $\frac{1}{m}\mathbb{Z}/\mathbb{Z}$. We have the eigenspace decomposition $\underline{h} = \bigoplus_{\hat{k}\in\frac{1}{m}\mathbb{Z}/\mathbb{Z}} \underline{h}_{\hat{k}}$ with respect to w, where $\underline{h}_{\hat{k}}$ corresponds to the eigenvalue $e^{-2\pi ik}$.

For each $k \in \frac{1}{m}\mathbb{Z}$, denote by $\underline{h}(k)$ a copy of $\underline{h}_{\hat{k}}$. Given $\alpha \in \underline{h}$, denote by $\alpha(k)$ the $\underline{h}_{\hat{k}}$-component of α, regarded as an element of the copy $\underline{h}(k)$.

Put $\hat{s}_w^{\pm} = \bigoplus_{\substack{k\in\frac{1}{m}\mathbb{Z}\\ k>0}} \underline{h}(\pm k)$ and define the Heisenberg Lie algebra $\hat{s}_w = \hat{s}_w^- \oplus \mathbb{C}c \oplus \hat{s}_w^+$ by the commutation relations

$$[h_1(j),h_2(k)] = j\delta_{j,-k}(h_1|h_2)c \quad \text{for } h_1 \in h_{\hat{j}},\ h_2 \in h_{\hat{k}};$$

$$(13.1) \qquad [c,h(j)] = 0 .$$

The Lie algebra $\hat{s}_w$ has a unique irreducible representation (F,π_0'), the Fock representation, such that $\pi_0'(c) = 1$ and there exists a non-zero vector, the vacuum vector, which is killed by $\hat{s}_+$. The space F may be identified with the symmetric algebra $S(\hat{s}_w^-)$ over $\hat{s}_w^-$ on which $c = 1$ and, for positive $k \in \frac{1}{m}\mathbb{Z}$, $h(-k)$ acts as a creation operator, i.e. the operator of multiplication by $h(-k)$, and $h(k)$ acts as an annihilation operator, i.e. a derivation of the algebra $S(\hat{s}_w^-)$, which kills 1, subject to relation (13.1), so that 1 is the vacuum vector.

Consider the (additive) group

$$L_w = \{(\alpha,\beta) \in \underline{h}_{\hat{0}} \oplus \underline{h} \mid \beta - w(\beta) \in \alpha + Q\},$$

and define on L_w the following bimultiplicative alternating function:

$$\psi((\alpha,\beta),(\alpha',\beta')) = \exp 2\pi i(\tfrac{1}{2}(\alpha|\alpha')+(\alpha|\beta')-(\alpha'|\beta)+(\beta|\beta'-w(\beta'))).$$

The group M_w is embeded in L_w in an obvious way, $\beta \to (0,\beta)$, so that the restriction of Ψ to M_w is the function ψ defined in Section 10. Note that $L_w^0 = \{(0,\beta) | \beta \in \underline{h}_{\hat{0}}\}$ is the identity component of L_w and that Ψ vanishes on $L_w^0 \times L_w^0$.

By a projective representation (U,τ) of a group Γ we mean a vector space U and a map $\tau : \Gamma \to \mathrm{Aut}\, U$ such that $\tau(\gamma_1)\tau(\gamma_2) \in \mathbb{C}^\times\, \tau(\gamma_1+\gamma_2)$. We say that another projective representation (U',τ') of Γ is equivalent to (U,τ) if there exists an isomorphism $\phi : U \xrightarrow{\sim} U'$ such that $\phi^{-1}\,\tau'(\gamma)\phi \in \mathbb{C}^\times\, \tau(\gamma)$ for all $\gamma \in \Gamma$.

The group L_w has a unique, up to equivalence, projective representation (U,π_0'') such that

(i) $\pi_0''(\gamma)\pi_0''(\gamma') = \Psi(\gamma,\gamma')\pi_0''(\gamma')\pi_0''(\gamma)$;

(ii) L_w^0 is diagonalizable and has a fixed vector;

(iii) the only operators commuting with all $\pi_0''(\gamma)$ are scalars.

The group $\tilde{S}_w$ considered earlier is isomorphic to the quotient of L_w by the subgroup $0 \oplus Q$. In the next section, we will construct explicitly a representation of the group $\hat{S}_w$, which induces a projective representation of $\tilde{S}_w$ and hence of L_w . This projective representation, which we denote by $(\overline{V}^+,\pi_0'')$, satisfies the properties (i), (ii) and (iii).

<u>Remark</u>. The radical of Ψ is $0 \oplus Q^*$. If w is non-degenerate, then $L_w = M_w$ and so $\dim \overline{V}^+ = c_w$; otherwise $\dim \overline{V}^+ = \infty$. If w is primitive, then $(\overline{V}^+,\pi_0'')$ is equivalent to the trivial 1-dimensional representation.

Let $\overline{V} = F \otimes_{\mathbb{C}} \overline{V}^+$. Given $\alpha \in \Delta$, introduce the following vertex operator:

$$X(\alpha,z) =: \exp - \sum_{\substack{j\in\frac{1}{m}\mathbb{Z} \\ j\neq 0}} \frac{1}{j} z^{-j}\, \pi_0'(\alpha(j)): \otimes T_\alpha(z) ,$$

where $T_\alpha(z) = \pi_0''((-p(\alpha),(1-w_*)^{-1}(\alpha-p(\alpha)))\pi_0''((0,(\frac{1}{2} + \frac{1}{2\pi i}\log z)p(\alpha)))$. Here p is the orthogonal projection of $\underline{h}$ on $\underline{h}_{\hat{0}}$ and w_* is the restriction of w to $\underline{h}_{\hat{0}}$; z^k stands for $e^{k\tau}$ and $\log z$ stands for τ , where τ is a complex parameter.

Decomposing by powers of z :

$X(\alpha, z) = \sum_k X_k(\alpha)z^k$, we obtain a collection of operators $X_k(\alpha)$ on $\overline{V}$.

Theorem. The identity operator, the creation and annihilation operators and the components $X_k(\alpha)$ of the vertex operators for $\alpha \in \Delta$, span a Lie algebra of operators on the vector space $\overline{V}$. This Lie algebra is isomorphic to $\hat{\underline{g}}$ and its representation on $\overline{V}$ is equivalent to the basic representation (V, π_0) of $\hat{\underline{g}}$.

14. We proceed to construct the group $\hat{S}_w$ and its representation on the space V^+ explicitly. Recall the bimultiplicative function $\varepsilon(\alpha,\beta)$ and the Chevalley basis elements e_α from Section 4, and the bimultiplicative function $B_{\alpha,\beta}$ from Section 12. Denote by $\mathbb{C}[Q]$ the complex vector space with basis $\{e(\alpha)\}_{\alpha\in Q}$ and by $\mathbb{C}[\exp \underline{h}_0]$ the complex vector space with basis $\{e^h\}_{h\in\underline{h}_0/2\pi i Q^w}$. Introduce the associative (non-commutative) algebra

$$A_w = \mathbb{C}[Q] \otimes_{\mathbb{C}} \mathbb{C}[\exp \underline{h}_0]$$

with the following multiplication:

$$e(\alpha)e(\beta) = \varepsilon(\alpha,\beta)\, B^{-1}_{\alpha,\beta}\, e(\alpha+\beta) ,$$
$$e^h\, e(\alpha) = e^{(\alpha|h)}\, e(\alpha)e^h ,$$
$$e^h\, e^{h'} = e^{h+h'} .$$

Here $e(\alpha)$ stands for $e(\alpha)\otimes 1$ and e^h stands for $1 \otimes e^h$.

The algebra A_w has the following representation τ on $\mathbb{C}[Q]$:

$$\tau(e(\alpha))e(\beta) = e(\alpha)e(\beta) ,$$
$$\tau(e^h)e(\beta) = e^h e(\beta)e^{-h} .$$

Introduce the function $\eta : Q \to \mathbb{C}^\times$ by:

$$e_{w(\alpha)} = \eta(\alpha)(\mathrm{Ad}\sigma)e_\alpha \quad \text{for} \quad \alpha \in \Delta ,$$
$$\eta(\alpha+\beta) = \varepsilon(\alpha,\beta)\varepsilon(w(\alpha),w(\beta))\eta(\alpha)\eta(\beta) .$$

Define an automorphism μ of the algebra A_w by:

$$\mu(e^h) = e^h ,\ \mu(e(\alpha)) = \eta(-\alpha)\, e^{-\pi i p(\alpha)} e(w(\alpha))e^{-\pi i p(\alpha)} .$$

Let A_w be the subgroup of the multiplicative group of the algebra A_w

consisting of the elements of the form $te(\alpha)e^h$, where $t \in \mathbb{C}^\times$, $\alpha \in Q$, $h \in \underline{h}_0$. Define a homomorphism μ_0 of $A_w^\times$ into its center by $\mu_0(a) = a^{-1}\mu(a)$, and let $\overline{S}_w = A_w^\times/\mu_0(A_w^\times)$. We now show that $\overline{S}_w$ is isomorphic to $\hat{S}_w$.

Define homomorphisms $\overline{\nu}_1 : \overline{S}_w \to \tilde{S}_w$ and $\overline{\pi}_0 : \overline{S}_w \to \mathrm{Aut}\, V$ by:

$$\overline{\nu}_1(te(\alpha)e^h) = h(\beta,\gamma)' \exp h ,$$

where $\beta = -p(\alpha)$, $\gamma = (1-w_*)^{-1}(\alpha-p(\alpha))$; $\overline{\pi}_0(te(\alpha)e^h) = tT_\alpha(e^{-\pi i})\exp \pi_0(h)$. Here $T_\alpha(z)$ for $\alpha \in Q$, $z \in \mathbb{C}^\times$ is defined by:

$$T_\alpha(z) = T_{e_\alpha}(z) \text{ for } \alpha \in \Delta , \; T_\alpha(z)T_\beta(z) = \varepsilon(\alpha,\beta)B_{\alpha,\beta}^{-1}T_{\alpha+\beta}(z) .$$

There exists a unique isomorphism $\overline{S}_w \to \hat{S}_w$ which identifies ν_1 with $\overline{\nu}_1$ and π_0 with $\overline{\pi}_0$; we identify $\overline{S}_w$ with $\hat{S}_w$ using this isomorphism. Note that e^h is identified with $\exp h$.

The space $U = \mathbb{C}[Q]/\tau((1-\mu)A_w)\mathbb{C}[Q]$ is a quotient representation of the representation τ of A_w. This is a representation of $A_w^\times$ on which $\mu_0(A_w^\times)$ acts trivially, thus giving rise to a representation of $\overline{S}_w$. Let U_0 be the fixed point set of center (G) on U.

For $\gamma \in Q$ such that $p(\gamma) = 0$, right multiplication by $e(\gamma)$ on $\mathbb{C}[Q]$ induces an endomorphism of U_0 which we denote by A_γ. The operators A_γ span the commuting algebra of the representation of $\overline{S}_w$ on U_0; this algebra is isomorphic to the algebra of $c_w \times c_w$-matrices over $\mathbb{C}$. Take a rank 1 projector in this algebra, say P, and put $\overline{V}^+ = P(U_0)$. The representation of $\overline{S}_w$ on $\overline{V}^+$ is equivalent to that of $\hat{S}_w$ on V^+.

15. Comments and questions.

A. (a) By the proposition in Section 9, the Irreducibility Theorem holds for <u>any</u> pair $(\hat{s},\hat{S})$. This is "philosophically" important.

(b) The Irreducibility Theorem was first proved [10] for the principal Heisenberg, then [2] for the homogeneous Heisenberg, and now for any Heisenberg. These three stages correspond to the appearance first of the Heisenberg Lie algebra $\hat{s}$, then of the "translation group" $\hat{S}/\hat{S}_0$, where $\hat{S}_0$ is the centralizer of the identity component of $\hat{S}$, and finally of the group $\hat{S}_0$, which is, essentially, a finite Heisenberg group.

B. (a) The other fundamental representations of level 1 may be treated in the same way.

(b) One can realize (V,π_0) as a space of functions, and describe the vertex operators, the Virasoro algebra, etc., in this realization (cf. [2]).

(c) Problem: construct intertwining operators $T_{w,w'}$ among the realizations of (V,π_0) .

(d) Taking $w \in \text{Aut } Q\backslash W$, one obtains, in a similar way, a construction of all representations of level 1 of all twisted affine Kac-Moody algebras.

C. (a) Formula (12.10) can be generalized to the case where $\beta\text{-}w(\beta) \in \alpha+Q^*$, so that $h(\alpha,\beta)' \in \widetilde{\text{Ad}(G)}$. This allows one to evaluate the action of the group elements $e(\alpha)$ of Section 14 on all fundamental representations by using the vertex operators.

(b) The embedding of center (G) into the group $\overline{S}_w$ of Section 14 can be given explicitly.

(c) The representation of $\hat{S}_w$ on V^+ can be realized as an induced representation, or as a space of sections of a bundle over H^w .

D. Let K be a simply-connected compact Lie group of type A, D, or E, let $\mathcal{K}$ be the group of C^∞ loops on K , and let $(\mathcal{V},\pi_0)$ be the basic projective unitary representation of $\mathcal{K}$ on a Hilbert space $\mathcal{V}$ [17]. Given a loop S of maximal tori of K , define the associated Heisenberg subgroup of $\mathcal{K}$ to be the subgroup $\tilde{S}$ consisting of all loops $p: S^1 \to K$ such that $p(\theta) \in S(\theta)$. It is reasonable to expect the following version of our irreducibility theorem: $(\mathcal{V},\pi_0)$ remains irreducible when restricted to $\tilde{S}$. (This is known in the case of a 1-point loop [17].)

E. (a) The group $\exp \underline{g}(0)$ is a covering group of G^σ , and V^{++} is a one-dimensional or fundamental representation of it.

(b) The groups $\hat{S}_0$ are of interest in the study of finite abelian and Heisenberg subgroups of semisimple Lie groups. The crucial commutator formula (10.3) was proved in this context.

(c) Problem. Find an integral formula for the commutator in $\hat{G}$ of preimages of two commuting elements of $\tilde{G}$.

F. The second author has given a description of the Heisenberg algebras

$\hat{s}_w$ for primitive w as centralizers of (possibly several) explicitly given loops. This is analogous to the use of Kostant's "cyclic element" in connection with the principal Heisenberg subalgebra (cf. [10]).

G. If $p(\alpha) = 0$, then formula (12.5) says that $T_a(z) = a(0)$ on V^+. This is a remarkable coincidence: the actions of a group element and a Lie algebra element coincide on V^+!

References

1. Carter, R.W., Conjugacy classes in the Weyl group, Compositio Math. 25 (1972), 1-59.

2. Frenkel, I.B., Kac, V.G., Basic representations of affine Lie algebras and dual resonance models, Invent. Math. 62 (1980), 23-66.

3. Frenkel, I.B., Lepowsky, J., Meurman, A., A natural representation of the Fischer-Griess Mouster with the modular function J as character, Proc. Natl. Acad. Sci. USA 81 (1984), 3256-3260.

4. Garland, H., The arithmetic theory of loop algebras, J. Algebra 53 (1978), 480-551.

5. Gross, D.J., Harvey, J.A., Martinec, E., Rohm, R., The heterotic string, Phys. Rev. Lett. 54 (1985), 502-505.
   Thierry-Mieg, J., Remarks concerning $E_8 \times E_8$ and D_{16} string theories (1984), Berkeley preprint.

6. Kac, V.G., Infinite dimensional Lie algebras and the Dedekind η-function, Funct. Anal. Appl. 8 (1974), 68-70.

7. Kac, V.G., Infinite-dimensional algebras, Dedekind's η-function, classical Möbius function and the very strange formula, Advances in Math. 30 (1978), 85-136.

8. Kac, V.G., An elucidation of "Infinite dimensional algebras...and the very strange formula". $E_8^{(1)}$ and the cube root of the modular invariant j, Advances in Math. 35 (1980), 264-273.

9. Kac, V.G., Infinite-dimensional Lie algebras. Second edition, Cambridge University Press, 1985.

10. Kac, V.G., Kazhdan, D.A., Lepowsky, J., Wilson, R.L., Realization of the basic representation of the Euclidean Lie algebras, Advances in Math. 42 (1981), 83-112.

11. Kac, V.G., Peterson, D.H., Infinite-dimensional Lie algebras, theta functions and modular forms, Advances in Math. 53 (1984), 125-264.

References, Cont.

12. Kac, V.G., Peterson, D.H., Unitary structure in representations of infinite-dimensional groups and a convexity theorem, Invent. Math. 76 (1984), 1-14.

13. Peterson, D.H., Kac, V.G., Infinite flag varieties and conjugacy theorems, Proc. Natl. Acad. Sci. USA 80 (1983), 1778-1782.

14. Peterson, D.H., Level 1 modules of affine Lie algebras, to appear.

15. Serre, J.-P., Cours d'arithmetique, Presses Universitaires de France, Paris, 1970.

16. Sugawara, H., A field theory of currents, Phys. Rev. 170 (1968), 1659-1662.

17. Segal, G., Unitary representations of some infinite dimensional groups, Comm. Math. Phys. 80 (1981), 301-342.

THE HETEROTIC STRING*

David Gross
Joseph Henry Laboratories
Princeton University
Princeton, New Jersey 08544

1. Introduction

Anomalies are good things. We have learned in recent years that they are ubiquitous features of chiral theories that possess local gauge symmetries, that arise due to the global structure of configuration space. In order to avoid the inconsistencies implied by such anomalies we are often led to strong constraints on the structure of these theories. Thus the study of anomalies provides us with another tool in the pursuit of uniqueness, and has already proved to have powerful predictive power.

When Jackiw and I explored, in 1972, the effect of chiral anomalies in non-abelian chiral gauge theories, we were concerned that these would render the newly revived unified gauge theories of the weak and electromagnetic interactions inconsistent. This indeed proved to be the case. However, we noticed (as did Bouchiat, Iliopoulos and Maiani) that the dangerous anomalies would cancel if the known leptons were appropriately paired with quarks in the, now standard, family patterns. We remarked that this required the existence of the charmed quark, postulated for other reasons by Glashow, Iliopoulos and Maiani. If our conclusion was somewhat tentative it was because at that time, before asymptotic freedom and QCD, quarks were not accorded the same degree of physical reality as leptons. This mechanism of anomaly cancellation has survived and has been reconfirmed by the subsequent discovery of the τ and the top and bottom quarks. It is the best evidence we have of the inherently chiral nature of the weak interactions, and of the fact that nature knows about potential anomalies and strives to avoid them.

In the last year, once again, the study of anomalies has led to powerful constraints on new theories and suggested new structures. The recent intense interest in string theories as candidates for unified theories of gravity and

---

*Research supported in part by NSF Grant PHY80-19754.

matter was spurred by the discovery of Green and Schwarz of a mechanism which eliminates anomalies in higher dimensional, chiral supergravity theories. Their anomaly cancellation mechanism provided a clue which led to the discovery of a totally new string theory--the Heterotic String Theory, which is an inherently chiral closed string theory that produces gauge interactions by compactification of some of its internal dimensions. This theory, whose structure I shall briefly review, provides us with a plausible candidate for a unified theory of everything.

2. String Theories

String theories offer a way of realizing the potential of supersymmetry, Kaluza-Klein and much more. They are based on an enormous increase in the number of degrees of freedom where, in addition to fermionic coordinates and extra dimensions, the basic entities are extended objects instead of points. Correspondingly the symmetry group is greatly enlarged in a way we are only beginning to comprehend. It has been clear for some time that the ten-dimensional superstring theory provides a consistent, finite theory which has as its low energy manifestation ten dimensional supergravity. Until recently, however, it was not clear how to construct realistic theories based on the string. In order to generate the observed chiral fermions one must start with a chiral string theory. Such a theory has potential anomalies, just like its field theoretic counterparts. These can be either the traditional gauge anomalies or gravitational anomalies. In either case they render the theory inconsistent. String theories come in two types. First there are the theories of closed strings, inherently neutral, whose low energy limit is pure N=2 supergravity. The chiral form of this theory is indeed anomaly free. However it does not contain Yang-Mills interactions and it is unlikely that they could emerge, together with the known fermions upon compactification. Open string theories, on the other hand, allow the introduction of gauge groups by the time honored method of attaching charges to the ends of the strings. String theories of this type can be constructed which yield, at low energies, N=1 supergravity with any Yang-Mills group. These however, in addition to being somewhat arbitrary, were suspected to be anomalous. The discovery, last summer, that for a particular gauge group--SO_{32}--the would be anomalies cancel, has greatly increased the phenomenological prospects of unified string theories.

The anomaly cancellation mechanism of Green and Schwarz can be understood in terms of the low energy field theory that emerges from the superstring, which is a slightly modified form of d=10 supergravity. One finds that the dangerous Lorentz and gauge anomalies cancel, if and only if, the gauge group is SO_{32} or $E_8 \times E_8$. The ordinary superstring theory cannot incorporate $E_8 \times E_8$. The apparent correspondence between the low energy limit of anomaly free superstring theories and anomaly free supergravity theories provided the motivation that led to the discovery of a new string theory, whose low energy limit contained an $E_8 \times E_8$ gauge group--the heterotic string. It is of more than academic interest to construct such a theory since the phenomenological prospects for an $E_8 \times E_8$ theory are much brighter.

String theories have many appealing features. First is the fact that even though they do represent a radical departure from ordinary QFT, they do so in the direction of increased symmetry and structure. Second, they yield for the first time consistent and well defined theories of gravity. String theories are inherently theories of gravity. Unlike ordinary QFT we do not have the option of turning gravity off. The gravitational, or closed string, sector of the theory must always be present even if one starts by considering open strings, since these can always join at their ends to form a closed string. One could even imagine discovering the graviton in the attempt to construct string theories of matter. In fact historically this happened for the dual resonance models--the graviton (or Pomeron) was first seen as a bound state of open strings. The problem of ultraviolet divergences is bypassed in string theories. It is the case that string theories contain no divergences in the ultraviolet. This is not too surprising considering the extended nature of strings, which softens their interaction. Alternatively one notes that interactions are introduced into the string theory by allowing the string coordinates, which are two dimensional fields, to propagate on world sheets with nontrivial topology (adding to the world sheet handles or holes). Thus from the point of view of the first quantized theory one doesn't introduce an interaction at all, and as long as reparametrization invariance is maintained there are simply no possible counterterms. In fact all the divergences that have ever appeared in string theories can be traced to infrared divergences that are an indication of vacuum instability. All string theories contain a massless scalar partner of the graviton, the dilaton. If one consructs a string theory by perturbing about a trial vacuum in which the dilaton has nonvanishing vacuum expectation value, then infrared divergences will occur when this massless particle goes into the vacuum. This is the source of the divergences that occur in the tree approximation of the open bosonic theory and in the one loop approximation of the closed bosonic string theory. Supersymmetry requires a vanishing dilaton tadpole, thus both the superstring and the heterotic string are completely finite (at least to one loop order).

Third, string theories are incredibly unique. Not only do they contain, in principle, no freely adjustable parameters, they also determine rather uniquely the choice of the gauge group of nature. Furthermore they fix the number of space-time dimensions to be ten.

Finally, as we shall discuss below, they led to phenomenologically attractive unified theories, which could very well describe the real world.

3. The Heterotic String

Previously known string theories are the bosonic theory in 26 dimensions (the Veneziano model) and the fermionic, superstring theory in ten dimensions (an outgrowth of the Ramond-Neveu-Schwarz string). The new string theory is consructed as a chiral hybrid of these. To see how this is possible let us recall how string theories are constructed.

Free string theories are constructed by first quantization of an action given by the invariant area of the world sheet swept out by the string, or by its supersymmetric generalization. For the bosonic string the action is

$$S = -\int d\tau d\sigma \, \frac{1}{4\pi\alpha'} \, [\eta_{\alpha\beta} g^{ab} \partial_a X^\alpha \partial_b X^\beta], \tag{1}$$

where $X^\alpha(\sigma,\tau)$ labels the space-time position of the string, embedded in some D-dimensional manifold ($\alpha=1,2,\ldots,D$), with σ,τ labeling the world sheet that the string sweeps out. It appears to be possible to construct consistent string theories as long as the above two dimensional sigma-model is conformally invariant. For the moment we take the big space to be flat, so that $\eta_{\alpha\beta}$ is the Minkowski metric. This is essentially a choice of vacuum for the quantum string theory. In order to describe the real world however one will be interested in non flat D-dimensional manifolds. The reparametrization invariance of the action (in σ,τ) permits one to choose the metric of the world sheet to be conformally flat and in which the timelike parameter of the world sheet, τ, is identified with light cone time. In this light cone gauge the theory reduces to a two-dimensinal free field theory of the physical degrees of freedom--the transverse coordinates of the string, subject to constraints. This procedure is valid however only in the critical dimension of 26 for the bosonic string and ten for the fermionic string. In other dimensions of space time the existence of conformal anomalies implies that the conformal degree of freedom of the internal metric does not decouple. If it is ignored there is a breakdown of world sheet reparametrization invariance.

In the critical dimension the physical degrees of freedom, being massless two-dimensional fields, can be decomposed into right and left movers, i.e. functions of $\tau-\sigma$ and $\tau+\sigma$ respectively. If we consider only closed strings then the right and left movers never mix. This separation is maintained even in the presence of string interactions, as long as we allow only orientable world sheets on which a handedness can be defined. This is because the interactions between closed strings are constructed order by order in perturbation theory, by simply modifying the topology of the world sheet on which the strings propagate. In terms of the first quantized two-dimensional theory no interaction is thereby introduced; the right and left movers still propagate freely and independently as massless fields. Thus there is in principle no obstacle to constructing the right and left moving sectors of a closed string in a different fashion, as long as each sector is separately consistent, and together can be regarded as a string embedded in ordinary space-time. This is the idea behind the construction of the heterotic string, which combines the right movers of the fermionic superstring with the left movers of the bosonic string. It is necessarily a theory of closed and orientable strings, since one can clearly distinguish an orientation on such a string. In some sense the heterotic string is inherently chiral; indeed we do not have the option, present in other closed string theories, of constructing a left-right symmetric theory.

The physical degrees of freedom of the right-moving sector of the fermionic superstring consist of eight transverse coordinates $X^i(\tau-\sigma)$ ($i=1,\ldots 8$) and eight Majorana-Weyl fermionic coordinates $S^a(\tau-\sigma)$. The physical degrees of freedom of the left-moving sector of the bosonic string consist of 24 transverse coordinates, $X^i(\tau+\sigma)$ and $X^I(\tau+\sigma)$, ($i=1,\ldots 8$, $I=1,\ldots 16$). Together they comprise the physical degrees of freedom of the heterotic string. The eight transverse right- and left-movers combine with the longitudinal coordinates to describe the position of the string embedded in ten-dimensional space. The extra fermionic and bosonic degrees of freedom parametrize an internal space.

The light cone action that yields the dynamics of these degrees of freedom can be derived from a manifestly covariant action, and one can easily quantize it. The only new feature that enters is the compactification and quantization of the extra 16 left-moving bosonic coordinates. It is this compactification, on a uniquely determined 16 dimensional compact space, that leads to the emergence of Yang-Mills interactions.

The transverse coordinates that describe a closed string are periodic functions of $0<\sigma<\pi$ and have the normal mode expansion

$$X^i(\tau-\sigma) = \frac{1}{2} X^i + \frac{1}{2} p^i(\tau-\sigma) + \frac{i}{2} \sum_{n\neq 0} \frac{\alpha_n^i}{n} e^{-2in(\tau-\sigma)}$$

$$X^i(\tau+\sigma) = \frac{1}{2} X^i + \frac{1}{2} p^i(\tau+\sigma) + \frac{i}{2} \sum_{n\neq 0} \frac{\tilde{\alpha}_n^i}{n} e^{-2in(\tau+\sigma)} \qquad (2)$$

where $x^i(p^i)$ are the center-of-mass coordinates (momenta) of the string, and α_n^i are creation ($n<0$) and annihilation operators ($n>0$). The right-moving fermionic coordinates have a similar expansion, as do the extra left-moving bosonic coordinates

$$X^I = x^I + p^I(\tau+\sigma) + \frac{i}{2} \sum \tilde{\alpha}^I_{n/n} \exp(-2in(\tau+\sigma)) \qquad (3)$$

(here, due to the constraint that X^I be left moving, $[x^I, p^J] = \frac{i}{2}\delta^{IJ}$).

In light cone gauge $X^+ = x^+ + p^+\tau$ and X^- is determined by solving the constraints that result from having chosen a conformally flat metric on the world sheet. This determines p^-, the generator of X^+ (or τ) translations, the light cone Hamiltonian, and thereby the string mass operator

$$(\text{mass})^2/4 = N + (\tilde{N}-1) + \frac{1}{2}(p^I)^2, \quad N = \tilde{N}-1 + \frac{1}{2}(p^I)^2, \qquad (4)$$

where $N(\tilde{N})$ are the number operators of the right- and left-moving modes of the string. The subtraction of -1 from $\tilde{N}$ is due to normal ordering and absent in the case of the right movers due to fermion-boson cancellation. The above constraint results from the invariance of the closed string under translation of σ. Consequently the would be tachyon of the bosonic string, for $\tilde{N}=0$ and $p^I=0$, is absent from the physical Hilbert space of the heterotic string, whose lowest mass state is massless.

The extra 16 left-moving coordinates of the heterotic string can be viewed as parametrizing an "internal" compact space T. This interpretation should not be taken too literally; in fact one can equally well represent these degrees of freedom by 32 real fermions. For consistency we take T to be a flat compact manifold, i.e. a 16 dimensional torus. Since closed strings contain gravity in their low energy limit we would expect that a compactified string theory will contain massless vector mesons associated with the isometries of the compact space. For T this would yield the 16 gauge bosons of $U(1)^{16}$. A remarkable feature of closed string theories is that for special choices of the compact space there will exist extra massless gauge bosons, which are in fact massless solitons. They combine with the Kaluza-Klein gauge bosons to fill out the adjoint representation of a simple lie group whose rank equals the dimension of T. In the case of the heterotic string the structure of T is so constrained by requirements of consistency that only two choices are possible. These produce the gauge bosons of $G = Spin(32)/Z_2$ or $E_8 \times E_8$.

To see how this comes about let us consider a general torus T (characterized by 136 parameters) which can be defined by identifying sides of the elementary cell of a lattice in R_{16}, Γ_{16} generated by the vectors e_i^I, I=1,...16; i=1...16. We normalize the lengths of the e_i's to be $\sqrt{2}$, and identify the center of mass coordinate X^I with its translation by $2\pi R$ in the direction of e_i, so that $X^I \equiv X^I + 2\pi \Sigma n_i R_i e_i^I$, for integer n_i. The mode expansion for the internal coordinates is

$$X^I(\sigma,\tau) = x^I + p^I\tau + 2L^I\sigma + (\text{oscillators}).$$

For a torus the allowed center of mass momenta are quantized to lie on the lattice dual to Γ, i.e. that generated by e_i^* (i=1,...16), $\Sigma_I \, e_i^{I*} \, e_j^I = \delta_{ij}$, so that

$$p^I = \frac{1}{\sqrt{2}} \sum_{i=1}^{16} \frac{m_i}{R_i} e_i^{*I}, \quad m_i = \text{integer} \tag{5}$$

The $L^I\sigma$ term arises because of the existence of soliton states. String theories contain solitons that arise because of the multiple connectedness of configuration space, a phenomenon which has no counterpart in the theory of points. The closed string configuration $X^I(\sigma,\tau)$ defines a map from $S^1(0\leq\sigma\leq\pi)$ onto T, and such maps fall into homotopy classes characterized by winding numbers L^I, that count how many times X^I winds around the torus T. The allowed winding numbers are

$$L^I = \frac{1}{\sqrt{2}} \sum_{i=1}^{16} n_i R_i e_i^I , \quad n_i = \text{integer} \tag{6}$$

String configurations with nonvanishing L are topologically stable. They must be included in the theory since they can be created in pairs.

In the case of the heterotic string X is left-moving and thus a function of $\tau+\sigma$. Therefore the allowed momenta must coincide with an allowed winding number. This severely constrains the choice of the torus. For example it is clear that the radii are highly restricted as well as the relation between the lattice Γ and its dual. The full constraints on T only emerge when we consider one loop radiative corrections to the heterotic string. The (Euclidean) two-dimensional world sheet which describes such a process is a torus. This torus is clearly symmetric under interchange of τ and σ. If this symmetry were violated this would be an indication of a global diffeomorphism (reparametrization) anomaly and would lead to various disasters. To achieve this symmetry the coefficients of τ and σ in X must span all the states on the same lattice. All T must have equal radii given by $R^2=\alpha'$, and the lattice Γ must be even (the square of the allowed momenta must be even integers) and self dual. Such lattices are extremely rare, they only exist in 8n dimensions. In our case of 16 dimensions there are just two such lattices, $\Gamma_8\times\Gamma_8$ and Γ_{16}. The first is the direct product of two Γ_8's, where Γ_8 is the root lattice of E_8. The lattice Γ_{16} consists of all the points of the root lattice of SO(32) plus additional points that correspond to spinor weights of Spin $(32)/Z_2$. On either of these tori the allowed momenta are

$$p^I = \sum_{i=1}^{16} n_i e_i^I \tag{7}$$

where n_i also measures the winding number in the ith direction around the torus. The values of $(p^I)^2$ are all even integers the smallest being 2. Each of these lattices has precisely 480 vectors of length squared 2. These will yield, in the heterotic string theory, 480 massless vector bosons. These 480 solitons are labeled by the weights of the adjoint representation of $G=E_8\times E_8$ or

Spin $(32)/Z_2$, and combine with the 16 massless vector bosons with zero weights (the Kaluza-Klein gauge bosons) to fill out the adjoint representation of G.

The physical states of the heterotic string are direct products of Fock space states $(|\rangle_R \times |\rangle_L)$ of the right-moving fermionic and the left-moving bosonic strings, subject to the constraint (4). The right-handed ground state is annihilated by α_n^i, S_n^a (n>0), N, and forms an irreducible representation of the fermionic zero mode oscillators S_o^a, and consists of 8 bosonic states $|i\rangle_R$ and 8 fermionic states $|a\rangle_R$. The left-handed ground state is annihilated by all the $\tilde{\alpha}_n^i$, $\tilde{\alpha}_n^I$ (n>0), N, and p^I. By itself it is a tachyon but is eliminated from the physical spectrum since $\tilde{N} + 1/2\,(p^I)^2 = N+1>0$. The ground state is therefore massless and consists of the direct product of $|i\rangle_R$ or $|a\rangle_R$ with $\tilde{\alpha}_{-1}^j|0\rangle_L$, $\tilde{\alpha}_{-1}^I|0\rangle_L$, $|P^I\rangle_L$ (where $(P^I)^2=2$). All these states have $N = \tilde{N} + 1/2\,(P^I)^2 - 1 = 0$. As expected they form irreducible ten dimensional, massless supermultiplets. The states $|i \text{ or } a\rangle_R \times \tilde{\alpha}_{-1}^j|0\rangle_L$ form the irreducible N=1, D=10 supergravity multiplet. The states $|i\rangle_R \times \tilde{\alpha}_{-1}^I|0\rangle_L$ and $|a\rangle_R \times \tilde{\alpha}_{-1}^I|0\rangle_L$ together with the states $|i \text{ or } a\rangle_R \times |P^I, (P^I)^2 = 2\rangle_L$, form an irreducible N=1, D=10 super Yang-Mills multiplet of G. It is amusing to think of the W^+ meson (assuming that the heterotic string does describe the real world) as a string soliton winding around a 16-dimensional torus.

In the heterotic string the excited states will contain arbitrary weight vectors, P^I, of the group G, and thus arbitrarily large representations. This in contrast to the open string theory which contains only the symmetric and antisymmetric tensor representations of SO(N).

It is straightforward to verify that the heterotic string is Lorentz invariant and N=1 supersymmetric in ten dimensions. This is because the generators of these symmetries act separately on the right and left movers, which are separately invariant since they are formulated in their critical dimensions. It is also easy to show that all the states form irreducible representations of the group G. Here we use the work of Frenkel, Kac, Segal and Lepowsky, who in fact used string theory vertex operators to construct representations of affine Lie algebras. The generator of the Lie algebra is constructed from the string vertex operator, and is of the form

$$E(K^I) = \int \frac{dz}{2\pi i z} : e^{2iK^I X^I(z)} : C(K^I), \qquad z = e^{2i(\tau+\sigma)}$$

It contains the translation operator $e^{2iK^I X^I}$ which translates the internal momentum (weight) by K^I, and an operator 1-cocycle C(K). This moment of the vertex commutes with the Hamiltonian, (4), and when acting on a heterotic string state shifts the momentum by K. It is easy to verify that the 480 E(K)'s, with $(K^I)^2=2$, plus the 16 operators P^I satisfy the Lie algebra of G (in the Chevalley basis). The other moments of the vertex generate the full Kac-Moody algebra. Therefore we have an explicit representation of the generators of G on the Fock space of the left movers of the heterotic string. Since the right movers are G invariant it follows that the free heterotic string is G invariant.

As indicated above it should be straightforward to introduce interactions in the heterotic string without destroying its essential features. In a functional integral approach one would simply integrate over world sheets with the topology of a sphere with handles attached. In the operator approach the heterotic vertex operators are easily constructed as products of operators that act on the right- and left-movers separately, the only new feature being the need to introduce operators that create the soliton states that wind around the internal torus. These vertices are then products of the vertex operators that appear in the bosonic string theory and those that appear in the superstring theory. It is relatively easy to use them to construct tree and loop diagrams in the light cone formalism, at least when considering scattering amplitudes involving external massless states. The heterotic string theory, even though it contains both gravitons and gauge bosons, is a closed string theory and thus contains only one kind of interaction--that describes the splitting of a closed string to form two closed strings. Thus, for example, Newton's constant is simply related to the Yang-Mills coupling by $G_N \sim \alpha' g^2$. To any given order in perturbation theory there is only one string diagram that contributes to a given process, which describes all possible particle exchanges, gravitational and gauge alike. The expressions that exhibit this duality are very beautiful.

We have explicitly evaluated some one loop amplitudes to confirm the expectation that they are finite. As discussed above, one must, at the one loop level, check that the amplitudes are invariant under the group of disconnected diffeomorphisms--modular invariance. This being the case the amplitudes are indeed finite.

We have thus constructed a new kind of closed string theory, in which a (almost) uniquely determined gauge symmetry group appears, which is as consistent and healthy as the superstring. The $E_8 \times E_8$ version of this theory is also quite promising as a candidate for a unified theory.

4. String Phenomenology

Most of the recent excitement concerning string theories has been generated by the discovery of a host of mechanisms, due to the work of Witten and of Candelas, Horowitz and Strominger, and of Dine, Kaplonovsky, Nappi, Seiberg and Rohm, which indicate how these theories could describe the real world. The resulting phenomenology, particularly in the case of the $E_8 \times E_8$ heterotic string, is quite promising.

The first issue that must be faced is that of the compactification of six of the dimensions of space. The heterotic string, described above, is formulated in 10 dimensional flat spacetime. This however is not necessary. A consistent string theory can be developed by quantizing the action (1), as long as the two dimensional field theory is conformally invariant. In other words it is not necessary that $\eta_{\alpha\beta}(x)$ be the Minkowski flat metric. It could well be a curved metric, in whch case the two dimensinal theory of the coordinates $X^{\alpha}(\sigma,\tau)$ would be a nontrivial σ-model, as long as this σ-model is conformally invariant. The choice of $\eta_{\alpha\beta}$ is equivalent to a choice of a trial vacuum state for the string theory. The condition that the two dimensional theory be conformally invariant is equivalent to demanding that the classical string equations are satisfied. Thus one can search for alternate vacuum states by searching for σ-models (actually supersymmetric σ-models), for which the β function (which is a local function of the metric $\eta_{\alpha\beta}$) vanishes. In addition one must check that the anomaly in the commutator of the stress energy tensor is not modified, so that the critical dimension remains equal to 10. Given such a theory one can construct the string theory by the usual procedure, since the conformal invariance guarantees the consistency of the Virasao algebra.

It has been shown that a sufficient condition for conformal invariance of supersymmetric, two dimensional, σ-models is that the background metric be Ricci flat. So one looks for six-dimensional compact Ricci flat manifolds. A famous class of these are the Calabi-Yau manifolds, which have SU(3) holonomy and are Ricci flat. They provide a starting point for the string theory constructed about a vacuum in four-dimensional Minkowski space. It is not sufficient, however, to simply have a Ricci flat curved six-dimensional space, it is also necessary to turn on an SU(3) subgroup of the $E_8 \times E_8'$ gauge group of string. Otherwise the right-handed internal fermionic degrees of freedom of the heterotic string would feel a nontrivial spin connection, whereas their left-handed partners would feel nothing--giving rise to (two-dimensional) gravitational anomalies. Therefore one must embed the spin connection in one of the E_8's, thereby breaking it down to E_6.

These Calabi-Yau compactifications, produce for each such manifold K, a consistent four-dimensional string vacuum, for which the gauge group is no larger than $E_6 \times E_8'$ and N=1 supersymmetry is preserved. In the presence of the background gauge fields there exist massless fermions (plus their supersymmetric scalar partners) belonging to the $\underset{\sim}{27}$ of E_6. This is good. E_6 is an attractive grand unified model and each $\underset{\sim}{27}$ can incorporate one generation of quarks and leptons. The number of generations is equal to half the Euler character of K and is normally quite large. If, however, there exists a discrete symmetry group Z, which acts freely on K, one can consider the smaller manifold K/Z whose Euler character is reduced by the dimension of Z. By this trick, and after some searching, manifolds have been constructed with 1,2,3,4,...etc generations.

This compactification scheme also produces a natural mechanism for the breaking of E_6 down to the observed low energy gauge group, since if K/Z is multiply connected one can wind Wilson loops around it. These non contractible Wilson loops act like Higgs bosons breaking E_6 down to the largest subgroup that commutes with all of them. By this procedure one can, without generating a cosmological constant, find vacua whose unbroken low energy gauge group is, say $SU_3 \times SU_2 \times U(1) \times U(1)$. Moreover there exists a natural mechanism for the existence of massless Higgs bosons which are weak isospin doublets without accompanying color triplets. Of course, it is also necessary to break the remaining N=1 supersymmetry. For this purpose the extra E_8' gauge group can play an important role. Below the compactification scale it yields a strong, confining gauge theory with no light matter fields. By producing a gluino condensate it can serve as a source for supersymmetry breaking. Detailed study of this possibility has shown that this occurs, to lowest order, without generating a cosmological constant.

5. Future Directions

Much work remains to be done in exploring the structure and the applications of string theory. First there are many techniques and methods of string theories that to date are only partially developed. We must fully develop the perturbative formalism for evaluating multi loop amplitudes, especially in the case of super and heterotic strings. This can and should be done in both the light cone and covariant formulations of the theory. The goal should be to develop the formalism at least to the point where the assertions of finiteness (vacuum stability) and supersymmetry can be proved rigorously to all orders in perturbation theory. A manifestly supersymmetric and covariant quantization of superstrings is still lacking. At a more difficult level we cannot be satisfied with our present understanding of the geometrical structureof string theories. In particular we lack a deep understanding of the origin of general coordinate and local gauge invariance. Recent attempts to construct covariant formulations of string field theory promise to clarify these issues. Finally we lack a formulation of the theory which could be used to explore nonperturbative structure.

Perhaps the most important issues are phenomenological. We would like to make contact with experiment as soon as possible. One might contemplate already, within the existing compactification schemes, a calculation of the Yukawa couplings of the Higgs bosons to the quarks and leptons--thereby deriving fermionic mass ratios. This and other explorations of the many possible vacua would yield important constraints, if not actual predictions. We also need to understand the dynamics that picks a unique ground state for the theory from the enormous number of potential vacua. What is the reason for the instability or inconsistency of the theory formulated in ten-dimensional flat space? Another related question is how the dilaton (or other Goldstone modes which correspond to parameters of the compactified manifold) gets a mass? Also, does the cosmological constant remain zero to all orders after supersymmetry is broken, and if so why?

Finally, even if we were to find a totally successful phenomenology, many interesting questions, regarding the high energy behavior of strings, would remain. Some of these can already be addressed and they might provide clues to the dynamics required for a satisfactory understanding of the low energy string theory. Given a consistent and finite theory of gravity there is nothing that prevents us from considering processes at arbitrarily large energies, say at

10^{100} Gev. We might suspect that in this regime string perturbation theory breaks down, but this has not been shown to be the case. If it does, then most likely there is a description of string theory which is more suited for discussing distances much smaller than the Planck scale. Perhaps our present formulation of string theory is in the nature of an effective Lagrangian which is appropriate only for describing infrared physics.

A hint that the nature of string dynamics does change at very short distances is provided by the existence of a limiting temperature for strings, at least when these are treated by perturbation theory. Since the density of states, d(m), increases exponentially with mass m, $d(m) \sim e^{\beta_c m}$, one finds that $T_c = \frac{1}{\beta_c}$ is a "limiting temperature" for the string. As one approaches this temperature one cannot maintain thermal equilibrium for free strings. Such a situation is not without precedent. Imagine that in the absence of QCD a string theory of hadrons had been developed (such as that indicated by the large N expansion of QCD). Such a theory would also have led to a limiting temperature of $T_c \sim 200$ Mev. In this case, however, we know that this is a sign of a phase transition, from confined hadronic flux tube strings ($T<T_c$) to an unconfined quark-gluon plasma ($T>T_c$). Correspondingly the appropriate short distance description of the strong itneractions is not in terms of hadronic strings, but rather in terms of quarks and gluons and color gauge interactions. Is there an analogous "unconfined" phase of string theory? If so what are the liberated constitutents and how do they interact?

Alternatively we might speculate that the present low energy ($\ll m_{pl}$) description of strings describes a broken symmetry phase, and the high temperature phase is characterized by a much larger symmetry group. This notion also leads to conceptual difficulties, since in the present framework of relativistic quantum mechanics it is hard to contemplate more symmetry than that manifested by string theory.

More likely the study of the short distance structure of strings will lead us to new ideas and concepts. These might not be of immediate practical consequence, although they could be of importance in understanding early cosmology, but they are bound to yield further insights into the structure of the theory.

REFERENCES

I have made no attempt to give detailed references to the material reviewed in this talk. An incomplete set of references to recent work on string theory is given below.

Superstrings

Reviews: J.H. Schwarz, Phys. Rep. 89 (1982) 223;

M.B. Green, Surveys in High Energy Physics 3 (1982) 127.

Anomaly Cancelation: M.B. Green and J.H. Schwarz, Phys. Lett. 149B (1984) 117.

Heterotic String

D.J. Gross, J.A. Harvey, E. Martinec, and R. Rohm, Phys. Rev. Lett. 54 (1985) 502; Princeton preprints "Heterotic String Theory I & II," to appear in Nucl. Phys. B.

String Phenomenology

P. Candelas, G. Horowitz, A. Strominger, and E. Witten, Santa Barbara preprint (1984).

E. Witten, "Symmetry Breaking Patterns in Superstring Models," Princeton preprint (1985).

M. Dine, V. Kaplunovsky, M. Mangano, C. Nappi, and N. Seiberg, "Superstring Model Building," IAS preprint (1985).

M. Dine, R. Rohm, N. Seiberg, and E. Witten, "Gluino Condensation in Superstring Models," IAS preprint (1985).

J.D. Breit, B. Ovrut, and G. Segre, Penn preprint (1985).

A. Strominger and E. Witten, IAS preprint (1985).

GAUGE INVARIANT FUNCTIONAL FIELD THEORY FOR BOSONIC STRINGS

by Thomas Banks

This talk was a brief summary of some work that I have been doing with M. Peskin on the connection between strings and gauge invariance. At the conference, I learned that similar results have been obtained by Kaku.

String theories are supposed to describe gravity and gauge interactions, but in their present formulation, no mention is made of gauge invariance or general covariance. We have found a formulation of free bosonic string theories which exhibits full off shell gauge invariance. The extension to superstrings would be immediate if we had a covariant first quantization procedure, but we do not yet know how to incorporate interactions.

The standard string model scattering amplitudes may be thought of [1,2] as limits of Green's functions for strings to propagate from one space time configuration to another:

$$G[X^1_\mu(\sigma), \ldots X^n_\mu(\sigma)]$$

Mimicking ordinary field theory, we write this as:

$$G[X^1_\mu(\sigma) \ldots X^n_\mu(\sigma)] = \langle \Phi[X^1_\mu(\sigma)] \ldots \Phi[X^n_\mu(\sigma)] \rangle$$

which suggests that the basic variable of the theory should be a functional field $\Phi[X_\mu(\sigma)]$. Writing (for the open string):

$$X^\mu(\sigma) = \hat{x}^\mu + i \sum_{n \neq 0} \alpha^\mu_n \frac{\cos n\sigma}{n} \qquad (1)$$

$$\frac{1}{i}\frac{\delta}{\delta X^\mu(\sigma)} \equiv P^\mu(\sigma) = \frac{1}{2\pi\alpha'}\left[\hat{p}^\mu + \sum_{n \neq 0} \alpha^\mu_n \cos n\sigma\right] \qquad (2)$$

$$[\alpha^\mu_n, \alpha^\nu_m] = 2in\alpha' \eta^{\mu\nu} \delta_{n+m,0} \qquad (3)$$

$$[\hat{x}^\mu, \hat{p}^\nu] = i\eta^{\mu\nu} \qquad (4)$$

$$\alpha' = 1/2 \text{ from now on}$$

we can realize $\Phi[X_\mu(\sigma)]$ as a ket $|\Phi\rangle$ in the Fock space based on the vacuum state:

$$\begin{aligned} \alpha^\mu_n |0,p\rangle &= 0 \qquad n>0 \\ \hat{P}_\mu |0,p\rangle &= P_\mu |0,p\rangle \end{aligned} \qquad (5)$$

The Virasoro generators [3] are:

$$L_n = -\frac{1}{2}\sum_{m=-\infty}^{\infty} :\alpha^{\mu}_{n-m}\alpha^{\mu}_{m}: = L^{+}_{-n} \qquad (6)$$

We choose our action for $\Phi[X_\mu(\sigma)]$ to be

$$S = \langle\Phi| P(L_0-1)P |\Phi\rangle \qquad (7)$$

where P is the projection operator satisfying

$$L_n P|\Psi\rangle = 0 \,, \quad n>0 \qquad (8)$$

for any $|\Psi\rangle$.

S is invariant under the gauge transformations

$$\delta|\Phi\rangle = \sum_{n>0} L_{-n}|\Lambda_n\rangle \qquad (9)$$

Note that since $[L_0, L^{+}_{n}L_n]=0$ $[L_0,P]=0$ and we can examine the form of the action for each L_0 eigenspace separately.

$$L_0 = \frac{1}{2}\hat{P}^2 + N \qquad N = \sum_{n>0}\alpha^{\mu}_{-n}\alpha^{\mu}_{n} \qquad (10)$$

For N = 0 we have states of the form

$$|\Phi_0\rangle = \int d^Dq\ \varphi(q)|0,q\rangle\ ; \quad \varphi^*(q)=\varphi(-q) \qquad (11)$$

which are annihilated by all the positive L_n . Thus

$$S(\Phi_0) = \int d^Dq\ \varphi^*(q)\left(\tfrac{1}{2}q^2-1\right)\varphi(q) \qquad (12)$$

which is the <u>off shell</u> action for a scalar tachyon.

At the next (massless) level we have

$$|\Phi_1\rangle = \int d^Dq\ A_\mu(q)\alpha^{\mu}_{-1}|0,q\rangle \qquad (13)$$

which is annihilated by L_n with $n\geq 2$ but satisfies

$$L_1|\Phi_1\rangle \propto \int d^Dq\ q^\mu A_\mu(q)|0,q\rangle \qquad (14)$$

Thus

$$P|\Phi_1\rangle = \int d^Dq\ \left(\eta^{\mu\nu} - \frac{q^\mu q^\nu}{q^2}\right)A_\nu(q)\alpha_{\mu-1}|0,q\rangle \qquad (15)$$

and

$$S(\Phi_1) = \frac{1}{2}\int d^Dq\ A_\mu(q)A_\nu(-q)(\eta^{\mu\nu}q^2 - q^\mu q^\nu) \qquad (16)$$

This is the Maxwell action for A_μ. Correspondingly, if we ask for a pure gauge functional (9) that belongs to the first level (13) we must choose:

$$|\Lambda_n\rangle = \delta_{n1}\int d^Dq\, \Lambda(q)\,|0,q\rangle \tag{17}$$

$\delta\phi_1 = L_{-1}|\Lambda_1\rangle$ is equivalent to $\delta A_\mu(q) = q_\mu \Lambda(q)$

Things become more interesting at the first positive mass-squared level. The states have the form:

$$|\phi_2\rangle = \int d^Dq\, \left(T_{\mu\nu}(q)\,\alpha^\mu_{-1}\alpha^\nu_{-1} + T_\mu(q)\,\alpha^\mu_{-2}\right)|0,q\rangle \tag{18}$$

and the gauge transformations are

$$\begin{aligned} \delta_1 T_{\mu\nu} &= \tfrac{1}{2}\left(q_\mu\Lambda_\nu + q_\nu\Lambda_\mu\right) \\ \delta_1 T_\mu &= \Lambda_\mu \end{aligned} \tag{19}$$

$$\delta_2 T_{\mu\nu} = \tfrac{1}{2}\eta_{\mu\nu}\Lambda \qquad \delta_2 T_\mu = q_\mu\Lambda \tag{20}$$

The projector is

$$\begin{aligned} P|\phi_2\rangle = \int d^Dq \Big\{ &\left(P^{\mu\nu,\lambda\kappa}T_{\lambda\kappa} + P^{\mu\nu,\lambda}T_\lambda\right)\alpha^\mu_{-1}\alpha^\nu_{-1} \\ &+ \left(P^{\mu\nu,\lambda}T_{\mu\nu} + P^{\kappa,\lambda}T_\kappa\right)\alpha^\lambda_{-2}\Big\}|0,q\rangle \end{aligned} \tag{21}$$

$$\begin{aligned} P^{\mu\nu,\lambda\kappa} = &\left(\Pi^{\mu\lambda}\Pi^{\nu\kappa} - \frac{1}{(D-1)}\Pi^{\mu\nu}\Pi^{\lambda\kappa}\right) \\ &+ \frac{B}{(D-1)^2q^2}(2q^2-1)^2\,\Pi^{\mu\nu}\Pi^{\lambda\kappa} \\ &+ \frac{B}{(D-1)q^2}(2q^2-1)\left(\Pi^{\mu\nu}\frac{q^\lambda q^\kappa}{q^2} + \frac{\Pi^{\lambda\kappa}q^\mu q^\nu}{q^2}\right) \\ &+ \frac{A}{q^2}\left(\frac{\Pi^{\mu\lambda}q^\nu q^\kappa}{q^2} + \text{permutations}\right) \\ &+ \frac{B}{q^2}\,\frac{q^\mu q^\nu q^\lambda q^\kappa}{q^4} \end{aligned} \tag{22}$$

$$P^{\lambda\kappa} = A\Pi^{\lambda\kappa} + \frac{Bq^{\lambda}q^{\kappa}}{q^2} \tag{23}$$

$$P^{\mu\nu,\lambda} = \frac{B}{(D-1)}\left(\frac{1-2q^2}{q^2}\right)\Pi^{\mu\nu}q^{\lambda} - \frac{A}{q^2}(\Pi^{\mu\lambda}q^{\nu}+\Pi^{\nu\lambda}q^{\mu}) - \frac{B}{q^2}\frac{q^{\mu}q^{\nu}q^{\lambda}}{q^2} \tag{24}$$

$$\Pi^{\mu\nu} = \eta^{\mu\nu} - \frac{q^{\mu}q^{\nu}}{q^2} \tag{25}$$

$$A = \frac{q^2}{q^2+2} \tag{26}$$

$$B = \frac{q^2}{q^2+1+\frac{(1-2q^2)^2}{D-1}} \tag{27}$$

The action $\langle\phi_2|P(\frac{q^2}{2}+1)P|\phi_2\rangle$ is not local in $T_{\mu\nu}$ and T_{μ}, but can be made local by the addition of auxiliary fields. In 26 dimensions the terms involving B(q) contribute only a single pole and only one auxiliary scalar field T(q) is needed. The action for $T_{\mu\nu}$, T_{μ} and T is

$$\begin{aligned}\int d^Dq\Big\{&\frac{q^2}{2}\left(\Pi^{\mu\lambda}\Pi^{\nu\kappa} - \frac{1}{D-1}\Pi^{\mu\nu}\Pi^{\lambda\kappa}\right)T_{\mu\nu}(q)T_{\lambda\kappa}(-q)\\ &-\frac{1}{2}\frac{D-2}{D-1}\frac{1}{q^2}\left|q^{\alpha}q^{\beta}T_{\alpha\beta} - q^2T_{\alpha}{}^{\alpha} + \frac{D-1}{2}\varphi q^2\right|^2\\ &+\frac{1}{2}\left|T_{\alpha\beta} - \frac{1}{2}(q_{\alpha}T_{\beta}+q_{\beta}T_{\alpha}) + q_{\alpha}q_{\beta}T - \eta_{\alpha\beta}\frac{T}{2}\right|^2\\ &-\frac{1}{2}\left|T_{\alpha}{}^{\alpha} - \varphi^{\alpha}T_{\alpha} + q^2T - \frac{D}{2}T\right|^2\Big\}\end{aligned} \tag{28}$$

It is invariant under (19,20) supplemented by

$$\delta_1 T = 0$$
$$\delta_2 T = \Lambda \tag{29}$$

T(q) can therefore be gauged away. When D ≠ 26 we need extra gauge invariant scalar fields which describe the Brower states: states which satisfy $L_n|\psi\rangle = 0$ but are not transverse. As is well known these lead to problems with unitarity in the interacting theory.

Higher levels can be described in a similar manner. We have recently found a closed formula for the projector P in terms of the generators of the Virasoro algebra.

The formalism for closed strings is a simple extension of the above, with two sets of oscillators α_n^μ and $\tilde{\alpha}_n^\mu$ (but only one center of mass momentum $\alpha_0^\mu = \tilde{\alpha}_0^\mu = \hat{p}^\mu$) and corresponding Virasoro generators L_n and $\tilde{L}_n$. The action is

$$S(\Phi) = \langle\Phi|P(L_0 + \tilde{L}_0 - 2)P|\Phi\rangle \tag{30}$$

where in addition to projecting on the subspace with $L_n = \tilde{L}_n = 0$ (n>0) P imposes the condition $(L_0 - \tilde{L}_0)P|\Phi\rangle = 0$. States that do not satisfy the latter condition do not seem to be necessary for a covariant off shell description of the string.

Functionals of the form $\int d^D q \; \varphi(q)|0,q\rangle$ describe the scalar tachyon of the closed string. The next level satisfying $L_0 = \tilde{L}_0$ has the form

$$\int d^D q \; T_{\mu\nu}(q) \alpha_{-1}^\mu \tilde{\alpha}_{-1}^\nu |0,q\rangle \tag{31}$$

The projector P breaks into two orthogonal pieces on this subspace. The first is the projector on transverse, antisymmetric tensors:

$$P_A^{\mu\nu,\lambda\kappa} = \frac{1}{2}\left(\pi^{\mu\lambda}\pi^{\nu\kappa} - \pi^{\mu\kappa}\pi^{\nu\lambda}\right) \tag{32}$$

This piece of the action is that of a two form gauge field.

$$\int d^D q \; \frac{1}{2} \; |q_{(\mu} A_{\nu\lambda)}|^2 \tag{33}$$

The second piece of the projector is

$$P_S^{\mu\nu,\lambda\kappa} = \frac{1}{2}\left(\Pi^{\mu\lambda}\Pi^{\nu\kappa} + \Pi^{\nu\lambda}\Pi^{\mu\kappa}\right) \tag{34}$$

If $h_{\mu\nu}$ is the symmetric piece of $T_{\mu\nu}$, the action for $h_{\mu\nu}$ is

$$\int d^D q \;\; h_{\mu\nu}(q) h_{\lambda\kappa}(-q) \; \frac{q^2}{2} \, P_S^{\mu\nu,\lambda\kappa} \tag{35}$$

This is nonlocal and we must introduce an auxiliary scalar field φ as above. The action is now

$$S = \int d^D x \left\{ \frac{1}{2} h_{\mu\nu} \Box h_{\mu\nu} + \frac{1}{2}(\partial_\nu h_{\mu\nu})^2 + \frac{1}{2}(\partial_\mu \varphi - \partial_\nu h_{\mu\nu})^2 \right\} \tag{36}$$

and is invariant under the linearized general coordinate transformation

$$\begin{aligned} \delta h_{\mu\nu} &= \partial_\mu \xi_\nu + \partial_\nu \xi_\mu \\ \delta \varphi &= 2\, \partial_\mu \xi^\mu \end{aligned} \tag{37}$$

Note that this is what we would expect if e^φ transforms as a scalar density of weight 2.

By choosing the gauge $\partial_\nu h_{\mu\nu} = 0$ we see that this system describes a massless graviton and a massless scalar, which is the correct particle content of the dual string at this level. $h_{\mu\nu}$ is related to the usual gravitational field variable $\hat{h}_{\mu\nu}$ (the one whose action is the linearized Einstein action) in this gauge by a formula of the form

$$h_{\mu\nu} = \hat{h}_{\mu\nu} + a\,\eta_{\mu\nu}\,\hat{h}^\mu_\mu \tag{38}$$

So far we have described the classical functional field theory of strings. We propose to quantize it by integrating over functionals $\Phi[x(\sigma)]$. However to do this correctly we must fix the gauge by the Fadeev-Popov procedure. Our gauge fixing condition is the analog of the Lorentz gauge in electrodynamics: we restrict ourselves to functionals satisfying

$$L_n |\Phi\rangle = 0 \qquad n > 0 \tag{39}$$

This will be called the Siegel [4] gauge. The action in this gauge is simple

$$S(\Phi) = \langle\Phi|(L_0 - 1)|\Phi\rangle \tag{40}$$

We compute the ghost action in the standard manner by varying the infinite set of gauge conditions with respect to the infinite number of gauge functionals $|\Lambda_n\rangle$. The result is

$$\sum_{m,n>0} \langle \hat{C}_m | L_m L_{-n} | C_n \rangle \tag{41}$$

Note that the ghost and anti-ghost fields carry an extra index. The ghost Lagrangian itself has a gauge invariance:

$$\delta|C_n\rangle = \sum_{m>0} L_{-m}|\Lambda_{nm}\rangle + \frac{1}{2}\sum_{m,k} V_{nm}^{k} L_{-k}|\Lambda_{nm}\rangle \tag{42}$$

$$|\Lambda_{nm}\rangle = -|\Lambda_{mn}\rangle$$

where the V's are defined by $[L_{-n}, L_{-m}] = \sum_{k>0} V_{nm}^{k} L_{-k} \quad (m,n>0)$
There is a similar transformation on $\hat{C}_n$. These invariances are similar to the gauge invariance of a one form action

$$S = \int (\partial_\mu V^\mu)^2 \tag{43}$$

to the two form gauge transformation

$$\delta V^\mu = \partial_\nu V^{\mu\nu} \qquad V^{\mu\nu} = -V^{\nu\mu} \tag{44}$$

They must of course be gauge fixed and we find ghosts of ghosts, which are two forms. Just as in the finite dimensional example (43), the two form ghost Lagrangian is singular and we must again fix the gauge, introducing a three form ghost etc. Pursuing this analogy we have found an interesting theory of differential forms in loop space, and an infinite number of ghost fields $C_{n_1 \cdots n_K, \hat{m}_1 \cdots \hat{m}_P}$. It turns out that these are just the Grassmann expansion coefficients of Siegel's (4) functional field $\Phi[X_\mu(\sigma), \theta(\sigma), \hat{\theta}(\sigma)]$. The actions found by repeatedly applying the Fadeev-Popov procedure to our action sum up to Siegel's action. The details are too complicated to reproduce here and will appear in our paper.

REFERENCES

1.Y. Nambu Lectures for the Copenhagen Summer Symposium 1970 unpublished

L. Susskind Nuovo Cimento 69A (1970) 457

2.A.M. Polyakov Phys. Lett. 103B, (1981) 207,211

3.M.A. Virasoro Phys Rev. D1 (1970), 2933

4.W. Siegel Phys. Lett. 142B,(1984),276 and 149B, (1984) 157-166

SYMPOSIUM ON ANOMALIES, GEOMETRY, TOPOLOGY

SUPERSTRINGS II

STEVE SHENKER

CHAIRMAN

UNIQUENESS OF SUPERSTRING ACTIONS

by

Lars Brink
Göteborg University

1. Introduction

Quantum field theories have had a tremendous success in the description of the strong, the weak and the electromagnetic interactions. The experimental evidence for non-abelian gauge field theories is very strong and theoretically they have been proven to be consistent at least as far as perturbative renormalizability is concerned[1)]. From a philosophical point of view we can, however, question why Nature has picked out just these models fitting the experimental data. They belong to a huge class of models which all seem to be theoretically consistent. A further question is how to fit in gravity into this scheme. This problem is really two-fold. Firstly, we seek a consistent quantum theory of gravity, and secondly we demand this theory to contain the correct strong, weak and electromagnetic interactions. Great hopes were extended to supergravity models[2)] and although being steps in the right direction these models do not seem to have a chance of being consistent quantum theories.

String theories[3)] on the other hand have been known for a long time, to contain gravitons as well as having seemingly good quantum properties. From this point of view it is natural to seek a truly unifying model among string theories. One bonus is presenting itself immediately. The number of possible models (we believe) is quite limited. If we insist on having models without tachyons and anomalies[4)] we only know of five possible superstring models: Type I with gauge group SO(32), Type II chiral and non-chiral and the two heterotic strings with gauge groups $E_8 \times E_8$ or spin(32)/Z_2[5)]. In the best of all worlds only one of these models should be fully quantum mechanically consistent, and in such a case Nature better use it. This is probably too pretentious an idea, but it forces us to consider the string models in more detail. We really would like to check if the models are finite in perturbation theory and ultimately we would like to understand also non-perturbative features. A further dream would be to understand how the four-dimensional Minkowski space is singled out from the ten-dimensional space in which the strings models are defined to start with.

The way we investigate point-particle theories is to work with the corresponding field theories. With string theories we would like to work in the same fashion. Field theories for superstrings have also been defined and one way to examine string theories would be to follow the same steps taken for non-abelian gauge field theories. This means that we want to be as fluent with field theories for strings as we are with field theories for point-particles. There are problems presenting themselves immediately. Field theories for strings are functional field theories, which at the outset are quite badly defined. However, we can always go to an oscillator basis and in this way functional expressions can be written in terms of well-defined sums. The second problem is that the field theories are only defined in the light-cone gauge so far[6]. In the absence of a covariant formalism we then have to understand how to examine a field theory in the light-cone gauge. We must understand finiteness or renormalizability, structure of counterterms etc. in the light-cone gauge.

This gauge is usually rather awkward in point-particle field theories (especially those containing gravity). The most important exception is N=4 supersymmetric Yang-Mills theory[7] in four dimensions which was proven to be finite using this gauge. For string theories, however, great simplifications occur and even if a covariant formalism is found, it is not clear that it would be superior for explicit computations. In this talk I will hence stick to the light-cone gauge and I will investigate how to find possible counterterms for field theories in this way. The main result[8] I will present is that there will be no possible counterterms to the superstring actions (other than the action itself). This is the first such case for a gravity theory and is a strong indication that the quantum theories exist.

2. Field Theories in the Light-Cone Gauge

To show how to work with field theories in the light-cone gauge I will start by indicating how it works for a vector field $A^{\mu}(x)$ in four dimensions. Starting with the ordinary gauge invariant action we must fix a gauge and we choose $A^+ \equiv \frac{1}{\sqrt{2}}(A^0+A^3) = 0$, the light-cone gauge. This is a physical gauge choice which can be implemented directly into the action. By considering the system in the light-cone frame with $x^+ \equiv \frac{1}{\sqrt{2}}(x^0+x^3)$ as the evolution parameter, the field $A^- \equiv \frac{1}{\sqrt{2}}(A^0-A^3)$ will be a non-propagating field which in a functional integral over the action can be integrated out. This amounts to inserting the equation of motion $A^- = A^-(A^1,A^2)$ back into the action, which is now written in terms of just the transverse components A^1 and A^2. These ones can be combined into an index-free complex field $A = \frac{1}{\sqrt{2}}(A^1+iA^2)$. The action is still Poincaré invariant. The appropriate generators are obtained by inserting the solution of A^- into the ones of the covariant formalism and by adding a gauge transformation such that the gauge choice is still valid. In an interacting theory some of the transformations are then non-linear[9), namely the ones that transform the system out of the quantization plane, $x^+ = \text{const}$.

The Poincaré generators contain the momentum p^-, which is the hamiltonian in the light-cone frame. Hence, if we know the Poincaré algebra for a certain interacting field theory we know the dynamics of it. In this way we can set up a general formalism by demanding closure of the Poincaré algebra. In principle we can construct all known field theories in this way. The procedure is perturbative and it means that gravity theories and theories with higher spins[10) are awkward in the sense that they contain an infinity of interaction terms written around a flat background. There are also explicit assumptions about the boundary conditions of the fields which could throw out topologically non-trivial cases.

In the sequel I will discuss first certain point-particle field theories containing gravity and show how possible new counterterms can be constructed by demanding closure of the algebra. Then I will discuss superstrings in the same context.

3. Kinetic Counterterms for Point-Particle Gravity Theories

Four-dimensional gravity is described by a complex field $\phi(x)$. Since we have a dimensionful coupling constant κ we will show that the kinetic

Lagrangian is not unique. (From now on I follow Ref. 8.) Consider first a Lagrangian

$$\mathcal{L}_0 = \frac{1}{2}(\bar{\phi}\,\Box\phi + \frac{\alpha}{2}\,\bar{\phi}\,\Box^2\phi) \tag{3.1}$$

with $\alpha \sim \kappa^2$. The first term is the ordinary kinetic term while the second one can be interpreted as a counterterm. The action is unique to this order in κ^2 if we insist on local terms. In the sequel we will assume that all quantum corrections respect (super-)Poincaré invariance and hence that all counterterms should be invariant.

To show the invariance of (3.1) we have to remember that the hamiltonian is a generator. It must be written in a first-order form. To understand the extra term we can rewrite the Lagrangian in first-order form as

$$\mathcal{L}_0 = \frac{1}{2}(\frac{1}{\partial_-}\pi\,\Box\,\bar{\phi} + \frac{1}{\partial_-}\bar{\pi}\,\Box\phi) - \frac{1}{2\alpha}(\bar{\phi}\phi - \frac{1}{\partial_-}\bar{\pi}\phi - \frac{1}{\partial_-}\pi\bar{\phi} + \frac{1}{\partial_-}\bar{\pi}\,\frac{1}{\partial_-}\pi). \tag{3.2}$$

The operator ∂_-^{-1} is defined such that $\partial_-(\partial_-^{-1}f(x^+)) = f(x^+)$. The expression (3.2) can be diagonalized into

$$\mathcal{L}_0 = \frac{1}{2}(\bar{\phi}_1\,\Box\,\phi_1 - \bar{\phi}_2\Box\,\phi_2 - \frac{2}{\alpha}\,\bar{\phi}_2\phi_2). \tag{3.3}$$

From this we conclude that (3.1) really describes two states, one massless positive-norm state and one massive ghost state. To show the Poincaré invariance we have to construct the generators. This is easily done for the Lagrangian (3.3). We write a generator G for the case $\alpha=0$ as

$$G = i\int d^3x\,\partial_-\bar{\phi}g\phi\,, \tag{3.4}$$

$$[G,\phi] = g\phi\,, \tag{3.5}$$

where we use the canonical commutation rule. For $\alpha=0$ we just let $\phi\to\begin{pmatrix}\phi_1\\ \phi_2\end{pmatrix}$ and let g become a 2×2 matrix. We can find such a representation

$$p^- = h = \frac{i}{2\partial_-}(\mathbb{1}\partial^{i\,2} - \mathbb{M}^2)$$

$$p^+ = i\,\mathbb{1}\partial_- \;, \quad p^i = -i\,\mathbb{1}\partial^i$$

$$j^{12} = -i\,\mathbb{1}(x^1\partial^2 - x^2\partial^1) - \Lambda$$

$$j^{+i} = -i\,\mathbb{1}(x^+\partial^i - x^i\partial^+)$$

$$j^{+-} = x^+h - i\,\mathbb{1}x^-\partial^+$$

$$j^{-i} = -i\,\mathbb{1}x^-\partial^i - x^ih + i\Lambda\frac{\partial^i}{\partial_-}\;, \tag{3.6}$$

where the mass matrix $\mathbb{M}^2 = \begin{bmatrix} 0 & 0 \\ 0 & -\frac{2}{\alpha} \end{bmatrix}$ and the helicity matrix $\Lambda = \begin{bmatrix} 2 & 0 \\ 0 & 0 \end{bmatrix}$. The extra term in (3.1) can be regarded as a new type of counterterm in the quantum theory. To see that such a term is allowed by the symmetry is hence equivalent to show that we can add a spinless massive mode in an invariant way.

We can now ask if we can add arbitrary powers of $\Box$'s to (3.1). This is indeed possible and one can show that any such action is invariant and is equivalent to adding the appropriate number of spinless massive modes.

One can so continue the analysis on the three-point level and also here it is possible to show that there are several possible terms. To really prove that the theory allows for an arbitrary number of counterterms one should close the algebra to all orders, but the existence of the terms found so far is a very strong indication that quantum gravity does not make sense.

A way out would be to find a symmetry that prevents counterterms other than the action itself from being invariant. Great hope was extended to supersymmetry in this respect. It is also true that supersymmetry improves the divergence properties of loops, but for every supergravity theory one can indeed find new types of counterterms[11)] (at least to the extent above) and also here we conclude that quantum supergravity does not make sense.

Here I will treat one supergravity model, the chiral N=2 supergravity in d=10[12]. This model is, of course, highly divergent in perturbation expansion, but since it has a string extension, it is a good starting point for the string discussion. The procedure and results for 4-dimensional theories are analogous. The N=2 supersymmetry algebra can be represented on a superspace x^{μ}, θ^{a}, where θ^{a} transforms as 8_s of SO(8) and the supergravity multiplet is described by a complex scalar field $\psi(x^{\mu},\theta^{a})$. The kinetic term is

$$S_0 = \int d^{10}x d^8\theta \;\psi \Box \psi \;. \tag{3.7}$$

Also in this case the super-Poincaré invariance allows us to have $\Box^n$-counterterms. Again it can be shown to be equivalent to being able to have massive multiplets. The new ingredient here is that we must extend the superspace. We augment the original one with another spinor $\tilde{\theta}^{\dot{a}}$ transforming as 8_c of SO(8). The super-Poincaré algebra is then represented as

$$q_1^{+a} = i\sqrt{2}\,\mathbb{1}\,\partial_-\theta^{a}, \qquad q_2^{+a} = \sqrt{2}\,\mathbb{1}\,\frac{\partial}{\partial\theta^{a}}$$

$$q_1^{-\dot{a}} = -i\,\mathbb{1}(\gamma^{i}\partial^{i}\theta)^{\dot{a}} - i\,\mathbb{M}\tilde{\theta}^{\dot{a}}$$

$$q_2^{-\dot{a}} = -\frac{1}{\partial_-}\Big[\mathbb{1}(\gamma^{i}\partial^{i}\frac{\partial}{\partial\theta})^{\dot{a}} - \mathbb{M}\frac{\partial}{\partial\tilde{\theta}_{\dot{a}}}\Big]$$

$$p^- = h = \frac{i}{2\partial_-}(\mathbb{1}\,\partial^{i\,2} - \mathbb{M}^2)$$

$$p^+ = i\,\mathbb{1}\,\partial_- \;; \qquad p^i = -i\,\mathbb{1}\,\partial^i$$

$$j^{i+} = i\,\mathbb{1}(x^i\partial_- + x^+\partial^i)$$

$$j^{ij} = -i\,\mathbb{1}(x^i\partial^j - x^j\partial^i + \frac{1}{2}\theta\gamma^{ij}\frac{\partial}{\partial\theta} + \frac{1}{2}\tilde{\theta}\gamma^{ij}\frac{\partial}{\partial\tilde{\theta}})$$

$$j^{+-} = x^+h - i\,\mathbb{1}(x^-\partial_- + \frac{1}{2}\theta\frac{\partial}{\partial\theta} - \frac{1}{2}\tilde{\theta}\frac{\partial}{\partial\tilde{\theta}})$$

$$j^{i-} = x^i h + i\,\mathbb{L}(x^-\partial^i + \frac{1}{2\partial_-}\theta\gamma^i\gamma\cdot\partial\,\frac{\partial}{\partial\theta} + \frac{1}{2\partial_-}\tilde{\theta}\gamma^i\gamma\cdot\partial\frac{\partial}{\partial\tilde{\theta}})$$

$$- \frac{i}{2\partial_-}\mathbb{M}(\tilde{\theta}\gamma^i\frac{\partial}{\partial\theta} - \theta\gamma^i\frac{\partial}{\partial\tilde{\theta}}) \ , \qquad (3.8)$$

with $\mathbb{M}$ as in (3.6). A new ingredient here is that we have had to add extra massive states to have a supersymmetric theory.

We can so find super-Poincaré invariant three-point functions by introducing such terms into the non-linearly realized generators. Also here we find an infinite class of possible terms showing quite strong indications for an infinite set of possible counterterms and hence possible quantum divergencies. The same is also true for four-dimensional supergravity theories.

4. Uniqueness of the Superstring Actions.

The analysis developed in the preceding section can now be attempted for superstring theories. Let me examine the chiral type II superstring field theory in this way[13]. For a string the field Ψ is a functional of the string configuration $\Sigma = (x^+, x^-, x^i(\sigma), \theta^a(\sigma))$. The parameter σ runs along the string. For convenience we have taken $0 \leq \sigma \leq 1$. Since we are treating the superstring in the light-cone gauge, the dependence on x^+, the light-cone time, and x^- is like for a point-particle. The super-Poincaré algebra must now be realized on the field using functional derivatives which we denote $\delta^i(\sigma) \equiv \frac{\delta}{\delta x^i(\sigma)}$ and $d^a(\sigma) \equiv \frac{\delta}{\delta\theta^a(\sigma)}$. Derivatives with respect to σ are written $a(\sigma) \equiv \frac{d}{d\sigma}a(\sigma)$. The super-Poincaré algebra acts on the field $\overline{\Psi}(\Sigma)$, which is a complex scalar superfield (satisfying certain mild constraints[13]) in the following way. We write the generators (for the free case)

$$G_2 = i\int D\Sigma\ \partial_-\Psi(\Sigma)g_2\Psi(\Sigma) \ , \qquad (4.1)$$

where $D\Sigma = dx^- D^8 x^i(\sigma) D^8\theta^a(\sigma)$, and the canonical commutation rule is

$$[\partial_-\Psi(\Sigma_1),\ \Psi(\Sigma_2)]_{x_1^+ = x_2^+} = -\frac{i}{2}\Delta^{17}(\Sigma_1,\Sigma_2) \ , \qquad (4.2)$$

with $\Delta^{17}(\Sigma_1,\Sigma_2) = \delta(x_1^- - x_2^-)\int d\sigma_0 \Delta^8[x_1^i(\sigma) - x_2^i(\sigma+\sigma_0)]\Delta^8[\theta_1^a(\sigma) - \theta_2^a(\sigma+\sigma_0)]$. Then

$$p^- = h = \frac{i}{2\partial_-}\int d\sigma(\delta^i\delta^i - x^i x^i + dd\frac{1}{\partial_-} - \theta\theta\partial_-) \equiv \int d\sigma\, h(\sigma)$$

$$p^+ = i\partial_-\ , \qquad p^i = -i\int d\sigma\ \delta^i$$

$$j^{ij} = -i\int d\sigma(x^i\delta^j - x^j\delta^i + \tfrac{1}{2}\theta\gamma^{ij}d)$$

$$j^{+i} = -i\int d\sigma(x^+\delta^i + x^i\partial_-)$$

$$j^{+-} = x^+h - ix^-\partial_- - \frac{i}{4}\int d\sigma[\theta^a, d^a] + 2i$$

$$j^{-i} = -\frac{i}{2}\int d\sigma(\{x^-(\sigma),\delta^i\} - i\{x^i, h(\sigma)\}$$

$$+ \tfrac{1}{2}[(\gamma^i\theta)^{\dot a}, (\gamma^j d)^{\dot a}]\frac{\delta^j}{\partial_-} - \tfrac{1}{2}(d\gamma^{ij}d\frac{1}{\partial_-} - \theta\gamma^{ij}\theta\partial_-)\frac{x^j}{\partial_-} - 4\,\frac{\delta^i}{\partial_-})$$

$$q_1^{+a} = i\sqrt{2}\int d\sigma\ \theta^a\partial_-\ , \quad q_1^{-\dot a} = -i\int d\sigma[(\gamma^i\theta)^{\dot a}\,\delta^i - (\gamma^i d)^{\dot a}\,\frac{x^i}{\partial_-}]$$

$$q_2^{+a} = \sqrt{2}\int d\sigma\ d^a \quad , \quad q_2^{-\dot a} = -\int d\sigma[(\gamma^i d)^a\,\frac{\delta^i}{\partial_-} + (\gamma^i\theta)^{\dot a}\,x^i]. \qquad (4.2)$$

The $x^-(\sigma)$ occurring in j^{-i} is determined by

$$x^-(\sigma) = -\frac{1}{\partial_-}(x^i\delta^i + \theta d)\ , \qquad (4.3)$$

a constraint, obtained when gauge-fixing the covariant one-string parameter-space action, that cannot be integrated explicitly.

Truncating the algebra to the point-particle case gives the algebra of the N=2 supergravity model of last section.

The question to ask now is if also the representation (4.2) can be extended in ways that would be interpreted as new kinds of counterterms. To check it we demand from the algebra, that it on the one hand reduces to (3.8) when the σ-dependence is truncated and on the other hand it takes the form (4.2) when the extra coordinate dependence is removed. To meet these conditions we seek an extension of the algebra in terms of a new spinor coordinate $\tilde\theta^{\dot a}(\sigma)$. We start by adding possible terms to the supersymmetry generators $q_{1,2}^{-\dot{a}}$.

$$q_1^{-\dot{a}} = -i\int d\sigma\{[\mathbb{L}(\gamma^i\theta)^{\dot{a}}\,\delta^i - (\gamma^i d)^{\dot{a}}\,\frac{x^i}{\partial_-}] + \mathbb{M}\tilde{\theta}^{\dot{a}} + \mathbb{F}^{\dot{a}}(\tilde{\theta},\tilde{d})\} \qquad (4.4)$$

$$q_2^{-\dot{a}} = -\int d\sigma\{\mathbb{L}[(\gamma^i d)^{\dot{a}}\,\frac{\delta^i}{\partial_-} + (\gamma^i\theta)^{\dot{a}}\,x^i] - \frac{\mathbb{M}}{\partial_-}\,\tilde{d}^{\dot{a}} - \frac{1}{\partial_-}\mathbb{G}^{\dot{a}}(\tilde{\theta},\tilde{d})\}\ , \qquad (4.5)$$

when $\mathbb{F}^{\dot{a}}$ and $\mathbb{G}^{\dot{a}}$ are at least trilinear expressions in $\tilde{\theta}$ an $\tilde{d}$ depending at least on one $\tilde{\theta}$ or $\tilde{d}$.

The relevant part of the algebra is

$$\{q_1^{-\dot{a}},\ q_1^{-\dot{b}}\} = \{q_2^{-\dot{a}},\ q_2^{-\dot{b}}\} = -2\delta^{\dot{a}\dot{b}}\int d\sigma x^-(\sigma), \qquad (4.6)$$

$$\{q_1^{-\dot{a}},\ q_2^{-\dot{b}}\} = 2\delta^{\dot{a}\dot{b}}\int d\sigma h(\sigma)\ . \qquad (4.7)$$

By a systematic procedure it is in fact possible to show that no $\mathbb{F}^{\dot{a}}$ and $\mathbb{G}^{\dot{a}}$ are possible and that <u>the algebra (4.2) is in fact unique!</u>

We have essentially tried to find a massive representation of the superstring theory and the impossibility to find such a one is quite natural. (One can also show this fact by using group theoretical arguments.)

With the unique form of the two-string functions in the algebra, we now ask what freedom there is for the three-string functions, the interaction terms. For this purpose we define

$$G_3 = i\int D\Sigma_1 D\Sigma_2\ \partial_-\Psi(\Sigma_1+\Sigma_2)g_3(\sigma_1,\sigma_2)\Psi(\Sigma_1)\Psi(\Sigma_2), \qquad (4.8)$$

where we demand Σ_1 and Σ_2 to have one point in common, the interaction point. To make the interaction local, σ_1 and σ_2 are taken infinitesimally near this point. To make the definition of the functional integrals precise one can expand the coordinates into normal modes and determine the coupling of three arbitrary states. Comparing with such a formalism convergence factors have to be inserted to damp singular behaviour of the functional operators near the interaction point.

To close the algebra at the three-string level one starts by considering the commutations among the Q_-'s. We let the operator q_{-3} in (4.8) be a general expression in terms of δ^i's, d^a's, θ^a's and x^i's. Grinding through the algebra leads after a long calculation <u>again to a unique solution</u> for the possible three-string interaction terms. The precise form for h_3 turns out to be

$$h_3 = u\partial_-^3 \sum_{n=0,2,4,6,8} C^{ij}_{a_1\ldots a_n} \underline{d}^{a_1}\ldots\underline{d}^{a_n} \underline{\bar{p}}^i \underline{p}^j \frac{\partial_{-1}^{\frac{n}{2}}\partial_{-2}^{\frac{n}{2}}}{\partial_-^{\frac{n}{2}}} , \tag{4.9}$$

where $\underline{p}^i = -i\underline{\delta}^i + \underline{x}^i$, $\underline{\bar{p}}^i = i\underline{\delta}^i + \underline{x}^i$ and

$$\begin{aligned}
C^{ij} &= \delta^{ij} \\
C^{ij}_{a_1a_2} &= -\frac{i}{2}\gamma^{ij}_{ab} \\
C^{ij}_{a_1a_2a_3a_4} &= -\frac{1}{4!}t^{ij}_{a_1a_2a_3a_4} \\
C^{ij}_{a_1\ldots a_6} &= \frac{i}{2\cdot 6!}\epsilon_{a_1\ldots a_8}\gamma^{ij}_{a_7a_8} \\
C^{ij}_{a_1\ldots a_8} &= \frac{1}{8!}\epsilon_{a_1\ldots a_8}\delta^{ij} .
\end{aligned} \tag{4.10}$$

The matrices used are defined by

$$u^{i\dot{a}}_{abc} = -\gamma^{ij}_{[ab}\gamma^{j}_{c]\dot{a}} , \quad t^{ij}_{abcd} = \gamma^{ik}_{[ab}\gamma^{jk}_{cd]} . \tag{4.11}$$

In the point-particle limit we recover the ordinary couplings of the supergravity theory.

In the supergravity theory there is an infinite sum of higher-order interaction terms. The algebra only closes order by order in the coupling constant. For the string theory, one can, however, argue that no higher-order terms than the three-string interaction is necessary to close the algebra[14] and hence we have a complete theory. To really convince oneself that the action is unique, it should be proven that no four-string term is possible. This is exceedingly likely, but remains to be proven.

Also for type I superstrings one can show that the actions are unique. For the "heterotic string"[5] there does not exist a field theoretic formulation yet. When such a formalism is developed it will probably follow the lines of the closed string theory described above. It is natural to believe that also its action will be unique, but it should, of course, be checked.

5. Conclusions

The absence of local counterterms other than the action itself is a strong indication that the superstring theories in contrast to supergravity theories are quantum mechanically consistent theories. The analysis performed here is essentially a classical one and a truly quantum mechanical one can only further constrain our results. The complete analysis can then very well show that some of the string models do show inconsistencies. Since string theories constitute a radical new concept, one must examine the perturbation expansion with great care. We must then convince ourselves that there are no overlapping divergences nor any divergences breaking the super-Poincaré invariance. There do seem to be good reasons to believe that the complete analysis will lead to superstring theories being finite. The question whether one model is singled out in this process is quite tantalizing and its answer is most important to find.

References

1. G. 't Hooft, Nucl. Phys. B35 (1971), 167.
2. For a recent review of this field, see M.J. Duff, B.E.W. Nilsson and C.N. Pope, Phys. Rep. in print.
3. For a review of superstring theory see J.H. Schwarz, Phys. Rep. 69 (1982), 223; M.B. Green, Surveys in High Energy Physics 3 (1983), 127; L. Brink, CERN-TH 4006/84 to be published in Proceedings from Nato Advanced Study Institute, "Supersymmetry", Bonn 1984.
4. M.B. Green and J.H. Schwarz, Phys. Lett. 149B (1984), 117.
5. D.J. Gross, J.A. Harvey, E. Martinec and R. Rohm, Phys. Rev. Lett. 55 (1985), 502 and Princeton preprint (1985).

6. M.B. Green and J.H. Schwarz, Nucl. Phys. B218 (1983), 43; M.B. Green, J.H. Schwarz and L. Brink, Nucl. Phys. B219 (1983), 437; M.B. Green and J.H. Schwarz, Nucl. Phys. B243 (1984), 475.
7. L. Brink, O. Lindgren and B.E.W. Nilsson, Nucl. Phys. B212 (1983), 401, Phys. Lett. 123B (1983), 323; S. Mandelstam, Nucl. Phys. B213 (1983), 149.
8. A.K.H. Bengtsson, L. Brink, M. Cederwall and M. Ögren, Nucl. Phys. B in print.
9. L. Brink, in 7th Johns Hopkins Workshop on Current Problems in High Energy Particle Theory, Bonn 1983 ed:s G. Domokos and S. Kövesi-Domokos, World Scientific.
10. A.K.H. Bengtsson, I. Bengtsson and L. Brink, Nucl. Phys. B227 (1983), 31
11. P.S. Howe and U. Lindström, Nucl. Phys. B181 (1981), 487; R.E. Kallosh, Phys. Lett. 99B (1981), 122.
12. M.B. Green and J.H. Schwarz, Phys. Lett. 122B (1983), 143.
13. The second reference in 6.
14. Last reference in 6.

HETEROTIC STRING INTERACTIONS

J. A. Harvey*
Joseph Henry Laboratories
Princeton University
Princeton, New Jersey 08544

Abstract

Some aspects of interacting heterotic strings are discussed. Vertex operators are introduced and various three-point amplitudes for scattering of massless string states are calculated. The low-energy field theory approximation to the heterotic string is described. A brief discussion of one-loop amplitudes and the restrictions due to modular invariance is presented.

*Research supported in part by NSF Grant PHY80-19754.

1. Introduction

There has been an upsurge of interest in superstring theories following the discovery by Green and Schwarz that gauge and gravitational anomalies cancel in ten-dimensions only for gauge group G=SO(32) or $E_8 \times E_8$.[1] The cancellation of anomalies for SO(32) follows from anomaly cancellation in the type I superstring theory with gauge group SO(32).[1,2] The understanding of anomaly cancellation for $E_8 \times E_8$ required the invention of a new type of "heterotic" superstring.[3] The construction of the free heterotic string is reviewed in the talk of D. Gross at this conference and has been described in detail in Ref. 3. The true test of string theory however, and much of the beauty of the heterotic string, lies in the construction of a consistent interacting theory. In this talk I will sketch some of the features of interacting heterotic strings. Full details can be found in Ref. 4.

2. Review of Free Heterotic String

In order to fix notation I will briefly review the ingredients of the free heterotic string. The physical degrees of freedom (in light-cone gauge) consist of the left-moving coordinates of the bosonic string

$$X^I(\tau+\sigma) = x^I + p^I(\tau+\sigma) + \frac{i}{2} \sum_{n\neq 0} \frac{\tilde{\alpha}^I_n}{n} e^{-2in(\tau+\sigma)}, \qquad I=1\ldots16$$

$$X^i(\tau+\sigma) = \frac{1}{2} x^i + \frac{1}{2} p^i(\tau+\sigma) + \frac{i}{2} \sum_{n\neq 0} \frac{\tilde{\alpha}^i_n}{n} e^{-2in(\tau+\sigma)}, \quad i=1\ldots8 \qquad (1)$$

and the right-moving coordinates of the superstring

$$X^i(\tau-\sigma) = \frac{1}{2} x^i + \frac{1}{2} p^i(\tau-\sigma) + \frac{i}{2} \sum_{n\neq 0} \frac{\tilde{\alpha}^i_n}{n} e^{-2in(\tau-\sigma)}, \qquad i=1\ldots8$$

$$S^a(\tau-\sigma) = \sum S^a_n \, e^{-2in(\tau-\sigma)} \qquad (2)$$

with

$$[x^i, p^i] = i\delta^{ij}, \; [\alpha^i_n, \alpha^j_m] = [\tilde{\alpha}^i_n, \tilde{\alpha}^j_m] = n\,\delta_{n+m,o}\,\delta^{ij}$$

$$[\alpha^n_i, \tilde{\alpha}^m_j] = 0, \; \{S^a_m, S^b_m\} = (\gamma^+h)\,\delta_{n+m,o}$$

$$\gamma^+ = \frac{1}{2}(\gamma^0 + \gamma^9), \ h = \frac{1}{2}(1 + \gamma'')$$

$$[\tilde{\alpha}^I_n, \tilde{\alpha}^J_m] = n\,\delta_{n+m,o}\,\delta^{IJ}, [x^I, P^I] = \frac{i}{2}\delta^{IJ}. \tag{3}$$

The X^I are coordinates on a maximal torus of Spin(32)/Z_2 or $E_8 \times E_8$. The restriction to these particular tori will be discussed later.

The one string Hilbert space is a direct product of the Hilbert spaces for the left- and right-moving degrees of freedom. Physical states must satisfy the constraint

$$N = \tilde{N} - 1 + \frac{1}{2}\sum_I (P^I)^2 \tag{4}$$

which follows from invariance under shifts in σ (N and $\tilde{N}$ are number operators in the right- and left-moving sectors respectively). The mass operator is given by

$$(\text{mass})^2 = 4\pi T\,\{N + \tilde{N} - 1 + \frac{1}{2}\sum_I (P^I)^2\} \tag{5}$$

where T is the string tension.

The existence of a fermion zero-mode in the right-moving sector implies that the ground state must be non-trivial since it must furnish a representation of the zero-mode anticommutation relations $\{S^a_o, S^b_o\} = (\gamma^+ h)^{ab}$. Since S^a_o transforms as an SO(8) spinor the ground state is a vector-spinor with 8 Bose components $|i\rangle$ i = 1...8 and 8 Fermi components $|a\rangle$ a = 1...8. The massless states therefore consist of a N=1 D=10 supergravity multiplet $(|i \text{ or } a\rangle_R \times \tilde{\alpha}^j_{-1}\,|0\rangle_L)$ and an N=1 D=10 Yang-Mills multiplet $(|i \text{ or } a\rangle_R \times \tilde{\alpha}^I_{-1}\,|0\rangle, |i \text{ or } a\rangle_R \times |P^I, (P^I)^2 = 2\rangle_L)$.

There is an alternate formulation where the 16 left-moving bosonic coordiantes I are replaced by 32 left-moving fermionic coordinates ψ^I. This formulation is particularly useful for discussing the coupling of the heterotic string to background fields. These two formulations provide equivalent ways of representating the current algebra or affine Lie algebra which is responsible for the gauge degrees of freedom of the heterotic string. In what follows I will use the bosonic formulation since vertex operators in this formalism are very similar to those of the Venenziano model or bosonic string.

3. Vertex Operators

In the first-quantized operator formalism, string interactions are constructed from vertex operators which give the amplitude for one string to split into two strings or for two strings to coalesce into a single string. In order to construct the low-energy field theory it is sufficient to construct vertex operators for the emission of massless string states which are then evaluated between initial and final massless string states. For simplicity I will only discuss vertex operators for bosonic states.

Since the Hilbert space of the heterotic string factorizes into left- and right-moving sectors the same is true of the vertex operators. The graviton multiplet is the direct product of the superstring ground state and the vector of the bosonic string. Thus the vertex operator for emission of a bosonic element of the graviton multiplet is

$$V_B^{grav}(k) = \frac{4g}{\pi}\,\rho^{\mu\nu}(k)\int_0^\pi d\sigma\, B^\mu\, \tilde{P}^\nu\, e^{ik_\mu X^\mu} \tag{6}$$

In this expression g is the string coupling constant and $\rho^{\mu\nu}$ is the polarization tensor ($k^\mu \rho_{\mu\nu} = 0$, $\rho^{\mu\nu} = \rho^{\nu\mu}$ for the graviton, $\rho^{\mu\nu} = -\rho^{\nu\mu}$ for the antisymmetric tensor field, and $\rho^{\mu\nu} = \eta^{\mu\nu}/\sqrt{8}$ for the dilaton). The integral over sigma corresponds to summing over the location of the emitted string.

The vertex operator given in Eq. (6) describes emission of a massless state with $k^+ = 0$ and is sufficient to describe amplitudes with fewer than 10 external particles. In practice one usually takes k^μ and $\rho^{\mu\nu}$ to be purely transverse in doing calculations and then assembles the result into a unique covariant expression. In this case we only need the transverse components of B^μ and $\tilde{P}^\nu$

$$B^i = P^i + \frac{1}{2} k^j R^{ij}$$

$$P^i = \frac{1}{2} p^i + \sum_{n\neq 0} \alpha_n^i e^{-2in(\tau-\sigma)}$$

$$R^{ij} = \frac{1}{8} \bar{S} \gamma^{ij} S \tag{7}$$

The bosonic part of the Yang-Mills multiplet consists of the states $|i\rangle_R \times \{\tilde{\alpha}^I_{-1}\ |0\rangle_L,\ |P^I,\ (P^I)^2 = 2\rangle_L\}$. The left-moving states are vectors of the bosonic string or tachyons of the bosonic string with momentum (=winding number) P^I in the internal dimension. The vertex operators for the Yang-Mills multiplet are thus

$$V^I_B(K) = \frac{4g}{\pi}\, \rho_\mu \int_0^\pi d\sigma\, B^\mu\, \mathcal{P}^I\, e^{ik_\mu X^\mu} \tag{8}$$

with

$$\mathcal{P}^I = P^I + \sum_{n\neq 0} \tilde{\alpha}^I_n\, e^{-2in(\tau+\sigma)} \tag{9}$$

and

$$V^{K^I}_B(k) = \frac{4g}{\pi}\, \rho_\mu \int_0^\pi d\sigma\, B^\mu\, e^{ik_\mu X^\mu}\ :e^{2iK^I X^I}:\ C(K) \tag{10}$$

The factor of two in the exponential is due to the fact that $2K^I$ generates translations in the internal space (see Eq. (3)). $C(K)$ is an operator cocycle which acts on left-moving states with internal momentum P^I as

$$C(K)|P\rangle = \varepsilon(K,P)|P\rangle. \tag{11}$$

The $C(K)$ form a projective representation of the translation group on the internal space

$$C(K)\, C(L) = \varepsilon(K,L)\, C(K+L) \tag{12}$$

where the two-cocycle $\varepsilon(K,L)$ can be chosen to be bilinear and to satisfy

$$\varepsilon(K,L)\, \varepsilon(L,K) = (-)^{K\cdot L}$$

$$\varepsilon(K,0) = -\varepsilon(K,-K) = 1. \tag{13}$$

4. Tree Amplitudes and Low-Energy Field Theory

It is well known that the interactions of massless string states at low energy correspond to Yang-Mills and gravitational interactions. The ten-dimensional field theory which corresponds to the low-energy limit of the heterotic string has proven to be a useful tool in attempts to obtain realistic phenomenology from string theory.[5] In this section I will sketch the derivation of this low-energy field theory.

A great deal of information is contained in the 3-point couplings of the heterotic string. These couplings can be computed without difficulty using the vertex operators (8) and (10). By comparing these amplitudes with amplitudes calculated in field theory, and by appealing to gauge and general coordinate invariance, it is possible to extract the terms of low dimension that appear in the effective field theory.* The bosonic terms which can be deduced from 3-point couplings are summarized by

$$\mathcal{L}_{bos} = \int d^{10}x\, e\, \{- \frac{1}{2\kappa^2} R - \frac{1}{8g_{10}^2} e^{-\kappa D/\sqrt{2}} (\mathrm{tr}\, F_{\mu\nu} F^{\mu\nu} - \mathrm{tr}\, R_{\mu\nu} R^{\mu\nu})$$

$$- \frac{1}{2} \partial_\mu D\, \partial^\mu D - \frac{3\kappa^2}{2g_{10}^4} e^{-\kappa D\sqrt{2}} H_{\mu\nu\rho} H^{\mu\nu\rho}\} \tag{14}$$

where g_{10} is the ten-dimensional gauge coupling and κ is the ten-dimensional gravitational coupling. In the heterotic string $g_{10}\sqrt{2\alpha'} = 2\kappa$ as compared to $g_{10}^2 \sim \kappa\alpha'$ in open string theories (implying that the relation between g_{10} and κ in the heterotic string survives compactification). In (14) tr indicates a trace in the vector representation of O(32) (for $F_{\mu\nu} F^{\mu\nu}$) or O(9,1) (for $R_{\mu\nu} R^{\mu\nu}$). D is the dilaton field rescaled so as to have a conventional kinetic energy term and $H_{\mu\nu\rho}$ is the generalized antisymmetric tensor field strength

$$H_{\mu\nu\rho} = \frac{1}{3} (\partial_\mu B_{\nu\rho} - \frac{1}{4} \mathrm{tr}\, (A_\mu F_{\nu\rho} - \frac{2}{3} A_\mu A_\nu A_\rho)$$

$$+ \frac{1}{4} \mathrm{tr}\, (\omega_\mu R_{\nu\rho} - \frac{2}{3} \omega_\mu \omega_\nu \omega_\rho) + \text{cyclic perm.}) \tag{15}$$

This Lagrangian is the bosonic part of the Chapline-Manton action except for the addition of higher derivative terms corresponding to the Lorentz Chern-Simons term in $H_{\mu\nu\rho}$[1] and the dilaton coupling to R^2.[8] I will now show that these new terms with the correct coefficients arise in the heterotic string.

Evaluating the vertex operator (6) with polarization tensor $\rho_2^{\mu\nu}$ and momentum k_2 between "graviton" states 1 and 3 with polarization tensors $\rho_1^{\alpha\beta}$, $\rho_3^{\lambda\rho}$ and momenta k_1, k_3 yields

---

*For alternate approaches see Refs. 6 and 7.

$$A(k_i) = 4g\, \rho_1^{\alpha\beta}\, \rho_2^{\mu\nu}\, \rho_3^{\lambda\rho}\, [t_{\alpha\mu\lambda}\, (\tfrac{1}{2}\, k_i)]\, [t_{\beta\nu\rho}\, (\tfrac{1}{2}\, k_i) + \frac{2\alpha'}{8}\, k_{2\beta} k_{3\nu} k_{1\rho})] \quad (16)$$

where

$$t^{\mu\nu\lambda}\, (\tfrac{1}{2}\, k_i) = \tfrac{1}{2}\, (k_2^\mu\, \eta^{\nu\lambda} + k_3^\nu\, \eta^{\mu\lambda} + k_1^\lambda\, \eta^{\mu\nu}). \quad (17)$$

The two factors entering the amplitude correspond to the usual Yang-Mills factor $t_{\alpha\mu\lambda}$ coming from the right-handed superstring and the Yang-Mills result with an $O(\alpha')$ correction coming from the left-handed bosonic string. The $O(\alpha')$ correction precisely corresponds to the new terms we are interested in.

First of all note that (16) vanishes if all three polarization tensors are antisymmetric or if all three are replaced by $\eta^{\mu\nu}$. Therefore there are no trilinear dilaton or antisymmetric tensor field couplings. If $\rho^{\mu\nu}$ is antisymmetric then for ρ_1 and ρ_3 symmetric only the $O(\alpha')$ term contributes and (16) reduces to

$$\frac{g}{4}\, \rho_1^{\alpha\beta}\, \rho_2^{\mu\nu}\, \rho_3^{\lambda\rho}\, [k_{2\rho} k_{1\nu} k_{3\alpha} k_{3\beta} \eta_{\mu\lambda} + k_{2\beta} k_{3\nu} k_{1\rho} k_{1\lambda} \eta_{\alpha\beta}] \quad (18)$$

It is not hard to see that this is equivalent at the linearized level to adding the Lorentz Chern-Simons term to $H_{\mu\nu\lambda}$ as in (15). If we take ρ_1 and ρ_3 to be symmetric and replace $\rho_2^{\mu\nu}$ by $1/\sqrt{8}\, \eta^{\mu\nu}$ (corresponding to the properly normalized dilaton vertex) then again only the $O(\alpha')$ term contributes and we find

$$-\frac{g}{4\sqrt{8}}\, \rho_1^{\alpha\beta}\, k_{3\alpha} k_{3\beta}\, \rho_3^{\lambda\rho} k_{1\lambda} k_{1\rho} \quad (19)$$

The general coordinate invariant generalization of this coupling must involve the dilaton coupling to a linear combination of R^2, $R_{\mu\nu}R^{\mu\nu}$, and $R_{\mu\nu\lambda\rho}R^{\mu\nu\lambda\rho}$. In linearized approximation with $g_{\mu\nu} = \eta_{\mu\nu} + 2\kappa\, h_{\mu\nu}$, $\partial^\mu h_{\mu\nu} = 0$ and $h_{\mu\nu}$ traceless only $R_{\mu\nu\lambda\rho} R^{\mu\nu\lambda\rho}$ contributes to the on-shell three-point coupling and its contribution reduces to $4k^2\, h_{\nu\lambda,\mu\rho}\, h^{\mu\rho,\nu\lambda}$. Using $g = g_{10}(2\alpha')^{-3/2} = 2\kappa(2\alpha')^{-2}$ it is easy to see that this corresponds to the amplitude (19).

The importance of these additional terms in compactifications of the heterotic string has been emphasized elsewhere.[5] I find it remarkable that they appear in such a simple form in the heterotic string. This seems a further indication that the "cross breeding" of the right-moving superstring and left-moving bosonic string is a very natural construction for reasons we do not yet fully understand.

The vertex operators described here can also be used to calculate four or higher point tree amplitudes using standard string techniques. The details can be found in Ref.4. It is also possible to calculate loop amplitudes by "sewing" together tree amplitudes. The consistency of one-loop amplitudes restricts the gauge group in the heterotic string to be precisely those for which ten-dimensional anomaly cancellation is possible,[1] i.e. SO(32) or $E_8 \times E_8$, as I will now discuss.

5. One Loop Amplitudes

The world sheet for a closed string one-loop amplitude has the topology of a torus. In constructing the one-loop amplitude we should sum over all such manifolds up to reparametrizations or diffeomorphisms. By choosing light-cone gauge we have fixed the gauge locally but we must still worry about global diffeomorphisms which cannot be reached continuously from the identity. The group of components of orientation preserving diffeomorphisms is known as the modular group.

The modular group can be viewed as the automorphism group of the fundamental group of the manifold. For example on the torus consider a curve which winds w_σ times around the σ direction and w_t times around the t direction. By slicing along constant t, performing a 2π twist, and then rejoining we take $(w_\sigma, w_t) \rightarrow (w_\sigma + w_t, w_t)$. It is useful to label a torus by a complex parameter τ, $\mathrm{Im}\tau > 0$ (not to be confused with the timelike parameter on the string world sheet) with the torus defined by $z \approx z+1$, $z \approx z+\tau$. The modular group then consists of the transformations

$$\tau \rightarrow \frac{a\tau+b}{c\tau+d} \quad a,b,c,d \text{ integer} \quad ad-bc = 1 \tag{20}$$

and is generated by $\tau \rightarrow \tau+1$ and $\tau \rightarrow -1/\tau$.

In order to obtain sensible and finite answers, one-loop heterotic string amplitudes must be invariant under modular transformations. To check this explicitly requires some detailed manipulation of elliptic functions which can be found in Ref. 4. I will just try to convey the outline here.

Consider the one-loop amplitude with four external charged gauge bosons. The amplitude has the general form

$$A \sim \int d\tau \, d\nu_1 d\nu_2 d\nu_3 \, F(\nu_i,\tau,k_i,P_i) \tag{21}$$

where $k_i(P_i)$ are the spacetime (internal) momenta of the external strings, the ν_i correspond to the location of the external strings on the torus and τ labels the "shape" of the torus as before. F splits into left- and right-moving pieces with the right-moving piece involving an integral over spacetime momenta and the left-moving piece involving a sum over internal momenta. Invariance under $\tau \to \tau+1$ is trivial, the key transformation is $\tau \to -1/\tau$ which corresponds to interchanging σ and t directions on the torus. The right-moving superstring part of the amplitude is known to be invariant under this transformation up to a power of τ. Therefore the left-moving part must also be invariant up to a power of τ which cancels the right-moving contribution.

As a trivial example of modular transformations consider

$$F(\tau,x,a) = F(\tau,x+a,a) = \sum_{n=-\infty}^{+\infty} e^{i\pi\tau(an+x)^2} \tag{22}$$

If we let Λ_a denote a one-dimensional lattice with spacing a and Λ_a^* the dual latice then it is easy to see by Fourier transforming F that

$$F(\tau,o,a) = \sum_{p\epsilon\Lambda_a} e^{i\pi\tau p^2} = \frac{1}{2\pi\alpha}\sqrt{\frac{1}{i\tau}} \sum_{p^*\epsilon\Lambda_a^*} e^{-i\pi p^{*2}/\tau} \tag{23}$$

Thus this lattice sum is related to the sum on the dual lattice by $\tau \to -1/\tau$.

In order for the left-moving part of the heterotic one-loop amplitude to transform correctly the theta function for the 16-dimensional lattice Γ

$$\theta_\Gamma(\tau) = \sum_{p\epsilon\Gamma} e^{i\pi\tau p^2}, \tag{24}$$

which occurs in the left-moving part of the one-loop amplitude must satisfy $\theta_\Gamma(-1/\tau) = \tau^8\theta_\Gamma(\tau)$. There is a unique lattice theta function with this property and amazingly it corresponds to the weight lattices of either $E_8 \times E_8$ or Spin $(32)/Z_2$. Thus only these two groups are allowed for the heterotic string.

6. Conclusions

The heterotic string has been brought roughly to the same stage of development as other superstring theories. Interactions have been introduced in a consistent fashion and one-loop amplitudes have been shown to be finite and modular invariant. From a phenomenological point of view the $E_8 \times E_8$ version appears particularly promising. It is remarkable that a construction which at first appears rather contrived should have such amazing properties. One hopes that a deeper understanding of string theory will reveal why nature seems to prefer the $E_8 \times E_8$ heterotic string over other superstring theories.

I would like to thank my collaborators D. Gross, E. Martinec and R. Rohm for many useful discussions. I also thank L. Dixon for discussions on modular invariance.

References

1. M.B. Green and J.H. Schwarz, Phys. Lett. 149B (1984) 117.
2. M.B. Green and J.H. Schwarz, CALT-68-1224 (1984).
3. D.J. Gross, J.A. Harvey, E. Martinec and R. Rohm, Phys. Rev. Lett. 54 (1985) 502, Nucl. Phys. B, in press.
4. D.J. Gross, J.A. Harvey, E. Martinec and R. Rohm, Princeton preprint (1985).
5. P. Candelas, G.T. Horowitz, A. Strominger and E. Witten, Princeton preprint (1984); E. Witten, Princeton preprints (1985).
6. M.B. Green, talk at this conference.
7. A. Sen, Fermilab preprints (1985); C.G. Callan, Jr., D. Friedan, E. Martinec, and M. Perry, Princeton preprint (1985).
8. The existence of this coupling was first deduced by D. Gross and E. Witten, unpublished.

COVARIANT APPROACH TO SUPERSTRINGS

Warren Siegel* †

Department of Physics

University of California

Berkeley, California 94720

Abstract

Lorentz-covariant BRST second-quantization of superstring field theory is studied by generalizing the corresponding analysis of the superparticle and bosonic string.

*This work supported by the National Science Foundation under Research Grant No. PHY85-40535.

†Address after September 1, 1985: University of Maryland, College Park, MD 20742.

1. INTRODUCTION

There are two major uses for theories of relativistic strings (see [1,2] for reviews): (1) In quantum chromodynamics there are good reasons to believe that the $1/N_{color}$ expansion is an accurate one for describing hadrons (see, e.g., [3]). In such an expansion mesons (and glueballs) appear as open (closed) strings (due to the topological structure of the Feynman graphs, as well as the fact that bound states have Regge behavior), and are the natural states (i.e., color singlets) for formulating the expansion (assuming confinement) [4]. (Baryons might then appear as their skyrmeons [5].) It would therefore be advantageous to formulate QCD directly as a string theory. (In fact, the original motivation for strings was a direct description of hadrons, since strings predict the observed linear Regge trajectories [1,2].) Although such an approach might be expected to sacrifice renormalizability (i.e., the underlying QCD could be needed to determine an infinite number of coupling constants in the string action), it has been suggested to the contrary that such a resummation would improve the (nonperturbative) renormalizability properties of QCD [6]. Furthermore, there are arguments to suggest that string theories which are consistent with the usual postulates of perturbative quantum field theory are not only renormalizable but finite (see below).

(2) String theories are the only known renormalizable theories of quantum gravity. Arguments suggest that even maximally extended supergravity has an infinite number of divergences beginning at eight loops [7] (or less [8]). Higher-derivative actions for gravity require Lee-Wick poles, which introduce ambiguities into higher-loop graphs [9], resulting in the introduction of an infinite number of arbitrary parameters, and thus nonrenormalizability (in spite of higher-loop finiteness). (As for theories of the graviton as a bound state , open-string theories are the only known ones.) On the other hand, the duality properties of string graphs (i.e., the fact that the two-dimensional surface describing a string Feynman graph is defined by just its global topology) imply that all string graphs can be represented by tree graphs (with

vertices of no more than four lines) with only *one-loop* (tadpole) insertions [10]. (String graphs related by stretching the two-dimensional surface are equivalent, and not counted separately.) This suggests that (barring anomalies in duality) string graphs have only one-loop divergences. Furthermore, since a two-loop overlapping divergence would thus be in conflict with duality, one is led to conclude that the one-loop subdivergences which would cause the overlapping divergence must also be absent [11], and thus string theories should be finite. (One-loop divergences, which are quadratic in powers of momentum cutoff, would thus always lead to one-loop duality anomalies, invisible in one-loop S-matrices, but showing up in two-loop S-matrices through the overlapping divergence.) Furthermore, the reduced number of graphs (e.g., only *one* at each order in perturbation theory for certain closed-string theories, where the only topological property is the number of loops) already suggests finiteness, since the lack of the usual resummation problems of field theory (which are due to an exponential increase in the number of graphs) could only occur in finite field theories, which lack renormalons [12] (other than instantons, which are no problem [13].) In fact, the known consistent interacting string theories (free of tachyons and anomalies [14,15]) are exactly those which are one-loop finite [2,16].

A major source of difficulties in string theories is the fact that they are generally formulated either as theories of "string mechanics," where the only variables are the (super)space-time coordinates of points on the string, or as string field theories in a light-cone gauge. A Lorentz- and gauge-covariant approach would have several advantages: (1) It would allow easier and more general construction of models, perhaps for four dimensions (in contrast to the known interacting models, which are ten-dimensional, and for which the necessary compactification hasn't been shown to be a dynamical consequence of the theory). In particular, it would be useful to have a direct construction of the QCD string, without having to sum the perturbation expansion of the underlying field theory. Since arguments for confinement generally require spacetime dimension $D \leq 4$, such a string would be expected to have critical dimension $D_c = 4$ (in contrast to the approach of Polyakov [17], based on modifications of the old models with $D_c = 10$ or 26). Since the QCD string has been missed by the usual string mechanics arguments (even at the level of classical string field theory), perhaps the known models are only a small subset of the general class of string field theories. (2) It would simplify both the results and evaluation of perturbation theory graphs. (E.g., in maximally extended supersymmetric Yang-Mills, one-loop propagator corrections vanish identically in Lorentz-covariant gauges with even only simple supersymmetry manifest [18], whereas in maximally supersymmetric light-cone gauges the results are expressed in terms of Spence functions [19]). (3) The use of a background field gauge would make duality manifest in the effective action, thus allowing a proof of all-loop finiteness. (4) A gauge-invariant string action would allow the study of semiclassical solutions (which are singular in light-cone gauges, where it's also hard to work in Euclidean space); topological properties (e.g., is the quantization of the string coupling in the QCD string as $1/N_{color}$ a general property of strings, due to Chern-Simons-like terms in the action?); and spontaneous symmetry breakdown. (5) Perhaps the Lee-Wick method could be applied to the (maximal-) unitarity-violating singularities in string theories for $D < D_c$, since the higher-loop properties of the method would be avoided due to duality. (6) If string theories fail at the phenomenological level, they could at least be used as models for the phenomenon of the bound-state graviton, for use as an alternative theory of quantum gravity. (Open strings produce closed strings as one-loop, two-string bound states, which include the graviton.) A covariant formulation would allow the study of this phenomenon, and in particular the anomaly in the naive local conservation of energy-momentum [20]: In the classical theory the energy-momentum tensor is conserved ($\partial \cdot T=0$), whereas in the quantum theory, due to the presence of the graviton and its general coordinate invariance, it's covariantly conserved ($\partial \cdot T \neq \nabla \cdot T=0$).

2. QUANTIZATION ALA BRST

Our method of covariant quantization of string field theory is based on the approach of Becchi, Rouet, and Stora, and of Tyutin, to quantizing Yang-Mills. Instead of applying this quantization to the string mechanics action (a method described below for the simpler case of the superparticle), we will use here the simpler method of considering directly the BRST quantization of the algebra of group generators which act on the string fields. (A similar approach has been used by Fradkin and Fradkina [21] for ordinary field theory.)

In general, the procedure is: (1) Find the appropriate gauge group, with generators G_i, and (graded) commutation relations (up to Schwinger-like terms)

$$[G_i,G_j\} = f_{ij}{}^k G_k .$$

(2) Construct the BRST operator

$$Q = c^i G_i + \tfrac{1}{2} c^j c^i f_{ij}{}^k \frac{\partial}{\partial c^k} \rightarrow Q^2=0.$$

This operator is defined to transform physical fields as a gauge transformation with the gauge parameters replaced by the ghosts c^i, and transform the ghosts in such a way that the BRST algebra closes. (3) Find a BRST-invariant action.

This procedure may be performed order-by-order in the coupling constants, in which case we first apply the above procedure to obtain a free Lagrangian of the form

$$L_0 = \tfrac{1}{2}\, \Phi K_0 \Phi\, , \quad [Q_0,\, K_0\,\} = 0 .$$

We then include interaction terms in Q, and demand that $Q^2 = 0$ order-by-order in perturbation theory:

$$Q = Q_0 + gQ_1 + \cdots, \quad Q^2 = 0 \rightarrow Q_0{}^2 = 0,\ \{Q_0,Q_1\} = 0,\ \cdots .$$

This gives the Lagrangian order-by-order: $Q_1 \rightarrow L_1$, etc.

3. BOSONIC STRING [22]

The mechanics of a free, nonsupersymmetric string is described in terms of the string spacetime coordinate $X(\sigma)$, where σ parametrizes the distance of that point along the length of the string.

A convenient operator for describing the free string is

$$\hat{P}(\sigma) = \frac{1}{\sqrt{2}}\left(i\frac{\delta}{\delta X} \pm X'\right)(\pm\sigma) \quad \text{on } \sigma\in[-\pi,\pi],$$

where $' = \partial/\partial\sigma$, and $\hat{P}$ is a single operator for the open string (defined on $[0,\pi]$, by using the $\pm$ for $\pm\sigma\in[0,\pm\pi]$) and two commuting operators (for the choice of $\pm$) for the closed string (defined on $[-\pi,\pi]$). The boundary conditions are such that $\hat{P}$ is always periodic, and expansion in modes (powers of $e^{i\sigma}$) gives harmonic oscillator creation and annihilation operators, except for the zero mode, which is the ordinary (center-of-mass) momentum ($p \sim \int d\sigma\, \hat{P}$). The appropriate group generators are now

$$G(\sigma) = \tfrac{1}{2}\hat{P}^2$$

(up to a constant, and including normal ordering), whose modes are the Virasoro operators, and in particular the zero mode is the string's harmonic-oscillator "Hamiltonian" $\sim -\delta^2/\delta X^2 + X'^2$. (We use units $\alpha'=1$.) The algebra of $G(\sigma)$ is identical to that of one-dimensional coordinate transformations (corresponding to two-dimensional conformal transformations in the string mechanics Lagrangian approach), up to a central charge (conformal anomaly) term. Introducing ghosts $\hat{C} = (1/\sqrt{2})\,(C \pm \delta/\delta\tilde{C})$ (analogous to $\hat{P}$), we thus have, according to the method of the previous section,

$$Q_0 = \int d\sigma\, \hat{C}\left(\tfrac{1}{2}\hat{P}^2 + i\hat{C}'\frac{\delta}{\delta\hat{C}}\right).$$

This operator generates BRST transformations on a string field functional $\Phi[X(\sigma), C(\sigma), \tilde{C}(\sigma)]$. (It was originally derived by fixing two-dimensional general coordinate invariance in quantum string mechanics[23], for which $G(\sigma)$ is the current, or energy-momentum tensor.) Absence of anomalous terms in $Q^2=0$ fixes $D_c=26$ (and the constant term in $G(\sigma)$).

If we define a kinetic operator $K = [\mathcal{O},Q\}$ for some operator $\mathcal{O}$, it satisfies BRST invariance $[Q,K\} = 0$ as a consequence of the Jacobi identities. The appropriate choice for the string is

$$\begin{cases} \text{open:} \quad \mathcal{O} = c\dfrac{\partial}{\partial c} & \rightarrow \quad K_0 = cH - \dfrac{\partial}{\partial c}\hat{H} \\ \text{closed:} \quad \mathcal{O} = \tilde{c}\tfrac{1}{2}\left[c,\dfrac{\partial}{\partial c}\right] & \rightarrow \quad K_0 = \tilde{c}\left(cH - \dfrac{\partial}{\partial c}\hat{H}\right) - \tfrac{1}{2}\left[c,\dfrac{\partial}{\partial c}\right](N_+ - N_-), \end{cases}$$

where c and $\tilde{c}$ are the zero modes of C and $\tilde{C}$. ($\tilde{C}$ has no zero mode for the open string.) All dynamics (i.e., p-dependence) is contained in the Hamiltonian H, which now includes ghost harmonic-oscillator contributions:

$$H = \int d\sigma \left(\tfrac{1}{2}\hat{P}^2 + i\hat{C}' \frac{\delta}{\delta\hat{C}}\right) \sim \Box - M^2,$$

where the mass operator M^2 is a harmonic oscillator number operator. ($\hat{H}$ is the kinetic operator for BRST auxiliary fields, and $N_+ - N_-$ is the kinetic operator for Lagrange multipliers which equate the number operators of clockwise and counterclockwise modes in the closed string.)

The three-point contribution to Q is expressed in terms of the "overlap integral", a δ-functional which equates points on a string to points on the two strings into which it splits. In analogy to the H terms in K_0 above (and consistent with $Q^2=0$ to this order),

$$Q_1 \sim \delta[X_1-X_{2,3}]\ \delta\,[C_1-C_{2,3}]\ \delta\,[\tilde{C}_1-\tilde{C}_{2,3}] \cdot \begin{cases} C\,(\sigma_{INT}): & \text{open} \\ C\,(\sigma_{INT})\tilde{C}(\sigma_{INT}): & \text{closed,} \end{cases}$$

where σ_{INT} is where the string splits.

Analyzing by means of an expansion of the string field Φ in terms of individual component fields (by a Taylor expansion in the nonzero modes of X, C, and $\tilde{C}$), we find: (1) All nonscalar fields appear as gauge fields in the usual way, with Stueckelberg formulations for the massive fields. (2) After performing field redefinitions which put the BRST transformations into canonical form, the Lagrangian is recognizable as the usual Faddeev-Popov quantized form: (gauge-invariant terms) + (BRST auxiliary field terms) + (BRST auxiliary field) $\cdot$ (gauge condition) + (ghost terms). (3) Not all components of physical fields appear at $C=\tilde{C}=0$: the traces appear at ghost levels, being replaced with physical modes. For example, the would-be metric tensor has a physical scalar (the "dilaton") as its trace, with the usual trace (the conformal mode, an auxiliary field) appearing at the second ghost level.

There is an important technical problem remaining for covariant bosonic string field theory: The gauge-invariant action is not yet known, but it can be found by reversing the BRST quantization on the action. (This is easy at the component level, but hard to do on the whole string field.) Along with this action comes the classical gauge invariance: The form of Q_0 suggests that the linearized transformations take the form

$$\delta\Phi\,[X] \sim \int d\sigma\, X'(\sigma)\cdot \frac{\delta}{\delta X(\sigma)}\,\Lambda_\sigma\,[X]$$

on a classical field $\Phi\,[X]$ in terms of a gauge parameter $\Lambda_\sigma\,[X]$. At this level it resembles σ-reparametrizations, but the form of the interactions suggests that the overlap integral should be incorporated in the group structure. (Also, as mentioned above, not all physical fields are contained in $\Phi[X]$.)

4. SUPERPARTICLE [24]

As mentioned earlier, Q_0 can also be derived from quantum mechanics, where the coordinates are functions of a proper-time parameter τ [25]. In the case of the supersymmetric particle, the appropriate Lagrangian, invariant under the supersymmetry transformation $\delta\theta = \epsilon$, $\delta x = i\epsilon\gamma\theta$ on the superspace coordinates, is

$$L = \dot{z}^M e_M{}^A(z)\, p_A - \lambda^i G_i(p_A)$$

$$= [(\dot{x} + i\,\dot{\theta}\gamma\theta)\cdot p + \dot{\theta}\pi] - [g\tfrac{1}{2}p^2 + \psi\,\not{p}\,\pi],$$

where $\dot{} = \partial/\partial\tau$ and $\lambda^i = (g,\psi)$ are gauge fields as well as Lagrange multipliers. Upon quantization, the supermomenta $p_A = (p,\pi)$ become the supersymmetry-covariant derivatives ($p_a = i\partial_a$, $\pi_\alpha = id_\alpha$) and $G_i = (\tfrac{1}{2}p^2,\ \not{p}\,\pi)$ the gauge-group generators and field equations (the Klein-Gordon operator and the "supersymmetric Dirac operator" [26]). Whereas $\tfrac{1}{2}p^2$ generates τ-reparametrizations, $\not{p}\pi$ generates a local spinorial invariance [27]:

$$\delta\theta = \not{p}\kappa,\ \delta x = \kappa(\gamma\pi - i\not{p}\gamma\theta),\ \delta\pi = -2ip^2\kappa,\ \delta p = 0,\ \delta\psi = \dot{\kappa},\ \delta g = 4i\psi\not{p}\kappa.$$

This action is a modification of the action of Brink and Schwarz [28] that allows for auxiliary fields in the corresponding field theory, due to the absence of their constraint $\pi = 0$.

The BRST operator follows from the method of section 2: Using the commutation relations $\{\pi,\pi\}=-2\not{p}$,

$$Q = cp^2 + \check{c}\not{p}\pi + (\check{c}\not{p}\check{c})\frac{\partial}{\partial c},$$

in terms of a scalar anticommuting ghost c and spinor commuting ghost $\check{c}$. (This corresponds to the covariant gauge g=1, $\psi=0$.)

5. SUPERSTRING ALGEBRA

In order to construct the group generators we first need the covariant operators generalizing $\hat{P}(\sigma)$ of the bosonic string and p and d of the superparticle. They should be covariant with respect to both conformal transformations (as for the bosonic string) and supersymmetry (as for the superparticle). We define these operators by their algebra, generalizing $[\hat{P}_a(\sigma_1), \hat{P}_b(\sigma_2)] = i\delta'(\sigma_2-\sigma_1)\eta_{ab}$ and $\{d_\alpha,d_\beta\}=2\gamma^a{}_{\alpha\beta}p_a$:

$$\{D_\alpha(\sigma_1),D_\beta(\sigma_2)\} = \delta(\sigma_2-\sigma_1)2\gamma^a{}_{\alpha\beta}P_a(\sigma_1),$$

$$[D_\alpha(\sigma_1), P_a(\sigma_2)] = \delta(\sigma_2-\sigma_1)2\gamma_{a\alpha\beta}\Omega^\beta(\sigma_1),$$

$$\{D_\alpha(\sigma_1),\Omega^\beta(\sigma_2)\} = i\delta'(\sigma_2-\sigma_1)\delta_\alpha{}^\beta,$$

$$[P_a(\sigma_1), P_b(\sigma_2)] = i\delta'(\sigma_2-\sigma_1)\eta_{ab} \qquad \text{(rest=0)}.$$

For consistency of the algebra $\gamma_{a\alpha(\beta}\gamma^a{}_{\gamma\delta)}=0$ (as well as $\gamma^a{}_{\alpha\beta} = \gamma^a{}_{\beta\alpha}$), which implies D=3, 4, 6, or 10 for simple supersymmetry (but more general cases are possible when P_a includes central charge components and D_α is an arbitrary type of spinor, and $\gamma^a{}_{\alpha\beta}$ are not the usual Dirac/Pauli matrices).

This algebra can be solved in terms of $\hat{P}_a$ (as defined previously), a spinor coordinate $\Theta^\alpha(\sigma)$, and its derivative $\delta/\delta\Theta^\alpha$:

$$D_\alpha = \frac{\delta}{\delta\Theta^\alpha} + \gamma^a{}_{\alpha\beta}\hat{P}_a\Theta^\beta + \frac{i}{2}\gamma_{a\alpha\beta}\gamma^a{}_{\gamma\delta}\Theta^\beta\Theta^\gamma\Theta'^\delta,$$

$$P_a = \hat{P}_a + i\gamma_{a\alpha\beta}\Theta^\alpha\Theta'^\beta,$$

$$\Omega^\alpha = i\Theta'^\alpha.$$

These are covariant under supersymmetry generated by

$$Q_\alpha = \int d\sigma \left(\frac{\delta}{\delta\Theta^\alpha} - \gamma^a{}_{\alpha\beta}\hat{P}_a\Theta^\beta - \frac{i}{6}\gamma_{a\alpha\beta}\gamma^a{}_{\gamma\delta}\Theta^\beta\Theta^\gamma\Theta'^\delta\right),$$

$$Q_a = \int d\sigma\, \hat{P}_a,$$

where $\{Q_\alpha, Q_\beta\} = -2\gamma^a{}_{\alpha\beta} Q_a$. They also transform covariantly, with weight 1, under conformal transformations generated by the generalized Virasoro operators

$$\tfrac{1}{2}P^2 + \Omega^\alpha D_\alpha = \tfrac{1}{2}\hat{P}^2 + i\Theta'^\alpha \frac{\delta}{\delta\Theta^\alpha}.$$

The group generators include these (which generalize $\frac{1}{2}\hat{P}^2$ of the bosonic string and $\frac{1}{2}p^2$ of the superparticle), and probably also $\not{P}D$ (generalizing $\not{p}\pi$ of the superparticle), as well as other operators needed to close the algebra.

The constraint on the generalized γ-matrices and the form of Q_α (if we constrain $D_\alpha = 0$) also arise from the covariant Green-Schwarz action for the superstring [29], suggesting that it should be modified as the Brink-Schwarz action for the superparticle was.

The γ-matrix constraint also follows from super-Yang-Mills [30], and the algebra above closely resembles the algebra of that theory in superspace [31] if we relate D_α, P_a, and Ω^α to the covariant derivatives and field strength ∇_α, ∇_a, and W^α. The Virasoro operators are then analogous to the background-field kinetic operator $-\frac{1}{2}\Box + iW^\alpha\nabla_\alpha$ [32].

To complete the quantization will require finding all the group generators and their algebra, the resulting BRST operator, and finally the BRST-invariant action.

REFERENCES

[1] Dual theory, ed. M. Jacob (North-Holland, Amsterdam, 1974); J. Scherk, Rev. Mod. Phys. 47 (1975) 123.

[2] J.H. Schwarz, Phys. Rep 89 (1982) 223; M.B. Green and J.H. Schwarz, Nucl. Phys. B243 (1984) 475.

[3] E. Witten, Nucl Phys. B149 (1979) 285.

[4] G. 't Hooft, Nucl Phys. B72 (1974) 461.

[5] T.H.R. Skyrme, Proc. Roy. Soc. A260 (1961) 227; E. Witten, Nucl Phys. B223 (1983) 433.

[6] G. 't Hooft, Phys. Lett. 109B (1982) 474.

[7] M.T. Grisaru and W. Siegel, Nucl. Phys. B201 (1982) 292, B206 (1982) 496.

[8] N. Marcus and A. Sagnotti, The ultraviolet behavior of N=4 Yang-Mills and the power counting of extended superspace, Caltech preprint CALT-68-1129 (June, 1984).

[9] R.E. Cutkosky, P.V. Landshoff, D.I. Olive, and J.C. Polkinghorne, Nucl. Phys. B12 (1969) 281.

[10] D.J. Gross, A. Neveu, J.Scherk, and J.H. Schwarz, Phys. Lett. 31B (1970) 592.

[11] I thank D. Boulware for drawing my attention to the overlapping divergence.

[12] G. 't Hooft, Can we make sense out of "quantum chromodynamics *in* The whys of subnuclear physics, proc. of the 1977 International School of Subnuclear Physics, Erice (Plenum, New York, 1979) p. 943.

[13] W.Y. Crutchfield II, Phys. Rev. D19 (1979) 2370.

[14] L. Alvarez-Gaumé and E. Witten, Nucl. Phys. B234 (1984) 269.

[15] M.B. Green and J.H. Schwarz, Phys. Lett. 149B (1984) 117.

[16] M.B. Green and J.H. Schwarz, Phys. Lett. 151B (1985) 21; D.J. Gross, J.A. Harvey, E. Martinec, and R. Rohm, Phys. Rev. Lett. 54 (1985) 502.

[17] A.M. Polykov, Phys. Lett. 103B (1981) 207, 211.

[18] M.T. Grisaru, W. Siegel, and M. Roček, Nucl Phys. B159 (1979) 429.

[19] M. Ögren, Light-cone integrals and finiteness of N=4 supersymmetric Yang-Mills theory, Göteborg preprint 84-15 (March, 1984).

[20] W.Siegel, Phys. Lett. 142B (1984) 276.

[21] E.S. Fradkin and T.E. Fradkina, Phys. Lett. 72B (1978) 343.

[22] W. Siegel, Phys. Lett. 149B (1984) 157, 162, 151B (1985) 391, 396.

[23] M. Kato and K. Ogawa, Nucl. Phys. B212 (1983) 443;
S. Hwang, Phys. Rev. D28 (1983) 2614.

[24] W. Siegel, Spacetime-supersymmetric quantum mechanics, Berkeley preprint UCB-PTH-85/11 (March, 1985).

[25] E.C.G. Stueckelberg, Helv. Phys. Acta 15 (1942) 23;
R.P. Feynman, Phys. Rev. 80 (1950) 440;
J. Schwinger, Phys. Rev. 82 (1951) 664;

[26] S.J. Gates, Jr., M.T. Grisaru, M. Roček, and W. Siegel, Superspace, *or* One thousand and one lessons in supersymmetry (Benjamin/Cummings, Reading, 1983) pp. 70,88.

[27] W. Siegel, Phys. Lett. 128B (1983) 397.

[28] L. Brink and J.H. Schwarz, Phys. Lett. 100B (1981) 310.

[29] M.B. Green and J.H. Schwarz, Phys. Lett. 136B (1984) 367, Nucl. Phys. B243 (1984) 285.

[30] L. Brink, J.H. Schwarz, and J. Scherk, Nucl. Phys. B121 (1977) 77.

[31] W. Siegel, Phys. Lett. 80B (1979) 220.

[32] M.T. Grisaru, W. Siegel, and M. Roček, Nucl. Phys. B159 (1979) 429;
M.T. Grisaru and W. Siegel, Nucl Phys. B201 (1982) 292, B206 (1982) 496;
S.J. Gates, Jr., M.T. Grisaru, M. Roček, and W. Siegel, Superspace, *or* One thousand and one lessons in supersymmetry (Benjamin/Cummings, Reading, 1983) pp. 25, 382, 383.

SUPERGAUGE FIELD THEORY OF SUPERSTRINGS

MICHIO KAKU and JOSEPH LYKKEN
City College of the City University of New York, N.Y., 10031

ABSTRACT

Years ago, we formulated the field theory of strings. [1] In this paper, we present the supergauge field theory of covariant superstrings. First, we derive the gauge covariant action for the field theory of strings [2]: $L = \Phi(X)^{\dagger} \mathbf{P} \left[i\,\partial_\tau - (L_o - 1) \right] \mathbf{P}\, \Phi(X)$, in the same way that Feynman derived the Schrodinger equation from the path integral formalism. The action is invariant under both the Lorentz group and a local gauge transformation that is generated by the Virasoro algebra: $\delta\Phi(X) = \sum_{n=1}^{\infty} \epsilon_{-n} L_{-n} \hat{\Phi}(X)$, where $\mathbf{P}$ is a projection operator which annihilates spurious states. We give three distinct formulations of this operator $\mathbf{P}$ to all orders, the first based on extracting the operator from the functional formulation of the Nambu-Goto action, and the second and third based on inverting the Shapovalov matrix on a Verma module. Unlike the previous field theory of strings defined in the light cone gauge, this action is manifestly Lorentz invariant as well as gauge invariant under local re-parametrizations of the string.

Second, we now generalize this result to write down the covariant field theory of superstrings [3] which is invariant under a local supersymmetric gauge transformation. We eliminate the bizarre, divergent commutators found previously for the superstring and construct the first and second quantized field theory of superstrings.

1. M. Kaku and K. Kikkawa, Phys. Rev. **D10** (1974) 1110, 1823.
2. M. Kaku, "Gauge Field Theory of Covariant Strings," CCNY preprint.
3. M. Kaku and J. Lykken, "Supergauge Field Theory of Covariant Superstrings," CCNY preprint.

1. Introduction

In contrast to the first quantized Nambu-Goto action, which is defined in terms of a vector $X_\mu(\sigma)$ which labels the position of the string, the second quantized field theory is defined in terms of a field $\Phi(X)$ which is a functional of all possible vibrations of the string. The theory is formally unitary, explicitly contains all interactions of splitting and joining strings, which must be put in by hand for the first quantized Nambu-Goto action, and the correct counting of perturbation diagrams is achieved without double counting.

The problem with the usual field theory of strings, however, is that it is defined only in the light cone gauge, where Lorentz covariance and re-parametrization invariance are both lost. Recently, a BRST formulation of the field theory of strings [4] has been written down, but again the Virosoro algebra is missing.

In the zero slope limit, it is easy to show that the light cone field theory of strings contains terms like $A_i\, \partial^2 A^i$. Furthermore, the the BRST action yields terms like $A_\mu\, \partial^2 A^\mu$. What we desire, however, is a gauge covariant action which yields the Maxwell action $(-1/4)F_{\mu\nu}F^{\mu\nu}$.

The key to this entire construction is to notice that the Maxwell action can be re-written as $A_\mu P^\mu{}_\nu\, \partial^2\, P^\nu{}_\lambda A^\lambda$, where $P^\mu{}_\nu$ is a projection operator which projects out transverse modes: $P_{\mu\nu}=\delta_{\mu\nu}-\partial_\mu\partial_\nu/\,\partial^2$. This projection operator guarantees that the action is invariant under $\delta A_\mu = \partial_\mu\Lambda$. The action for the free graviton can be written in exactly the same manner. We generalize this now to all spins.

2. From first to second quantization

We begin our discussion by extracting out the second quantized theory from the first quantized theory in exactly the same way that Feynman originally extracted the Schrodinger equation from the first quantized action of a point particle.

We begin, as Feynman did, with the Green's function connecting a state that begins at X_i and propagates to X_j and will eventually slice up the interval into finite intervals i, i+1, i+2,...j. This Green's function $G(X_i, X_j)$ can be written either in first or in second quantized formalisms, i.e. either with the position vector X_μ as the independent variable, or with a field functional $\Phi(X)$ composed of all excitations of the position vector. We will use the following to *derive* an expression for $L(\Phi)$:

$$\int_{X_i}^{X_j} DX \exp i \int L(X)\, d\sigma d\tau = \int D\Phi^\dagger(X)\, D\Phi(X)\;\; \Phi^\dagger(X_i)\, \Phi(X_j) \exp i \int L(\Phi) DX$$

4. W. Siegel, Phys. Lett. **148B** (1984) 556; **149B** (1984) 157, 162.

where $L(X) = \sqrt{g_{01}^2 - g_{00} g_{11}}$. If we define the conjugate momentum $P_\mu = \frac{\delta L}{\delta \dot{X}^\mu}$, then our first class constraints read: $P_\mu^2 + (\partial_\sigma X_\mu)^2 \equiv 0$; $P_\mu \, \partial_\sigma X^\mu \equiv 0$. Converting to the second order formalism, we can show that this Green's function can be written as:

$$G(X_i, X_j) = \int_{X_i}^{X_j} DX \, DP \, D\lambda \, D\rho \, \Delta \, \exp i \left\{ \int L(P,X) \, d\sigma d\tau \right\} \tag{2.1}$$

$$L(P,X) = P\dot{X} + (\tfrac{1}{2}\lambda)(P^2 + X'^2) + \rho(PX') \tag{2.2}$$

(Δ represents the measure and possible Fadeev-Popov determinants, which we keep unspecified.) This action is explicitly invariant under a local gauge rotation with parameters $\epsilon(\sigma)$ and $\eta(\sigma)$:

$$\delta X_\mu = \epsilon P_\mu + \eta X_\mu' ; \quad \delta P_\mu = \partial_\sigma (\epsilon X_\mu' + \eta P_\mu)$$

$$\delta\lambda = -\dot{\epsilon} + \lambda'\eta - \eta'\lambda + \rho'\epsilon - \epsilon'\rho$$

$$\delta\rho = -\dot{\delta} + \epsilon'\lambda - \lambda'\epsilon + \rho'\eta - \eta'\rho \tag{2.3}$$

This local gauge transformation guarantees that we can eliminate all ghosts.

The transition to the second quantized theory is now made by slicing up the interval from i to j into small finite intervals. Labeling each τ slice by i, i+1, i+2,,,. we can now make the transition to quantum operators for each slice:

$$\int_{X_i}^{X_j} DX \, DP \, \exp i \int d\sigma \, d\tau \, P_\mu \dot{X}^\mu \rightarrow \int \prod_{n=i}^{j-1} DX_n \, DP_n \, \exp i \int d\sigma \, P_{i,\mu} (X_i^\mu - X_{i+1}^\mu)$$

$$= \int \prod_{n=i}^{j-1} \langle X_n | P_n \rangle DX_n \; DP_n \; \langle P_n | X_{n+1} \rangle \tag{2.4}$$

$$|X\rangle \equiv \prod_{n=1}^{\infty} |X_n\rangle \equiv \prod_{n=1}^{\infty} \exp(-\tfrac{1}{2}X_n^2 - i\sqrt{2}X_n a^\dagger_n + \tfrac{1}{2}a^\dagger_n \, a^\dagger_n)|0\rangle$$

$$|P\rangle \equiv \prod_{n=1}^{\infty} |P_n\rangle \equiv \prod_{n=1}^{\infty} \exp(-\tfrac{1}{2}P_n^2 + \sqrt{2}P_n a^\dagger_n - \tfrac{1}{2}a^\dagger_n \, a^\dagger_n)|0\rangle \tag{2.5}$$

Sandwiched between the various slices, of course, we must insert $\delta(P^2 + X'^2)\,\delta(PX')$, which represent the first class constraints taken at each slice. Now let us find an explicit operator expansion of $\Phi(X)$ itself. Let us define $|\Phi\rangle$ as an arbitrary state vector in the Hilbert space of harmonic oscillators. Obviously, this means

$$|\Phi\rangle \equiv \phi(x_o)|0\rangle + A(x_o)^\mu a^\dagger_{1\mu}|0\rangle + g^{\mu\nu}(x_o)\, a^\dagger_{1\mu} a^\dagger_{1\mu} + \cdots \tag{2.6}$$

where the state $|\Phi\rangle$ contains the tachyon, the photon, a massive graviton, etc.

If we now take the matrix element of $|X>$ with $<\Phi|$, then we arrive at the usual expansion of the field Φ in terms of Hermite polynomials [1]:

$$\Phi(X) \equiv <\Phi|X> \equiv \phi(x_o) \prod_{\substack{n=1 \\ \alpha=1,26}}^{\infty} H_o(X_{n,\alpha}) + A^{\mu}(x_o) H_1(X_{1\mu}) \prod_{\substack{n=1 \\ n\neq 1,\mu\neq\alpha}}^{\infty} H_o(X_n) + \cdots \quad (2.7)$$

At each time slice labelled by i, the local gauge invariance guarantees that we have enough symmetry to eliminate the ghost states. In Dirac quantization, we can apply the first class constraints directly onto the state vectors:

$$\int d\sigma \exp in\sigma \left[\hat{P}_{\mu}^{2} + 2\hat{P}_{\mu}X^{\mu\prime} + X^{\prime 2}\right] |\Phi> \equiv L_n |\Phi> = 0. \quad (2.8)$$

This means that we are allowed to extract out all the spurious states out of $|\Phi>$ with a projection operator that we will call **P** . We will now give three distinct formulations of this operator **P** : (a) in terms of a Hilbert space projection operator [5] $\mathbf{P} = \sum |R_i><R_i|$ summed over all real states which satisfy $L_n |R_i> = 0$ (b) in terms of a summation over operators [6] composed of arbitrarily large products over the elements of the L's $\mathbf{P} = \sum L_{-n} F_n(L_o) L_n + \dots$ (c) in terms of string operators by extracting the projection operator directly from the Feynman functional at each τ slice.

3. First method: projection operators for each level

It will be helpful to first define some mathematical concepts from the theory of affine Lie (Kac-Moody) algebras [7]: let the *highest weight vacuum vector* be a state $|R>$ which satisfies $L_n |R> = 0$ for all positive n. We know that we can reproduce the entire representation associated with $|R>$ if we apply all possible lowering step operators. Similarly, let the *universal enveloping algebra* $U(L_{-n})$ consist of all possible products that we can form from L_{-n}. A typical element of the enveloping algebra is $\mathbf{L}_{-I} \equiv L_{-1}^{\lambda_1} L_{-2}^{\lambda_2} \cdots L_{-n}^{\lambda_n} \in U(L_{-n})$

Let p(N) equal the number of partitions that we can make of the integer N. Let I equal any integer from 1 to p(N). If we let $N = |I| = \sum_{i=1}^{n} i\,\lambda_i$, then I simply counts all possible partitions of the integer $N = |I|$. Now, the set of all states created by applying the universal enveloping algebra (the set of all products of lowering operators) to the hightest weight vacuum vector $|R>$ merely creates the entire multiplet, called the

5. See R.C. Brower and C.B. Thorn, Nucl. Phys. **B31** (1971) 163-182 where the on-shell projection operator is constructed.
6. B. L. Feigin and D. B. Fuchs, Sov. Math. Doklady 27 (1983), No. 2, 465-9.
7. V. Kac, *Infinite Dimensional Lie Algebras* Birkhauser, Boston, 1983.

Verma module: V(h,c) = $U(L_{-n})|R>$ where $L_o|R> = h|R>$ and c is the dimension of space time appearing in the universal extension (Schwinger term). Notice that all the vectors in the multiplet or the Verma module are spurious states except the highest weight vacuum vector |R>. Using the notation of Feigin-Fuchs, let us now define |I> $\equiv L_{-I}|0>$. Then we can define *the Shapovalov matrix as [8]:*

$$S_{IJ}^N(p^2) = <I|J> = <0|L_I\ L_{-J}|0> \tag{3.1}$$

for |I| = |J| = N and h = p^2 . *Given the Shapovalov matrix, we can now write down an expression for* **P** *to all orders.* Let us define $\mathbf{P}^{R_n}$ as the projection operator which projects onto real states at the nth level, while $\mathbf{P}^{S_n}$ is the off mass shell spurious particle projection operator at that level. For example, $\mathbf{P}^{R_o} = |0><0|$ and $\mathbf{P}^{R_1} = 1_1 - (2p^2)^{-1}L_1\,\mathbf{P}^{R_o}\,L_{-1}$. We now iterate, calculating the nth level from the n-1 level (levels are ranked by the eigenvalue of the number operator on the Hilbert space):

$$\mathbf{P} = \sum_{N=0}^{\infty} \mathbf{P}^{R_N} = \sum_{N=0}^{\infty} 1_N - \mathbf{P}^{S_N}$$

$$\mathbf{P}^{S_N} = \sum_{M=1}^{N} \sum_{\substack{I\,J=1 \\ |I|=|J|=M}}^{p(N-M)} \mathbf{L}_{-I}\,(S^{-1})_{IJ}^{N-M}(p^2+M)\,\mathbf{P}^{R_M}\,\mathbf{L}_J \tag{3.2}$$

It is easy to show that $\mathbf{P}^2 = \mathbf{P}$, $\mathbf{P}|R> = |R>$, $<R|\mathbf{P} = <R|$, and that $<R|L_n\ \mathbf{P} = \mathbf{P}\ L_{-n}|R> = 0$ for any highest weight vacuum vector |R>. *Notice that if the Shapovalov matrix is known, then we know* **P** *to all orders.* Since the divergences of the Shapovalov are well-known and have been isolated by Kac [9], we know that it is possible over a wide range of parameters p^2 and c to construct the *off-shell* projection operator.

4. Second method: power expansion in $U(L_{-n})$

Rather than expand **P** in terms of $\sum |R_i><R_i|$, we can also expand in all orders in elements of the universal enveloping algebra and its conjugate. Following the method of Feigin-Fuchs, who created a generalized Casimir operator by this same power expansion, we can show that **P**= 1 − $\mathbf{P}^S$ and

$$\mathbf{P}^S = \sum_{N=1}^{\infty} \sum_{\substack{I\,J=1 \\ |I|=|J|=N}}^{p(N)} \mathbf{L}_{-I}\ F_{IJ}^N(L_o)\ \mathbf{L}_J$$

8. N.N. Shapovalov, Func. Anal. Appl. 6 (1972) 307-312.
9. V. Kac, Lect. Notes in Physics, vol. 94, 441-5 (1979).

$$F^N_{IJ}(L_o) \equiv \left[\delta_{IL} - A^{N-1}_{IL}(L_o)\right](S^{-1})^N_{LJ}(L_o)$$

$$\sum_{M=1}^{N-1} \sum_{\substack{I,J=1 \\ |I|=|J|=N}}^{p(M)} \mathbf{L}_{-I}\, F^M_{IJ}(L_o)\, \mathbf{L}_J \;\; \mathbf{L}_{-S}\,|R> \equiv \mathbf{L}_{-P}\;\; A^{N-1}_{PS}(L_o)\,|R> \qquad (4.1)$$

where $S^N_{IJ}(L_o)\,|R> \equiv L_I\, L_{-J}\,|R>$ and S^N is determined iteratively from A^{N-1}. Notice that we have, to all orders, an expression for the projection operator in terms of a simple power expansion in operators composed out of the universal enveloping algebra and the Shapovalov matrix.

5. Third method: extraction of the operators from the functional

We only sketch the last method, which consists of extracting directly out of the Feynman functional the operator expression which corresponds to the delta functions we found arising from the first class constraints, the Virasoro conditions.

Since the transition from Feynman path integrals to harmonic oscillators is not that transparent, it will be first instructive to do a simpler case, where we have explicitly fixed the gauge and extracted out the field theory lagrangian. In this way, we can rigorously construct the field theory lagrangian from the Feynman path integral. Let us now, as an exercise, break the Virasoro gauge invariance by choosing a gauge.

Choosing the conformal gauge $\lambda=1, \rho=0$ in our previous calculation of the gauge invariance of P and X, we can calculate the Fadeev-Popov determinant. We are left with $-\delta\lambda=\dot{\epsilon}-\eta$ and $-\delta\rho=\dot{\eta}+\epsilon$. When we calculate the Fadeev-Popov ghost associated with this gauge, we find a new term in our action:

$$p^1_\theta\,(\partial_\sigma+\partial_\tau)\,\theta^1 + p^2_\theta\,(\partial_\tau-\partial_\sigma)\,\theta^2 \qquad (5.1)$$

The two Fadeev Popov ghosts associated with the conformal gauge therefore effectively *reduce the 26 dimensional excitations of the string down to 24 excitations.* Because the ghost particle now contains a τ derivative in the action, we must also let it contribute to the bra and ket vectors when we time slice the functional. Our Green's function now becomes $G\,(X_i\,\theta_i\,;\,X_{i+1},\theta_{i+1})$ which can be rewritten as:

$$<X_i\;\theta_i\,|P_i\;p_{\theta i}>\int DP_i\;Dp_{\theta i}<P_i\;p_{\theta i}\,|X_{i+1}\;\theta_{i+1}>\;\exp i\int d\sigma\,[P_i^{\,2}+(\partial_\sigma X)^2+p_{\theta i}\rho\partial_\sigma\theta_i]$$

where we have combined the spinors into one two dimensional spinor and ρ is the Pauli spin matrix σ_z . In order to actually perform the integration over the canonical momenta, we will find it useful to first calculate the matrix element between two ordinary string states:

$$<X_i\,|X_j> = \prod_n^\infty \delta(X_{ni}-X_{nj}) = <X_j\,|\Phi>\int D\Phi^*_n\;D\Phi_n\;\exp-\sum_n^\infty \Phi^*_n\;\Phi_n\;\;<\Phi|X_j>$$

$$= \int D\Phi^\dagger(X)\, D\Phi(X)\ \Phi(X_i)^\dagger\, \Phi(X_j)\, \exp - \int DX\ \Phi^\dagger(X)\, \Phi(X)$$

Now modify this matrix element by inserting $e^{iH\Delta\tau}$ between the state vectors:

$$<X_i\,|\,e^{\,iH\Delta\tau}\,|\,X_{i+1}> = \int D\Phi^\dagger(X) D\Phi(X)\ \Phi(X_i)^\dagger \Phi(X_{i+1})$$

$$\exp i \int DX \left\{ \Phi^\dagger(X_i)[\Phi(X_i) - \Phi(X_{i+1})] + i\,\Phi(X_{i+1})^\dagger H(X_{i+1})\Phi(X_{i+1})\Delta\tau \right\}$$

Notice that in the continuum limit, this expression reduces to the Lagrangian for the Schrodinger equation for an infinite number of free fields: $L=\Phi(X)^\dagger\,[\,i\,\partial_\tau - H\,]\,\Phi(X)$ where the expression for the Hamiltonian is just L_o , where we add in the contribution of the two ghost particles in the Hamiltonian. Similarly, we can convert *any* expression in the path integral into operator language via these techniques.

In the case of the gauge covariant theory, we proceed in the same way, systematically converting c-number expressions into operator expressions level by level. We find that the net effect of having the terms $\delta[P^2 + (\partial_\sigma X)^2]\,\delta[P\,\partial_\sigma X]$ is to eliminate the ghost terms level by level, which simply reproduces the projection operator. The method is, however, rather tedious and we refer the reader to [2] for more details.

Our next task is to generalize our previous methods to superstrings. This can be accomplished in two ways, either via the Neveu-Schwarz- Ramond model, or through the Green-Schwarz model. We first generalize our methods to the NRS model, which is straightforward. Using the same methods as before, we find easily: $\mathbf{G}_{-I} \equiv G_{-1/2}^{\lambda_{-1/2}}\, G_{-3/2}^{\lambda_{3/2}} \cdots G_{-n}^{\lambda_n}$ and $S_{IJ} \equiv <0|G_I G_{-J}|0>$. and:

$$\mathbf{P} = \sum_{N=0}^{\infty} \left\{ 1_N - \sum_{M=1/2}^{N} \sum_{\substack{I,J=1/2 \\ |I|=|J|=M}}^{p(N-M)} \mathbf{G}_{-I}\, (S^{-1})_{IJ}^{N-M}(p^2+M)\, \mathbf{P}^{R_M}\, \mathbf{G}_J \right\} \tag{5.2}$$

where p represents the number of distinct partitions of a half-integer or interger. Notice that the generalization to the Neveu-Schwarz model is straightforward, since G is the square root of L. The same methods apply to the Ramond model.

6. Field theory of the superstring

Our main interest now lies in trying to generalize these methods to the superstring model of Green and Schwarz:

$$L = -\sqrt{-g}\; - i\,\partial_\tau X_\mu\, \bar\theta\gamma^\mu\partial_\sigma\rho\theta\; + i\,\partial_\sigma X_\mu\, \bar\theta\gamma^\mu\partial_\tau\rho\theta\; + \bar\theta^1\gamma_\mu\partial_\tau\theta^1\, \bar\theta^2\gamma^\mu\partial_\sigma\theta^2 - \bar\theta^1\gamma_\mu\partial_\sigma\theta^1\, \bar\theta^2\gamma^\mu\partial_\tau\theta^2$$

where $g = -(\Pi_\tau\Pi_\sigma)^2 + (\Pi_\tau\Pi_\tau)(\Pi_\sigma\Pi_\sigma)$ and

$$\Pi_{\tau\mu} = \partial_\tau X_\mu - i\,\bar\theta\gamma_\mu\partial_\tau\theta: \quad \Pi_{\sigma\mu} = \partial_\sigma X_\mu - i\,\bar\theta\gamma_\mu\partial_\sigma\theta$$

It is straightforward to write down their action in second order formalism, using the conjugate pairs (P,X) and ($\bar{p}_\theta^a , \theta^a$) . θ is a Majorana-Weyl spinor in 10 dimensional space with 16+16 independent components. Notice that we are explicitly introducing the spinor conjugate to the spinor. If we define $P_\mu \equiv \frac{\delta L}{\delta X^\mu}$ and $\bar{p}_\theta \equiv \frac{\delta L}{\delta \theta}$ we find a new expression for the Green-Schwarz action in second order form. After a certain amount of algebra, we find that their theory can be *exactly* expressed as:

$$Z = \int DX\, DP\, D\theta\, D\bar{p}_\theta\, D\lambda\, D\rho\, D\epsilon^a\ \Delta \exp i \int L(P,X;\, \bar{p}_\theta^a ,\theta^a) d\sigma\, d\tau \tag{6.1}$$

$$L(P,X;\bar{p}_\theta^a,\theta^a) = P_\mu \dot{X}^\mu - \bar{p}_\theta \dot{\theta} + \frac{\lambda}{2}(\pi_o^2 + \pi_1^2) + \rho(\pi_o \pi_1) + \bar{Q}^a \epsilon^a \tag{6.2}$$

$$\pi_o^2 + \pi_1^2 \equiv 0 \quad ; \quad \pi_o \pi_1 \equiv 0$$

$$\pi_{o\mu} \equiv P_\mu + i\bar{\theta}\gamma_\mu \partial_\sigma \rho \theta \quad ; \quad \pi_{1\mu} \equiv \partial_\sigma X_\mu - i\bar{\theta}\gamma_\mu \partial_\sigma \theta$$

$$\bar{Q}^1 \equiv \bar{p}_\theta^1 - i\bar{\theta}^1 \gamma_\mu \pi_o^\mu + i\bar{\theta}^1 \gamma_\mu \pi_1^\mu - \bar{\theta}^1 \gamma_\mu \partial_\sigma \theta^1\, \bar{\theta}^1 \gamma^\mu \equiv 0$$

$$\bar{Q}^2 \equiv \bar{p}_\theta^2 - i\bar{\theta}^2 \gamma_\mu \pi_o^\mu - i\bar{\theta}^2 \gamma_\mu \pi_1^\mu + \bar{\theta}_2 \gamma_\mu \partial_\sigma \theta^2\, \bar{\theta}^2 \gamma^\mu \equiv 0 \tag{6.3}$$

where ρ^{ab} is the Pauli matrix σ_z and λ, ρ, ϵ are Lagrange multipliers.

Taking linear combinations of these constraints, we can easily diagonalize our primary constraints so that the fermionic and bosonic components decouple:

$$L_+ \equiv \pi_o^2 + \pi_1^2 - 2\bar{Q}\rho \partial_\sigma \theta \equiv P^2 + X'^2 + 2\bar{p}_\theta \rho \partial_\sigma \theta \equiv 0.$$

$$L_- \equiv 2\pi_o \pi_1 - 2\bar{Q}\, \partial_\sigma \theta \equiv 2PX' - 2\bar{p}_\theta \partial_\sigma \theta \equiv 0. \tag{6.4}$$

We now proceed to the quantization of the model. Whenever the momenta appear in the path integral, they can be replaced by a partial derivative because:

$$P_\mu \exp iP\dot{X} = -i\, \partial_\mu \exp iP\dot{X}$$

$$\bar{p}_\theta \exp -i\bar{p}_\theta \dot{\theta} = -i\, \partial_\theta \exp -i\bar{p}_\theta \dot{\theta} \tag{6.5}$$

Using this replacement of c-numbers by their operator counterpart, we easily find the canonical commutation relations:

$$\Big[P_\mu(\sigma), X_\nu(\bar{\sigma}) \Big]_- = -i\, \delta_{\mu\nu}\, \delta(\sigma - \bar{\sigma}); \qquad \Big\{ \bar{p}_\theta^\alpha(\sigma), \theta^\beta(\bar{\sigma}) \Big\}_+ = -i\, \zeta^{\alpha\beta}\, \delta(\sigma - \bar{\sigma})$$

$$\int d\sigma\, d\bar{\sigma} \Big\{ \bar{Q}(\sigma)\epsilon^a(\sigma), \bar{Q}(\bar{\sigma})\epsilon^b(\bar{\sigma}) \Big\}_- = \int d\sigma [\, \bar{\epsilon}^{[a} \gamma_\mu (\pi_o^\mu - \pi_1^\mu \rho)\, \epsilon^{b]}]$$

$$\int d\sigma\, d\bar{\sigma} \Big[f(\sigma) L_\pm(\sigma), g(\bar{\sigma}) L_\pm(\bar{\sigma}) \Big]_- = -2i \int d\sigma (f'g - g'f) L_-(\sigma)$$

$$\int d\sigma\, d\bar{\sigma} \Big[f(\sigma) L_+(\sigma), g(\bar{\sigma}) L_-(\bar{\sigma}) \Big]_- = -2i \int d\sigma (f'g - g'f) L_+(\sigma) \tag{6.6}$$

where ζ equals the projection onto Majorana-Weyl spinors.

Let us now examine the counting of fermion states. Formally, it appears as if we have 16+16 first class constraints in the Q's. But this cannot be true, because local supersymmetry only has 8+8 components. Therefore, *Q is a non-trivial mixture of first and second class constraints.* This is the origin of the problem found earlier [10] in attempts to quantize the superstring. A naive quantization of the theory will have terms proportional to $1/\pi^2$, which is not well-defined. This problem arises because the original action contained terms proportional to $\bar{\theta}\pi_\mu\gamma^\mu\dot{\theta}$. A naive quantization of the model would define the canonical conjugate to θ as $\bar{\theta}\pi_\mu\gamma^\mu$, which would result in the commutator between two θ 's having a term proportional to $1/\pi_\mu\gamma^\mu$, which is absurd.

Notice that the algebra of the Q's do not close on the π's, a sure sign that there are second class constraints in the theory. The problem is that it is formally impossible to decompose a 16 dimensional Majorana-Weyl spinor down to 8 components. The 16 component spinor is the smallest spinor representation of the Lorentz group.

In the light cone gauge, this problem is simply solved by contracting the spinor onto $k_\mu\gamma^\mu$, where the fact that $k^2=0$ forces the spinor $k_\mu\gamma^\mu\theta$ to have only eight independent components, i.e. it satisfies eight linear constraints $k_\mu\gamma^\mu(k_\nu\gamma^\nu\theta) = 0$. Using this analogy, we realize that we actually have a non-zero vector in the theory, the vector $\pi_{\pm\mu}$. Using this fact, we can now construct projection operators for the Green-Schwarz theory which hold because of the primary constraint $\pi^2=0$:

$$\mathbf{P}_a = 1 + \gamma^\mu\gamma^\nu\,[\pi_{\mu-}\pi_{\mu+}]/\,[2\pi_+\pi_-]; \quad \mathbf{P}_b = 1 + \gamma^\mu\gamma^\nu[\pi_{\mu+}\pi_{\mu-}]/\,[2\pi_+\pi_-] \tag{6.7}$$

where $\pi_\pm \equiv \pi_o \pm \pi_1$, and $\mathbf{P}_a + \mathbf{P}_b = 1$; $\mathbf{P}_a\mathbf{P}_b = \delta_{ab}\mathbf{P}_a$

$$\pi_{\mu+}\gamma^\mu\mathbf{P}_a = \pi_{\mu-}\gamma^\mu\mathbf{P}_b = \mathbf{P}_a\pi_{\mu-}\gamma^\mu = \mathbf{P}_b\pi_{\mu+}\gamma^\mu = 0.$$

Notice that these identities hold modulo the first class constraints. We can now reduce 16+16 component Majorana-Weyl spinors down to 8+8 component spinors without violating Lorentz invariance. Let us, therefore, write down the new set of 8+8 first class spinor constraints which generate supersymmetry:

$$\bar{S}^1 \equiv \bar{Q}^1\,\pi_{\mu-}\gamma^\mu; \quad \bar{S}^2 \equiv \bar{Q}^2\,\pi_{\mu+}\gamma^\mu \tag{6.8}$$

and the set of 8+8 second class constraints:

$$\bar{T}^1 \equiv \bar{Q}^1\,\pi_{\mu+}\gamma^\mu; \quad \bar{T}_2 \equiv \bar{Q}^2\,\pi_{\mu-}\gamma^\mu \tag{6.9}$$

---

10. M.B. Green and J.H. Schwarz, Nucl. Phys. **B243** (1984) 285-306

We will find that the first class constraints do indeed close, while the second class constraints do not close, as required:

$$\int d\sigma\, d\bar{\sigma} \left[f(\sigma) L_{\pm}(\sigma), \bar{S}^a(\bar{\sigma})\, \epsilon(\bar{\sigma}) \right]_- = (-1)^{\frac{1}{2}(a \pm a)}\, i \int d\sigma\, \bar{S}^a (f'\epsilon - f\epsilon')$$

$$\int d\sigma\, d\bar{\sigma} \left[\bar{S}^a(\sigma)\epsilon(\sigma), \bar{S}^b(\bar{\sigma})\eta(\bar{\sigma}) \right]_- =$$

$$\delta^{ab} \int d\sigma \left[\bar{\epsilon}\pi^a_\mu \gamma^\mu \eta \;\; (L_+ + (-1)^a L_-) + (-1)^a [8\bar{S}^a \eta\, \bar{\epsilon}\partial_\sigma \theta^a + 2\bar{S}^a \gamma^\mu \partial_\sigma \theta^b \;\; \bar{\eta}\gamma_\mu \epsilon \right] - (\epsilon \longleftrightarrow \eta)$$

$$\int d\sigma\, d\bar{\sigma} \left[\bar{T}^a(\sigma)\epsilon(\sigma), \bar{T}^b(\bar{\sigma})\epsilon(\bar{\sigma}) \right]_- = -2\delta^{ab} \int d\sigma (\pi_o^2 - \pi_1^2) \bar{\epsilon}\pi^a_\mu \gamma^\mu \eta$$

where $\pi^1 = \pi_-$; $\pi^2 = \pi_+$ and modulo terms which vanish on the constraints. However, we cannot as yet make the transition to the second quantized field theory from the Feynman path integral. The reason is because second class constraints cannot naively be applied on the state vectors of the theory. Because the second class constraints do not close on themselves, the application of the anti-commutator of two second class constraints onto state vectors will lead to contradictions. Because of this, we will be forced to adopt the formalism of Dirac brackets. Functionally, this simply means that there is an extra delta function in the measure corresponding to the 8+8 second class constraints. In order to proceed to the second quantized theory, we must construct the projection operator onto real states out of the Dirac brackets. This means that we must adopt the following modification of all naive commutators:

$$[X, Y] \rightarrow [X, Y]^* = [X, Y] - [X, \phi^a] (C^{-1})^{ab} [\phi^b, Y]$$

where ϕ represents the second class constraints given by the T's and the C matrix is simply proportional to the inverse of $\pi_+\pi_-$. Notice that this operator can be power expanded into normal modes, $\int d\sigma \exp in\sigma\, [\pi_+\pi_-]^{-1}$, much like the usual Virasoro generators, because the inverse operator is well-defined, unlike the operator $\pi^2_\pm$, which is proportional to the first class constraints and hence has no inverse. Unfortunately, however, this considerably complicates normal ordering of the operators.

At this point, notice that the theory is completely well-defined. All commutators now close among themselves because all constraints are now first class. We can now construct the Verma module corresponding to this theory in exactly the same way as before and write down the second quantized field theory, which has the same action as before except that the number of fields is much larger and we must take into account the Dirac brackets. Unfortunately, the limited space of this article does not permit any more detailed discussion of the field theory. Interested readers can find more details in ref [2] and [3].

7. Acknowledgments

This work was supported in part by NSF PHY-82-15364 and CUNY-FRAP-RF 13873. We are happy to acknowledge many fruitful conversations with Bunji Sakita on the functional formalism for strings. Note added: after this work was done, we discovered that T. Hori and K. Kamimura also discovered the use of operators $\pi_{\pm}$ in reducing the first quantized supersymmetry generators down to 8+8 components. Our thrust, however, has been in the direction of constructing the second quantized field theory. Also, at the Argonne conference, we met T. Banks, who independently with M. Peskin came across the idea of using spurious particle projection operators to construct the covariant field theory for bosonic strings. Although our approaches differed somehwhat, upon comparing our results we found similarities in our power expansion of the projection operator.

SUPERSTRINGS AT HIGH TEMPERATURE

Mark J. Bowick
Yale University, Physics Department
New Haven, CT 06511

It is important to study superstrings[1] at high temperature since in this regime string dynamics will differ from point-like dynamics. Such a study will also be useful in considering the novel cosmologies that may arise from the large number of particle species at large mass that are associated with the higher modes of strings.[2]

The first quantity to determine is the level density of various superstring theories. Using generating-function techniques the degeneracy of the mass operator can be computed. The level density is generically of the form $\rho(m) = m^{-a} \exp(bm)$.

The values of a and b are given below for different superstring theories, with α' the Regge slope parameter.

$$\begin{array}{llll} \text{Type I} & \text{superstrings :} & a = 9/2 & b = \pi\sqrt{8}\ \sqrt{\alpha'} \\ \text{Type II} & \text{superstrings :} & a = 10 & b = \pi\sqrt{8}\ \sqrt{\alpha'} \\ \text{Heterotic} & \text{superstrings :} & a = 10 & b = \pi\,(2+\sqrt{2})\ \pi\sqrt{\alpha'} \end{array} \tag{1}$$

Consider now the thermodynamics of an ideal gas of superstrings. The canonical partition function in 10 space-time dimensions is[3]

$$\ln Z = \frac{V}{(2\pi)^9} \int_\zeta^\infty \rho(m)dm \int d^9k \ \ln \left[\frac{1 + e^{-\beta\sqrt{k^2+m^2}}}{1 - e^{-\beta\sqrt{k^2+m^2}}}\right] \tag{2}$$

where ζ is an infrared cutoff above which the level density is of the form given above. As the temperature T approaches $T_o = 1/b$ (the Hagedorn[4] limiting temperature)

$$\ln Z \to \left(\frac{T\,T_o}{T_o - T}\right)^{\frac{11}{2}-a} \Gamma\left(\frac{11}{2} - a,\ \zeta\frac{(T_o - T)}{T\,T_o}\right) \tag{3}$$

For Type I superstrings the pressure, density and specific heat diverge as T approaches T_o. For Type II and heterotic strings these observables are all finite.

The canonical ensemble is valid provided the mean-square energy fluctuations are not large.[5,6] But for $a > D+3/2$ (in D space-time dimensions) the energy fluctuations become large above a critical energy density. The fundamental ensemble to use in this case is the microcanonical ensemble. For $a > 13/2$ in 10 dimensions (Type II and Heterotic strings) one finds that the density of states as a function of the total energy E has the same form as the level density $\rho(m)$ i.e. $\Omega(E_s) = E_s^{-a} \exp(bE_s)$ with E_s the total energy in massive string excitations. This gives, however, negative specific heat $C = -1/T^2(\partial^2 S/\partial E^2)^{-1} = -1/T^2(E^2/a)$ $(S = \ln \Omega)$. This is reminiscent of the thermodynamics of black holes[7] which also have negative specific heat. So far the zero modes of the string have been ignored. When these are included it is found that it is possible to have thermodynamic equilibrium between the massive and massless modes of the strings for temperature above the Hagedorn limiting temperature. Maximising the total entropy one finds the condition for thermodynamic equilibrium to be $b\,T_{max} = [20\,bE - 9a \pm \sqrt{81\,a^2 + 40\,abE}]/20\,(bE - a)$. Thus the energy in the massless modes is limited to be $E_o < E-[a\,T_{max}/b\,T_{max}-1]$. The corresponding condition for black holes of mass M is that $E_{radiation} < 1/4\,M$. Thus it is possible to pass through the Hagedorn temperature where the canonical partition function diverges. What happens at this temperature is uncertain. There may be a phase transition. If so it may have significant cosmological implications.

References

1. J.H. Schwarz, Phys. Rep. 89, 223 (1982); M.B. Green, Surveys in High Energy Physics 3, 127 (1983).
2. K. Huang and S. Weinberg, Phys. Rev. Lett. 25, 895 (1970).
3. M.J. Bowick and L.C.R. Wijewardhana, Yale Preprint YTP 85-04 (1985), to be published in Phys. Rev. Lett.
4. R. Hagedorn, Nuovo Cimento Suppl. 3, 147 (1965).
5. S. Frautschi, Phys. Rev. D3, 2821 (1971).
6. R. Carlitz, Phys. Rev. D5, 3231 (1972).
7. S.W. Hawking, Phys. Rev. D13, 191 (1975).

GHOST-FREE R^2 ACTION ARISING IN STRING THEORY

Barton Zwiebach+, University of California, Berkeley, California 94720.

This short note is a brief summary of results reported in [1] and of some further developments which were presented at this symposium.

Zero slope limits of string theories [2,3] yield field theories we are familiar with, such as Yang-Mills, gravity, and ten-dimensional supergravity. Small slope corrections can be thought as giving additional interactions to the above field theories. Very little is known about these interactions. It was recently reported in [4] that an $(R_{\mu\nu\rho\sigma})^2$ term arises as an additional interaction in the heterotic string producing a dramatic improvement as far as the possibilities of achieving a realistic dimensional reduction.

How is it possible that string theories, well known to be free of ghosts, have R^2 interactions that define ghost-infested theories ? * This question has a straightforward answer [1] : For dimensions higher than four there is a unique nontrivial ghost-free action made out of a combination of squared curvatures, and string theories use this action. The action is $\int d^Dx\,(g)^{\frac{1}{2}}\,y_4$, with $y_4 = (R_{\mu\nu\rho\sigma})^2 - 4\,(R_{\mu\nu})^2 + R^2$. Only for this combination one finds that expanding around flat space the dangerous leading terms containing two fields and four derivatives cancel up to a total derivative and thus the y_4 action gives no propagator corrections; it is a pure interaction.

I wish to emphazise why strings must use the precise combination indicated in y_4. Consider the small slope expansion of closed oriented bosonic strings at the tree level. The scattering amplitude for three on-shell gravitons has a term with four momenta that could only arise from a curvature squared term. Here one can identify the $(R_{\mu\nu\rho\sigma})^2$term but not the presence of the $(R_{\mu\nu})^2$ and R^2 terms which do not contribute to this amplitude**. The argument that follows for their appearance is therefore indirect; I believe, however, that it is conclusive. It is not possible to have propagator corrections at the tree level in closed oriented string theory, therefore whatever interaction vertices exist in the string the terms in the action that represent them should not modify the propagators. There is only one R^2 theory satisfying this requirement, namely y_4 . Beyond the tree level, one loop propagator corrections have never been found to give rise to ghosts, moreover in superstrings one loop propagator corrections vanish. Thus if ghosts would have been found at the tree level (by not using y_4) this problem would not get fixed by higher corrections.

The y_4 action is the dimensionally continued form of the four-dimensional Euler invariant χ^4, where the dimensional continuation is done expanding the two Levi-Civita symbols in χ^4 and letting the indices run over D-dimensions.***

---

* This question was raised to me by W. Siegel.

** These terms do contribute to higher point amplitudes. Their effects should be visible in the amplitude for scattering of four gravitons.

*** Upon reduction to four dimensions the invariant y_4 yields the true topological invariant χ^4 plus other interactions.

+ Work supported in part by NSF Grant PHY-84-06608

In this way it is possible to construct the dimensional continuation y_{2n} of any Euler density χ^{2n}. M. B. Halpern and the author noted [1] that y_2 is just the Einstein action, and given that strings use y_4 we were led to think that perhaps the gravitational interactions in the string use all the y's. It is clear now that things are not that simple. Let us consider a few string theories. In the Shapiro-Virasoro model (26-dimensional bosonic string) the scattering amplitude for three gravitons reveals the presence of the Einstein action (y_2), of y_4 and of an interaction made out of curvatures cubed that could not arise from y_6. In type II superstrings (A and B) one finds only the Einstein term in the three graviton scattering. Thus these strings do not use y_4 (they may use y_6). In heterotic strings y_2 and y_4 are present. In these last two cases the presence of y_6 could be detected in the four graviton scattering amplitude but the required calculations have not yet been performed. How far can one go in this tree level expansion ? Suppose one insists on constructing this expansion using only the massless fields. A field theory that reproduces the full dual N-particle amplitudes, which for N greater or equal to four have all powers of momenta due to the exchanges of massive states, will require all numbers of spatial derivatives. Thus, for example, the four-graviton amplitude requires terms with four curvatures and all numbers of derivatives sprinkled in them, five-particle amplitudes may require new structures, and so on. It is not clear whether or not a pattern could be found.

Apart from their use in string theories, gravity theories based on the y's may be very special. Zumino has rewritten these actions in the language of forms in a way that it is then simple to see that for any dimension D only the y_{2n} with $2n \leq D$ are different from zero and that the leading term of the expansion of y_{2n} around flat space, the term with n fields and 2n derivatives, is always a total derivative [5]. This cancellation of leading terms is crucial for y_4 in order to avoid ghosts, but for higher y_{2n}, which around flat space are interactions regardless of this leading cancellation, the significance is not clear. It is likely that a rationale can be found studying the expansion of these invariants around curved space, since around curved space the higher y's are not necessarily pure interactions (they can contribute to propagators).

Interactions such as the ones arising from y_4 illustrate the subtle but yet enormously important way in which string theories can differ from the field theories that arise in their zero slope limit.

References

[1] B. Zwiebach, Curvature Squared Terms and String Theories, UC Berkeley preprint UCB-PTH-85/10, Phys. Lett. B, to appear.

[2] J. Scherk, Nucl. Phys. B31 (1971) 222; N. Nakanishi, Prog. Theor. Phys. 48 (1972) 355.

[3] A. Neveu and J. Scherk, Nucl. Phys. B36 (1972) 155; J. L. Gervais and A. Neveu, Nucl. Phys. B46(1972) 381; J. Scherk and J. H. Schwarz, Nucl. Phys. B81 (1974) 118; M. B. Green, J. H. Schwarz and L. Brink, Nucl. Phys. B198 (1982) 474.

[4] P. Candelas, G. T. Horowitz, A. Strominger and E. Witten, St. Barbara NSF-ITP-84-170; D. Gross and E. Witten, to appear.

[5] B. Zumino, Gravity Theories in More than Four Dimensions, UC Berkeley preprint UCB-PTH-85/13.

SYMPOSIUM ON ANOMALIES, GEOMETRY, TOPOLOGY

COMPACTIFICATION

ANDREW STROMINGER

CHAIRMAN

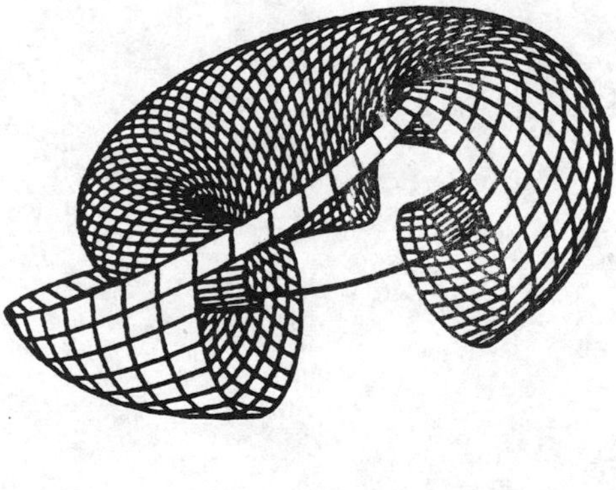

SUPERSTRING PHENOMENOLOGY*

P. Candelas
Center for Theoretical Physics
University of Texas, Austin TX 78712

Gary T. Horowitz
Department of Physics
University of California
Santa Barbara, California 93106

Andrew Strominger
The Institute for Advanced Study
Princeton, N.J. 08540

Edward Witten
Joseph Henry Laboratories
Princeton University
Princeton, N.J. 08544

ABSTRACT

We discuss some recent work on Kaluza-Klein compactifications of superstring theories and the resulting low energy phenomenology. The string theory approach to compactification is emphasized as opposed to the effective field theory approach. An attempt is made to keep the discussion non-technical.

A number of remarkable developments have recently taken place[1,2] in the theory of superstrings.[3] These new developments inspire optimism that superstrings provide both the first mathematically consistent quantum theory of gravity and the first truly unified theory of all forces and matter. The ultimate test of any physical theory, however, is not mathematical consistency, but confrontation with experiment. Historically, this confrontation has been crucial in the development as well as the testing of new theories. This has made the development of a quantum theory of gravity exceedingly difficult, since quantum gravitational effects are presumably only directly observable at 10^{19} GeV, and are thus beyond the reach of present day experiment.

A remarkable feature of superstring theories is that they should in principle lead to many low energy predictions. An attempt at exploring these predictions was made in ref. [4] and will be reviewed here. The basic reason predictions are possible is that it is very difficult to construct a consistent quantum theory of gravity, and those theories that have been found to survive the many consistency requirements have almost no freedom to adjust coupling constants,[5] alter the gauge group[1] or add or subtract particles.[3*] Thus, if the theory is correct, it must predict all the masses and couplings of the observed elementary particles!

Superstring theories appear to be consistent only if the dimension of spacetime is ten and the gauge group, if any, is $E_8 x E_8$ or SO(32). On the one hand these constraints are desirable in that they are precisely the type of restrictions

---

*However, some loss of predictive power could occur if the full quantum theory turns out to have degenerate vacua.

one would hope to arise in a truly unified theory. On the other hand, they are at first sight disappointing since we certainly do not observe ten dimensions or SO(32) or $E_8 x E_8$ gauge symmetries. Clearly, if these theories are to have some connection with nature we must find a way to reduce both the dimension of spacetime and the gauge group. The idea we are going to discuss is based on the modern incarnation[6] of the old Kaluza-Klein program that some of the spacelike dimensions are compactified and small enough to not be directly observable.

One can discuss compactifications either in terms of a low energy effective field theory determined from the string, or directly in terms of the string theory. Here we discuss only the latter approach. The reader is referred to reference [4] for an effective field theory approach which leads to equivalent conclusions. We will try to review the main results in a non-technical manner and ignore certain generalizations. For further details see reference [4].

As discussed by Green and Schwarz,[3] the superstring theory is a field theory with an infinite number of fields. Among these many fields is a massless spin two field. In view of general arguments,[7] this strongly suggests that superstrings must in a suitable approximation give rise to general relativity. In general relativistic field theories the geometry of spacetime is not fixed, and one can expand around curved backgrounds. One is thereby led to attempt an expansion of the superstring theory around backgrounds other than flat ten dimensional Minkowski space. Phenomenologically interesting backgrounds are of the form $M^4 x K$, where K is some small six dimensional space and M^4 is four dimensional Minkowski space.

It is not at all obvious that there exists a consistent expansion around such backgrounds. Indeed, a considerable effort was required to demonstrate the consistency of the superstring theory expanded around flat M^{10}. On a curved background, we begin with a generalization of the superstring action:

$$S = -\frac{1}{4\pi\alpha'}\int d\sigma d\tau \sqrt{-q}\,(q^{\alpha\beta} g_{\mu\nu}\partial_\alpha X^\mu \partial_\beta X^\nu + \text{superpartners})$$

$$\alpha, \beta = 0,1$$

$$\mu, \nu = 0,1,\ldots,9 \tag{1}$$

where we simply replace the flat metric $\eta_{\mu\nu}$ on M^{10} with the curved metric $g_{\mu\nu}(X)$ on $M^4 \times K$. $X^\mu(\sigma,\tau)$ is the location of the string world sheet in spacetime and $q_{\alpha\beta}$ is the world sheet metric. S contains no kinetic term for $q_{\alpha\beta}$, so one does not expect to treat $q_{\alpha\beta}$ as a dynamical variable of the theory. Instead, one attempts to solve for $q_{\alpha\beta}$ (up to gauge freedom) via its equation of motion

$$\frac{\delta S}{\delta q_{\alpha\beta}} = 0 \tag{2}$$

The theory described by equation (1) can be viewed as a two dimensional supersymmetric non-linear σ-model with dynamical fields $X^\mu(\sigma,\tau)$ (plus fermions) and internal space $M^4 \times K$. Equation (2) requires the stress energy tensor $T_{\alpha\beta}$ of this two dimensional field theory to vanish. Classically, this can always be achieved. However, quantum mechanically, (2) becomes an operator equation. The trace of this equation takes the form:

$$T^\alpha_{\ \alpha} = aR + \beta_{\mu\nu}\partial_\alpha X^\mu \partial_\beta X^\nu q^{\alpha\beta} + \text{superpartner} \tag{3}$$

where R is the scalar curvature of the metric $q_{\alpha\beta}$, a is a coefficient depending on the dimension of spacetime and $\beta_{\mu\nu}$ is the β-"function" associated with the spacetime metric. If this trace does not vanish, then the equation of motion (2) for $q_{\alpha\beta}$ cannot be imposed and additional dynamics must be introduced for $q_{\alpha\beta}$.[8] Whether or not this can be done in a consistent fashion remains an open question. Even if it can, however, the resulting "Polyakov" string theory probably does not contain massless particles and is therefore not relevant as a theory of the fundamental interactions.

Fortunately, there are special cases in which $T^{\alpha}_{\ \alpha} = 0$. This condition is related to a local scale invariance of the two dimensional σ model. Classically, S is invariant under the transformations:

$$x^{\mu} \to x^{\mu}$$
$$q_{\alpha\beta} \to \Omega^2 q_{\alpha\beta} \tag{4}$$

which implies $T^{\alpha}_{\ \alpha} = 0$. However in the quantum theory, ultraviolet regulators usually destroy this scale invariance. For finite theories, however, this is not the case. Supersymmetric non-linear σ models on a flat two dimensional world sheet are known to be finite (assuming the existence of appropriate regulators) for Ricci flat internal spaces and N=2 or N=4 supersymmetry, and are believed to be finite for Ricci flat spaces and N=1 supersymmetry.[9] Scale invariance on a curved world sheet requires in addition that the dimension of spacetime be the critical dimension 10. Thus Ricci flatness of the internal space $M^4 \times K$ is, in the present framework, essential for consistent superstring compactifications.[10]

Of particular interest is the heterotic superstring,[2] because it probably has the best phenomenology (and because its hard to believe that nature declined such a good opportunity to base itself on exceptional groups). Recall that in this theory the fields are divided into left moving and right moving modes on the world sheet. In the fermionic representation there is a right moving anticommuting ten dimensional Majorana-Weyl spinor S, and 32 left moving anticommuting two dimensional Majorana-Weyl spinors ψ^m m=1,···, 32 which are spacetime scalars. For the SO(32) superstring, ψ^m is in the fundamental representation of the group, while for $E_8 \times E_8$ the situation is more complicated.[2] The presence of gauge interactions in this theory suggests that one should be able to expand about a background configuration that has a non-zero Yang-Mills field as well as non-zero curvature. In this case, the light cone action for the heterotic superstring becomes:[2,11]

$$S^H_{LC} = -\frac{1}{4\pi\alpha'}\int d\sigma d\tau(\partial_\alpha X^i\partial^\alpha X^j g_{ij} + i\bar{S}\gamma^-\mathcal{D}_+S$$

$$+ \psi^m\mathcal{D}_-\psi^m + F^A{}_{ij}\bar{S}\gamma^-\gamma^i\gamma^j S T^A{}_{mn}\psi^m\psi^n) \qquad (5)$$

where $i,j = 1,\ldots,8$ run only over the transverse space $R^2 \times K$ and S obeys the light cone condition $\gamma^+S = 0$. $F^A{}_{ij}$ is the SO(32) or $E_8 \times E_8$ background Yang-Mills field, and $T^A{}_{mn}$ the appropriate generators. $\mathcal{D}_\pm$ is a covariant derivative with respect to both the background gauge and spin connections. It acts on the left movers as $\mathcal{D}_-\psi = \partial_-\psi + (\partial_-X^j)A_j\psi$ (with $\partial_\pm = \frac{\partial}{\partial\tau} \pm \frac{\partial}{\partial\sigma}$) and on the right movers as $\mathcal{D}_+S = \partial_+S + (\partial_+X^j)\omega_j S$. It is related to the spacetime gauge covariant derivative $\mathcal{D}_j$ by $\mathcal{D}_\pm = (\partial_\pm X^j)\mathcal{D}_j$.

The heterotic superstring corresponds to an $N = \frac{1}{2}$ supersymmetric non-linear σ model, as the supersymmetry acts on the right movers only. In general this is insufficient to insure that the σ model trace anomaly vanishes, even on a Ricci flat background. However, if you set the background gauge field A_i equal to the spin connection ω_i then a remarkable thing happens. Since ω_i must take values in a subgroup of SO(8) rather than SO(32) or $E_8 \times E_8$, many of the ψ's decouple from the gauge field and just satisfy a free Dirac equation. Their contribution to the trace anomaly will be cancelled by ghosts just as in the expansion about flat space without background gauge fields. The remaining ψ's now enter symmetrically with the components of the spinor S, and one recovers a left right symmetry in this sector of the theory. An N=1 (at least) world sheet supersymmetry then results* and the trace anomaly will vanish if the geometry is Ricci flat.

---

*Actually, the N=1 world sheet supersymmetry will not be obvious in the form of the action (5) unless the geometry is not only Ricci flat but Kähler. Otherwise the supersymmetry is apparent in the Ramond Neveu-Schwarz formulation of this theory. See Reference [11] for details.

Another consistency requirement is the absence of anomalies in the four dimensional Lorentz algebra. In particular, there are potential anomalies in the commutator $[M^{i-},M^{j-}]$ associated with the value of the two point function of T_{++} in the σ model. In the critical dimension, for background geometries $M^4 \times K$, this anomaly has been shown not to arise in lowest non-trivial order when K is Ricci-flat,[11] and presumably does not arise at higher orders either.

So far we have found that if one looks for a string state that can be described just by a background geometry, and assumes the relevant conditions are obeyed for all values of the sigma model coupling, then consistency forces the background geometry to be Ricci flat, and the background gauge connection A to equal the background spin connection ω. Have we found all the consistency requirements? Hopefully the answer is no, because these constraints do not uniquely determine a background configuration. Further consistency requirements might be useful in narrowing the range of potential vacuum configurations for the superstring theory.

We have argued that (modulo the above comments) one can construct a consistent first quantized string theory on Ricci flat manifolds with $A = \omega$, but it remains to be shown that such backgrounds provide solutions to the full superstring theory. What is meant by this statement is that the vacuum expectation values of all tadpoles vanish. In a scalar field theory with potential $V(\varphi) = \varphi$, for example, setting the background scalar field to zero is not the semiclassical approximation to a solution of the theory because the tadpole $\langle 0|\varphi|0\rangle$ does not vanish. The superstring theory is a field theory with an infinite number of fields, so one similarly requires that $\langle 0|\Phi|0\rangle = 0$, where Φ is any operator that creates a tadpole.

There is a simple argument which shows that to all orders in the σ-model, but tree level in the string theory, all the tadpoles vanish for the background configurations we have discussed. Consider, for example, the operator

$\Phi_D = q^{\alpha\beta} g_{ij} \partial_\alpha X^i \partial_\beta X^j$, which creates a scalar dilaton field. For backgrounds with no trace anomaly, this operator scales as $\Phi_D \to \Omega^{-2} \Phi_D$ under the two dimensional scale transformations (4). However, since the world sheet in tree level string calculations can (after stereographic projection) be taken to be a plane which is invariant under these transformations, the expectation value $\langle 0 | \Phi_D | 0 \rangle$ must vanish. Similar arguments can be made for the other tadpoles.

Having shown that Ricci flat manifolds with $A = \omega$ provide solutions of the superstring theory at tree level, one still needs to check their classical stability before they can be called vacuum solutions.[12] A general argument for perturbative stability can be made in the special case where the resulting theory has N=1 spacetime supersymmetry (as distinct from world sheet supersymmetry). This may also be the most phenomenologically interesting case, since without spacetime supersymmetry at the compactification scale there is likely to be a serious hierarchy problem. With N=1 spacetime supersymmetry, the Hamiltonian for perturbations around the supersymmetric background can be written $H = Q^+ Q$, where Q is the supercharge operator for spacetime supersymmetry. In light cone gauge the absence of ghosts is manifest, so H acts on a positive norm Hilbert space and its expectation value in any state is therefore non-negative. This ensures perturbative vacuum stability.

What is the condition for N=1 spacetime supersymmetry? In flat space, the action (5) is invariant under the supersymmetry transformations[2,3]

$$\delta_\epsilon X^i = (p^+)^{-1/2} \bar{\epsilon} \gamma^i S$$

$$\delta_\epsilon S = i(p^+)^{-1/2} \gamma_- \gamma_\mu (\partial_- X^\mu) \epsilon \qquad (6)$$

where $\mu = 0, \cdots, 9$ and ϵ is a right moving ten dimensional Majorana-Weyl spinor.

The commutator of two supersymmetry transformations is a translation:

$$[\delta_1, \delta_2]\, X^i = \xi^- \partial_- X^i + a^i$$
$$[\delta_1, \delta_2]\, S = \xi^- \partial_- S$$

where

$$\xi^- = -\frac{2i}{p^+}\bar{\epsilon}^{(1)}\gamma_-\epsilon^{(2)}$$
$$a^i = -2i\bar{\epsilon}^{(1)}\gamma^i\epsilon^{(2)} \,. \qquad (7)$$

A curved background admits spacetime supersymmetry if there exists supersymmetries parameterized by $\epsilon^{(1)}$ and $\epsilon^{(2)}$ such that a^i is any spatial translation of the transverse $R^2 X K$. (Four dimensional Lorentz invariance then insures the full four dimensional Poincare supersymmetry.)

Unlike S, ϵ need not obey the light cone condition $\gamma^+ S = 0$. There are correspondingly two types of supersymmetry transformations characterized by $\gamma^+\epsilon_+ = 0$ and $\gamma^-\epsilon_- = 0$ of positive and negative "transverse chirality." If $\epsilon^{(1)}$ and $\epsilon^{(2)}$ have the same transverse chirality then a^i can be easily seen to vanish. Both types of world sheet supersymmetries are thus necessary to ensure spacetime supersymmetry. The transformation laws for ϵ_+ are particularly simple:

$$\delta X^i = 0$$
$$\delta S = -2i\sqrt{p^+}\,\epsilon_+ \qquad (8)$$

The action (5) will be invariant under this transformation if ϵ_+ is a covariantly constant spinor on the transverse space.* This follows since the first and third term in (5) are trivially invariant, and the second term gives a total derivative when $\mathcal{D}_+\epsilon_+ = 0$. The last term also vanishes because when $A = \omega$,

* More precisely, ϵ_+ is the restriction to the world sheet of a covariantly constant spinor on $\mathbb{R}^2 \times K$.

the gauge and metric curvatures are also equal and $F^A_{ij}\gamma^i\gamma^j\epsilon_+ = 0$ is just the integrability condition for $\mathcal{D}_j\epsilon_+ = 0$. Under these conditions there are always ϵ_- supersymmetries as well since these are just the usual supersymmetries of the non-linear σ model.

Thus we have learned that N=1 (or greater) spacetime supersymmetry follows from the existence of a covariantly constant spinor on the internal manifold K. This restriction can be understood in terms of a group known as the holonomy group of K. If a spinor (or vector) is parallel transported around a closed loop in K, it will undergo some O(6) rotation. The group of all rotations that can be generated in this way is the holonomy group. For example, the holonomy group of flat space is trivial while the holonomy group of the standard metric connection on the six sphere is O(6). The existence of a covariantly constant spinor says that the holonomy group of K cannot be the full O(6) since there is at least one spinor that is not rotated under parallel transport. In fact it implies that the holonomy group is at most an SU(3) subgroup of O(6). (We are interested in the case where it is precisely SU(3), otherwise the manifold K must have zero Euler number which we will soon see leads to severe problems with phenomenology.) A manifold with U(3) (or smaller) holonomy is known as a complex Kähler manifold.

The requirement that K be a three complex dimensional Ricci flat Kähler manifold is quite a restrictive one. To better understand the nature of this restriction, we consider the requirements on K individually. Recall that a six dimensional real manifold can be viewed as patches of $\mathbb{R}^6$ which are "glued together" at the edges by identifying points of one patch with those of another in a smooth (i.e. C^∞) manner. Similarly, a three dimensional complex manifold can be viewed as patches of $\mathbb{C}^3$ glued together in a holomorphic i.e. complex analytic manner. Since holomorphic functions are always smooth, it is clear that every complex three manifold can be viewed as a real six manifold.

However, the converse is not always the case. For example, although it is not obvious, the familiar manifolds S^6 and $S^2 x S^4$ cannot be viewed as complex manifolds, although $S^3 x S^3$ and $S^1 x S^5$ can.

To understand the Kähler condition we must discuss the metric. The analog of a positive definite metric for a real manifold is a hermitian metric for a complex manifold. Given a hermitian metric one can define a unique (torsion free, metric compatible) covariant derivative. Now consider a vector V such that for any function f depending only on the complex coordinates $\bar{z}^i$ and not on z^i we have

$$V^i \nabla_i f = 0 \quad (9)$$

Such a vector is called holomorphic. In most cases, if one starts with a holomorphic vector and parallel transports it along a curve, then the vector will not remain holomorphic. However, there are special metrics for which this difficulty doesn't occur, namely those with U(3) holonomy. These special metrics are called <u>Kähler</u>. Not every complex manifold admits a Kähler metric. For example, no metric on $S^3 x S^3$ or $S^1 x S^5$ can be Kähler, although $S^2 x S^2 x S^2$ does admit Kähler metrics. One can view a Kähler manifold as the nicest type of complex manifold in that the metric structure and the complex structure are compatible in the above sense.

Having restricted ourselves from arbitrary Riemannian six manifolds to complex manifolds to Kähler manifolds, there remains one final restriction - our space must be Ricci flat. In general there is a topological obstruction to finding a Ricci flat metric on a Kähler manifold. This is known as the first Chern class. For example, in two dimensions, the first Chern class is related to the Euler number. In this case it is well known that the only compact two manifold which admits a Ricci flat metric is the one with zero Euler number i.e. the torus. Calabi conjectured that in higher dimensions the first

Chern class was the only obstruction and that if it vanishes a Ricci flat metric always exists.[13] Calabi's conjecture was proved twenty years later by Yau.[14] This result is of great significance to us for the following reason. Whereas Ricci flat Kähler metrics are in general quite complicated, Kähler manifolds with vanishing first Chern class can be constructed quite easily - as we now indicate. We call such manifolds Calabi-Yau manifolds (if their Euler number is non-zero) although it should be noted that the theorems proved by these mathematicians are really more general than we consider here.

Perhaps the simplest example of a Calabi-Yau manifold is the following. Start with $\mathbb{C}^5$ with coordinates $(z_1,\ldots z_5)$ and consider the subspace satisfying

$$\sum_{i=1}^{5} z_i^5 = 0. \qquad (10)$$

This is a four dimensional complex manifold. Notice that if (z_i) is a solution so is $\lambda(z_i)$. Now identify each non-zero solution (z_i) with $\lambda(z_i)$ for all complex $\lambda \neq 0$. Let Y_0 denote the resulting three complex dimensional manifold. One can show that Y_0 has vanishing first Chern class and hence admits a Ricci flat Kähler metric. Although this space is simple to construct, its topology is surprisingly complicated. For example, it turns out that the Euler number χ of Y_0 is -200. Therefore every vector field on this space must vanish in at least 200 points!*

Many other examples of Ricci flat Kähler spaces can be constructed.[15,16] However, its important to note that although there are an infinite number of complex three manifolds that admit Kähler metrics, it is likely that only a <u>finite</u> number of these admit Ricci flat Kähler metrics.[15]

---

*Strictly speaking, this statement is only true for vector fields whose zeros are non-degenerate.

Having found a vacuum configuration of the superstring theory, we can now extract the low energy effective field theory. Recall that the gauge connection was assumed to acquire an expectation value equal to that of the spin connection, which is valued in SU(3) (because K has SU(3) holonomy). For the heterotic superstring with an $E_8 x E_8$ gauge field this breaks the gauge group down to $E_8 x E_6$. The theory contains fermions (gluinos) in the adjoint representation. The adjoint (248) of E_8 decomposes as $(1,78)\oplus(3,27)\oplus(\overline{3},\overline{27})\oplus(8,1)$ under $SU(3) x E_6$.

Let n^L_{27} and n^R_{27} be the number of left and right handed massless fermion multiplets in four dimensions transforming as a 27 under E_6, and let $N = n^L_{27} - n^R_{27}$. Since the difference between left and right is just a matter of definition, the number of generations is $|N|$. Because the fundamental theory contains ten dimensional Weyl fermions massless chiral fermions on M^4 are associated, in the usual way, with chiral zero modes of the Dirac operator on K. Fermions transforming in the 27 of E_6 also transform in the 3 of SU(3). Hence $N = n^L_{27} - n^R_{27}$ is just the index of the (gauge coupled) Dirac operator on K acting on spinors in the 3 representation of SU(3). Now since the SU(3) Yang-Mills potential is equal to the spin connection, this index can depend only on the geometry of K. But the index is a topological invariant. Hence, it can depend only on the topology of K. In fact it turns out that N is simply one half the Euler number χ of K. So the number of generations is $|N| = \frac{1}{2} |\chi(K)|$.

This is a solution of the long-standing chiral fermion problem in Kaluza-Klein theories.[17] To our knowledge there is no previous case of a supersymmetric Kaluza-Klein compactification that produced a chiral spectrum of fermions. In the present case, not only are chiral fermions naturally obtained, but they are in the correct representation (27) of of a realistic grand unified group E_6.[18] It is remarkable that superstring theory, which was developed to solve the problem of quantum gravity, also solves the chiral fermion problem.

Returning now to the manifold Y_0, we see that this particular example would predict 100 families, which is considerably more than we need and in serious conflict with cosmology (among other things). Fortunately, there is a general procedure for constructing a new Calabi-Yau manifold from an old one such that the absolute value of the Euler number is reduced. This procedure is applicable whenever there exists a group of discrete symmetries that leave no point fixed (except, of course, for the identity which leaves every point fixed). A simple example of this is provided by S^2, which has a Z_2 symmetry that maps each point to the antipodal point. If we identify points related by this Z_2 we obtain a new manifold $\frac{S^2}{Z_2} = RP^2$. Roughly speaking RP^2 is "half as big" as S^2, and has half the Euler number. This can be easily seen by using the formula for the Euler number expressed as an integral of the curvature. In general, if the discrete group has n elements the new Euler number will be $\frac{1}{n}$ times the old one.

For the manifold Y_0, consider the group generated by

$$\begin{aligned} A&: (z_1,z_2,z_3,z_4,z_5) = (z_5,z_1,z_2,z_3,z_4) \\ B&: (z_1,z_2,z_3,z_4,z_5) = (\alpha z_1, \alpha^2 z_2, \alpha^3 z_3, \alpha^4 z_4, z_5) \end{aligned} \tag{11}$$

where $\alpha \equiv e^{2\pi i/5}$. It is clear that A and B each take solutions of (10) into solutions and hence are symmetries of Y_0. It is also clear that $A^5 = B^5 =$ identity so that the group of symmetries generated by A and B is $Z_5 x Z_5$. Somewhat less clear but not hard to verify is that no element of this group has fixed points except for the identity. It is this last requirement which rules out more general symmetries such as non-cyclic permutations and multiplying the z_i with powers of α other than those given by powers of B. By identifying points related by this symmetry group, we obtain a new Ricci flat Kähler manifold $Y = Y_0/Z_5 x Z_5$ with Euler number

$$\chi(Y) = \chi(Y_0)/25 = -8 \qquad (12)$$

(Unlike RP^2, Y is still orientable.) So the superstring theory formulated on Y predicts four generations. Other Calabi-Yau manifolds have been found that predict one, two, three or four generations.[15,16]

So far we have seen that the superstring theory can produce a reasonable number of generations of quarks and leptons in the required representation of a realistic grand unified group. However there are at least two more ingredients that are essential for a realistic E_6 theory: mechanisms for breaking E_6 down to a baryon number conserving group at the GUT scale and for Weinberg-Salam symmetry breaking.[18] The Higgs fields responsible for the latter can be found in the superpartners of the quarks and leptons. The former occurs in a fashion unique to Kaluza-Klein theories, as we now explain.

Quotient spaces such as $Y_0/Z_5 x Z_5$ or S^2/Z_2 are not simply connected. Consider for example the line on the two sphere extending from the north to south pole. On S^2/Z_2 this line becomes a non-contractible loop. However if we go twice around this loop on S^2/Z_2, it can be obtained from a closed loop on S^2 which is contractible (i.e. $\Pi_1(S^2/Z_2) = Z_2$). Similarly Y has loops which are contractible after transversing five times. Now consider the expectation value:

$$U = \langle \exp(i\oint_\Gamma A_m dx^m) \rangle \qquad (13)$$

where A_m lies in an Abelian subgroup of E_6 and Γ is a non-contractible loop. U is then an element of E_6. In general U can acquire an expectation value even if the E_6 field strength vanishes.[19] However if we wrap five times around Γ Stokes theorem can then be used to relate the path ordered exponential to the integral of the curvature over a two surface spanning the loop. Since the E_6 field strength vanishes for vacuum configurations, this implies $U^5 = 1$.

An expectation value for U breaks the E_6 gauge symmetry. Fermion zero modes that are not neutral under U acquire masses, as do gauge fields that do not commute with U. Thus the effects of U resemble in this respect those of a Higgs field in the adjoint representation. This is precisely what is required for GUT symmetry breaking, and allows one to break E_6 down to, for example, $SU(3)xSU(2)xU(1)^3$.

Having obtained these initial successes, one should now proceed to compute particle lifetimes, masses and coupling constants. These quantities turn out to depend on more refined topological properties of the internal manifold K.[16,20] For the Y manifold discussed in this paper there is a serious problem with rapid proton decay.[5,21] There might be a Calabi-Yau manifold with appropriate topological properties for which such difficulties are absent. Another problem is supersymmetry breaking.[12] At present no phenomenologically viable mechanism has been found. Finally, assuming a Calabi-Yau manifold is found that has all the right properties, one would like to understand why superstring theory prefers this one over any other. Or, indeed, why is four spacetime dimensions preferred at all?

These are serious problems and certainly worthy of attention. However, it is an unprecedented and exciting state of affairs that we are judging a potential unification of quantum mechanics and gravity on the basis of low energy phenomenology.

Acknowledgments

We are grateful to E. Martinec for useful conversations. This work was supported in part by NSF grants PHY80-19754, PHY81-07384, and PHY82-05717.

REFERENCES

1. M.B. Green and J.H. Schwarz, Phys. Lett. 149B (1984) 117.
2. D.J. Gross, J.A. Harvey, E. Martinec and R. Rohm, Phys. Rev. Lett. 54 (1985) 502 and Princeton preprints.
3. M.B. Green and J.H. Schwarz, Nucl. Phys. B181 (1981) 502, B198 (1982) 252, B198 (1982) 441; Phys. Lett. 109B (1982) 444; M.B. Green, J.H. Schwarz, and L. Brink, Nucl. Phys. B198 (1982) 474.
4. P. Candelas, G.T. Horowitz, A. Strominger and E. Witten, to appear in Nucl. Phys. B. (1985).
5. E. Witten, Phys. Lett. 149B (1984) 351.
6. J. Scherk and J.H. Schwarz, Phys. Lett. 57B (1975) 463; E. Cremmer and J. Scherk, Nucl. Phys. B103 (1976) 399.
7. R.P. Feynman, Proc. Chapel Hill Conference (1957), S. Weinberg, Phys. Rev. D138 (1965) 988, S. Deser, Gen. Relativity and Grav. 1 (1970) 9.
8. A.M. Polyakov, Phys. Lett. 103B (1981) 207, 211.
9. D.Z. Freedman and P.K. Townsend, Nucl. Phys. B177 (1981) 443; L. Alvarez-Gaumé and D.Z. Freedman, Phys. Rev. D22 (1980) 846; Commun. Math. Phys. 80 (1981) 282; A. Ya. Morozov, A.M. Perelmov and M.A. Shifman, ITEP preprint; C.M. Hull unpublished; L. Alvarez-Gaumé and P. Ginsparg, in proceedings of the Argonne Symposium on Anomalies, Geometry and Topology.
10. This point was independently made by D. Friedan and S. Shanker, unpublished talk given at the Aspen Summer Institute (1984). See also E. Witten, Comm. Math. Phys. 92 (1984) 455 and C. Lovelace, Phys. Lett. 135B (1984) 75.
11. C. Callan, D. Friedan, E. Martinec and M. Perry, Princeton preprint (1985).
12. Whether or not they remain solutions at the quantum level is of course an important and non trivial question that we do not address here. See M. Dine, R. Rohm, N. Seiberg and E. Witten, to appear Phys. Lett. B (1985), M. Dine and N. Seiberg, IAS preprint (1985), and V. Kaplunovsky, to appear.

13. E. Calabi, in Algebraic Geometry and Topology: A symposium in Honor of S. Lefschetz (Princeton University Press, 1957) p. 78.
14. S.-T. Yau, Proc. Natl. Acad. Sci. 74 (1977) 1798.
15. S.-T. Yau in proceedings of the Argonne Symposium on Anomalies, Geometry and Topology.
16. A. Strominger and E. Witten, to appear in Comm. Math. Phys.
17. E. Witten, Nucl. Phys. B186 (1981) 412. Work on this problem can be found in G. Chapline and R. Slansky, Nucl. Phys. B209 (1982) 461; C. Wetterich, Nucl. Phys. B223 (1983) 109; S. Randjbar-Daemi, A. Salam and S. Strathdee, Nucl. Phys. B214 (1983) 491; E. Witten to appear in the Proceedings of the 1983 Shelter Island II Conference (MIT press, 1985); D. Olive and P. West, Nucl. Phys. B217 (1983) 248; G. Chapline and B. Grossman, Phys. Lett. 125B (1984) 109; P.H. Frampton and K. Yamamoto, Phys. Rev. Lett. 125B (1984) 109; S. Weinberg, Phys. Lett. 138B (1984) 47; P.H. Frampton and T.W. Kephardt, Phys. Rev. Lett. 53 (1984) 867; I.G. Koh and H. Nishino, Trieste preprint ICTP/84/129.
18. F. Gürsey, P. Ramond and P. Sikivie, Phys. Lett. 60B (1976) 177; F. Gürsey and P. Sikivie, Phys. Rev. Lett. 36 (1976) 775; P. Ramond, Nucl. Phys. B110 (1976) 214.
19. Y. Hosotani, Phys. Lett. 129B (1983) 193.
20. E. Witten, to appear Nucl. Phys. B.
21. M. Dine, V. Kaplunovsky, C. Nappi, M. Mangano and N. Seiberg, Princeton preprint (1985).

Compact Three Dimensional Kähler Manifolds with Zero Ricci Curvature

by Shing-Tung Yau
Department of Mathematics, U.C. San Diego

In memory of my sister Shing Wu and my brother Shing Yuk. Both of them gave their strongest support at the early stage of my career while they were struggling for their own life.

In this article, we review the construction of compact manifolds with zero Ricci curvature. In the appendix, we construct three examples of such manifolds with Euler number equal to -6. It is a joint work with my student Tian. The problem of constructing a compact manifold with zero Ricci curvature which is not flat was one of the major problems in differential geometry. In fact, S. Bochner told the author that ever since he discovered his famous vanishing theorem in the forties, he always wondered about the existence of such manifolds. His student Calabi was motivated by his question to look for such manifolds. Calabi noticed that the simplicity of the Ricci tensor in Kähler geometry should be exploited. The vanishing of the Ricci tensor implies the vanishing of the first Chern class of the manifold. He boldly put forth the conjecture that the converse is true. This involves solving non-linear elliptic equations on manifolds. For quite a long time very few geometers believed this conjecture until 1976, the author ([10], [11]) demonstrated the solvability of the equation. While it is still not known how to write the metric in a closed form, one should certainly be able to obtain information by numerical methods.

The first significant result on Ricci flat manifolds was a corollary of the theorem of Gromoll-Meyer [3] which says that every compact Ricci flat manifold is the quotient of $R^k \times M^{n-k}$ by a discrete group of isometrics which act on the product without fixed points. Here R^k is the euclidean space and M^{n-k} is a compact simply connected manifold with zero Ricci curvature.

This corollary shows that "basic" compact manifolds with zero Ricci curvature are those with finite fundamental group. For compact four dimensional manifolds, the only known example of such manifolds are the K-3 surfaces and their quotients (see [10]). It can be proved (see [4]) that if a compact simply connected four dimensional spin manifold with non-zero index admits a metric with zero scalar curvature, then the manifold is the K-3 surface and the metric is Kähler with zero Ricci curvature. It also follows from the above theorem of Gromoll-Meyer that a compact six dimensional Ricci flat manifold with nonzero Euler number must have finite fundamental group.

There had been a lot of efforts in attempting to exhibit Ricci flat metrics on the K-3 surfaces in a closed form. Calabi [1] wrote down a lot of complete Kähler metrics with zero Ricci curvature on non-compact manifolds. This includes the Eguchi-Hanson metric studied by physicists. For a survey of what was known by physicists one can consult [6]. It should be pointed out that we do not even know whether S^4 admits a Ricci flat metric or not.

For the rest of this paper, we shall discuss the construction of compact Ricci flat Kähler manifolds. As was mentioned above, the problem is reduced to constructing compact Kähler manifolds with zero first Chern class. (Throughout this paper cohomology class is taken with real coefficient). Hence we are looking for compact Kähler manifolds which support a volume form $(\sqrt{-1})^n\, V\, dz^1 \wedge \cdots \wedge dz^n \wedge d\bar{z}^1 \wedge \cdots \wedge d\bar{z}^n$ with the property $\frac{\partial^2 \log V}{\partial z^i \partial \bar{z}^j} = 0$. Such a volume form will exist if one can find a holomorphic n-form $h\, dz^1 \wedge \cdots \wedge dz^n$ with $h \neq 0$ because $(\sqrt{-1})^n |h|^2\, dz^1 \wedge \cdots \wedge dz^n \wedge d\bar{z}^1 \wedge \cdots \wedge d\bar{z}^n$ will be such a volume form.

One way to construct a non-zero holomorphic n-form is as follows. First one constructs a meromorphic n-form $\tilde{h}\, dz^1 \wedge \cdots \wedge dz^n \wedge d\bar{z}^1 \wedge \cdots \wedge d\bar{z}^n$. Let D_o (and D_∞) be the complex subvariety defined by the zeroes (and poles respectively) of $\tilde{h}$, counting multiplicity. Then $(D_0) - (D_\infty)$ is called the canonical divisor of $\tilde{h}$. If such a divisor is linearly equivalent to zero, i.e., if one finds a meromorphic function f whose zero divisor is D_o and polar divisor is D_∞ , then $f^{-1}\, \tilde{h}\, dz^1 \wedge \cdots \wedge dz^n$ is a non-zero holomorphic n-form.

Let us now describe the ways of constructing manifolds with zero first Chern class.

(1) The complex torus has of course zero first Chern class.

(2) Let M be a compact Kähler manifold and V be a holomorphic vector bundle over M such that $C_1(V) = C_1(M)$. Then if V admits a holomorphic section S which is transversal to the zero section of V, the zero set of S is a complex submanifold of M with zero first Chern class. A useful special case is the following. Let V be the direct sum of holomorphic line bundles $L_1, \ldots, L_k$ so that each L_i non-singular admits a holomorphic section S_i and the non-singular submanifolds $S_i = 0$ are in general position. Then the submanifold defined by $S_1 = 0, S_2 = 0, \ldots, S_k = 0$ is a nonsingular submanifold N with $C_1 = 0$ if $C_1(M) = \sum_i C_1(L_i)$. In case the manifold N is three dimensional, its Euler number is given by the evaluation of the cohomology class $C_3(M) - C_2(M) \cup C_1(M) + \frac{C_1^3(M)}{3} - \frac{1}{3} \sum_i C_1(L_i)^3$ on the

homology class N. Three special cases will be discussed in the following.

(i) When M is $\mathbb{C}P^n$ and $\{S_i = 0\}$ are hypersurfaces defined by polynomials with degree n_i, the condition is $\sum_i n_i = n+1$ and the Euler number is

$$\left(\frac{(n+1)n(n-1)}{3} - \frac{(n+1)^2 n}{2} + \frac{(n+1)^3 n}{3} - \frac{1}{3}\sum_i n_i^3 \right) n_1 \cdots n_k$$

(ii) When M is $M_1 \times \mathbb{C}P^1$ where M_1 is a three dimensional manifold with very ample anticanonical line bundle, we can take the non-singular hypersurface N of M to be a hyperplane section of M if M is embedded into a higher dimensional projective space by the anticanonical line bundle. The first Chern class of N is zero and its Euler number is

$$2\, C_3(M_1) - 2\, C_1(M_1)^3 - 48$$

If M_1 is $\mathbb{C}P^3$, the Euler number of N is -168. There are many choices of M_1 (see [5], [7]).

(iii) When $M = M_1 \times M_2$ where M_i are two dimensional complex surfaces with very ample anticanonical line bundle, we can take a generic hyperplane section of the embedding of M by the anticanonical line bundle. The resulting manifold has zero first Chern class and its Euler number is $-2C_1^2(M_1)\, C_1^2(M_2)$. Note that if M_i are cubic hypersurface in $\mathbb{C}P^3$, this number is -18.

(iv) In (i) (ii) and (iii), we take one hyperplane section of the manifold M. We can of course take two hyperplane sections also. For example, in $\mathbb{C}P^3 \times \mathbb{C}P^2$, one can take the complete intersection of two hypersurfaces, one of bidegree (1, 2) and the other of bidegree (3, 1). Bidegree (1, 2) means that it is defined by a polynomial which is of degree one restricted to $\mathbb{C}P^3$ and of degree two restricted to $\mathbb{C}P^2$. One can also take the cubic hypersurface M in $\mathbb{C}P^4$ and let Σ be a surface which admits two embeddings by two line bundles L_1 and L_2 into the projective space so that $C_1(L_1) + C_1(L_2) = C_1(\Sigma)$. Then for each embedding by L_i, we can take a hypersurface N_i of $M \times \Sigma$ by intersecting $M \times \Sigma$ with a hypersurface of bidegree (1, 1) in the product projective space. We can assume N_1 intersects N_2 transversally. The Euler number of $N_1 \cap N_2$ is

$$-6\,[C_1^2(\Sigma) + 3C_1(L_1)C_1(L_2)]$$

(v) Some of the natural space may have singularities. For example, the weighted projective space which is the quotient of $\mathbb{C}^{n+1} - \{0\}$ by an action $[z_0, z_1, \ldots, z_n] \to [t^{i_0}z_0, t^{i_1}z_1, t^{i_2}z_2, \cdots t^{i_n}z_n]$ with $t \neq 0$. We can take a submanifold of such spaces as long as it avoids the singularities. As in the case of $\mathbb{C}P^n$, we can take complete intersection of hypersurfaces in the orbit space which are defined by homogeneous polynomials with each variable z_k counted with weight i_k. If these polynominals have degree a_j and $\sum_j a_j = \sum_{k=0}^{n} i_k$, we obtain manifolds with zero first Chern class as long as it avoids the singularities. If the dimension of the complete intersection is m, then its Euler number is the m-th coefficient of the formed power series. $\pi_k (1 + i_k x)\, \pi_k (1 + a_k x)^{-1}$ multiplied with $\pi\, a_k(\pi\, i_k)^{-1}$. For example, let $i_0 = i_1 = i_2 = i_3 = 1$, $i_4 = 2$ and $a = 6$. Then we can find such manifold with Euler number -204.

(3) Let M be a compact three dimensional complex variety with codimension $\geqslant 2$ singularities. Let M' denote the nonsingular part of M. Suppose that there exists a volume element on M' with zero Ricci curvature. Let U be a neighborhood of $M \backslash M'$ so that for some complex manifold $\tilde{U}$ with zero first Chern class, we can find a proper holomorphic map $\pi : \tilde{U} \to U$ which is one to one on $\pi^{-1}(U \cap M')$. Let $\hat{M}$ be the complex manifold obtained from M by replacing U by $\tilde{U}$. Then $\hat{M}$ has zero first Chern class.

One way to obtain singularity which can be resolved to manifolds with zero first Chern class is to multiply vectors in $\mathbb{C}^n$ by the n-th root of unity. This gives rise to an action of the cyclic group Z_n. The quotient manifold $\mathbb{C}^n/Z_n$ has an isolated singularity. By blowing up once, one obtains a manifold with zero first Chern class. This construction can be done fiberwise on a holomorphic vector bundle.

The group action mentioned above has the property that the singularity can be resolved by a single blowing up. There can be more complicated singularities. For example, we can have a cyclic group Z_n acting on $\mathbb{C}^2$ so that after resolving the singularity of $\mathbb{C}^2/Z_n$ by blowing up several times, one obtains a manifold with zero first Chern class. This action has the form $(z_1, z_2) \to (\omega z_1, \omega^{-1} z_2)$ where ω is the n-th root of unity.

(i) Let M be a three dimensional compact Kähler manifold with zero first Chern class. Let G be a finite group of biholomorphic transformations acting on M so that for some finite number of points $\{p_1, \ldots, p_m\}$ and finite number of disjoint non-singular holomorphic curves $\{C_1, \ldots, C_\ell\}$, the group G acts freely on the set $M \backslash \{p_1, \ldots, p_m\} \backslash \{C_1, \ldots, C_\ell\}$. Suppose that for all i, the group $\{g \mid g(p_i) = p_i\}$ acts in a neighborhood of p_i by scalar multiplication by the cubic root of unity. Let $G_i = \{g \mid g(C_i) \subset C_i\}$ and G'_i be the subgroup that fixes C_i pointwise. Suppose that G_i/G'_i acts freely on C_i and G'_i acts as a cyclic group of order k_i on the normal bundle of C_i so that on each fiber, it acts like $(z_1, z_2) \to (\omega_i z_1, \omega_i^{-1} z_2)$ where ω_i is the k_i-th root of unity. With all these assumptions we can form M/G and resolve the singularities. In this way we obtain a new Kähler manifold with zero first Chern class whose Euler number is:

$$\frac{1}{|G|}\left[\chi(M) - m - \sum_{i=1}^{\ell} \chi(C_i)\right] + 3m + \sum_{i=1}^{\ell} (k_i + 1)\chi(C_i)\frac{|G'_i|}{|G|}.$$

Instead of using cyclic groups acting on the normal bundle of C_i, one can also use other finite groups such as dihedral groups, tetrahedral groups, octahedral and isosahedral groups. We mention here two examples.

(a) Let ω be the cubic root of unity. It can act on a one dimensional complex torus with three fixed points. Hence it can act on the three dimensional complex torus with 27 fixed points. Taking the quotient and blowing up 27 points, one obtains a Kähler manifold with zero first Chern class and Euler number 72.

(b) Let $\sum$ be the quartic surface in $\mathbb{C}P^3$. Let Z_2 act on $\sum$ with a fixed curve of genus 3. It also acts on the one dimensional torus T with four fixed points. Hence it acts on $\sum \times T$ with four fixed curves. Taking the quotient and resolving the singularity, we obtain a Kähler manifold with zero first Chern class and Euler number -24. It is not hard to find free action of Z_2 so that we can make the Euler number to be -12.

(4) Let M be a compact Kähler manifold so that for some nonsingular hypersurfaces $D_1, D_2, \ldots, D_m$; the canonical divisor of M is linearly equivalent to $\sum_i (k_i - 1)D_i$ where k_i are positive integers. Suppose that there exists a group G of holomorphic transformations which acts on M and freely on $M \setminus \bigcup_{i=1}^{m} D_i$. Let G_i be the subgroup which fixes every point of D_i . Then we assume that G_i is a cyclic group with order k_i . For each point x in $D_i \cap D_j$, we assume that the subgroup of G which leaves invariant a neighborhood of x is generated by those G_i with $x \in D_i$. Then we conclude that M/G is a compact Kähler manifold with zero first Chern class. Its Euler number is $\frac{1}{|G|} \chi(M \setminus \bigcup_i D_i) + \chi(\bigcup_i D_i/G)$

(5) Let D be a non-singular divisor in a compact Kähler manifold M. Then it defines a line bundle L. If $C_1(L)$ is divisible by n or if the homology class represented by D is divisible by n, then there exists a line bundle $\tilde{L}$ so that $\tilde{L}^n = L$. Furthermore, there is a natural bundle homomorphism $\pi : \tilde{L} \to L$. If s is the section of L which defines D $\hat{M} = \pi^{-1}(s(M))$ will be a non-singular manifold which is an n-fold cover of M branched along D. The first Chern class of $\hat{M}$ is zero if $nC_1(M) = (n-1)\, C_1(L) = (n-1)[D]$. The Euler number of $\hat{M}$ is $n\chi(M) - (n-1)\chi(D)$.

As a consequence, if $n\, C_1(M)$ is divisible by $n - 1$ and $K_M^{-\frac{n}{n-1}}$ is very ample, then we can find a n-fold branch cover $\hat{M}$ of M with zero first Chern class. Its Euler number is $n\, C_3(M) - \frac{n^2}{(n-1)^2} C_1(M)^3 - 24\, n$. In particular, if $M = \Sigma \times \mathbb{C}P^1$ where Σ is a compact Kähler surface such that $2K_{\Sigma}^{-1}$ gives a projective embedding of Σ . Then we can find a two-fold branch cover $\hat{M}$ of M with zero first Chern class whose Euler number is $-28\, C_1^2(\Sigma)$. If $C_1(\Sigma)$ is divisible by two and $3K_{\Sigma}^{-1/2}$ gives a projective embedding of Σ , we can find a three-fold branch cover with zero first Chern class whose Euler number is $-\frac{39}{2} C_1^2(\Sigma)$. (Note that Σ can be $\mathbb{C}P^1 \times \mathbb{C}P^1$ in both cases.) We can also take M to be complete intersections of hypersurfaces $H_1, \ldots, H_\ell$ in $\mathbb{C}P^N$ with $\sum_{i=1}^{\ell} \deg H_i < N + 1$.

(i) Let M be a nonsingular hypersurface of degree six in $\mathbb{C}P^4$ which is invariant under an involution of $\mathbb{C}P^4$ fixing a hyperplane. Then the quotient of M by this involution is a compact Kähler manifold with zero first Chern class. Similarly, if M is a nonsingular hypersurface of degree eight in $\mathbb{C}P^4$ which is invariant under Z_4 action by multiplying $\sqrt{-1}$ on one of the coordinates, then M/Z_4 is a compact Kähler manifold with zero first Chern class. The former has Euler number -204 and the latter -296.

(ii) Let G be the group on $\mathbb{C}P^4$ generated by involutions which map z_i to $-z_i$ and keep the other coordinates fixed. Let M be the hypersurface $\sum_i z_i^{10} = 0$. Then M/G is a compact Kähler manifold with zero first Chern class.

(iii) Let M′ be a four dimensional manifold in $\mathbb{C}P^m$ so that it is invariant under the map $[z_0, z_1, ..., z_m] \to [\omega z_0, z_1, ..., z_m]$ where ω is the n-th primitive root of unity. Suppose M′ does not contain [1, 0, ..., 0]. Then there is a hyperplane H in $\mathbb{C}P^m$ so that $M' \cap H$ is nonsingular and invariant under the above Z_n action. Its quotient has zero first Chern class. Its Euler number is $\frac{1}{n} C_3(M') H + \frac{3n-4}{n} H^4 + \frac{n-2}{n} C_2(M') H$. **Similarly, if M′ is the product of two quartic surfaces in $\mathbb{C}P^3$, we can take the hypersurface of bidegree (1, 1) in M′ which is invariant under an action of $Z_2 \times Z_2$. Its quotient will be a compact manifold with zero first Chern class and itsEuler number 16.**

(6) Let $\sum$ be a compact Kähler surface with positive first Chern class. Then by suitably taking a fiber space over $\sum$ with generic fiber equal to an elliptic curve, we can construct three dimensional manifolds with zero first Chern class. We shall give a more complete account on this construction elsewhere.

Appendix

(G. Tian and S.-T. Yau)

Here we construct two complex 3-folds with trivial canonical bundles and Euler numbers -6.

(1) Let $\sum_1$, $\sum_2$ be cubic surfaces in $\mathbb{C}P^3$, i.e.,

$$\textstyle\sum_1 = \{x_o^3 + x_1^3 + x_2^3 + x_3^3 = 0\} \subset \mathbb{C}P^3$$

$$\textstyle\sum_2 = \{y_o^3 + y_1^3 + y_2^3 + y_3^3 = 0\} \subset \mathbb{C}P^3$$

where $[x_0, x_1, x_2, x_3]$, $[y_0, y_1, y_2, y_3]$ are homogeneous coordinates of $\mathbb{C}P^2$.

$$H = \left\{[x_0, x_1, x_2, x_3]\,[y_0, y_1, y_2, y_3] \,|\, x_0y_0 + x_1y_1 + x_2y_2 + x_3y_3 = 0\right\}$$

is a hyperplane of $\mathbb{C}P^3 \times \mathbb{C}P^3$.

$$\text{Put } M = (\textstyle\sum_1 \times \sum_2) \cap H.$$

Then M is non-singular because the form

$$\Omega = (\sum_{i=0}^{3} x_i^2 dx_i) \wedge (\sum_{j=0}^{3} y_j^2 dy_j) \wedge (\sum_{k=0}^{3} x_k dy_k + y_k dx_k)$$

is non-zero on M.

Furthermore, the first Chern class of M is zero and its Euler number is -18. This can be seen from the adjoint formula for normal bundles and the total Chern class of cubic surfaces.

Define $\sigma : \mathbb{C}P^3 \times \mathbb{C}P^3 \to \mathbb{C}P^3 \times \mathbb{C}P^3$ by sending $[x_0, x_1, x_2, x_3] \times [y_0, y_1, y_2, y_3] \to [x_1, x_2, x_0, \omega x_3] \times [y_1, y_2, y_0, \omega^2 y_3]$, where $\omega = e^{\frac{2\pi\sqrt{-1}}{3}}$. It is easy to see that σ acts on M freely and $\sigma^3 = id$.

By Lefschez theorem, M is simply-connected.

Now putting $V = M/\sigma$, then V is a Kähler manifold with the properties we require.

Moreover, a straight computation shows

$$b^1(V) = b^5(V)\ 0,\ h^{2,0}(V) = h^{0,2}(V) = 0$$

$$h^{1,1}(V) = 2,\ h^{3,0}(V) = h^{0,3}(V) = 1,\ h^{2,1}(V) = h^{1,2}(V) = 5$$

and $\pi_1(V) = Z_3$ since M is simply-connected.

(2) The second one is a little more complicated.

Define varieties $M_\delta = | [x_0, x_1, x_2] \times [y_0, y_1, y_2] \in \mathbb{C}P^2 \times \mathbb{C}P^2 |$

$$\left\{ \sum_{i=0}^{2} x_i^3 y_i^3 + \delta\left(\sum_{i=0}^{2} x_i^3 y_{i+1}^3 + \sum_{i=0}^{2} x_{i+1}^3 y_i^3\right) = 0 \right\}$$

where $\delta \in C$, $x_{i+3} = x_i$, $y_{i+3} = y_i$.

It is straight to verify that $\{M_\delta\}_{\delta \in C}$ has no base point, so by the Bertini theorem, M_δ is non-singular for almost all $\delta \in C$.

As before, using the adjoint formula, we have

$$C_1(M_\delta) = 0, \chi(M_\delta) = -162 \text{ for non-singular } M_\delta .$$

By Lefschez theorem, M_δ is simply-connected, so M_δ has trivial canonical bundle.

Define

$$\sigma_1 : \mathbb{C}P^2 \times \mathbb{C}P^2 \to \mathbb{C}P^2 \times \mathbb{C}P^2$$

$$[x_0, x_1, x_2] \times [y_0, y_1, y_2] \to [x_1, x_2, x_0] \times [y_1, y_2, y_0]$$

$$\sigma_2 : \mathbb{C}P^2 \times \mathbb{C}P^2 \to \mathbb{C}P^2 \times \mathbb{C}P^2$$

$$[x_0, x_1, x_2] \times [y_0, y_1, y_2] \to [x_0, \omega x_1, \omega^2 x_2] \times [y_0, \omega y_1, \omega^2 y_2]$$

Then it is easy to see that σ_1, σ_2 acts on M_δ freely for almost all δ and $\{\sigma_1, \sigma_2\} = Z_3 \times Z_3$.

$$\text{Put } \tilde{V}_\delta = M_\delta / \{\sigma_1, \sigma_2\}.$$

Then $\tilde{V}_\delta$ are Kähler manifolds with trivial canonical bundles and Euler numbers -18 for almost all $\delta \in C$.

Unfortunately, one cannot find any automorphism of order 3, which acts on $\tilde{V}_\delta$ freely. Hence we make the following construction.

Define $\sigma_3 : \mathbb{C}P^2 \times \mathbb{C}P^2 \to \mathbb{C}P^2 \times \mathbb{C}P^2$, $[x_0, x_1, x_2] \times [y_0, y_1, y_2] \to [x_0, x_1, x_2] \times [y_0, \omega y_1, \omega^2 y_2]$, then $\sigma_3 \cdot \sigma_1 = \sigma_1 \cdot \sigma_3$, $\sigma_2 \cdot \sigma_3 = \sigma_3 \cdot \sigma_2$, $\sigma_3^3 = \text{id}$, and σ_3 acts on M_δ . Hence σ_3 induces an automorphism on $\tilde{V}_\delta$, which we denote by σ_3 , also.

On M_δ , σ_3 has three fixed tori:

$$\left\{ x_0^3 + \delta(x_1^3 + x_2^3) = 0 \right\} \times [1, 0, 0]$$

$$\left\{ x_1^3 + \delta(x_0^3 + x_2^3) = 0 \right\} \times [0, 1, 0]$$

$$\left\{x_2^3 + \delta(x_0^3 + x_1^3) = 0\right\} \times [0, 0, 1]$$

Therefore, σ_3 has a fixed torus T_1 in V_δ, the image of the above tori under projection $M_\delta \to V_\delta = M_\delta/\{\sigma_1, \sigma_2\}$.

Since $\sigma_2^2\sigma_3 : [x_0, x_1, x_2] \times [y_0, y_1, y_2] \to [x_0, \omega^2 x_1, \omega^2 x_2] \times [y_0, y_1, y_2]$, σ_3 has another fixed torus T_2 in V_δ. One can see that T_1 is disjoint from T_2, and σ_3 acts on the normal bundles of T_1, T_2 by $\begin{pmatrix} \omega & o \\ o & \omega^{-1} \end{pmatrix}, \begin{pmatrix} \omega^{-1} & o \\ o & \omega \end{pmatrix}$ respectively.

Now we can resolve the two singular tori of $\tilde{V}_\delta/\sigma_3$ to get the required manifold V_δ. Its Euler number is

$$\chi(V_\delta) = \frac{\chi(\tilde{V}_\delta) - \chi(T_1) - \chi(T_2)}{3} + \sum_{i=1}^{4} \chi(D_i)$$

$$= \chi(\tilde{V}_\delta)/3 = -6\,,$$

i.e., V_δ is what we need. Furthermore, a straight computation shows: $\pi_1(V_\delta) = Z_3 \oplus Z_3$ (using Van Kampen theorem) and $b_1(V_\delta) = b_5(V_\delta) = 0$, $h^{1,1}(V_\delta) = 2$, $h^{2,0}(V_\delta) = 0$, $H^{2,1}(V_\delta) = 9$.

(3) Here we give another example.

Let $\sum_1$ = cubic suface in $\mathbb{C}P^3$, i.e. $\sum_1 = \{x_0^3 + x_1^3 + s_2^3 + x_3^3 = 0\}$.

$\sum_2$ = intersection of two quadratics $\mathbb{C}P^4$,

i.e, $\sum_2 = \{[y_0, y_1, y_2, y_3, y_4] \mid \sum_{i=0}^{4} a_i y_i^2 = 0\,, \sum_{i=0}^{4} b_i y_i^2 = 0\}$.

where $a = (a_0, ..., a_4)$, $b = (b_0, ..., b_1, ..., b_4) \in C^5$

$M_{(a,b,\delta)} = (\sum_1 \times \sum_2) \cap \{x_3y_3 + \delta x_4 y_4 = 0\}$. $\delta \in C$.

It is easy to see that there is no base point for the system $\{M_{(a,b,\delta)}\}$, so by Bertini's theorem, for almost all (a, b, δ), $M_{(a,b,\delta)}$ is non-singular.

Let

$$\sigma : [x_0, x_1, x_2, x_3] \times [y_0, y_1, y_2, y_3, y_4] \to [x_0, x_1, x_2, x_3] \times [-y_0, -y_1, y_2, y_3, y_4]$$

$$\sigma : [x_0, x_1, x_2, x_3] \times [y_0, y_1, y_2, y_3, y_4] \to [x_0, x_1, x_2, x_3] \times [-y_0, y_1, -y_2, y_3, y_4]$$

then $\sigma_1^2 = \sigma_2^2 = \text{id}$. $G = \{\sigma_1, \sigma_2\} = \{\text{id}, \sigma_1, \sigma_2, \sigma_1\sigma_2\} = Z_2 \oplus Z_2$. Furthermore, σ_1 has fixed points consisting of four disjoint tori:

$$\Sigma_1 \cap \{x_3y_3 + x_4y_4 = 0\} \times \{a_2y_2^2 + a_3y_3^2 + a_4y_4^2 = 0 \, , \, b_2y_2^2 + b_3y_3^2 + b_4y_4^2 = 0\}$$

for almost all (a, b, δ), and σ_1 acts on the normal bundles of these tori by $\begin{pmatrix} -1 & 0 \\ 0 & -1 \end{pmatrix}$.

The same argument works also for $\sigma_2, \sigma_1 \cdot \sigma_2$. Hence we know that G has twelve disjoint tori as fixed points and G acts on the normal bundles by $\begin{pmatrix} -1 & 0 \\ 0 & -1 \end{pmatrix}$.

Taking the quotient M/G and blowing up these twelve singular tori in M/G, we obtain a new algebraic manifold V.

$$\chi(V) = \frac{1}{4}\chi(M) \, . \quad C_1(V) = C_1(M) \, .$$

But one can easily see that $C_1(M) = 0$, and the Euler number is $\chi(M) = -24$. Therefore, $C_1(V) = 0$, $\chi(V) = -6$. Note that V is simply-connected.

References

(1) E. Calabi, Métriques Kähleriennes et fibres holomorphes, Ann. Sci. Ec. Norm. Sup. Paris, 4 me Sér. 12 (1979) 269-294.

(2) E. Calabi, Isometric families of Kähler structures, in The Chern Symposium 1979, Springer-Verlag.

(3) D. Gromoll and W. Meyer, The splitting theorem for manifolds of nonnegative Ricci curvature, J. Diff. Geom. 6 (1971).

(4) N. Hitchin, Compact four dimensional Einstein manifolds, J. Diff. Geom. 9 (1974), 435-441.

(5) V.A. Iskovskih, Fano 3-folds I, II, Izv. Akad. Nank USSR Ser. Mat. 41 (1977), 516-562; 42 (1978), 469-506.

(6) M. Perry, Gravitational instantons, in Seminar on Differential Geometry, edited by S.-T. Yau, Ann. Math. Studies, Princeton (1982), 603-630.

(7) S. Mori and S. Mukai, Classification of Fano 3-folds with $B_2 \geqslant 2$, Manuscripta Math. 36 (1981), 147-162.

(8) A. Strominger and E. Witten, to appear.

(9) P. Candelas, G. Horowitz, A. Strominger and E. Witten, to appear.

(10) S.-T. Yau, Calabi's conjecture and some new results in algebraic geometry, Proc. Natl. Acad. Sci. USA 74 (1977), 1798-1799.

(11) S.-T. Yau, On the Ricci curvature of compact Kähler manifolds and complex Monge-Ampère equations I, Comm. Pure Appl. Math. 31 (1978), 339-411.

DYNAMICAL SUPERSYMMETRY BREAKING IN SUPERSTRING THEORIES

Michael Dine
The Institute for Advanced Study
Princeton, NJ 08540

Abstract

For superstring theories compactified on Calabi Yau spaces with vanishing three index antisymmetric tensor field, H, gluino condensation lifts the vacuum degeneracy and causes a runaway to weak coupling and large manifolds. With a non-vanishing H, supersymmetry is broken and the cosmological constant vanishes in the leading approximation.

The anomaly free superstrings[1,2] are believed to be consistent quantum theories incorporating gauge and gravitational interactions. This is remarkable in itself, but many features of the $E_8 \times E_8$ version of the heterotic string[2] make it a plausible candidate for a truly unified theory of the known forces.[3,4] As discovered by Candelas, Horowitz, Strominger, and Witten, these theories possess classical ground states in which six of the ten dimensions are compactified to "Calabi-Yau" spaces, manifolds of SU(3) holonomy. In these ground states, four-dimensional space is flat Minkowski space, i.e. the cosmological constant vanishes. The low energy, four-dimensional theory possesses an unbroken N = 1 local supersymmetry; it can possess a reasonable gauge symmetry, such as SU(3) x SU(2) x U(1) x U(1). These are repetitive generations of chiral fermions. Other exciting features of these compactifications have been reviewed by Witten[4] and Horowitz[5] at this meeting.

The presence of a low energy supersymmetry is a particularly desirable feature. It can explain why the Weinberg-Salam Higgs doublets are light, and if dynamically broken, may explain why M_W is so much smaller than the Planck mass or compactification (unification) scale. In the past few years, our understanding of dynamical supersymmetry breaking has progressed significantly.[6-12] Using a variety of techniques, it is now possible to determine, in most theories, whether or not supersymmetry is broken.[10] Ryan Rhome, Nathan Seiberg, Ed Witten, and myself have studied the problem of dynamical supersymmetry breaking in string theories.[13]

At low energies, we have to consider a conventional field theory of massless particles, including higher dimension operators coming from integrating out higher Kaluza-Klein and string modes. It is not hard to show that no appreciable supersymmetry breaking can come from the ordinary SU(3) x SU(2) x U(1) (x other E_6 subgroups).[10] Any such breaking will be much smaller than Λ_{QCD}. Thus the obvious place to look for supersymmetry breaking is the second E_8. (This E_8 may be broken to some smaller group by expectation values of Wilson lines. As long as the remaining subgroup contains a non-abelian part, the following discussion goes through unaltered.) We wish to ask then, whether this group can serve as the "hidden sector" of a supergravity theory. Of course, it is crucial that supersymmetry be broken without generating a cosmological constant.

First consider what happens in the limit $M_p \to \infty$. The theory then becomes an ordinary supersymmetric gauge theory of gluons A_μ and gluinos, λ. From the Witten index, effective Lagrangian arguments, and instanton calculations, it is known that these theories do not break supersymmetry, and it is believed that the discrete chiral symmetry (Z_{60} for E_8) of these theories is broken by a gluino condensate, $\langle\lambda\lambda\rangle \sim \Lambda^3$. Here Λ is the scale of the E_8 theory, related to M_{GUT} and the unified coupling g^2 by $\Lambda = M_{GUT} \exp(-\frac{1}{2b_o g^2})$.

At the next order in $\frac{1}{M_p}$, other fields couple to the E_8 sector. In particular, there is an axion-dilaton multiplet which couples. The ten-dimensional theory[14] contains a dilaton field, ϕ, with coupling $L^{(10)} = -\frac{\phi}{4} F_{AB}^{\ 2} + \ldots$ Classically, this field has no potential. Different $\langle\phi\rangle$ label physically distinct vacua; $\langle\phi\rangle$ acts, for example, as the effective gauge coupling. There are, of course, many other terms in this Lagrangian which I have not written here. There is one term, however, which is missing from the Lagrangian presented by Chapline and Manton which will play a particularly important role in our discussion. This is a four-gluino coupling $\Delta L^{(10)} = -\frac{\kappa^2}{16}(\bar{\lambda}\Gamma_{ABC}\lambda)^2$. This term is required for the supersymmetry of the Lagrangian, as one can check either using the 10-dimensional transformation laws directly, or by reducing the Lagrangian to four dimensions and casting it in the form of a general N=1 supergravity Lagrangian.[15]

When we reduce the Lagrangian to four dimensions, there are in fact two dilatons. Recall that classically (and in perturbation theory) the radius of the Calabi-Yau space is undetermined.[3] Corresponding to this "breathing mode" of the manifold is a massless field in four dimensions, $\sigma(x)$.[16] Calling $M_{GUT} = M_p e^{-2\sigma(x)} = R^{-1}$, one finds upon reduction to four dimensions, $L^{(4)} = -\frac{1}{4}\phi e^{3\sigma} F_{\mu\nu}^2 + aF\tilde{F} + e^{-3/2\sigma} \lambda \not{D} \lambda + e^{-3\sigma}(\lambda\lambda)^2 + \ldots$ Here the axion field, $a(x)$, comes from the antisymmetric tensor field $B_{\mu\nu}$, with four-dimensional indices. The effective four dimensional gauge coupling, at the unification scale, is $g_{eff}^{-2}(M_{GUT}) = \phi e^{3\sigma} \equiv Y$. So $Y \to \infty$ corresponds to weak coupling. The fields σ and ϕ are undetermined classically and in perturbation theory. Thus we are free to work in a vacuum with arbitrarily weak coupling, and where higher dimension operators can be neglected with arbitrary accuracy. We wish to ask whether non-perturbative effects lift this degeneracy and determine g_{eff}^2 and R.

In global supersymmetry, a nearly identical problem involving coupling an axion multiplet to a gauge theory arises.[10] Consider, for example, supersymmetric QCD with gauge group SU(3), and two chiral multiplets Q and $\bar{Q}$. in the 3 and $\bar{3}$ representation. This theory has a non-anomalous R-symmetry, under which $Q \to e^{-2i\alpha}Q(\theta e^{-i\alpha})$. Classically this theory possesses a large vacuum degeneracy: $\langle Q^i\rangle = \langle \bar{Q}_i\rangle^+ = v\delta_{i3}$. In these vacua, SU(3) is broken to SU(2), and there is a single light chiral field, $\Phi = (\bar{Q}Q)^{\frac{1}{2}}$; $\langle\Phi\rangle = v$. Writing $\Phi = v + \phi + i\pi + \theta\psi + \theta^2 F_\phi$, it is easy to see that at one loop the following coupling between Φ and the SU(2) gauge fields is generated: $\frac{1}{4}\int d^2\theta\left(\frac{1}{g^2} + \frac{b_o}{8\pi}\ln(\Phi)\right) W_\alpha^2$. The real part is $\left(\frac{1}{g^2} + \frac{b_o}{8\pi^2}\ln(v+\phi)\right)(F^2 + i\bar{\lambda}\not{D}\lambda)$. This is just the renormalization of the SU(2) coupling, as in a grand unified theory. The imaginary part is $\frac{b_o\pi}{v} F\tilde{F}$, the "axion" coupling. This coupling is in fact necessary in order that the non-anomalous R-symmetry be properly realized in the low energy Lagrangian. Under this symmetry, $\frac{\pi}{v} \to \frac{\pi}{v} - 2\alpha$, but the corresponding shift in the Lagrangian is precisely canceled by the $F\tilde{F}$ term generated by the chiral rotation of the SU(2) gluino fields.

This Lagrangian also has a $\frac{1}{v} F_\phi \lambda\lambda$ coupling. Correspondingly, there is a potential, $\frac{1}{v^2}|\langle\lambda\lambda\rangle|^2$. $\langle\lambda\lambda\rangle$ is itself, however, a function of v through the renormalization group. A simple calculation gives $\langle\lambda\lambda\rangle \alpha \frac{\Lambda^4}{v}$, where Λ is the SU(3) scale. This suggests that there should be a potential $\frac{1}{v^4}$. Below the SU(2) scale, we can integrate out the gauge fields and write an effective Lagrangian for Φ alone. The superpotential in this Lagrangian is uniquely determined by symmetry considerations, $W \alpha \frac{1}{\Phi}$. This gives, again, $V \sim \frac{1}{v^4}$, verifying the naive argument.

In the string theory, we can perform a quite similar analysis. Again, the theory possesses four gluino couplings. Since $\langle\lambda\lambda\rangle \sim \Lambda^3 \sim M_{GUT}{}^3 \times \exp(\frac{3}{2b_o}(Y+ia))$ (the dependence of the condensate on the axion phase follows from simple anomaly considerations), we expect $V \sim |\langle\lambda\lambda\rangle|^2 \sim \exp(-\frac{3y}{b_o})$, up to power law corrections in X and Y. The ground state of the string appears to be at weak coupling, and probably at flat ten-dimensional space. (It should be stressed that there is no cosmological out here; at any point, the cosmological constant is of order $m_{3/2}{}^4$.)

There is, however, a possible way out. If one examines the corrected Chapline-Manton action, one notices that the three index antisymmetric tensor H and the gluino condensate λ enter in the form of a perfect square, $L^{(10)} \sim \phi^2(H_{ABC} - \frac{\sqrt{2}}{24}\phi^{-1}\bar{\lambda}\Gamma_{ABC}\lambda)^2$. From the point of view of 10 dimensions, the light gluinos are proportional to the covariantly constant spinor, η. Thus the gluino condensate is proportional to the covariantly constant holomorphic 3-form, $\varepsilon_{ijk} \sim \bar{\eta}\,\Gamma_{ijk}\,\eta$. Suppose $H_{ijk} = c\varepsilon_{ijk}$, for some constant c. (The corresponding equation for B can be solved locally; globally it has Dirac string singularities.) Then the fields Y and a will adjust to give a value for the gluino condensate which precisely cancels H in the perfect square. Thus, at the minimum of the Y potential, the cosmological constant will vanish. On the other hand, examining the 10 dimensional transformation laws, one finds that supersymmetry is broken at the minimum.

This can all be understood from a four dimensional viewpoint. Define $X = e^{\sigma}\phi^{-1} + ib$, $Y = e^{3\sigma}\phi + ia$ ($\mathrm{Re}\,Y = \frac{1}{g^2}$). Dimensional reduction yields a four dimensional supergravity theory with Kahler potential $K(X,Y) = -\ln(Y+Y^*) - 3\ln(X+X^*)$ (similar to "no-scale" models). Only the field Y couples to gauge fields ($\sim \int d^2\theta Y W_\alpha^2$), and there is a superpotential $W = M_p^3 c$ (note c is not renormalized). For $c \to 0$, this Lagrangian is symmetric under shift of X by $X \to X + i\gamma$. It also has a non-anomalous R-symmetry, under which $Y \to Y + \frac{2}{3} i\alpha b_o$, $\theta \to \theta e^{-i\alpha}$. As in supersymmetric QCD, integrating out the E_8 sector must give an effective Lagrangian which respects these symmetries. Again, the superpotential is unique: $W_{eff} = M_p^3(c + h\, e^{-3/2b_o Y})$. The potential is easily computed: $V_{eff} = \frac{1}{X^3 Y} |c + \frac{3h}{2b_o} Y \exp(\frac{-3Y}{2b_o})|^2$. Clearly the cosmological constant vanishes at the minimum. One finds that supersymmetry is broken: $m_{3/2} \sim c \frac{M_{GUT}^3}{M_p^2}$. Also, $\langle X\rangle$ is obviously undetermined, so the scalar component of X is massless. The components of Y have masses of order $m_{3/2}$. At this order, the gaugino and matter fields are massless.

In conclusion, we see that, to obtain a reasonable ground state, some of the assumptions of Candelas et al must be abandoned. In particular, we need $\langle H\rangle \neq 0$. In this case, we can obtain broken supersymmetry and, to lowest order, zero cosmological constant. Obviously, this work leaves over many questions and problems. Clearly one would like to compute the other soft breaking terms in the low energy theory. More urgently, one must determine whether the cosmological constant continues to vanish as one includes higher order corrections. The consistency of having $\langle H\rangle \neq 0$ must be investigated. For example, from the point of view of the non-linear sigma model, such a background H corresponds to the presence of a Wess-Zumino term. According to Witten and Rohm,[17] this term is quantized; the constant we have called c is of order one. This immediately raises at least two concerns: can the soft breakings be small enough? since $\langle\lambda\lambda\rangle \sim M_{GUT}^3$, can we trust, even qualitatively, our analysis? For the moment, however, the results we have presented are sufficiently intriguing to merit further investigation.

Acknowledgement

Research supported by NSF Grant No. PHY 82-17352.

References

1. M. B. Green and J. H. Schwarz, Phys. Lett. 149B (1984) 117.
2. D. J. Gross, J. A. Harvey, E. Martinec, and R. Rohm, Phys. Rev. Lett. 54 (1985) 502, Princeton preprint (1985) and to appear.
3. P. Candelas, G. Horowitz, A. Strominger, and E. Witten, Santa Barbara preprint (1984); E. Witten, Princeton preprint (1985).
4. E. Witten, these proceedings.
5. G. Horowitz, these proceedings.
6. E. Witten, Nucl. Phys. B188 (1981) 513.
7. E. Witten, Nucl. Phys. B202 (1982) 253.
8. G. Veneziano and S. Yankielowicz, Phys. Lett. 113B (1982) 321.
9. V. A. Novikov, M. A. Shifman, V. I. Vainshtein, M. B. Voloshin, and V. I. Zakharov, Nucl. Phys. B229 (1983) 394; V. A. Novikov, M. A. Shifman, A. I Vainshtein, and V. I. Zakharov, Nucl. Phys. B229 (1983) 381, 407.
10. I. Affleck, M. Dine, and N. Seiberg, Nucl. Phys. B241 (1984) 493, and I.A.S. preprint (1984).
11. D. Amati, G. C. Rossi, and S. Veneziano, CERN preprint TH3907/84.
12. S. Ferrara, L. Girardello, and H. P. Nilles, Phys. Lett. 125B (1983) 457.
13. M. Dine, R. Rohm, N. Seiberg, and E. Witten, Institute for Advanced Study preprint (1985).
14. E. Bergshoeff, M. de Roo, B. de Wit, and P. van Nieuwenhuysen, Nucl. Phys. B195 (1982); G. F. Chapline and N. S. Manton, Phys. Lett. 120B (1983) 105.
15. E. Cremmer, S. Ferrara, L. Girardello, and A. van Proeyen, Nucl. Phys. B212 (1983) 413.
16. E. Witten, Princeton University preprint (1985).
17. R. Rohm and E. Witten, to appear.

SUPERSTRING PHENOMENOLOGY

Paul H. Frampton
Department of Physics and Astronomy, University of North Carolina
Chapel Hill, NC 27514

ABSTRACT

An SU(8) phenomenology and other aspects of superstrings are discussed

One motivation for examining higher-dimensional Yang-Mills theory in even dimensions $d = 2n > 4$ was to attempt to explain fermion quantum numbers, and the number of fermion families, from the extra chiral anomaly cancellation conditions. Chiral fermions in d=4 require gauge fields in $d = 2n > 4$ hence giving an "anti-Kaluza-Klein" philosophy in which the low-energy gauge group does not come from an isometry group.

Although these studies were originally string motivated, it became apparent that the zero-slope limit of supersymmetric Yang-Mills theory in ten dimensions was apparently anomalous for any gauge group, and hence just one year ago all superstrings seemed doomed phenomenologically.(1) Studies of anti-Kaluza-Klein theories were made in other even dimensions d = 6, 8, and 12. Last summer, a miracle happened in that the O(32) string theory in ten dimensions was found to be anomaly-free.(2) How could the earlier analysis have been right for every case except O(32)? One way of explaining this is that the earlier work was based on a field theory prejudice that quantum corrections are one loop. String theory involves Planck's constant in a more subtle way and the same diagram can be both 1 loop and zero loop in the point limit; the closed strings have an inherent Planck's constant relative to open strings, and this is how the orientable nonplanar string cancels the chiral anomaly for O(32). Because the gauge coupling is now unified with gravitation, and the quantum corrections are better controlled, we are led(3) to examine chiral fermions in d = 4 starting with supersymmetric gauge theories in d = 10 with group O(32) and the anomaly-free alternative E(8) x E(8).

The group O(32) does not allow an O(10) GUT subgroup because if we embed $32 = 16 + \overline{16}$ the adjoint 496 is vectorial. We may embed SU(N) but this leads for any choice of 6-dimensional compact manifold to a trivial family replication with arbitrary family number. Also the persistence of unbroken U(1) symmetries makes e.g. the SU(5) model phenomenologically unattractive.

The alternative group E(8) x E(8)' is much more promising. E(8) has several interesting subalgebras e.g. SU(3) x E(6), O(16) and SU(9). We choose[3] SU(9) where the adjoint transforms as $248 = 80 + 84 + \overline{84}$, and under an SU(8) x U(1) subgroup this becomes

$$248 = (63,0) + (8,+3) + (\overline{8},-3) + (1,0) + (56,+1) + (\overline{56},-1) + (28,-2) + (\overline{28},+2)$$

Now consider compactification on a manifold which is a product of three 2-spheres, and with the U(1) gauge field in monopole configurations with charges m_1, m_2, m_3. Then it is easy to show that the chiral fermions in four dimensions corresponds to $M[56 + 8(\overline{28}) + 27(8)]$ of SU(8) where $M = m_1 m_2 m_3$. This requires a multiple of six families; if the rank of the group is further reduced in compactification the number of families becomes arbitrary. Absence of a local triangle anomaly in d = 4 follows from the special algebraic properties of E(8). This particular compactification is at least a field theoretic illustration; we did not investigate consistency at the string level.

We have also re-examined[4] non-string Kaluza-Klein theory in the light of the new anomaly cancellation mechanism invented by the superstring. The situation for d = 4 is, of course, unchanged but for all even $d = 2n \geq 6$ the nonleading gauge anomalies, gravitational anomalies and mixed anomalies may always be cancelled by adding antisymmetric field(s) which transform with Chern-Simons classes. Only the leading gauge anomaly must be cancelled by choice of the fermion representation. If one ever became disenchanted with strings, this new freedom will be exploited in model building.

1. P. H. Frampton, Fifth Workshop in Grand Unification, World Scientific (1984) p. 494 and references therein.
2. M. B. Green and J. H. Schwarz, Phys. Lett. 149B, 117 (1984).
3. P. H. Frampton, H. van Dam and K. Yamamoto, Phys. Rev. Lett. 54, 1114 (1985).
4. P. H. Frampton and K. Yamamoto, IFP-244-UNC, Phys. Lett. B (to appear).

Some Compactifications of Superstrings

K. Pilch and A. N. Schellekens
Institute for Theoretical Physics
State University of New York at Stony Brook
Stony Brook, New York 11794

One of the serious obstacles on the way towards successful superstring phenomenology is the problem of finding the right vacuum. In [1] Calabi-Yau spaces were proposed as the most likely candidates. Although the arguments in favor of this choice - unbroken supersymmetry and string consistency - are persuasive, they are not rigorous, and alternatives have not been ruled out.

In [2] we have investigated a large class of such alternatives, obtained by compactifying six dimensions on arbitrary manifolds, with a classical Yang-Mills field that is equal to the spin connection. Global existence of the field strength of the antisymmetric tensor field, with its Yang-Mills and Lorentz Chern-Simons terms [3,4] requires in most cases that the Yang -Mills generators Λ^a and the Lorentz generates T^a satisfy a trace condition

$$\mathrm{Tr}\,\Lambda^a\Lambda^b = 30\,\mathrm{Tr}\,T^aT^b \qquad (1)$$

This is a non-trivial condition, which cannot be satisfied for most Yang-Mills groups. Fortunately, SO(32) and $E_8 \times E_8$ are among the very few groups for which it can be satisfied.

Irreducible six-dimensional manifolds can have holonomy groups SO(6), SU(3), SU(3) x U(1) or SU(2) x U(1). This last group is the holonomy group of the symmetric space $S_p(4)/SU(2) \times U(1)$, which does not admit spinors. Since the first two groups have been studied completely in [1], we focus our attention on six-dimensional Kahler manifolds. To satisfy (1) we have to know the allowed U(1) charges. This is determined by the first Chern class of the manifold. We have restricted ourselves to manifolds with a quantization condition not finer than CP_3. There are large numbers of such manifolds.

Using the E_8 trace-identities [4,5] we construct all embeddings of SU(3) x U(1) in $E_8 \times E_8$ that satisfy (1). There are four, and in all four cases the unbroken group contains a factor SO(10) or SU(5). Furthermore the chiral fermions are always in the (16) or $(5)+(\overline{10})$ representations of these groups. In [2] we have derived expressions for the multiplicity of these generations in terms of the three Chern numbers of the tangent bundle of the manifolds.

The most interesting manifolds appear to be the so-called Fano 3-folds, which have positive first Chern class, and have been classified [6]. Two manifolds are especially interesting. They are $SU(3)/U(1)^2$ and the intersection of a cubic curve with CP_4, which have respectively Euler characteristic 6 and -6. Both manifolds give rise to three generations of (16)'s of SO(10). The other Fano 3-folds that we know give either not enough generations, or at least eight, which seems a bit too much. The manifold CP_3 gives either two, one or zero generations, depending on the embedding of the holonomy group.

For zero first Chern class we obtain of course the Calabi-Yau spaces, and for negative first Chern class there are large numbers of manifolds constructed as complete intersections of algebraic varieties in CP_n. These manifolds all have very large (and negative) Euler characteristics, and would lead to hundreds or thousands of generations. It is interesting that condition (1), which follows from the requirement of global existence of the H-field, is precisely what is needed to obtain the standard model. For arbitrary SU(3) subgroups of E_8, the coefficient is always a multiple of 30. We have constructed all possible SU(3) subgroups using index sum rules [5]. Of these, only the one that satisfies (1) leads to an acceptable spectrum.

If the manifold is reducible (e.g. a product of three two-dimensional manifolds), one can also obtain the standard model under the same conditions, but now there are also many other possibilities, mostly without chiral fermions. A new feature is the possibility of obtaining SU(4)xSU(2)xSU(2) unification.

[1] P. Candelas, G. T. Horowitz, A. Strominger and E. Witten, Nucl. Phys. B. (to appear)

[2] K. Pilch and A. N. Schellekens, Stony Brook preprint ITP-SB-85-14

[3] E. Bergshoeff, M.de Roo, B. deWit and P.van Nieuwenhuizen, Nucl. Phys. B195 (1982)97; G.F.Chapline and N.S.Manton, Phys.Lett 120B (1983) 105.

[4] M. B. Green and J. H. Schwarz, Phys. Lett. 149B (1984) 117.

[5] S. Okubo and J. Patera, J.Math. Phys. 24(1983), 2722; 25(1984) 1114.

[6] V. A. Iskovskih and V.V.Sokurov, Springer Lecture Notes In Mathematics No. 732; Algebraic Geometry (Copenhagen 1978);

SYMPOSIUM ON ANOMALIES, GEOMETRY, TOPOLOGY

CHARGE FRACTIONALIZATION

ANTTI NIEMI

CHAIRMAN

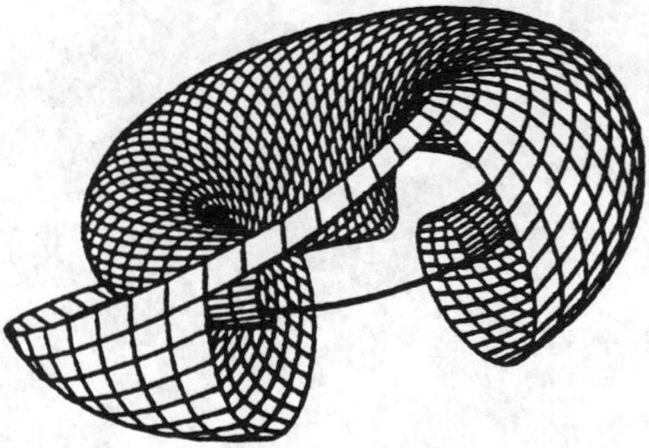

CHIRAL ANOMALIES IN A MAGNETIC MONOPOLE BACKGROUND

Haralambos Panagopoulos

Laboratoire de Physique Nucléaire
Université de Montréal
Montréal, Québec H3C 3J7, Canada

Introduction

Many authors have recently discussed fermionic systems in the presence of a magnetic monopole, particularly as a context for the catalysis of proton decay.[1,2] For such systems chiral anomalies play a crucial role: Various scattering processes among the fermions are allowed or not, depending on the value of the axial current; also, in certain cases, chiral symmetry breaking can be decided on the basis of the commutation of electric charge with axial charge[3], which can have anomalous contributions.

Two questions were the point of departure for this work: First, the singularity of a point monopole at the origin means that expressions involving the magnetic field throughout all space must be looked at more closely; these include the anomalous commutator between electric and axial charge and the anomalous divergence of the axial current. Second, very often in discussing fermion-monopole systems, attention is restricted to fermion wave functions of lowest angular momentum, and anomaly equations are used to describe transitions between different fermionic states in this wave[4]; it is therefore natural to ask whether the anomaly equations remain unchanged there, that is, whether they are saturated by the fermionic currents of lowest angular momentum, or receive contributions from higher partial waves.

To resolve these questions we calculate the above anomaly equations in a partial wave expansion. We study the Abelian and non-Abelian cases separately and work for simplicity with massless fermions. We will see that, to both questions, non-trivial answers are obtained. In addition, our results help set the record straight for contradictory statements which have only too often appeared in the literature. Finally, some results concerning fractional charges and the correspondence between Abelian and non-Abelian fermion-monopole systems will be discussed.

a) Abelian Case

In the presence of an everywhere regular electromagnetic field, there is a standard expression for the commutator of the time components of the electric and axial currents[5]:

$$<0|[j_0(\vec{x}),j^5_0(\vec{y})]|0> = -\frac{ie}{2\pi^2}\,\vec{B}(\vec{y})\cdot\vec{\nabla}_{\vec{x}}\,\delta^3(\vec{x}-\vec{y}), \tag{1}$$

obtained by evaluating a triangle diagram in the Bjorken limit. An alternative expression is[6]:

$$<0|[j_0(\vec{x}),j^5_0(\vec{y})]|0> = -\frac{ie}{2\pi^2}\,\vec{B}(\vec{x})\cdot\vec{\nabla}_{\vec{x}}\,\delta^3(\vec{x}-\vec{y}) \tag{2}$$

Equations (1) and (2) are equivalent and one can easily go from one to the other, provided: $\vec{\nabla}\cdot\vec{B} = 0$. Thus, for $\vec{\nabla}\cdot\vec{B} \neq 0$, which of course is the case of interest for a magnetic monopole field, the two equations are no longer equivalent; in addition, their integrated versions for the commutator of the two charges give also different answers, one zero and the other non-zero. Clearly, we must choose the correct expression among the two.

What we will then compute is the commutator $[Q^f,Q^g_5]$, where:

$$Q^f = \int d^3x\,\Psi^\dagger(\vec{x})\Psi(\vec{x})\,f(r),\qquad Q^g_5 = \int d^3x\,\Psi^\dagger(\vec{x})\gamma_5\Psi(\vec{x})\,g(r)$$

are the electric and axial charges. Here, $f(r)$ and $g(r)$ are smooth functions which are often required to tend to zero as $r\to\infty$, in order to make the charges well-defined. Since we expect a c-number value for this commutator when calculated in a fixed background gauge field, we calculate instead:

$$<0|[Q^f,Q^g_5]|0>$$

Expanding the field $\Psi(\vec{x})$ in eigenstates of the Dirac Hamiltonian:

$$[\vec{\alpha}\cdot(-i\vec{\nabla}-e\vec{A})]\,u^\alpha_{Ejm} = E\,u^\alpha_{Ejm} \tag{3}$$

$$\Psi(\vec{x},t) = \frac{1}{\pi}\sum_{jm\alpha}\Big[\int_0^\infty dE\,e^{-iEt}\,b^\alpha_{Ejm}\,u^\alpha_{Ejm}(r,\Omega)+\int_0^\infty dE\,e^{-iEt}\,d^{\alpha\dagger}_{Ejm}\,v^\alpha_{Ejm}(r,\Omega)\Big] \tag{4}$$

for each value of the energy and angular momentum there are two eigenstates, which in standard notation[7], are:

$$u^1_{Ejm}(\vec{x}) = \frac{1}{r}\begin{pmatrix} F^1_{Ej}(r)\,\xi^1_{jm}(\Omega) \\ G^1_{Ej}(r)\,\xi^2_{jm}(\Omega)\end{pmatrix},\quad u^2_{Ejm}(\vec{x}) = \frac{1}{r}\begin{pmatrix} F^2_{Ej}(r)\,\xi^2_{jm}(\Omega) \\ G^2_{Ej}(r)\,\xi^1_{jm}(\Omega)\end{pmatrix} \tag{5}$$

The functions ξ^1_{jm}, ξ^2_{jm} are monopole harmonics; for $j= |q|-1/2$ (lowest angular momentum) only one state exists for every value of (E,m).

With these ingredients, the commutator becomes:

$$<0|[Q^f,Q_5^g]|0> = \frac{1}{\pi^2}\int d^3r \int d^3r' \; f(r)\; g(r') \cdot \sum_{jm\alpha}\sum_{j'm'\alpha'} \int_{-\infty}^{0} dE \int_0^{\infty} dE' \cdot \tag{6}$$
$$\cdot[(v_{Ejm}^{\alpha *}(\vec{x})\; u_{E'j'm'}^{\alpha'}(\vec{x}))\;(u_{E'j'm'}^{\alpha' *}(\vec{x}')\gamma_5 v_{Ejm}^{\alpha}(\vec{x}')) - c.c.]$$

Already at this stage, by writing (6) in terms of monopole harmonics and using their orthogonality properties, we find that the contribution of higher partial waves vanishes: The lowest partial wave saturates this equation. For this wave, the eigenstates of H are:

$$u_{Ej_0m} = \frac{1}{r}\,\chi_E(r)\;\eta_{jm}(\Omega) \tag{7}$$

with $\eta_{jm}(\Omega)$ a monopole harmonic for $j=|q|-1/2$ and $\chi_E(r)$ given by:

$$\chi_E(r) = e^{i\theta\gamma_5/2}\cdot\begin{pmatrix} i\sin(Er+\pi/4) \\ \cos(Er+\pi/4)\end{pmatrix} \tag{8}$$

(θ is a constant angle parameterizing the boundary condition for all $j=|q|-1/2$ wave functions, as required in order to render H self-adjoint[8]). The commutator now reads:

$$<0|[Q^f,Q_5^g]|0> = \frac{2q}{\pi^2}\int dr\int dr' \; f(r)\; g(r') \int_{-\infty}^{0} dE \int_0^{\infty} dE' \cdot$$
$$\cdot[(\chi_E^{\dagger}(r)\chi_{E'}(r))\;(\chi_{E'}^{\dagger}(r')\gamma_5\chi_E(r')) - c.c.],\quad \gamma_5 = \begin{pmatrix} 0 & 1 \\ 1 & 0\end{pmatrix} \tag{9}$$

To evaluate the energy integrals we regularize by point-splitting. Since the task here was, among other things, to find regularizations for expressions which would otherwise be ambiguous, it is worth mentioning at this stage that different ways of regularizing Eq.9 lead to the same answer. Point-splitting then gives:

$$<0|[Q^f,Q_5^g]|0> = \lim_{\varepsilon\to 0}\frac{-4qi}{\pi^2}\int dr\; dr' \; f(r)g(r')\left\{\frac{(r+r')\;\varepsilon}{[(r+r')^2+\varepsilon^2]^2} + \frac{(r-r')\;\varepsilon}{[(r-r')^2+\varepsilon^2]^2}\right\}$$
$$= \frac{qi}{\pi}\int_0^{\infty} dr\;[f'(r)g(r) - g'(r)f(r)] - \frac{qi}{\pi}f(0)g(0) \tag{10}$$

From Eq.10 we can see the original source of ambiguity, if we recall that:

$$\delta'(x) = -\frac{2}{\pi}\lim_{\varepsilon\to 0}\frac{\varepsilon x}{(\varepsilon^2+x^2)^2} \tag{11}$$

Thus, in particular, (10) involves $\delta'(r+r')$, which on the half-line $r,r'>0$ is by itself ambiguous.

We now integrate both Eqs.1 and 2 with $\int dr'dr\; f(r)\; g(r')$ to compare with our final answer. Eq.1 gives the result (11), while Eq.2 doesn't and must be rejected. As a corollary we find, by setting $f(r)=1$, that:

$$[Q,Q_5^g] = 0 \tag{12}$$

in disagreement with some statements of this kind in the literature.

We turn now to the anomalous divergence of the axial current. To find a non-zero divergence, we add to the monopole an extra electrostatic potential $V(r)$, $V(0)<\infty$, so that: $F^{\mu\nu}\tilde{F}_{\mu\nu} = 4\vec{E}\cdot\vec{B} \neq 0$. The fermion wave functions will now satisfy:

$$H\,\psi(\vec{x}) \equiv [\,\vec{\alpha}\cdot(-i\vec{\nabla} - e\vec{A}) + V(r)]\,\psi(\vec{x}) = E\,\psi(\vec{x}) \tag{13}$$

We calculate:
$$<0|\,\partial_\mu j^\mu_5\,|0> = \partial_\mu <0|\,\tfrac{1}{2}[\Psi(\vec{x}),\,\gamma^\mu\gamma_5\,\Psi(\vec{x})]|0> \tag{14}$$
$$= \frac{1}{2\pi}\,\partial_i\,\{\textstyle\sum_{\alpha jm}(\int_{-\infty}^{0}dE - \int_0^\infty dE)\,\psi^{\alpha *}_{Ejm}(\vec{x})\begin{pmatrix}\sigma^i & \\ & \sigma^i\end{pmatrix}\psi^{\alpha}_{Ejm}(\vec{x})\}$$

Higher partial waves do not contribute again by: $\sum_m \xi^{\alpha *}_{jm}(\vec{\sigma}\cdot\hat{r})\xi^{\alpha}_{jm} = 0$. Only the lowest partial wave remains, giving:

$$<0|\,\partial_\mu j^\mu_5\,|0> = \frac{q}{4\pi^2}\,\partial_i\,\{\,\frac{\hat{r}_i}{r^2}\,(\int_{-\infty}^{0}dE - \int_0^\infty dE)\,\chi^\dagger_E(r)\chi_E(r)\} \tag{15}$$

where $\chi_E(r)$ satisfies the j=0 version of the Dirac equation (13):

$$-i\gamma_5\frac{d}{dr}\,\chi_E(r) = (\,E - V(r))\,\chi_E(r) \tag{16}$$

with solutions:
$$\chi_E(r) = e^{-i\gamma_5\int_0^r V(r)dr}\,.\,e^{i\theta\gamma_5/2}\,.\begin{pmatrix} i\sin(Er+\pi/4) \\ \cos(Er+\pi/4)\end{pmatrix} \tag{17}$$

Point-splitting in the radial direction (note that, since the radial component of the gauge potential vanishes, no path-ordered phase is needed to maintain the gauge invariance of j^μ_5), we get:

$$<0|\,\partial_\mu j^\mu_5\,|0> = \lim_{\varepsilon\to 0}\frac{-q}{2\pi^2}\,\partial_i\,\{\frac{\hat{r}_i}{r^2}\int_0^\infty dE\,\sin\varepsilon E\,\sin\int_{r-\varepsilon/2}^{r+\varepsilon/2} dr' V(r')\,\} \tag{18}$$
$$= -\,\frac{q}{2\pi^2}\,\partial_i\,\{\frac{\hat{r}_i}{r^2}\,V(r)\} = -\,\frac{q}{2\pi^2 r^2}\,\frac{dV(r)}{dr} - \frac{2q}{\pi}\,V(0)\delta^3(\vec{r})$$

Using the expression for the gauge potentials: $A^i = \frac{g}{r\sin\theta}\,(1-\cos\theta)\,\hat{\phi}^i$ and: $A^0 = \frac{1}{e}\,V(r)$, we can verify that: $-\,\frac{e^2}{16\pi^2}\,\varepsilon^{\mu\nu\rho\sigma}F_{\mu\nu}F_{\rho\sigma} = -qV'(r)/2\pi^2r^2$. Therefore:

$$<0|\,\partial_\mu j^\mu_5\,|0> = -\,\frac{e^2}{16\pi^2}\,\varepsilon^{\mu\nu\rho\sigma}F_{\mu\nu}F_{\rho\sigma} - \frac{2q}{\pi}\,V(0)\,\delta^3(\vec{r}) \tag{19}$$

Thus, aside from a δ-function contribution, we have found the usual value for the divergence of the chiral current; in the process, we have also seen that this equation as well is saturated by the lowest partial wave.

b) Non-Abelian Case

We consider a dyon described by the SU(2) monopole gauge fields:

$$A^a_i(\vec{x}) = \varepsilon_{aij}x_j\,\frac{K(r)-1}{er^2}\,, \qquad K(r) = 1 + \mathcal{O}(r^2),\; r\to 0 \tag{20}$$

plus an additional time component: $A^a_0(\vec{x}) = x_a J(r)/er^2$, so that the Dirac Hamiltonian now reads:

$$H\,\psi(\vec{x}) \equiv [\,\vec{\alpha}\cdot(-i\vec{\nabla} + \frac{e}{2}\,\tau^a\vec{A}^a) - \frac{1}{2}\,\vec{\tau}\cdot\hat{x}\,\frac{J(r)}{r}\,]\,\psi(\vec{x}) = E\,\psi(\vec{x}) \tag{21}$$

Since all gauge fields are non-singular in this case, we do not expect any modifications to the anomaly equations; however, the decomposition into partial waves now will become non-trivial.

The final answer for the anomalous divergence must be:

$$<0|\,\partial_\mu j_5^\mu\,|0>_{tot} = -\frac{e^2}{16\pi^2}\,\mathrm{Tr}\,\varepsilon_{\mu\nu\rho\sigma}F^{\mu\nu}F^{\rho\sigma} = \partial_i\,\{\frac{x_i(K(r)^2-1)J(r)}{4\pi^2r^2}\} \tag{22}$$

We can now expand the axial current in Dirac eigenstates as before. The symmetry of higher partial waves no longer leads to a vanishing contribution as in the Abelian case. To show in the simplest way what this contribution is, let's compute it for the lowest angular momentum and compare to the total divergence, Eq.22. For j=0 the Dirac equation reads:

$$[\,-i\,\frac{d}{dr}\,\tau_3\rho_3 - \frac{K(r)}{r}\,\tau_2\rho_3 + \frac{1}{2}\,\frac{J(r)}{r}\,\tau_3\,]\,\chi_E(r) = E\,\chi_E(r) \tag{23}$$

Or, to put it in standard form, using:

$$\tilde{\chi}_E(r) \equiv \exp(\,\frac{i\rho_3}{2}\int_0^r J(r)\,\frac{dr}{r}\,)\,\chi_E(r)\;, \qquad \tau_i=\sigma\otimes 1,\quad \rho_i=1\otimes\sigma_i \tag{24}$$

we have: $$[\,-i\,\frac{d}{dr}\,\tau_3\rho_3 - \frac{K(r)}{r}\,\tau_2\rho_3\,]\,\tilde{\chi}_E(r) = E\,\tilde{\chi}_E(r) \tag{25}$$

From this equation, $\tilde{\chi}_E(r)$ is obtained either explicitly (for K(r) being the Prasad-Sommerfield expression), or formally as a path-ordered exponential in general. Thus we have, for j=0:

$$\begin{aligned}<0|\,\partial_\mu j_5^\mu\,|0>_{j=0} &= \lim_{\varepsilon\to 0}\,\partial_i\,\{\frac{-\hat{x}_i}{8\pi^2r^2}\int_0^\infty dE\,\chi_E^\dagger(r+\frac{\varepsilon}{2})\,\tau_3\,\chi_E(r-\frac{\varepsilon}{2}) + \mathrm{c.c.}\,\}\\ &= \lim_{\varepsilon\to 0}\,\partial_i\,\{\frac{-\hat{x}_i}{8\pi^2r^2}\int_0^\infty dE\,\tilde{\chi}_E^\dagger(r+\frac{\varepsilon}{2})\,\tau_3\exp(\frac{i\gamma_5}{2}\int_{r-\varepsilon/2}^{r+\varepsilon/2} dr\,\frac{J(r)}{r})\,\tilde{\chi}_E(r-\frac{\varepsilon}{2}) + \mathrm{c.c.}\}\\ &= \partial_i\,\{\frac{-x_iJ(r)}{4\pi^2r^2}\}\end{aligned} \tag{26}$$

Comparing Eq.26 with Eq.22, we see that $<0|\,\partial_\mu j_5^\mu|0>_{j=0}$ equals:

$$<0|\,\partial_\mu j_5^\mu\,|0>_{j=0} = -\frac{e^2}{16\pi^2}\,\mathrm{Tr}\,\varepsilon_{\mu\nu\rho\sigma}F^{\mu\nu}F^{\rho\sigma}\Big|_{K(r)=0} \tag{27}$$

The part of the anomaly involving K(r) is the contribution of the higher partial waves. Now, K(r) is a function which falls off exponentially outside the monopole core, so we see that in many instances it is indeed safe to ignore higher partial waves when using the anomaly equation. It is worth noting, however, that inside the core their contribution is increasingly larger (tending to infinity as $r\to 0$, but still with a finite spatial integral).

To conclude the discussion on chiral anomalies, we saw that a Dirac eigenstate expansion of the fermionic currents in a monopole (dyon) background gives the following results:

In the Abelian case: a) We identify $[j_0(\vec{x}), j_0^5(\vec{y})] = -\frac{ie}{2\pi^2} \vec{B}(\vec{y})\cdot\vec{\nabla}_{\vec{x}}\, \delta^3(\vec{x}-\vec{y})$ as the correct expression for the anomalous commutator. b) As a consequence, we see that the electric charge in fact commutes with the regularized axial charge. c) The anomalous divergence equation acquires an extra contribution, with support at the origin. d) The lowest partial wave saturates both anomaly equations.

In the non-Abelian case: a) The higher partial waves do contribute to the anomalous divergence, but only at distances comparable to the monopole core. b) Inside the core, this contribution grows singular, but with a finite integral.

Finally, we turn briefly to a computation of fermion number and a comparison of the properties of Abelian and non-Abelian systems[9]. A most obvious difference between them is the need to introduce some self-adjoint extension parameters in the Abelian system (one boundary angle in the simplest case), which, despite their appearance as a mathematical artifact, affect the physics of the problem. Now, given that in the limit of a vanishing monopole core the non-Abelian monopole becomes identical to the Abelian one and can be modeled by it for computational simplicity, does the same relation exist also for the corresponding fermionic systems? In particular, what will play the role of the boundary angle θ in the non-Abelian case?

D'Hoker and Farhi[10] have demonstrated that in this limit the Dirac Hamiltonian (3) can be obtained from the following non-Abelian one:

$$H = \vec{\alpha}\cdot(-i\vec{\nabla} + \frac{e}{2}\vec{A}^a\tau^a) + \beta M_+ e^{i\omega_+\gamma_5}(\frac{1}{2} + \frac{1}{2}\hat{r}^a\tau^a\phi(r)) + \beta M_- e^{i\omega_-\gamma_5}(\frac{1}{2} - \frac{1}{2}\hat{r}^a\tau^a\phi(r)) \quad (28)$$

describing (outside the core) two fermions of opposite charges and masses M_+, M_-, if, in addition, $M_+ \gg M_-$ so that the M_+ fermion decouples, while its chiral angle ω_+ plays the role of θ. In that case, we show that the properties of the vacuum can also be reduced to the Abelian properties. For general M_+, M_- however, this non-Abelian system presents a more intricate structure: even though the positive and negative charge components of the fermion wave function obey decoupled equations in the limit of infinite monopole mass, their boundary conditions at the origin are mixed by the monopole. This mixing results in an effective long-range coupling of the fermions, shifting the charge density and fermion number density of the vacuum at distances from the monopole of the order of the inverse fermion mass. Thus, for the fermion number density, we find:

$$\rho(r) = \frac{M_+M_-\sin(\omega_+-\omega_-)}{\pi}\int_0^\infty dE\,\frac{e^{-2r(E^2+M_+^2)^{1/2}}+e^{-2r(E^2+M_-^2)^{1/2}}}{(E^2+M_+^2)^{1/2}(E^2+M_-^2)^{1/2}+E^2+M_+M_-\cos(\omega_+-\omega_-)}$$

$$= \rho_+(r) + \rho_-(r) + \rho_I(r) \tag{29}$$

ρ_+, ρ_- are densities for uncoupled fermions and $\rho_I(r)$ is and interference term with range: $\rho_I(r) \sim e^{-M_\pm r}$. We also remark here that an index-type calculation can be used for the total fermion number $n_F \equiv \int\rho(r)\,dr = \frac{\omega_+-\omega_-}{2\pi}$, but not for $\rho(r)$ itself so that the interference cannot be seen in this way.

The properties of this system can again be imitated by an Abelian one which is now larger, containing two fermion species of opposite charge; this time, the self-adjoint extension is a particular choice from a family parameterized by elements of U(2). Other choices for the self-adjoint extension will model non-Abelian cases with a Kobayashi-Maskawa mass mixing. In general self-adjoint extensions are seen to have just the right form and number of parameters to model the possible non-Abelian Hamiltonians; in this way, these parameters, which in general span U(n), can be given a physical interpretation in terms of chiral angles and K-M matrix elements.

Acknowledgements

This work was done partly in collaboration with Hidenaga Yamagishi. It is also a pleasure to thank E.D'Hoker, E.Farhi and L.Vinet for many useful conversations.

References

1. V.A.Rubakov, Nucl.Phys.B203, 311 (1982).
2. C.G.Callan,Jr. Nucl.Phys. B212, 391 (1983).
3. H.Panagopoulos and H.Yamagishi, M.I.T. preprint #1159.
4. A.Sen, Phys.Rev. D28, 876 (1983).
5. R.Jackiw, in "Lectures on Current Algebra and Applications" Princeton U. Press (1972).
6. C.Besson, Ph.D. Thesis, Princeton U. (1981).
7. Y.Kazama, C.N.Yang and A.S.Goldhaber, Phys.Rev. D15, 2287 (1977).
8. H.Yamagishi, Phys.Rev. D27, 2323 (1983).
9. H.Panagopoulos, U. de Montréal preprint, to appear in Phys.Rev. D
10. E.D'Hoker and E.Farhi, Phys.Lett. 127B, 360 (1983).

FRACTIONAL CHARGE IN A NUT-SHELL*

D. BOYANOVSKY AND R. BLANKENBECLER

Stanford Linear Accelerator Center
Stanford University, Stanford, California, 94305

ABSTRACT

We study the physics of charge fractionalization using simple methods. The strategy is to count the number of states of the theory with solitons relative to the same theory with trivial background fields. The interplay between high and low energy contributions is exposed and the topological properties clarified.

* Work supported by the Department of Energy, contract DE – AC03 – 76SF00515.

We study fermions interacting with static external background fields with non-trivial topology. The physics of the problem is simple. The spatial variations of the background fields (b.f.) (gradients) act as "localized" scattering potentials. The spectrum of the free problem is modified. Bound states may be formed (some of them of topological origin), and there is a change in the density of continuum states with respect to the free problem (constant or trivial fields).

Since the spatial variations of the (b.f.) are localized, the change in the density of states is finite. The continuum wave functions are phase shifted near the region of the spatial variations. We study the case when the theory is not CP-invariant, where there is no ambiguity arising from states at zero energy.

The vacuum charge is related to the asymmetry between the positive and negative part of the spectrum (Atiyah-Patodi-Singer invariant)

$$Q = -\frac{1}{2}\,\eta \tag{1}$$

As a measure of the asymmetry in the spectrum of the Hamiltonian H we introduce the fundamental quantity $B(E)$ given by

$$B(E) = \det\left[\frac{H+E}{H-E}\right] \tag{2}$$

$B(E)$ compares the positive and negative parts of the spectrum. We also introduce the even part of the resolvent and odd part of the density of states.

$$G_e = \frac{1}{2}T_r\left[\frac{1}{H+E} + \frac{1}{H-E}\right] = \frac{1}{2}\,\frac{d}{dE}\,\ell n\; B(E) \tag{3}$$

$$\rho_{\rm odd} = \frac{1}{2\pi}\,Im\; G_e(E+i\eta) \tag{4}$$

Then

$$\eta = 2\int_0^\infty \rho_{\rm odd}(E)\,dE = \int_0^\infty [\rho(E) - \rho(-E)]\,dE \tag{5}$$

Regulators are not necessary: the localized spatial variations induce finite changes in the density of states (DOS) and $B(E)$ is a direct comparison of the positive and negative energy spectrum of the full H. We write above the continuum thresholds

$$B(E) = |B(E)|e^{i\delta(E)} \tag{6}$$

where $\delta(E) = \delta^+(E) - \delta^-(E)$ (difference of phase shifts for $E > 0$ and $E < 0$). Therefore

$$\eta = N^+ - N^- + \frac{1}{\pi}[\delta(\infty) - \delta(E_T)] \tag{7}$$

where $N^{\pm}$ is the number of positive and negative energy bound states and E_T = threshold energy.

The most general Hamiltonian of interest in 1-spatial dimension is

$$H = -i\sigma_2 \frac{d}{dx} + \sigma_1 \phi(x) + \sigma_3 K(x) \tag{8}$$

$$H\psi = E\psi \tag{9}$$

Writing

$$\phi(x) = \rho(x)\ \cos\theta(x) \qquad K(x) = \rho(x)\ \sin\theta(x) \tag{10}$$

and performing a chiral rotation

$$\psi(x) = e^{i\sigma_2 \theta(x)}\ \chi(x)\ , \tag{11}$$

we find

$$B(E) = \frac{T_\chi(E)}{T_\chi(-E)} \tag{12}$$

where T_χ is the transmission coefficient of the spinors χ that are eigenspinors of the transformed Hamiltonian

$$H_\chi = -i\sigma_2 \frac{d}{dx} + \frac{1}{2}\frac{d\theta}{dx} + \rho(x)\sigma_1 \tag{13}$$

The spinors χ are, asymptotically, eigenstates of charge conjugation (σ_3). Positive and negative energy spinors interact with opposite sign with the potential ($\theta'(x)$); this is the basic reason for the asymmetry in the spectrum (notice that the spectrum of $H_\chi(\theta' = 0)$ is symmetric). We have studied the cases:

$$\phi(x) = \begin{cases} -\phi & x < 0 \\ \phi(>0) & x > 0 \end{cases} \qquad K(x) = \begin{cases} K & x < -d \\ K_0 & -d < x < d \\ K & x > d \end{cases} \tag{14}$$

and also

$$\phi(x) = \begin{cases} -\phi & x < -d \\ 0 & -d < x < d \\ \phi & x > d \end{cases} \qquad K(x) = \begin{cases} K & x < -d \\ K_0 & -d < x < d \\ K & x > d \end{cases} \tag{15}$$

These examples provide a setting in which the adiabatic approximation breaks down and also the chiral angle $\theta(x)$ winds by 2π, allowing us to understand whether these ambiguities have any influence on the vacuum charge.

For $d = 0$ these examples correspond to the $K =$ constant case, where we find that there is an operator U such that $\{ H, U\} = 0$. The existence of U ensures that the net number of levels crossing $E = 0$ in the process of deforming $\phi(x)$ is zero (zero spectral flow). We find for this case

$$\delta(\infty) = \Delta\theta \equiv \theta(x = +\infty) - \theta(x = -\infty), \qquad -\pi \leq \Delta\theta \leq \pi \tag{16}$$

$$N^+ - N^- = \frac{1}{2}\,\text{sign}(K)[\text{sign}(\phi_+) - \text{sign}(\phi_-)]; \quad \phi_\pm = \phi(x = \pm\infty) \tag{17}$$

and

$$\frac{\delta(0)}{\pi} = N^+ - N^-$$

Therefore $\delta(0)/\pi$ cancels the bound states contribution (Levinson's) theorem, but only when there is no spectral flow. When there is spectral flow, $\delta(0)/\pi$ adds to $N^+ - N^-$. The threshold phase shift $\delta(0)$ changes by π (or $-\pi$) when a new bound state emerges from the positive or negative continuum; therefore η does not change when new bound states appear.

For $K_0 < 0$ and $d \neq 0$, $\Delta\theta$ jumps by 2π; however for $d \ll 1/|K_0|$ no bound state crosses $E = 0$ (no spectral flow). This trivial 2π is compensated by a change of 2π in $\delta(0)$ and is associated to the definition of the branches of $\delta(E)$ and not to new bound states. Therefore $[\delta(\infty) - \delta(0)]$ stays invariant ($\delta(\infty) = \Delta\theta$).

When $d > 1/|K_0|$, one bound state crosses $E = 0$ but $\delta(\infty) - \delta(0)$ remains constant; η jumps by $+2$, and spectral flow has occured. Although the winding of $\Delta\theta$ by 2π may indicate spectral flow and a change in the vacuum charge Q by one unit, this does not occur unless this change in fields takes place over a distance $d \gg \rho(x)$ ($\rho(x)$ = local mass term). The integral values of the charge depend on this spectral flow and local details of the b.f. For the charge conjugate case ($K \to 0^+$) with a soliton profile

$$N^+ - N^- = 1; \qquad \delta(\infty) = \pi; \qquad \delta(0) = \pi$$
$$\eta = 1 + \frac{1}{\pi}[\pi - \pi] \tag{18}$$

The bound state (at $E = 0$) is the Jackiw-Rebbi-Schrieffer "zero mode." Expression (18) exposes the interplay between high and low energy contributions.

We have also studied the vacuum charge in 2+1 dimensions for the case

$$H = i\not{D} + m\sigma_3 \qquad i\not{D} = i\not{\partial} - \not{A}\ , \tag{19}$$

where A_μ corresponds to a static vortex. For constant m, there is no spectral flow as in $1+1$ dimension (for K = constant). In Ref. (3) we showed that the phase shift at infinite energy is

$$\frac{\delta(\infty)}{\pi} = -\text{sign}(m) \int d^2x\ \epsilon_{ij}\ F_{ij}$$

this phase shift at infinite energy is completely determined by the axial anomaly in $1+1$ –Euclidean dimensions where the vortex plays the role of an instanton.

We also found that because of the long range nature of the gauge fields there are $\delta(\infty)/\pi$ states at threshold $E = \pm m$ and the vacuum charge is

$$Q = \frac{1}{2}\ \text{sign}\ (m) \int d^2x\ \epsilon_{ij} F_{ij}\ .$$

The relation between the chiral anomaly in $1+1$ dimensions and the vacuum charge in $2+1$ dimensions is easily understood. The operator $i\not{\partial} - \not{A}$ in H is the $1+1$ –

dimensional Dirac operator; with topologically non-trival A_μ, this operator has "zero modes." These zero modes are eigenstates of σ_3 therefore they are eigenstates of H with energies $E = \pm m$, i.e. threshold states. The sign of the energy depends on the sign of the mass and the flux of the vortex. The sign (m) factor in the expression for the charge plays the same role as the $\pm$ in the 1–dimensional case; these states are filled or empty depending on sign (m).

Some of these states are bound states, but there are also resonant states (non-normalizable). For a sphericaly symmetric vortex the "zero mode" wavefunction behaves as

$$\psi_0 \underset{r\to\infty}{\sim} r^{J-F} \quad \text{where} \quad J = \text{angular momentum}$$

$$F = \text{vortex flux} .$$

In general we write the η-invariant as

$$\eta = \eta_{SF} + \eta_V \ ,$$

Where η_{SF} is a local quantity, i.e. it has information about details of the b.f. It only has contributions from low energy $(\delta(0), N^{\pm})$ and is an even integer or zero. It corresponds to spectral flow (energy levels crossing zero).

In contrast η_V is a topological invariant and completely determined by $\delta(\infty)$ i.e. is a high energy property of the theory. Since it is a high energy property it can be easily computed, and directly related to the anomaly in one less dimension and topological indices (Callias, Atiyah-Singer, etc).

There is a very important physical aspect that relates fractionalization to anomalies. The phase shift at infinite energies is independent of the mass scale ρ in the Hamiltonian. A non-zero phase shift at large energies implies that the energy levels are shifted relative to the non-interacting system. Since the large eigenvalues are shifted equally, the density of states (the energy derivative of the phase shifts) goes to zero as $1/E^3$ as $E \to \infty$.

The total deficit of continuum states cannot depend on the mass scale. It is given by $\delta(\infty) - \delta(0)$ and $\delta(0) \sim n\pi$ (n = integer). The mass and the potential range R set the scale of the density of states as a function of energy. As the mass $\to 0$ and $R \to \infty$, the continuum relative density of states becomes a δ-function at $E = 0$.

REFERENCES

1. R. Jackiw and C. Rebbi, Phys. Rev. D13, 3398 (1976); R. Jackiw and J. R. Schrieffer, Nucl. Phys. B190 [FS3], 253 (1981).

2. J. Goldstone and F. Wilczek, Phys. Rev. Lett. 47, 968 (1981).

3. R. Blankenbecler and D. Boyanovsky, SLAC-PUB-3430; 3567 (to be published in Phys. Rev. D 1985). I. Schmidt *et al.*, SLAC-PUB-3590 (to be published in Phys. Rev. D 1985).

4. A. Niemi and G. W. Semenoff, Phys. Rev. D30, 809 (1984).

5. M. Stone, Illinois preprint ILL-(TH)-84-51 (1984).

HIDDEN SUPERSYMMETRY AND FERMION NUMBER FRACTIONALIZATION

R. Akhoury
University of California, Los Angeles, CA 90024

ABSTRACT. We discuss how a "hidden supersymmetry" of the underlying field theories can be used to interpret and to calculate fermion number fractionalization in different dimensions. This is made possible by relating it to a corresponding Witten index of the "hidden supersymmetry." The closely related anomalies in odd dimensions are also briefly discussed.

I. INTRODUCTION.

In the last few years the study of quantum field theories of fermions coupled to external fields has unearthed many novel features. In particular, the interactions of fermions with topological solitons were shown to give rise to quantum states with fractional fermion numbers.[1] This is the phenomenon of fermion number fractionalization.

Here we discuss a way to calculate and to interpret charge fractionalization using a hidden supersymmetry of the underlying field theories. The induced charge will be related to a "Witten Index"[2] of a supersymmetric quantum mechanical Hamiltonian and the "bosons" and "fermions" will be shown to correspond to particles ($E > 0$) and to antiparticles ($E < 0$) respectively. In the following, we will also discuss the interpretation of the induced charge Q as a spectral asymmetry which measures the relative distortion of the local density of states of positive and negative energy states. Furthermore, the asymmetry for the general case will be related to that for the charge conjugation symmetric limit by an integral transform.

We will first discuss fermion number fractionalization in 1+1 dimensions and then in 3+1 dimensions. The method is easily generalizable to any arbitrary number of dimensions. Next we briefly discuss the closely related phenomenon of anomalies in odd dimensions.[3] This work was carried out in collaboration with A. Comtet.[4]

II. CHARGE FRACTIONALIZATION IN 1+1D.

In order to see how quantum states with fractional fermion number can arise in this manner, consider the following Lagrangian in 1+1D.

$$L = \overline{\psi}(i\not{\partial} - \phi(x) - i\gamma^5 m)\,\psi\ . \tag{1}$$

$\phi(x)$ is a static external soliton and the Hamiltonian of the system is given by

$$-i\frac{\partial}{\partial t}\psi = H_D\psi = \left(i\gamma^5\frac{\partial}{\partial x} - \gamma^o\phi(x) - im\gamma^1 \right)\psi . \qquad (2)$$

For m = 0, the Hamiltonian H_D possesses a conjugation symmetry which can be made explicit by choosing the following representation of the Dirac matrices: $\gamma^o = \sigma_2$, $\gamma^1 = i\sigma_3$, $\gamma^5 = \sigma_1$. Then

$$H_D^{m=0} = -(\sigma^1 P + \sigma^2\phi(x))$$

and $\{H_D^{m=0}, \sigma_3\} = 0$. This shows that σ_3 serves as a conjugation matrix; the energy eigenmodes are symmetric about E = 0, i.e.

$$H_D^{m=0}\psi_E = E\psi_E$$

$$\sigma_3\psi_E = \psi_{-E} \quad .$$

This symmetry is the origin of the hidden supersymmetry in calculations of fermion number fractionalization.

Before we proceed further, it will be useful to discuss certain concepts from supersymmetric quantum mechanics and to develop a procedure for calculating the Witten index.[5]

The most general charge of a supersymmetric quantum mechanics in one dimension is[6]

$$Q = \sigma_1 P + \sigma_2\phi(x)$$

$$Q^2 = H = P^2 + \phi^2 + \sigma_3\phi' = \begin{pmatrix} H_- & 0 \\ 0 & H_+ \end{pmatrix} .$$

The fermion number operator is $(-1)^F$ with the property that $\{Q,(-1)^F\} = 0$, whence it is easily identified that $(-1)^F \Longleftrightarrow -\sigma_3$. The Hamiltonian acts on states $\begin{pmatrix} |f\rangle \\ |b\rangle \end{pmatrix}$. States with fermion number ±1 are termed "bosons" and "fermions" respectively. The Witten index, $\Delta(\beta)$ is defined as:

$$\Delta(\beta) = \mathrm{Tr}(-1)^F e^{-\beta H} = \mathrm{Tr}(e^{-\beta H_+} - e^{-\beta H_-}) \qquad (3)$$

and can be conveniently expressed in terms of the heat kernels:

$$K_\pm(x,y,\beta) = \langle y| e^{-\beta H_\pm} |x\rangle .$$

These satisfy the differential equations,

$$\left(\frac{d}{d\beta} - \frac{d^2}{dx^2} + \phi^2 \mp \phi' \right) K_\pm = 0 \ . \qquad (4)$$

In terms of these heat kernels the Witten index may be written as:

$$\Delta(\beta) = \int dx[K_+(x,x,\beta) - K_-(x,x,\beta)]$$
$$\sim n_+^{E=0} - n_-^{E=0} + \int (\rho_+(E) - \rho_-(E)) \, e^{-\beta E} \, dE \ . \qquad (5)$$

$n_\pm^{E=0}$ are respectively the number of normalizable zero energy states of $H_\pm$. From (5) it is clear that $\Delta(\beta)$ measures the spectral asymmetry, with respect to the Hamiltonian $H_\pm$. In the presence of a soliton ($\phi(x) \underset{x\to\infty}{\to} \phi_+$, $\phi(x) \underset{x\to-\infty}{\to} \phi_-$), ρ_+, ρ_- are not Fermi-Bose paired.[5] In order to compute the Witten index, we use the following identity true in any dimension,

$$\Delta(\beta) - \Delta(0) = \int_0^\beta \frac{d\Delta}{d\beta} \, d\beta \ . \qquad (6)$$

$\Delta(0)$ is just the "anomaly" and it was shown in Ref. 5 that $d\Delta/d\beta$ is a surface term.

In our one-dimensional example,

$$\frac{d\Delta}{d\beta} = \text{surface term} = \int dx \, \frac{1}{2} \frac{d}{dx} \left(\frac{d}{dx} + 2\phi \right) K_+(x,x,\beta) \ .$$

Thus, to evaluate $d\Delta/d\beta$ only the asymptotic form of the heat kernel will be needed. Further, since there is no anomaly in odd dimensions, $\Delta(0) = 0$ and[5]

$$\Delta(\beta) = \frac{1}{2} \, [(\text{sign}\phi) \, \text{erf}(\sqrt{\beta}|\phi|)]_{-\infty}^{\infty} \ . \qquad (7)$$

We will see later how this can be generalized to three dimensions.

Returning now to the problem of fermion number fractionalization in 1+1D, the induced charge is given by

$$Q = \int \langle j^o \rangle \, dx = \frac{1}{2} \int dx \langle [\psi^\dagger(x), \psi(x)] \rangle \ . \qquad (8)$$

Since $\phi(x)$ is static, the propagator can be written as:

$$S(\tau_x, x, \tau_y, y) = \int_C \frac{dE}{2\pi} \, e^{-iE(\tau_x - \tau_y)} \, S_E(x,y)$$

where C encloses all the occupied states. Thus,

$$Q = \frac{1}{2}\int dx \int \frac{dE}{2\pi} \mathrm{Tr}(\gamma_o S_E + \gamma_o S_{-E})$$

$$= -m \int dx \int \frac{dE}{2\pi} \mathrm{Tr}\ \sigma_3 \langle x| \frac{1}{-\partial_x^{\ 2}+\phi^2+\sigma_3\phi^1+E^2+m^2} |x\rangle \ .$$

Using the Schwinger proper time formalism

$$Q = -m \int dx \int \frac{dE}{2\pi} \int_0^\infty dT\ e^{-(m^2+E^2)T}\ \mathrm{Tr}\ \sigma_3\ e^{-TH}$$

$$H = -\partial_x^{\ 2} + \phi^2 + \sigma_3\phi^1 \tag{9}$$

which is the supersymmetric Hamiltonian introduced earlier. Thus Q can be expressed in terms of spectral asymmetry of H. This spectral asymmetry is given by the Witten index introduced earlier. Since σ_3 serves as a conjugation matrix distinguishing particles from antiparticles, and since we may identify $(-1)^F \Longleftrightarrow -\sigma_3$, the particles ($E > 0$) and antiparticles ($E < 0$) correspond to "bosons" and "fermions" of the hidden supersymmetry for which the Witten index,

$$\Delta(T) = \int dx\ \mathrm{Tr}\ -\sigma_3\ e^{-TH} \ .$$

Expression (9) now becomes,

$$Q = m \int \frac{dE}{2\pi} \int_0^\infty e^{-(m^2+E^2)T}\ \Delta(T)\ dT = \int_0^\infty \frac{e^{-T}}{\sqrt{T}}\ \Delta(T/m^2)\ \frac{dT}{2\pi} \ . \tag{10}$$

This was first obtained in Ref. 7 using different methods. If we write Q as the spectral asymmetry between density of states for particles and antiparticles,

$$Q = \frac{1}{2}\int_0^\infty dE(\rho(E) - \rho(-E)) \ .$$

Then

$$\rho(E) - \rho(-E) = \frac{m}{\pi}\int_0^\infty dT\ e^{-(m^2+E^2)T}\ \Delta(T) \ . \tag{11}$$

The LHS measures the spectral asymmetry for the general case with $m \neq 0$ whereas on the RHS, $\Delta(T)$ measures that for the charge conjugation limit with $m = 0$. Substituting (7) for $\Delta(T)$ in (11) one obtains the usual expression for Q, i.e.

$$Q = \frac{1}{2\pi}\left(\tan^{-1}\frac{\phi_+}{m} - \tan^{-1}\frac{\phi_-}{m} \right) .$$

Similar considerations can be generalized to higher dimensions and we indicate how it works for 3+1D.

III. CHARGE FRACTIONALIZATION IN 3+1D.

We consider the interaction of fermions in a magnetic monopole background with $A_o{}^a = 0$.

$$L = (i\partial\!\!\!/ + \gamma_\mu A_\mu - \phi(x) + im\gamma_5)\, \psi .$$

The Hamiltonian is given by:

$$-i\partial_o\psi = H_D\psi = (i\alpha^k\partial^k + \alpha^k A^k - \beta(\phi - i\gamma_5 m))\, \psi . \qquad (12)$$

When $m = 0$, once again there is a conjugation symmetry with $i\beta\gamma_5$ as the conjugation matrix:

$$\{H_D, i\beta\gamma_5\} = 0$$

and we may identify $(-1)^F \Longleftrightarrow i\beta\gamma_5$ with the "bosons" and "fermions" of the hidden supersymmetry identified with the particles and antiparticles as before. Identical arguments as before allow us to write the induced charge as

$$Q = m \int \frac{dE}{2\pi} \int_0^\infty dT\, e^{-T(m^2+E^2)}\, \Delta(T) \qquad (13)$$

where the $\Delta(T)$ is the Witten index for a 3D system:

$$\Delta(T) = \int d^3x\, \mathrm{Tr}(e^{-\beta H_+} - e^{-\beta H_-})$$

$$H_\pm = -\nabla^2 - \sigma_k B_k \mp \sigma_k[\nabla_k, \phi] + \phi^2$$

$$\nabla_k = \partial_k - iA_k \text{ and } B_k \text{ is the magnetic field .} \qquad (14)$$

This is the appropriate generalization of the 1+1D case. It can be shown[4] that once again $d\Delta(T)/dT$ is a surface term. Using the asymptotic forms of the various background fields, i.e.

$$A_i(x) \to \frac{1}{|\underset{\sim}{x}|} \; , \quad \phi(x) \to O(1) \; , \quad [\nabla_k,\phi] \to 0 \; , \quad B_k(x) \to \frac{1}{|\underset{\sim}{x}|^2}$$

and the fact that in 3D, $\Delta(0) = 0$, we obtain

$$\Delta(T) = \frac{\sqrt{T}}{(4\pi)^{3/2}} \int_0^1 dx \int \mathrm{Tr} \, \frac{e^{-Tx\phi_o^2}}{\sqrt{x}} \, B_i \phi_o d\Sigma_i$$

which yields for SU(2) fermions in the adjoint representation the following expression for Q by substituting in (13)

$$Q = \frac{1}{\pi} \left[\tan^{-1} \frac{|\phi_o|}{m} \right] \iint \frac{d\Sigma_i}{4\pi} B_i^a \frac{\phi^a}{|\phi^a|} \; .$$

IV. CHARGE FRACTIONALIZATION IN 2+1D.

We next very briefly discuss charge fractionalization in QED in 2+1D with static external gauge fields coupled to fermions ($A_o = 0$). Here the only contribution to $\Delta(T)$ comes from $\Delta(0)$ in (6) in contradiction to the two earlier cases discussed.

The induced charge may be written as:

$$Q = m \int \frac{dE}{2\pi} \int_0^\infty dT \; e^{-T(m^2+E^2)} \; \Delta(T) \qquad (15)$$

with

$$\Delta(T) = \mathrm{Tr}_2 \gamma_o \; e^{-T(i\not{D})_2^2} \qquad (16)$$

where the subscript "2" above denotes the corresponding operation in 2 dimensions. Since γ_o in 3D plays the role of γ_5 in 2D, and since in 2D the index is T independent, we get

$$\Delta(T) = \Delta(0) = \text{2-D anomaly} \; ,$$

whence

$$Q = \int \langle j^o \rangle \, dx = \frac{e}{2} \frac{m}{|m|} \int \frac{eB}{2\pi} d^2x \; . \qquad (17)$$

The parity violating part of the effective action in 3D has its origin in this fermion number fractionalization.[8] This parity violating part of effective action is written as

$$\Gamma^P_{eff} = \frac{1}{2} [\mathrm{Tr}\ \ell n(i\not{D}+im) - \mathrm{Tr}\ \ell n(i\not{D}-im)]$$
$$= \int d^3x \frac{e^2}{16\pi} \varepsilon_{\mu\nu\alpha} A^\mu F^{\nu\alpha} \frac{m}{|m|} .$$

The induced charge is

$$Q = \int \langle j^o \rangle d^2x \quad \text{with} \quad \langle j^\mu \rangle = \frac{\delta\Gamma^P_{eff}}{\delta A_\mu} ,$$

$\langle j^o \rangle$ is exactly the expression obtained in (17) which establishes the connection with charge fractionalization. Since Γ^P_{eff} has its origin in charge fractionalization which is depleted at finite temperatures, we expect a similar behavior for Γ^P_{eff}. In fact, this can be computed for gauge fields in a periodic box length $[0,\beta]$ in time and $[L_1,L_2]$ in spatial direction with the following configuration

$$F_{12} = B , \quad A_1 = -\frac{Bx_2}{2} , \quad A_2 = \frac{Bx_1}{2} , \quad A_3 = A \text{ (constant)} .$$

The result[4] is an expression for Γ^P_{eff} at finite temperature:

$$\Gamma^P_{eff} = \frac{e\beta}{2\pi} \arctan\left[\tanh\frac{\beta m}{2} \tan\frac{\beta eA}{2} \right] L_1 L_2$$

which decreases with increasing temperature as expected.

ACKNOWLEDGEMENT. This work is supported in part by the National Science Foundation under Grant # PHY-83-14188.

REFERENCES.

1. R. Jackiw, C. Rebbi, Phys. Rev. D13, 3398 (1976); J. Goldstone, F. Wilczek, Phys. Rev. Lett. 47, 468 (1981); A. J. Niemi, G. W. Semenoff, Phys. Rev. D30, 809 (1984) and references therein.
2. E. Witten, Nucl. Phys. B202, 253 (1982).
3. N. Redlich, Phys. Rev. Lett. 52, 1 (1984); A. J. Niemi, G. W. Semenoff, Phys. Rev. Lett. 51, 2077 (1983); L. Alvarez-Gaumé, S. De-la Pietra, G. Moore, Harvard Preprint, HUTP-84/A028.
4. R. Akhoury, A. Comtet, UCLA Preprint, UCLA/85/TEP/2.
5. R. Akhoury, A. Comtet, Nucl. Phys. B246, 253 (1984).
6. E. Witten, Nucl. Phys. B185, 513 (1981).

7. A. J. Niemi, Phys. Lett. 146B, 213 (1984).
8. A. J. Niemi, G. W. Semenoff, Phys. Rev. Lett. 51, 2077 (1983).

Twist and Topology in ^{3}He-A

Michael Stone
Department of Physics
University of Illinois at Urbana-Champaign
1110 West Green Streèt
Urbana, IL 61801

Abstract

I give an account of the role of "charge fractionalization" in the mass current of superfluid Helium-3. The topologically induced charge is seen to account for some of the puzzling features of the current.

Introduction

Most of this conference has been about esoteric mathematics applied to systems which, while they may describe the real world, are not readily studied in the laboratory. It is comforting that there do exist, in condensed matter, a number of simple and experimentally realizable systems where topological considerations, very similar to those that occur in high energy physics, substantially influence the physics. Well known examples are the fractionally charged solitons in polyacetylene[1)] and the quantum hall effect.[2)] I shall describe here another example: that of the superfluid phases of ^{3}He - expecially the A phase.

Helium 3 is a fermi-liquid which undergoes a phase transition to a superfluid at a temperature in the order of 1mK. At the transition temperature Cooper pairs form in a manner similar to a superconductor.

The main differences between the superfluid and the superconductor are that the former is electrically neutral, unlike the electron gas in a metal, and the Cooper pairs form in a p-state instead of an s-state. The A phase is characterized by an order parameter which is an orthonormal triad of vectors $\underline{\ell}$, $\underline{w}_1$, $\underline{w}_2$ where $\underline{\ell} = \underline{w}_1 \times \underline{w}_2$. A spatial variation in the orientation of the triad gives rise to a mass current which at zero temperature has been calculated to be[3)]

$$\underline{g} = \rho \underline{V}_s + \frac{1}{4} \rho \, \underline{\nabla} \times \underline{\ell} - \rho/2 \, \underline{\ell} \, (\underline{\ell} \cdot \underline{\nabla} \times \underline{\ell}) \tag{1}$$

where

$$(V_s)_i = \frac{1}{2} \underline{w}_1 \cdot \nabla_i \underline{w}_2 \tag{2}$$

The first term is the supercurrent which could be obtained by just giving all the atoms a common momentum. The second can be understood loosely as arising from the orbital motion of the Cooper pairs, which have angular momentum ℓ, in the same way that a bound current $\underline{\nabla} \times \underline{M}$ occurs in a system with magnetic dipole density $\underline{M}$. The last term, called the twist term, is harder to account for and has given rise to some puzzlement. To see why this is so consider a slab of fluid between two walls at 0,a. Let. the order parameter be independant of x,y and suppose that the boundaries impose the condition that ℓ be normal to the wall at the boundary but allowed to vary with z elsewhere. Then integrating 1) to find the total transverse (ie x,y) mass flow one gets zero from the first two terms but, in general, a non-zero answer from the twist term. This contradicts the well known result from quantum mechanics that translation invariance of the wave function implies zero total momentum; since if the order parameter is independent of x,y so is the wave-function. We have found a version of what is called the McClure-Takagi paradox.[4)]

2) ^{3}He-A and the Dirac Equation

As a model for ^{3}He consider the partition function of a four-fermi interacting field:

$$Z = \int d[\psi]\, d[\psi^*] \exp - \int_0^\beta \{\psi^*(\partial_\tau + H)\, \psi - \frac{\lambda}{2}\, \psi^* \psi^* \psi\psi\} d\tau \qquad (2.1)$$

$$H = - \frac{1}{2m}\, \nabla^2 - \mu \qquad (2.2)$$

where the attractive interaction creates a condensate

$$\langle\psi\psi\rangle = \Delta \qquad (2.3)$$

(there are spin and space indices on the grassman field ψ, but I shall suppress them. Δ is antisymmetric in these indices). In terms of Δ

$$Z = \int d[\Delta]\, d[\Delta^\dagger]\, d[\psi]\, d[\psi^*] \exp - \int_0^\beta \{\psi^*(\partial_\tau + H)\, \psi - \Delta^\dagger \psi\psi - \Delta\psi^*\psi^*\}\, d\tau$$

$$\times \exp - \int \frac{2}{\lambda}\, |\Delta|^2 d\tau \qquad (2.4)$$

If we assume $|\Delta|^2$ is fixed we just have to consider the grassman quadratic form

$$\frac{1}{2}\, (\psi^*, \psi) \begin{bmatrix} \partial_\tau + H & \Delta \\ \Delta^\dagger & \partial_\tau - H^T \end{bmatrix} \begin{bmatrix} \psi \\ \psi^* \end{bmatrix} \qquad (2.5)$$

which can be diagonalized by a substitution

$$\psi = \sum_n (u^{(n)}\chi_n + (v^{(n)})^* \chi_n^*)$$

$$\psi^* = \sum_n (v^{(n)}\chi_n + (u^{(n)})^* \chi_n^*) \tag{2.6}$$

to the form:

$$\frac{1}{2}\sum_n (\chi_n^* \; \chi_n) \begin{bmatrix} \partial_\tau + E_n & \\ & \partial_\tau - E_n \end{bmatrix} \begin{bmatrix} \chi_n \\ \chi_n^* \end{bmatrix} \tag{2.7}$$

For states near the fermi surface we can put,[5] (for variation in the Z direction only).

$$(u_n^0, v_n^0) = \left(u_n(z), v_n(z)\right) e^{i\underline{p}\cdot\underline{r}} , \quad |p| = p_f \tag{2.8}$$

and for the A phase $\Delta = \Delta\ (r,r')$ has fourier transform:

$$\int d^3r\ e^{-i\underline{p}\cdot\underline{r}}\ \Delta(R + r/2,\ R - r/2) = i\ \frac{\Delta}{p_f}\ \underline{p}\cdot(\underline{w}_1(R) + i\ \underline{w}_2(R)) \tag{2.9}$$

so the eigenvalue equation for E_n becomes

$$E_n u_n = -\,i\,\frac{p_z}{m}\,\partial_z u_n + i\,\frac{\Delta}{p_f}\,(\underline{w}_1\cdot\underline{p} + i\,\underline{w}_2\cdot\underline{p})\,v_n$$

$$E_n v_n = +\,i\,\frac{p_z}{m}\,\partial_z v_n - i\,\frac{\Delta}{p_f}\,(\underline{w}_1\cdot\underline{p} - i\,\underline{w}_2\cdot\underline{p})\,u_n \tag{2.10}$$

which is the Hamiltonian from the 1+1 dimensional Dirac action:

$$\bar{\psi}\,(\gamma^{\mu}\partial_{\mu}+\phi_1+i\,\phi_2\gamma_5)\psi$$

$$\phi_1 \propto \underline{w}_1\cdot\underline{p} \qquad (2.11)$$

$$\phi_2 \propto \underline{w}_2\cdot\underline{p}$$

which is of the form discussed in the talks by Boyanovski and Semenof in this volume.

3. The Mass Current and the Origin of Twist

The mass current can easily be calculated to be

$$g = \int \frac{d^2p}{(2\pi)^2}\,\underline{p} \sum_{\substack{\text{negative}\\ E_n}} |u_n|^2 \qquad (3.1)$$

(where the sum on p comes from putting periodic boundary conditions in the x,y directions).

Now we can use the well known results from charge fractionalization

$$\sum_{E_n<0} (|u|^2+|v|^2) = \langle\bar{\psi}\,\gamma^0\psi\rangle = j_0$$

$$\sum_{E_n<0} (|u|^2-|v|^2) = \langle\bar{\psi}\,\gamma^0\gamma^5\psi\rangle = j_1 \qquad (3.2)$$

$$j_{\mu} = \frac{\varepsilon_{\mu\nu}}{2\pi}\,\partial_{\nu}\tan^{-1}\phi_2/\phi_1$$

In the static case we are considering here $j_1 = 0$ so

$$\underline{g} = \frac{1}{4\pi}\int \frac{d^2p}{(2\pi)^2}\,\underline{p}\,\mathrm{sgn}\,(p_z)\,\partial_z\tan^{-1}\left(\frac{p\cdot w_1}{p\cdot w_2}\right) \qquad (3.3)$$

where the sgn (p_z) comes from observing that two values of p_z occur on the fermi surface for each pair p_x, p_y and the role of positive and negative energies is reversed between them.

Equation 3.3 is not new. In a slightly modified form it is the expression for the current due to Volovik and Mineev.[6)] However the advantage of deriving it via charge fractionalisation is that there are no paradoxes there. We know that, if we find a fractional charge at a soliton in polyacetylene, the balance of the charge is found elsewhere. Thus in our context there must be currents induced on the walls of the container (where 1.1 does not apply) in just the same way that charges are induced at the end of the polyacetylene molecule.

To finish up let me just indicate how the twist term comes out of 3.3: If ℓ, w_1, w_2 all start and end the same, then $\tan^{-1}(p\cdot w_2)/(p\cdot w_1)$ can return to its initial value or increase by $2\pi n$. Thus those $\underline{p}$ contribute that have been wound around by $\underline{\ell}$. Using

$$(p_x, p_y)\, dp_x \times dp_y = \frac{1}{3}\, d\left((p_x, p_y)\, p_x dp_y - p_y dp_x\right)$$

we can convert the integral over them to one over z

$$\int \underline{p}_\perp dp_x \times dp_y = \frac{p_F^{\;3}}{3} \int \underline{\ell}_\perp (\hat{\underline{z}} \cdot (\underline{\ell} \times d\underline{\ell})$$

$$= -\frac{p_F^{\;3}}{3} \int \underline{\ell}_{\;\perp} (\underline{\ell} \cdot (\Delta \times \underline{\ell})\, dz$$

$$\int \underline{g}_{\;\perp} dz = -\frac{p_f^{\;3}}{3\cdot(2\pi)^2} \int dz\, \left(\underline{\ell}_\perp (\underline{\ell}\cdot\underline{\Delta}\times\underline{\ell})\right)$$

and $\rho = \frac{4}{3} \cdot \frac{\pi p_f^3}{(2\pi)^3}$ so the net transverse current is produced by just by those momenta for which there is an integer topological "charge".

Acknowledgements

The work described here was done in collaboration with Paul Muzikar and Anupam Garg.[7] Work supported by NSF Grant DMR84-15063.

References

1) W. P. Su, J. R. Schrieffer, A. J. Heeger, Phys. Rev. Lett. 42, 1968 (1979).

2) R. B. Laughlin, Phys. Rev. Lett. 50, 1395, (1983).

3) a) M. C. Cross, J. Low Temp. Phys. 21, 525 (1975).
b) N. D. Mermin, P. Muzikar, Phys. Rev. B21, 980 (1980).

4) There are various formulations of this paradox: See Ref. 3b) and M. G. McClure, S. Takagi, Phys. Rev. Lett. 43, 596, (1979).

5) T. L. Ho, J. R. Fulco, J. R. Schrieffer, F. Wilczek, Phys. Rev. Lett. 52, 1524 (1984).

6) G. E. Volovik, V. P. Mineev, Sov. Phys. JETP 54, 524 (1981).

7) M. Stone, A. Garg, P. Muzikar, Illinois preprint.

INDEX THEORY ANALYSIS OF FERMION NUMBER FRACTIONIZATION

A.J. Niemi *
Institute for Advanced Study
Princeton, NJ 08540, USA †

and

G.W. Semenoff ‡
Department of Physics
University of British Columbia
Vancouver, B.C., V6T 2A6 Canada

I. Introduction

In their original work, Jackiw and Rebbi [1] showed that topologically nontrivial background fields induce zero modes for certain conjugation symmetric Dirac Hamiltonians and that the ensuing ground state degeneracy leads to quantum states with fractional fermion number. This relation between zero modes and fermion number fractionization suggested an index theory analysis of the problem and motivated Callias [2] to derive an open infinite space index theorem for a special class of Dirac operators. Subsequent analysis by Goldstone and Wilczek [3] revealed that even in the more general case of Dirac operators without conjugation symmetry the topological invariance of the fermion number persists, at least in the adiabatic limit. However, it was also obvious that known index theorems did not provide a setting for the analysis. It was then realized that the ground state fermion number N is always proportional to the η-invariant or spectral asymmetry of the Dirac Hamiltonian [4],

$$N = -\frac{1}{2}\eta_H = -\frac{1}{2}\lim_{\beta\to 0+}\sum_n sign(E_n)e^{-\beta E_n^2} \tag{1}$$

where E_n are the eigenvalues of the Hamiltonian. (Notice that on an open infinite manifold the spectrum of H in general contains a continuum contribution and the definition of η_H requires some care [5]: (1) must then be understood as an integral over the odd part of the spectral density of H.)

The η-invariant was originally introduced in the mathematics literature by Atiyah, Patodi and Singer [6]. They found that in addition to the pertinent characteristic classes,

---

* Research supported in part by Department of Energy Grant no. DE-AC02-76ER02220

† On leave from Helsinki University of Technology. Espoo. Finland

‡ Supported in part by the Natural Sciences and Engineering Research Council of Canada

on an open compact manifold the index of a Dirac operator is also related to the η-invariant of another Dirac operator defined on the boundary of the manifold. However, since the Dirac Hamiltonians that arise in the analysis of fermion number fractionization are not generally defined on compact closed manifolds the methods by Atiyah, Patodi and Singer could not be used directly for computation of the η-invariants that arise there.

A technique for calculating η_H for a large class of Dirac operators on open infinite spaces was developed by Niemi, Paranjape and Semenoff [7] - [10]. Their work provided a complete mathematical analysis of fermion number fractionization in a large class of field theory models and the invariance of η_H under local variations of the background fields led to the identification of the odd part of the spectral density as a topological quantity [5]. However, it was also obvious that certain interesting Dirac operators cannot be represented in the form analyzed in [7] - [10]. For these more general operators the η-invariant depends on the local details of the background fields and acquires a *spectral flow* contribution (*i.e.* eigenvalues crossing zero). Niemi and Semenoff [11] observed that since the spectral flow of a Dirac Hamiltonian can be related to the index of a Dirac operator in one higher dimension, the proper mathematical setting for the fermion number fractionization problem is obtained using a family index theorem. They also derived the appropriate index theorem thus generalizing the Atiyah-Patodi-Singer index theorem to open infinite manifolds.

In this article we review our work on the topological analysis of fermion number fractionization. In section II we exhibit the relation between the ground state fermion number and the η-invariant of the pertinent Dirac Hamiltonian. In section III we derive an expression for η_H for the family of Dirac operators analyzed in [7] - [10] and give a few examples. In section IV we explain the family index theorem approach for the computation of η_H and in section V we show how this index theorem can be used to compute the fermion number.

II. Vacuum Fermion Number in Quantum Field Theory

Consider a system of fermions with dynamics governed by a Dirac Hamiltonian $H(Q)$ where Q stands for generic, static background fields. Quantization proceeds by solving for the energy eigenstates of $H(Q)$,

$$H\psi_n(x) = E_n\psi_n(x) \tag{2}$$

and expanding the field operator,

$$\Psi(x,t) = \sum_{E_n>0} \mathbf{a}_n\psi_n(x)e^{iE_nt} + \sum_{E_n<0} \mathbf{b}_n^\dagger\psi_n(x)e^{iE_nt} \tag{3}$$

where $\mathbf{a}_n$, $\mathbf{b}_n^+$ are the fermionic annihilation and creation operators.

$$\{\mathbf{a}_n, \mathbf{a}_m^\dagger\} = \{\mathbf{b}_n, \mathbf{b}_m^\dagger\} = \delta_{n,m} \tag{4}$$

with all other anticommutators vanishing. The Fock vacuum satisfies

$$\mathbf{a}_n|0>=\mathbf{b}_n|0>=0 \tag{5}$$

and the ground state expectation value of the fermion number operator is given by

$$<\mathbf{N}>=N=\frac{1}{2}\int dx\ <0|\left[\Psi^\dagger(x),\Psi(x)\right]|0>=-\frac{1}{2}\eta_H \tag{6}$$

III. Computation of the η-invariant

For a large class of Dirac operators η_H is invariant under local variations of the background fields and can be computed exactly. These operators have the property that in some representation of the Dirac and internal matrices they can be represented in the form

$$H=\begin{pmatrix} m & \mathcal{D} \\ \mathcal{D}^\dagger & -m \end{pmatrix}=H_0+m\Gamma^C \tag{7}$$

where m is a (real) constant and $\mathcal{D}$ an operator of the form

$$\mathcal{D}=i\vec{\gamma}\cdot\vec{\nabla}+Q(x) \tag{8}$$

and $Q(x)$ denotes the (arbitrary) background fields.

The operator H_0 anticommutes with the chirality matrix Γ^C and consequently its spectrum is symmetric. Thus, in the special case where $m=0$, only the zero modes of H_0 can contribute to η_{H_0}, each entering the relation (1) with an ambiguous sign. The corresponding fermion number was computed by Jackiw and Rebbi:

$$N=+\frac{1}{2}(\#\ of\ occupied\ zero\ modes)-\frac{1}{2}(\#\ of\ unoccupied\ zero\ modes) \tag{9}$$

Partial information on the number of zero modes can be obtained from the index of H_0.

$$Index\ H_0=DimKer\ \mathcal{D}-DimKer\ \mathcal{D}^\dagger \tag{10}$$

For many Dirac operators either $DimKer\ \mathcal{D}$ or $DimKer\ \mathcal{D}^\dagger$ vanishes. In such cases the index of H_0 counts the total number of zero modes and therefore completely determines the possible values of the fermion number.

In the more general case where $m\neq 0$

$$H^2=H_0^2+m^2\geq m^2 \tag{11}$$

and consequently the operator H does not have zero modes. Furthermore, in general its spectrum is not symmetric. In addition to the zero modes of H_0 *i.e.* the eigenvalues of H

with $E = \pm m$, the continuum eigenvalues of H will also contribute to (1). Following [7] - [10] we compute (1) as follows: Using the integral representation

$$sign(E) = \int_{-\infty}^{\infty} \frac{d\omega}{\pi} \frac{E}{E^2 + \omega^2} \tag{12}$$

η_H can be written as the operator trace

$$\eta_H = \lim_{\beta \to 0+} \int_{-\infty}^{\infty} \frac{d\omega}{\pi} \int dx \, tr < x| \frac{H}{H^2 + \omega^2} e^{-\beta H^2} |x > \tag{13}$$

where "tr" denotes a pointwise trace over the Dirac and internal indices. Since $\{\Gamma^C, H_0\} = 0$ we get

$$\eta_H = \lim_{\beta \to 0+} \int_{-\infty}^{\infty} \frac{d\omega}{\pi} \, m e^{-\beta m^2} \int dx \, tr < x|\Gamma^C \frac{1}{H_0^2 + m^2 + \omega^2} e^{-\beta H_0^2} |x > \tag{14}$$

which can be written as

$$\eta_H = sign(m) \lim_{\beta \to 0+} \int dx \, tr < x|\Gamma^C e^{-\beta H_0^2}|x > +$$

$$+ \lim_{\beta \to 0} \int_{-\infty}^{\infty} \frac{d\omega}{2\pi} \frac{m e^{-\beta m^2}}{m^2 + \omega^2} \int dx \, \vec{\nabla} \cdot tr < x| i \vec{\Gamma} \Gamma^C \frac{H_0}{H_0^2 + m^2 + \omega^2} e^{-\beta H_0^2} |x > \tag{15}$$

where

$$\vec{\Gamma} = \begin{pmatrix} 0 & \vec{\gamma} \\ \vec{\gamma}^\dagger & 0 \end{pmatrix} \tag{16}$$

are the Dirac matrices constructed from those in $\mathcal{D}$.

The first term on the *r.h.s.* of (15) can be computed using the asymptotic $\beta \to 0$ expansion [12]

$$tr < x|\Gamma^C e^{-\beta H_0^2}|x > \stackrel{\beta \to 0+}{\longrightarrow} \sum_{n=\frac{d}{2}} \beta^{n-\frac{d}{2}} \mathcal{B}_n(x) \tag{17}$$

where $\mathcal{B}_n$ are the pertinent characteristic classes. In odd dimensions this contribution is absent and in even dimensions it is proportional to the chiral anomaly: Indeed, (15) can be recast in a form where it resembles an integrated continuity equation for a chiral fermionic current, the *l.h.s.* arises from the fermion mass term and the first term on the *r.h.s.* is the chiral anomaly [9], [10]. In the $\beta \to 0$ limit we have

$$\eta_H = sign(m) \int dx \, \mathcal{B}_{\frac{d}{2}}(x) +$$

$$+\int_{-\infty}^{\infty} \frac{d\omega}{2\pi} \frac{m}{m^2+\omega^2} \oint d\Sigma \cdot tr < x|\vec{\Gamma}\Gamma^C \frac{H_0}{H_0^2+m^2+\omega^2}|x> \tag{18}$$

For background fields with sufficiently smooth asymptotic behaviour the second term in (18) can be computed by a large distance expansion of the integrand in inverse powers of $|x|$. Since the first term in (18) (*i.e.* the chiral anomaly term) can always be computed, (18) then provides a practical scheme for the computation of the fermion number for Dirac operators of the form (7) [4], [10].

We now consider some examples:

(i) for $d = 1$, consider

$$H = i\sigma^2 \frac{d}{dx} + \sigma^1\phi(x) + \sigma^3 m \tag{19}$$

which is of the form (7) with

$$\mathcal{D} = \frac{d}{dx} + \phi(x) \tag{20}$$

Here the anomaly term in (18) is absent and the surface integral yields [7]

$$\eta_H = \frac{1}{\pi}\left\{tan^{-1}(\frac{\phi(\infty)}{m}) - tan^{-1}(\frac{\phi(-\infty)}{m})\right\} \tag{21}$$

(ii) for $d = 2$ we consider

$$H = i\sigma^1(\partial_x + ieA_x) + i\sigma^2(\partial_y + ieA_y) + \sigma^3 m \tag{22}$$

Here

$$\mathcal{D} = i\frac{d}{dx} - A_x + \frac{d}{dy} + iA_y \tag{23}$$

and only the anomaly term contributes [9],

$$\eta_H = sign(m)\frac{e}{2\pi}\int d^2x\, B(x) \tag{24}$$

where $B(x)$ is the $d = 2$ magnetic field.

(iii) for $d = 3$ consider

$$H = i\vec{\alpha}\cdot\vec{\nabla} + \vec{\alpha}\cdot\vec{A} - \beta(\mu - im\gamma^5 + \Phi) \tag{25}$$

Here

$$\mathcal{D} = i\vec{\sigma}\cdot\vec{\nabla} + \vec{\sigma}\cdot\vec{A} + i(\mu + \Phi) \tag{26}$$

and $\vec{A}$, Φ are in the isospin-T representation of $SU(2)$ with a magnetic monopole profile. The anomaly term is absent and the surface term in (18) yields [8], [10]

$$\eta_H = \frac{2\nu}{\pi}\sum_{j=-T}^{T} j\, tan^{-1}\left(\frac{\mu + j\varphi}{m}\right) \tag{27}$$

where φ is the asymptotic length of Φ and

$$\nu = \frac{1}{4\pi}\oint d\vec{\Sigma}\cdot\vec{B}^a\frac{\Phi^a}{\varphi} \tag{28}$$

is the monopole number

(iv) for $d = 4$ consider

$$H = i\gamma^E_\mu D_\mu + \gamma^5 m \tag{29}$$

where D_μ is the gauge covariant derivative with an $SU(2)$ isospin-T background field. Now

$$\mathcal{D} = i\sigma^\mu\nabla^\mu + \sigma^\mu A^\mu \tag{30}$$

and only the anomaly term contributes [10],

$$\eta_H = sign(m)\frac{e^2}{16\pi^2}\int dx\; tr\{F\widetilde{F}\} \tag{31}$$

IV. An Index Theorem for Open Infinite Spaces

There are many interesting Dirac Hamiltonians that can not be represented in the form (7). In such cases the previous formalism does not apply directly. In this section we shall describe a generalization that can be used to compute the η-invariant of an *arbitrary* Dirac Hamiltonian. This technique is based on an open infinite space version of the Atiyah-Patodi-Singer index theorem derived in [11].

Consider the $d+1$ dimensional Dirac equation

$$i\frac{\partial}{\partial t}\psi(x,t) = H\psi(x,t) \tag{32}$$

where H is a Hamiltonian defined in the background of a topological soliton. This Hamiltonian is of the form

$$H = \frac{1}{i}\gamma^0\vec{\gamma}\cdot\vec{\nabla} + Q(x) \tag{33}$$

where $Q(x)$ includes all background fields. We assume that these background fields are static and without loss of generality we also assume that the eigenvalues E_n of H are nonvanishing. In order to compute η_H we first introduce a one-parameter family of Dirac Hamiltonians H_τ with $\tau \in (-\infty, \infty)$ by extending $Q(x)$ to a τ-dependent field $Q(x,\tau)$. We choose

$$\lim_{\tau\to+\infty} H_\tau = H \qquad \& \qquad \lim_{\tau\to-\infty} H_\tau = H_0 \tag{34}$$

where H_0 is some conveniently chosen Hamiltonian for which the η-invariant can be computed independently (*e.g.* a free field Hamiltonian). We assume that the background field $Q(x,\tau)$ is a slowly varying, *adiabatic* function of τ. We also assume that the Dirac equation (32) is obeyed for all values of τ. Consider the fermionic current

$$j_\mu(x,t;\tau) = \frac{1}{2} < 0|\left[\bar{\Psi}, \gamma^\mu\Psi\right]|0> \tag{35}$$

In the adiabatic limit the field operators in (35) admit an eigenmode expansion such as (3) but with the energy eigenstates now the eigenstates of the Hamiltonian H_τ. We choose the state $|0>$ in (35) to be the Fock vacuum corresponding to the Hamiltonian H. This means that in the eigenmode expansion of Ψ we use creation and annihilation operators $\mathbf{a}_n$, $\mathbf{b}_m^\dagger$ that are determined at $\tau = \infty$ *i.e.* these operators are τ-independent. The current (35) is then normal ordered with respect to the $\tau = \infty$ ground state and is conserved, $\partial^\mu j_\mu = 0$, for every value of τ. By time translation invariance of the background fields the fermion number

$$< 0|\mathbf{N}_\tau|0 >= \int dx\, j^0(x,t;\tau) \tag{36}$$

is time independent. However, in general it does depend in a nontrivial way on the parameter τ. If we consider the divergence of j_μ with respect to the spatial variables x^i *and* the parameter τ (with Euclidean metric) we find that

$$\partial_\mu j_\mu = \Delta(x,\tau) \tag{37}$$

where $\Delta(x,\tau)$ reflects the τ-dependence of (36). (Notice that this implies a particular extension of j^μ in the parameter τ which we shall discuss in more detail later.) If we integrate (37) over the (x_i,τ) space we obtain

$$\int_{\tau=+\infty} dx\, j_0(x,\tau) \; - \; \int_{\tau=-\infty} dx\, j_0(x,\tau) \tag{38}$$

$$= \int_{-\infty}^{\infty} d\tau \frac{\partial}{\partial\tau} \int dx\, j_0(x,\tau) = -\int_{-\infty}^{\infty} d\tau \oint dS^i j_i(x,\tau) + \int d\tau dx\, \Delta(x,\tau) \tag{39}$$

The first term in (38) gives the desired ground state fermion number of the original Hamiltonian H. However, since the state $|0>$ in (35) is the Fock vacuum at $\tau = \infty$, the second term does not necessarily yield the ground state fermion number of H_0 but corresponds to the fermion number of an *excited* $\tau = -\infty$ state: The eigenvalues $E_n(\tau)$ are in general nontrivial functions of the parameter τ and it is possible that for some values $\tau_1 < \tau_2 < ... < \tau_n$ some number $\sharp(\tau_1), ..., \sharp(\tau_n)$ of these eigenvalues cross zero. Whenever an eigenvalue $E(\tau)$ crosses from negative to positive (positive to negative) values the corresponding expansion (3) of the second quantized field operator must be modified accordingly. A state which was quantized as an antifermion (fermion) for negative values of $E(\tau)$ must be reinterpreted as a fermion (antifermion) for positive values of $E(\tau)$ and we conclude that the second term in (38) differs from the $\tau = -\infty$ ground state fermion number by the signed sum of the eigenvalue crossing *i.e.* by the *spectral flow* of the family H_τ:

$$\int_{\tau=-\infty} dx\, j^0(x,\tau) = N_{-\infty} + (\textit{spectral flow}) = -\frac{1}{2}\eta_{H_0} + (\textit{spectral flow}) \tag{40}$$

As a consequence of the spectral flow η_{H_τ} becomes a discontinuous function of τ with discontinuity ± 2 for each eigenvalue $E(\tau)$ that crosses zero from negative values to positive values or vice versa. However, for all values of τ the ground state fermion number is proportional to the pertinent η-invariant,

$$N_\tau = -\frac{1}{2}\eta_{H_\tau} \tag{41}$$

with a proper limiting prescription at τ_i. If we write η_{H_τ} as a sum of its continuous part $\eta_{cont}\{H_\tau\}$ and discontinuous part $\eta_{disc}\{H_\tau\}$,

$$\eta_{H_\tau} = \eta_{cont}\{H_\tau\} + \eta_{disc}\{H_\tau\} \tag{42}$$

we find for the $\tau = \pm\infty$ ground state fermion numbers

$$N_\infty - N_{-\infty} = -\frac{1}{2}\{\eta_H - \eta_{H_0}\} = -\frac{1}{2}\int_{-\infty}^{\infty} d\tau \, \frac{d}{d\tau}\eta_{cont}\{H_\tau\} - \frac{1}{2}\sum_i \eta_{disc}\{H_{\tau_i}\} \tag{43}$$

Comparing (43) with (38), (39) we then conclude that

$$N_\infty = -\frac{1}{2}\eta_H = \int_{\tau=+\infty} dx \; j^0(x,\tau) \tag{44}$$

$$N_{-\infty} = -\frac{1}{2}\eta_{H_0} = \int_{\tau=-\infty} dx \; j^0(x,\tau) - \frac{1}{2}\sum_i \eta_{disc}\{H_{\tau_i}\} \tag{45}$$

$$\frac{1}{2}\int_{-\infty}^{\infty} d\tau \; \frac{d}{d\tau}\eta_{cont}\{H_\tau\} = \int_{-\infty}^{\infty} d\tau \oint dS^i j_i(x,\tau) - \int d\tau dx \; \Delta(x,\tau) \tag{46}$$

We now wish to relate the quantities (44) - (46) to the index of a Dirac operator. If we introduce

$$L = i\gamma^0\partial_\tau + i\gamma^0 H_\tau \tag{47}$$

the spectral flow of the family H_τ is proportional to the index of the (Euclidean) Dirac operator

$$\not{D} = \begin{bmatrix} 0 & L \\ L^\dagger & 0 \end{bmatrix} \tag{48}$$

$$\frac{1}{2}\sum_i \eta_{disc}\{H_{\tau_i}\} = Index\,\not{D} \tag{49}$$

We define the Euclidean Dirac matrices

$$\Gamma^0 = \begin{pmatrix} 0 & \gamma^0 \\ \gamma^0 & 0 \end{pmatrix} \qquad\qquad \Gamma^i = \begin{pmatrix} 0 & i\gamma^i \\ i\gamma^i & 0 \end{pmatrix} \tag{50}$$

that satisfy the algebra

$$\{\Gamma^\mu, \Gamma^\nu\} = 2\delta^{\mu\nu} \tag{51}$$

and we write (48) as

$$\not{D} = i\Gamma^0\partial_\tau + i\Gamma^i\partial_i + K(x) \equiv i\vec{\Gamma}\cdot\vec{\nabla} + K(x) \tag{52}$$

where

$$K = \begin{pmatrix} 0 & i\gamma^0 Q(x) \\ -iQ(x)\gamma^0 & 0 \end{pmatrix} \tag{53}$$

In analogy with (7) we introduce the constant matrix Γ^C and define

$$\not{D}_z = \not{D} + z\Gamma^C \tag{54}$$

This operator is of the form (7). Since

$$\lim_{z\to 0+} \eta\{\not{D}_z\} = -Index\,\not{D} \tag{55}$$

we find from (15), (49) that

$$-Index\,\not{D} = -\frac{1}{2}\sum_i \eta_{disc}\{H_{\tau_i}\} = \lim_{\beta\to 0+}\int dx\; tr < x|\Gamma^C e^{-\beta\,\not{D}^2}|x > +$$

$$+\lim_{z,\beta\to 0+}\int_{-\infty}^{\infty}\frac{d\omega}{2\pi}\frac{ze^{-\beta z^2}}{z^2+\omega^2}\int dx\;\vec{\nabla}\cdot tr < x|i\vec{\Gamma}\Gamma^C\frac{\not{D}}{\not{D}^2+z^2+\omega^2}e^{-\beta\,\not{D}^2}|x > \tag{56}$$

We define

$$\vec{J}(z,\beta) = \int_{-\infty}^{\infty}\frac{d\omega}{2\pi}\;\frac{ze^{-\beta z^2}}{z^2+\omega^2}tr < x|i\vec{\Gamma}\Gamma^C\frac{\not{D}}{\not{D}^2+z^2+\omega^2}e^{-\beta\,\not{D}^2}|x > \tag{57}$$

Converting the space integral in (56) into a surface integral we get

$$\int dx\;\vec{\nabla}\cdot\vec{J}(z,\beta) = \int_{\tau=\infty} dy\;J^0(z,\beta) + \int_{\tau=-\infty} dy\;J^0(z,\beta) + \int_{-\infty}^{\infty} d\tau \oint_{r=\infty} dS^i\;J^i(z,\beta) \tag{58}$$

and if we compare (56),(58) with (43) - (45) we conclude that we can choose

$$N_\infty = -\frac{1}{2}\eta_H = \int_{\tau=+\infty} dx\; j^0(x,\tau) = \lim_{z,\beta\to 0+}\int_{\tau=\infty} dy\;J^0(z,\beta) \tag{59}$$

$$N_{-\infty} = -\frac{1}{2}\eta_{H_0} = \int_{=-\infty} dx\; j^0(x,\tau) - \frac{1}{2}\sum_i \eta_{disc}\{H_{\tau_i}\} =$$

$$= \lim_{z,\beta \to 0+} \int_{\tau=-\infty} dy\ J^0(z,\beta) \tag{60}$$

$$\frac{1}{2}\int_{-\infty}^{\infty} d\tau\ \frac{d}{d\tau}\eta_{cont}\{H_\tau\} = \lim_{\beta\to 0+} \int dx\ tr < x|\Gamma^C e^{-\beta\ \not{D}^2}|x> +$$

$$+ \lim_{z,\beta\to 0+} \int_{-\infty}^{\infty} d\tau \oint_{\tau=\infty} dS^i\ J^i(z,\beta) \tag{61}$$

Comparing (61) with (46) it is obvious that there is certain arbitrariness in identifying the terms on the *r.h.s.* of these equations. This arbitrariness reflects the arbitrariness in identifying the family H_τ and the operator (47). However, consistently with (59), (60) we *choose*

$$\lim_{\beta\to 0+} \int dx\ tr < x|\Gamma^C e^{-\beta\ \not{D}^2}|x> = -\int d\tau dx\ \Delta(x,\tau) \stackrel{def.}{=} \Delta \tag{62}$$

$$\lim_{z,\beta\to 0+} \int_{-\infty}^{\infty} d\tau \oint_{\tau=\infty} dS^i\ J^i(z,\beta) = \int_{-\infty}^{\infty} d\tau \oint dS^i j_i(x,\tau) \stackrel{def.}{=} \frac{1}{2}\eta_{bdy} \tag{63}$$

Combining (56), (59) - (63) we then find the open infinite space index theorem [11]

$$-Index\ \not{D} = \Delta + \frac{1}{2}\eta_H - \frac{1}{2}\eta_{H_0} + \frac{1}{2}\eta_{bdy} \tag{64}$$

Furthermore, by general covariance we can find a boundary operator $\mathcal{L}$ (assumed to be hermitean; see [11]) that yields the restriction of (48) to the boundary at infinity in $(x_i,\tau) \simeq R^{d+1}$ and agrees pointwise with the operator H at $\tau = +\infty$ and H_0 at $\tau = -\infty$ so that

$$\lim_{z,\beta\to 0+} \int d\Sigma^i\ J^i(z,\beta) = \frac{1}{2}\eta_{\mathcal{L}} = \frac{1}{2}\eta_H - \frac{1}{2}\eta_{H_0} + \frac{1}{2}\eta_{bdy} \tag{65}$$

The index theorem (64) then becomes [11]

$$-Index\ \not{D} = \Delta + \frac{1}{2}\eta_{\mathcal{L}} \tag{66}$$

which is a generalization of the Atiyah-Patodi-Singer index theorem to open infinite manifolds.

V. An Example

We shall now use the index theorem (64) to compute the η-invariant of an operator that does not admit the representation (7). We consider the 1-dimensional Hamiltonian

$$H = \begin{pmatrix} \phi_1 & -\partial_x + \phi_2 \\ \partial_x + \phi_2 & -\phi_1 \end{pmatrix} = i\sigma^2\partial_x + \sigma^3\phi_1 + \sigma^1\phi_2 \tag{67}$$

where the background fields $\phi_1(x)$ and $\phi_2(x)$ are arbitrary smooth functions of x with the limits

$$\phi_1(\pm\infty) = a_\pm \qquad \phi_2(\pm\infty) = b_\pm \tag{68}$$

We introduce the parameter $\tau \in (-\infty, \infty)$ and extend the background fields to smooth functions of x and τ. We choose these extensions in such a way that both $\phi_1(x, -\infty)$ and $\phi_2(x, -\infty)$ are independent of x,

$$\phi_1(x, -\infty) \equiv a_+ \qquad \phi_2(x, -\infty) \equiv b_- \tag{69}$$

The comparison Hamiltonian introduced in (34) then becomes

$$H_0 = \begin{pmatrix} a_+ & -\partial_x + b_- \\ \partial_x + b_- & -a_+ \end{pmatrix} \tag{70}$$

Since a_+ is a constant this Hamiltonian is of the form (7) and from (21) we conclude that it has a vanishing η-invariant.

On the boundary $x = -\infty$ we choose ϕ_1 to be an arbitrary smooth function of τ and ϕ_2 to be a constant such that

$$\phi_1(-\infty, \tau \to \pm\infty) \to a_\mp \qquad \phi_2(-\infty, \tau) \equiv b_- \tag{71}$$

Similarly, on the boundary $x = +\infty$ we choose

$$\phi_1(\infty, \tau) \equiv a_+ \qquad \phi_2(\infty, \tau \to \pm\infty) \to b_\pm \tag{72}$$

The operator L in (47) is then of the form

$$L = i\sigma^1\partial_\tau + i\sigma^3\partial_x - \sigma_2\phi_1 + i\phi_2 \tag{73}$$

and the pertinent restriction of $\not{D}$ to the spatial boundary yields the operator $\mathcal{L}$ introduced in (65), (66) as an Hermitean operator with

$$\mathcal{L} = i\sigma^2\partial_\tau - \sigma^1\phi_1(x) - \sigma^3 b_- \qquad x = -\infty \tag{74}$$

$$\mathcal{L} = -i\sigma^2\partial_\tau + \sigma^1 a_+ + \sigma^3\phi_2 \qquad x = +\infty \tag{75}$$

Consequently (63) becomes

$$\lim_{z,\beta \to 0+} \int dS^i J^i(z, \beta) =$$

$$= \frac{1}{\pi}\int_0^\infty d\hat{\omega}\int_{-\infty}^{\infty} d\tau\, \{tr < \tau,\infty|\frac{\mathcal{L}}{\mathcal{L}^2+\hat{\omega}^2}|\tau,\infty> - tr < \tau,-\infty|\frac{\mathcal{L}}{\mathcal{L}^2+\hat{\omega}^2}|\tau,-\infty>\} \tag{76}$$

This is half the difference in the η-invariants of the operators (74) and (75). Clearly, both of these operators can be represented in the form (7) and from (21) we find

$$\eta_{\mathcal{L}}(x=\infty) - \eta_{\mathcal{L}}(x=-\infty) = \frac{1}{\pi}\left\{arctan[\frac{b_+}{a_+}] - arctan[\frac{b_-}{a_-}]\right\} \tag{77}$$

Since the η-invariant of the comparison Hamiltonian (70) vanishes we find by combining these results with the index theorem (64) that the fermion number corresponding to the operator H in (67) is given by

$$N = -\frac{1}{2}\eta_H = \frac{1}{2\pi}\left\{arctan[\frac{b_+}{a_+}] - arctan[\frac{b_-}{a_-}]\right\} + Index\, \not{D} \tag{78}$$

In the general case the index in (78) is quite difficult to compute. However, since this index is an integer it does not contribute to the *fractional* part of the fermion number which is given by the first term.

References

[1] R. Jackiw and C. Rebbi, Phys. Rev. **D13** (1976) 3398
[2] C. Callias, Comm. Math. Phys. **62** (1978) 213
[3] J. Goldstone and F. Wilczek, Phys. Rev. Lett. **47** (1981) 986
[4] A.J. Niemi and G.W. Semenoff. Physics Report *to appear*
[5] A.J. Niemi, Nucl.Phys. **B253** (1985) 14
[6] M. Atiyah, V. Patodi and I. Singer, Bull. London Math. Soc. **5** (1973) 229
[7] A.J. Niemi and G.W. Semenoff. Phys. Lett. **B135** (1984) 121
[8] M.B. Paranjape and G.W. Semenoff, Phys. Lett. **B132** (1983) 369
[9] A.J. Niemi and G.W. Semenoff, Phys. Rev. Lett. **51** (1983) 2077
[10] A.J. Niemi and G.W. Semenoff, Phys. Rev. **D30** (1984) 809
[11] A.J. Niemi and G.W. Semenoff, IAS preprint (1985)
[12] P. Gilkey, *The Index Theorem And the Heat Equation* (Publish of Perish, Inc. 1974)

SYMPOSIUM ON ANOMALIES, GEOMETRY, TOPOLOGY

EFFECTIVE LAGRANGIANS

EDWARD FARHI

CHAIRMAN

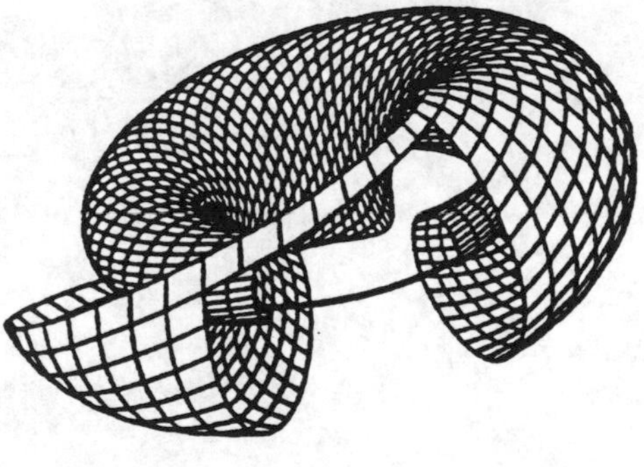

SKYRMION PHENOMENOLOGY

Chiara R. Nappi†
Joseph Henry Laboratories
Princeton University
Princeton, New Jersey 08544

The non-linear field theory

$$\mathcal{L} = \frac{F_\pi^2}{16} \mathrm{Tr}(\partial_\mu U \, \partial_\mu U^+) + \frac{1}{32e^2} \mathrm{Tr}[U\partial_\mu U^+, U\partial_\nu U^+]^2 \tag{1}$$

was suggested by Skyrme[1] as a unified theory of mesons and baryons, with the mesons being the elementary fields $\pi(x)$ in

$$U(x) = e^{2i\vec{\tau}\cdot\vec{\pi}(x)/F_\pi} \tag{2}$$

and the baryons arising as solitons. After the recent revival of this idea,[2,3] a lot of work has been done to test the validity of this approach. I will report on some recent results , and comment on some aspects of the phenomenological status of the subject.

SU(2) Results

All the results in the case of two flavors are based on the Skyrme ansatz

$$U_0 = e^{iF(r)\,\vec{\tau}\cdot\hat{x}} \tag{3}$$

for the classical soliton and on its quantization by the method of collective coordinate. This is achieved by substituting U_0 with $A(t)\, U_0\, A(t)^{-1}$, where $A(t) \in SU(2)$. Straightforward quantization of the collective coordinte $A(t)$ leads to the Hamiltonian

$$M_{B=1} = M(F) + \frac{1}{2I(F)} J(J+1) \tag{4}$$

where the classical mass $M(F)$ and the moment of inertia of inertia $I(F)$ are model dependent quantities. In [4] the parameters F_π and e in (1) were determined by fitting (4) to the nucleon and delta masses. This

---

†Research supported in part by NSF Grant PHY80-19754.

gave F_π = 130 Mev (experimentally it is 186 MeV) and e = 5.45 (e is unknown experimentally). All other static properties of baryons such as magnetic moments, g-factors and charge-radii came out, in average, to within 30% of their experimental values (see table).[4] In the non-chiral case obtained by adding to the Lagrangian the chiral symmetry breaking piece

$$\frac{1}{8} m_\pi{}^2 F_\pi{}^2 \, tr(U-2) \qquad (5)$$

F_π is lowered to 108 MeV, while the other predictions basically remain the same.[5] Some improvement in the results was noticed in a model with the ω-vector meson coupled to the pions.[6] Currently the same analysis is being carried out in a model with the ρ vector meson instead.[7] The last two models above have to be viewed as precursors of a more complete model containing pions, omega and rho all. The hope is that the more realistic the model is the better it will reproduce baryon properties.

Quantity	Skyrme Model with m_π=0	Skyrme Model with $m_\pi \neq 0$	ω-Vector Model	Experiment
m_N(Mev)	input	input	input	938.9
m_π(Mev)	--	input	input	138
m_ω(Mev)	--	--	input	782.4
m_Δ(Mev)	input	input	input	1232
F_π(Mev)	129	108	124	186
$\langle r^2\rangle^{1/2}_{I=0}$(fm)	.59	.68	.74	.72
$\langle r^2\rangle^{1/2}_{I=1}$(fm)	--	1.04	1.06	.88
$\langle r^2\rangle^{1/2}_{M,J=0}$(fm)	.92	.95	.92	.81
$\langle r^2\rangle_{M,I=1}$(fm)	--	1.04	1.02	.80
μ_p	1.87	1.97	2.34	2.79
μ_n	-1.31	-1.24	-1.46	-1.91
g_A	.61	.65	.82	1.23
$g_{\pi NN}$	8.9	11.9	13.0	13.5
σ(Mev)	--	49	53	36±20
$g_{\pi N\Delta}$	13.2	17.8	19.5	20.3
$\mu_{N\Delta}$	2.3	2.3	2.7	3.3

Recently, a lot of attention has been focused on the study of dynamical properties of Skyrmions. Pion-nucleon resonances have been studied[8,9,10] in the Skyrme model by looking at small fluctuations around the Skyrmion. This is the usual procedure when one wants to calculate scattering of field quanta off the soliton. Again one adopts a semiclassical expansion around the static solution. In the Skyrme ansatz we take

$$F(r)\ \vec{r}\cdot\vec{\tau} \rightarrow (F(r)\vec{r} + \delta\vec{F}(\vec{x},t))\cdot\vec{\tau} \tag{6}$$

which still preserves the I+J symmetry. The part of the Lagrangian quadratic in $\delta\vec{F}$ provides the scattering phase shifts, while higher powers in δF give rise to loop corrections. Since δF is order $N_C^{-1/2}$ and the scale of the Lagrangian is $F_\pi^2 \sim \frac{1}{e^2} \sim N_C$, the leading contribution of δF is order 1, and the loops are down by powers of $1/N_C$. So the $1/N_C$ expansion justifies the small vibration analysis, as well as the semiclassical expansion in (4). In the treatment of rotational modes we neglected the vibrational modes, and the coupling between the rotational and vibrational modes. In the study of small vibrations we adopt the same approximation. Justification for this has to be found again in the framework of the large N_C expansion. Breit and myself studied the small oscillation equation for the singlet channel with I+J=0 in the Skyrme model. Our ansatz was simply

$$U(\vec{x},t) = e^{i[F(r) + \delta F(r,t)]\ \hat{x}\cdot\vec{\tau}} \tag{7}$$

and we studied scattering solutions of the small oscillation equation for $\delta F(r,t) = e^{-ie F_\pi \omega t}\,\delta F(r)$. We fitted $F(r)$ for large r to $a(\omega)\ j_1(\omega r) + b(\omega)\ n_1(\omega r)$, where j_1 and n_1 are the usual spherical Bessel functions of order 1 and found the phase shift

$$\delta(\omega) = \tan^{-1}\left[-\frac{b(\omega)}{a(\omega)}\right] \tag{8}$$

The Siegen group[9] and the SLAC group[10,11] have investigated other channels by expanding the pion field in (6) in terms of vector spherical harmonics. They have also figured out how to relate pion-scattering from elementary unrotated Skyrmions with physical pion-nucleon or pion-delta scattering. This requires restoring the rotations, i.e. the collective coordinates, and projecting out the states of definite spin and isospin. In particular, the SLAC group has computed the phase shifts and associated nucleon and delta resonances in all the partial waves up to L=8 and pion energies up to 3 GeV and compared them with the available experimental data. They choose the parameters F_π and e in (1) by using a least square fit for all resonances and get F_π=150 MeV and e=4.79. From (4) the nucleon and delta masses come out around 200 MeV too high, but the resonances are matched within 8% in average. In most partial waves they find good agreement with experiment, except for the S, P and D waves. (The discrepancies in these low waves is probably due to mixing with the translational and rotational zero-modes of the chiral soliton.) The values of F_π=150 MeV and e=4.79 obtained from a fit to the entire resonance spectrum also give reasonable values for the static properties (except for the nucleon and delta masses, as already said.)

In conclusion, I would say that for the two flavor case the soliton picture of baryons looks pretty good, both qualitatively and quantitatively. Particularly satisfying are the model independent relations for coupling constants and magnetic moments,[4,12] and the model-independent and energy-independent sumrules between partial wave $\pi N\to\pi N$ and $\pi N\to\pi\Delta$ amplitudes,[11,9] all of which are reasonably well satisfied in Nature. Moreover, the numerical predictions are as good as one can expect, given the extreme simplicity of the models and the crude approximations involved (we should at least introduce corrections in $1/N_c$). Next we analyze the situation with three flavors.

SU(3) Results

All SU(3) results are based on an SU(3) ansatz for the B=1 soliton that is a straightforward generalization of the SU(2) ansatz and consist in embedding the SU(2) Skyrme soliton in an SU(3) matrix[3,13] as follows

$$U_0 = \left(\begin{array}{cc|c} \multicolumn{2}{c|}{e^{iF(r)\,\hat{x}\cdot\vec{\tau}}} & \begin{matrix}0\\0\end{matrix} \\ \hline 0 & 0 & 1 \end{array}\right) \tag{9}$$

As in the SU(2) case we rotate the Skyrmion

$$U_0 \to U(\vec{x},t) = A(t)\, U_0\, A^{-1}(t) \qquad A\varepsilon\, SU(3)$$

The SU(3) soliton $U(\vec{x},t)$ is invariant under λ_8 transformations

$$A \to A\, e^{i\theta\, \lambda_8/2} \tag{10}$$

Under the above transformation the baryon wave function picks up a phase[12]

$$\psi(A\, e^{i\theta\, \lambda_8/2}) = \psi(A)\, e^{i\theta\, N_c/2\sqrt{3}} \tag{11}$$

The numbers of colors N_c comes in because of the Wess-Zumino term $N_c\Gamma$. From (11) it follows that the representations of SU(3) of lowest dimensionality must be the $\underset{\sim}{8}$ and the $\underset{\sim}{10}$, and they come with the right spin S = 1/2 and S = 3/2 respectively.[3,13] In the space of collective coordinates A the wavefunctions for the baryons as well as the various observables can be expressed in terms of the matrices $D^{(n)}_{a,b}(A)$, i.e. the unitary matrices for the representation (n) of the SU(3) transformation A. The expectation value of an operator will therefore appear as an integral over group space and will be evaluated as a sum over products of Clebsh-Gordan coefficients. Along these lines we can derive various model independent relations for baryons, like mass relations, F/D ratios, decays, etc.[13,14] As an example I will discuss here hyperon magnetic moments as analyzed by Adkins and myself.[11] The only new prediction for the octet magnetic moments is

$$\frac{\mu_n}{\mu_p} = -\frac{3}{4} \tag{12}$$

The experimental value of this ratio is -0.685. All other relations between magnetic moments of the octet are just the SU(3) Coleman-Glashow results combined with (12). For the decuplet we get

$$\mu_{10} = \frac{15}{16}\, Q\, \mu_p \tag{13}$$

similar to and experimentally indistinguishable from the SU(6) result $\mu_{10} = Q\,\mu_p$. Since SU(3) is not an exact symmetry, and experimental departures from the Coleman-Glashow relations are significant, we introduce SU(3) flavor breaking corrections. In the attempt of improving our results further we also introduce corrections of higher order in $1/N_c$, by adding operators with the quantum number of the magnetic moment, but containing a single time derivative of the collective coordinate $\dot{A}$. Our final relations are

$$(\mu_p + \mu_n) + \frac{3}{2}(\mu_{\Sigma^+} + \mu_{\Sigma^-}) + (\mu_{\Xi^0} + \mu_{\Xi^-}) + \mu_{\Lambda^0} = 0 \tag{14}$$

and

$$\frac{2}{3\sqrt{3}}\mu_{\Lambda\Sigma} - \frac{1}{3}(\mu_{\Sigma^+} - \mu_{\Sigma^-}) - \frac{1}{3}(\mu_{\Xi^0} - \mu_{\Xi^-}) + (\mu_p + \mu_n) + \frac{2}{3}\mu_{\Lambda^0} = 0 \tag{15}$$

The left-hand side of (14) is 0.24 ± 0.09, while the left-hand of (15) is 0.19 $^{+.10}_{-.07}$. Both equations hold to within 2.7 standard deviations. In general, the SU(3) model independent relations are not as good as the SU(2) ones. This might simply be due to the fact that SU(3) is not such a good symmetry as SU(2) is. Or, as suggested in [15], this might be due to the fact that with three flavors the spin and quantum numbers of baryons depend on N_c in a more intricate way than in the two flavor case, so making the extrapolation from large N_c to the real world less smooth.

Moving to model dependent results, the generalization to SU(3) of (4) by means of the ansatz (8) is

$$M_{B=1} = M(F) + \frac{J(J+1)}{2I(F)} + \frac{1}{2k(F)} \left(C_2 - J(J+1) - \frac{N_c^{\,2}}{12}\right) \qquad (16)$$

Above M(F), I(F) an k(F) are model dependent quantities (M(F) and I(F) are exactly the same as in (4)) and C_2 is the SU(3) quadratic Casimir. We have written (16) in a form that clearly separates the contribution of the strange quark. The first two terms are precisely those present in the two flavor version of the model, and the third term is a result of adding the strange quark. This last one, although it comes totally from the collective coordinates, is not of order $1/N_c$ like the SU(2) piece, but of order 1, as one would expect from large N_c QCD considerations. This is because both k and C_2-J(J+1) - $N_c^{\,2}/12$ are of order N_c, so their ratio is of order 1.[16] By fitting (16) in the Skyrme model to the octet (J=1/2, C_2=3) and decuplet (J=3/2, C_2=6) centers of mass, M_8=1151 MeV and M_{10}=1382 MeV, one determines in the chiral limit F_π=114 MeV and e=5.25.[17]

Of course one would like to break chiral and SU(3) symmetry. This can be done by introducing in the Hamiltonian the term

$$H_M = \pi F_\pi^{\,2} \alpha \left\{\mu^2 - \frac{(m_k^{\,2} - m_\pi^{\,2})}{3} \mathrm{Tr}\left(\lambda_8 A \lambda_8 A^{-1}\right)\right\} \qquad (17)$$

Above μ^2 is the mean square meson octet mass, experimentally $\mu^2 = (410)^2$ MeV^2, and α is the model dependent integral

$$\alpha = \int_0^\infty r^2 \left(1 - \cos F\right) dr \qquad (18)$$

The first piece in (21) is the chiral symmetry breaking term analogous to (6), and the second piece is the SU(3) symmetry breaking piece. If we fit now M_8 and M_{10}, we predict a value for F_π considerably worse than in the SU(2) case.[17,18,19,20] Infact the σ term in the three flavor case comes out around 300 MeV (not unreasonably, since the mass of the strange quark is in that range), while instead in the two flavor case it was only around 50 MeV.[5] So the big contribution from the symmetry breaking piece lowers F_π considerably (i.e. $F_\pi \sim 80$ MeV). Chemtob[21] claims however that, although F_π is so low, one still gets good predictions for the static properties of the nucleon, which are actually improved with respect to the two flavor case. A prediction that is surely worsened by such a low F_π is the mass of the strange dibaryon, which infact comes out unreasonably low. The H, originally discovered in the MIT bag model with a mass $M_\pi = 2150$ MeV,[22] has been recently rediscovered[23] as a soliton of baryon number B=2 in the Skyrme model. It corresponds to the "spherically symmetric" ansatz based on an SU(3) subgroup of SU(3)

$$U_H(\vec{x}) = \exp\left\{ ix\cdot\vec{\Lambda}\, f(r) + i[(x\cdot\vec{\Lambda})^2 - \tfrac{2}{3}]\, g(r)\right\} \qquad (19)$$

with $f(0) = g(0) = \pi$ and $f(\infty) = g(\infty) = 0$. Above $\Lambda_1=\lambda_7$, $\Lambda_2=-\lambda_5$ and $\Lambda_3=\lambda_2$. The mass of the H has been recently estimated[18,19] in the Skyrme model. The various estimates all come out much lower than the bag model prediction. Since the mass of the H is so crucial in determining its stability with respect to strong decay into baryon, Yost and myself[20] have computed it in the model with the ω vector meson mentioned above. We come up with an even lower value of M_H, namely M_H=1130 MeV. In the process, we discover that the omega model highly overestimates the contribution of the strange quark to the nucleon mass. The Skyrme model has a similar problem, but the overestimate of the strange quark contribution seems less severe.[18,19] Since the contribution from the strange quarks comes all from the collective coordinates, this makes our semiclassical approximation rather unjustified. Again, there might be various explanations for all this. SU(3) is not a good symmetry, and the symmetry breaking term is therefore too big and disruptive. Maybe strange quarks should not be introduced in chiral models on the same footing as up and down quarks, but in some alternative way. Progress in this direction has been recently made with a model which couples kaons to an SU(2) chiral Lagrangian, thus breaking SU(3) from the start.[24] Another explanation could be related to the fact that in this treatment we have neglected more degrees of freedom, like radial and flavor excitations (both order 1 in N_c) and their zero point corrections. One could hope that zero mode corrections would sum up to give rise to a kind of Casimir effect, with a negative contribution to the energy,[19] which would rescue the prediction for F_π. Infact if one adds an overall constant M_x to $M_{B=1}$ in (16), one can fit M_8 and M_{10} by using the experimental value of F_π = 186 MeV. One then predicts e = 4.81 and M_x = -485 MeV. However, these values of F_π and e give worse predictions for the static properties than those shown in the table. Of course a three-parameter fit for F_π, e and M_x would surely improve matters. For instance, the choice F_π = 150 MeV and e = 4.79 as obtained in [10] and $M_x \sim$ -200 MeV would fit within a few percent resonances as well as proton and delta masses, and give good predictions for the static properties. Finally, one should remember that we are working with models that are only a crude approximation of the theory of all mesons and their resonances to which QCD is equivalent in the large N_c limit. Maybe if we had correct model, we would not have the above mentioned problems. In conclusion, it is not clear at the moment how to interpret the numerical failures of the SU(3) Skyrmions. The question is whether they are intrinsic to the approach of baryons as solitons, or maybe due to the fact that we are still missing something.

References

1. T.H.R. Skyrme, Proc. Roy. Soc. A260, 127 (1961).
2. N.K. Pak and H.C. Tze, Ann. Phys. 117, 164 (1979); J. Gibson and H. C. Tze, Nucl. Phys. B183, 524 (1981); A.P. Balachandran, V.P. Nair, S.G. Rajeev, and A. Stern, Phys. Rev. Lett. 49, 1124 (1982), Phys. Rev. D27, 1153 (1983). For an update on recent developments see "Solitons in Nuclear and Elementary Particle Physics," edited by A. Chodos, E. Hadjimichael and C. Tze, World Scientific, and references therein.
3. E. Witten, Nucl. Phys. B223, 433 (1983), ibid, 422.
4. G. Adkins, C.R. Nappi and E. Witten, Nucl. Phys. B228, 552 (1983).
5. G. Adkins and C.R. Nappi, Nucl. Phys. B233, 109 (1984).
6. G. Adkins and C.R. Nappi, Phys. Lett. 137B, 251 (1984).
7. G. Adkins, to appear.

8. J. Breit and C.R. Nappi, Phys. Rev. Lett. 53, 889 (1984); C. Hajduk and B. Schwesinger, Phys. Lett. 140B, 172 (1984); I. Zahed, U.G. Meissner and V.B. Kauffuss, Nucl. Phys. A426, 525 (1984), K.F. Liu, J.S. Zhang and G.R.E. Black, Phys. Rev. D30, 2015 (1984); L.C. Biedenharn, Y. Dothan and M. Tarlini, Phys Rev. D31, 649 (1985); J. Breit, Phys. Lett. B (to appear).
9. H. Walliser and G. Eckart, Nucl. Phys. A429, 514 (1984); A. Hayashi, G. Eckart, G. Holzworth and H. Wallíser, Phys. Lett. 147B, 5 (1984).
10. M.P. Mattis and M. Karliner, SLAC-Pub-3539, Dec. 1984.
11. M.P. Mattis and M. Peskin, SLAC-Pub-3538, Dec. 1984.
12. G. Adkins and C.R. Nappi, Nucl. Phys. B249, 507 (1985).
13. E. Guadagnini, Nucl. Phys. B236, 35 (1984); S. Jain and S.R. Wadia, TIFR/TH/84-7; L.C. Biedenharn and Y. Dothan, Duke preprint (1985).
14. M.S. Sriram, H.S. Mani and R. Ramachandran, Phys. Rev. D30, 1141 (1984); J. Bijnens, H. Sonoda and M.B. Wise, Phys. Lett. 140B, 421 (1984).
15. E. Witten, in "Solitons in Nuclear and Elementary Particle Physics, edited by A. Chodos, E. Hadjimichael and C. Tze, World Scientific (1984).
16. V.S. Kaplunovsky, "Exotic Skyrmions," to appear.
17. P.O. Mazur, M.A. Nowak and M. Praszalowicz, Phys. Lett. 147B, 137 (1984); M. Praszalowicz, CERN-TH-4114/85.
18. R.L. Jaffe and C.L.Korpa, MIT Preprint CTP #1233 (1985).
19. A.P. Balachandran, F. Lizzi, V.G.J. Rodgers and A. Stern, Syracuse preprint SU4222-296 (1985).
20. S.A. Yost and C.R. Nappi, Princeton preprint (1985).
21. M. Chemtob, CEN preprint 1984, to appear in Zeitschrift für Physik C.
22. R.L. Jaffe, Phys. Rev. Lett. 38, 195 (1977).
23. A.P. Balachandran, A. Barducci, F. Lizzi, V.G.J. Rogers and A. Stern, Phys. Rev. Lett. 52, 887 (1984).
24. C.G. Callan and I. Klebanov, to appear.

QUANTIZATION AMBIGUITIES IN CHIRAL MODELS

A. P. Balachandran
Physics Department, Syracuse University, Syracuse, NY 13210

1. INTRODUCTION

In the chiral model, the ansatz which leads to the classical static solitonic configuration is not invariant under generic global flavour rotations. When flavour symmetry is unbroken, a flavour rotation of the static solution in general leads to another distinct static solution with exactly the same energy. The existence of such a classical degeneracy suggests that the quantum properties of the low lying excitations can be well approximated by introducing collective coordinates for the flavour rotations and quantizing just these modes. Such an approximation can be called the collective coordinate approximation (CCA). In practice, we occasionally improve this approximation by quantizing modes such as the breather mode. As these additional modes are normally topologically trivial, they do not affect the qualitative properties of the states such as whether they are bosons or fermions. If there are ambiguities in the quantization of the soliton in the CCA, they do not normally resolve these ambiguities either.

In this talk, the qualitative properties of the CCA will be discussed and it will be shown that for any number N_f of flavours, there is a soliton which can be quantized in N_f different ways in such an approximation. this result has been obtained by the Syracuse-Oregon group and by Rabinovici et al. independently. There are reasons to suspect that for $N_f \geq 3$, the quantization ambiguity is a deficiency of the CCA and that it can be resolved by quantizing certain additional modes.

2. A HIERARCHY OF SOLITONS

We begin the discussion by indicating the construction of a hierarchy of classical ansatze with a high degree of symmetry which can lead to static solitonic solutions. Let W be such an ansatz. It is not difficult to argue that the highest possible symmetry of W is the following generalized spherical symmetry:

$$-i(\vec{x} \times \vec{\nabla})_i W + [\Lambda_i, W] = 0 .$$

Here, Λ_i generate any SU(2) or SO(3) subgroup of $SU(N_f)$. For $N_f = 3$, the Skyrme soliton is based on the choice $\Lambda_i = \lambda_i$ ($i \leqslant 3$) while the H meson is based on the choice $\Lambda_1 = \lambda_7$, $\Lambda_2 = -\lambda_5$, $\Lambda_3 = \lambda_2$. See the references for explicit forms of W in these cases. When there are altogether N_f flavours and Λ_i generate an SU(2) algebra acting nontrivially on the first D flavours [and hence characterized by "angular momentum" (D-1)/2], let us call the classical soliton as the (N_f,D) soliton. For three flavours, the classical Skyrmion is the (3,2) soliton and the classical H meson is the (3,3) soliton.

We shall see below that in the CCA, there is an N_f-fold ambiguity in quantizing the "maximal" (N_f,N_f) soliton and that this ambiguity disappears when it is imbedded in N_f+1 flavours. Thus there are two ways to quantize the (2,2) soliton (the two flavour Skyrmion), one way to quantize the (3,2) soliton, three ways to quantize the (3,3) soliton (the three flavour H meson) etc.

3. QUANTIZATION OF COLLECTIVE COORDINATES

If U is the chiral field on space time that we wish to quantize, we set $U = A(t)W\,A(t)^\dagger$ in the CCA. Since U is invariant under the action $A \rightarrow Az$ where z is in the center Z_{N_f} of $SU(N_f)$, it can be regarded as a function of W and Ad A where $A \rightarrow \mathrm{Ad}\,A$ defines the adjoint representation of $SU(N_f)$. Thus we can think of $\mathrm{Ad}\,A_{ij}$ as the collective coordinates. The Lagrangian L for $\mathrm{Ad}\,A_{ij}$ can be derived from the field theoretic Lagrangian, its quantization leads to an approximate description of the low lying excitations.

Let $\mathrm{Ad}\,\hat{A}$ be the operator which represents Ad A in quantum mechanics. We can go about as follows to get an explicit realization of $\mathrm{Ad}\,\hat{A}$: Let $\mathcal{H}$ be the Hibert space of functions on A, the scalar product on $\mathcal{H}$ is defined using the invariant measure on $SU(N_f)$. The definition of $\mathrm{Ad}\hat{A}$ is

$$[\mathrm{Ad}\,\hat{A}_{ij}\alpha](A) = \mathrm{Ad}\,A_{ij}\alpha(A) .$$

The task of setting up the quantum states is not yet complete, however. The additional surgeries we have to do on $\mathcal{H}$ are best illustrated by examples.

a) The (2,2) Soliton: For the (2,2) soliton (which on quantization becomes the nucleon), W is $\cos\theta(r) + i\vec{\tau}\cdot\hat{x}\sin\theta(r)$. It follows from the definition $U = A(t)W\,A(t)$ that the only transformations on A which leave U invariant are generated by $A \to Az$, $z = -1$ and correspond to the center Z_2 of SU(2). The significance of this remark will become clear below. Further this Z_2 can be realized on $\mathcal{H}$ by defining the operator U(z) where $[U(z)\alpha](A) = \alpha(Az)$. Since $Ad(Az) = Ad\,A$, it follows that $[Ad\,\hat{A}, U(z)] = 0$. Thus by Schur's lemma, the representation of $Ad\,\hat{A}$ on $\mathcal{H}$ is reducible. Its reduction is achieved by writing $\mathcal{H} = \mathcal{H}^{(0)} \oplus \mathcal{H}^{(1)}$ where on $\mathcal{H}^{(\nu)}$, U(z) has the value $(-1)^{\nu}$. We can therefore quantize the system in two ways, using either $\mathcal{H}^{(0)}$ or $\mathcal{H}^{(1)}$. The former leads to bosonic states and the latter to fermionic states. These results are originally due to Skyrme and Williams.

b) The (3.2) Soliton. The ansatz W for this soliton consists of the trivial inbedding of the (2,2) soliton in three flavours. It commutes with the hypercharge Y. An important consequence is that U is invariant under a gauge (time dependent) transformation of A: $U \to U$ when $A(t) \to A(t)e^{iY\xi(t)}$. Since the observable field is U, we should be able to rewrite the equations of motion for A in terms of U, and without involving A. Thus these equations should be invariant under the preceding U(1) group generated by "right" hypercharge. In this way, we can infer that L can change at most by a total time derivative under this gauge transformation: $L \to L + d\chi/dt$. The form of χ will depend on the Wess-Zumino term, see the references for details. In any event, we see that if $\hat{Y}$ is the quantum mechanical generator of the gauge group, we can compute it using Noether's principle, and as with Gauss's law in electrodynamics therefrom find a constraint on the states. When the Wess-Zumino term is absent, $\hat{Y}$ is zero on states, otherwise it is a calculable constant. This constraint picks out a family of states and resolves the Z_2 quantization ambiguity of the (2,2) soliton. These results are due to Witten. Note that now $Ad\,\hat{A}$ is not gauge invariant, $[Ad\,\hat{A}, \hat{Y}] \neq 0$, and hence is not an observable. The observables are functions of $\hat{A}$ which commute with $\hat{Y}$.

c) The (3,3) Soliton: The classical ansatz W is a polynomial in $\Lambda.\hat{x}$ where the matrices Λ_i now describe "angular momentum" 1 and act irreducibly on three flavours. As a consequence the transformations on A which leave U invariant consist only of the center Z_3 of SU(3). There are no gauge transformations on A which leave U invariant. If $z = e^{2\pi i/3}\mathbb{1} \varepsilon Z_3$, we can define a representation of z and hence of Z_3 on $\mathcal{H}$ via the operator U(z) where $[U(z)\alpha](A) = \alpha(Az)$. It commutes with $Ad\,\hat{A}$ since $Ad(Az) = Ad\,A$. The representation of Ad $\hat{A}$ on $\mathcal{H}$ is thus reducible. We achieve the reduction by writing $\mathcal{H}=\bigoplus_{\nu=0}^{2}\mathcal{H}^{(\nu)}$ where on $^{(\nu)}$, U(z) has the value $[e^{2\pi i/3}]^{\nu}$. There are thus three ways of quantizing the (3,3) soliton, they are distinguished by their trialities.

d) <u>The (4,3) Soliton.</u> When the H meson ansatz is imbedded in the obvious way in four flavours, it commutes with the matrix (1,1,1,-3) diagonal. A U(1) gauge symmetry thus appears resolving the Z_3 quantization ambiguity of the (3,3) soliton.

Of course now the (4,4) soliton suffers from a Z_4 quantization ambiguity.

4. CONCLUDING REMARKS

There are reasons to suspect that for $N_f \geqslant 3$, these quantization ambiguities are caused by the collective coordinate approximation and are not present in the full quantum chiral field theory (QCFT). Consider for instance the three flavour QCFT without the CCA. With the canonical choice of the Wess-Zumino term, the usual Skyrmion is uniquely predicted to have triality zero in this theory. Further in this theory, there are histories with finite action S(U) where the field U is continuously evolved from the dibaryon configuration to a configuration with two widely separated Skyrmions. Thus unless there are unexpected cancellations between these histories, the dibaryon-two Skyrmion vertex is nonzero and the dibaryon has triality zero (by triality conservation) in QCFT. The freedom to use Hilbert spaces with any triality is not available in the unapproximated QCFT.

The topological properties important for quantization are $H^2(Q,Z)$ and $\pi_1(Q)$ where Q is the configuration space. It is possible to show that for $N_f \geqslant 3$, these groups are not the same for Q = Ad SU(N_f) (the configuration space in the CCA] and for Q = the space of chiral fields at a given time. This is another way to see that the relevant topological properties of the chiral fields are not reproduced in the CCA.

The preceding discussion suggests that the topological deficiency of the CCA for $N_f \geqslant 3$ can be corrected by quantizing new modes which describe the tunnelling of the dibaryon to two Skyrmions. It is not clear how to implement this improvement in a practically useful way. It is also not clear whether such an improvement is phenomenologically significant.

This work was supported by the Department of Energy under Contract Number DE-AC02-76ER03533.

REFERENCES

A. P. Balachandran, F. Lizzi, V. G. J. Rodgers and A. Stern, Nuclear Physics B (in press); E. Rabinovici, A. Schwimmer and S. Yankielowicz, Nuclear Physics B248, 523 (1984). Closely related papers are R. L. Jaffe and C. L. Korba, MIT preprint (1985); S. A. Yost and C. R. Nappi, Princeton preprint (1985). Further references may be found in these papers and in "Solitons in Nuclear and Elementary Particle Physics", Proceedings of the 1984 Lewes Workshop, Editors: A. Chodos, E. Hadjimichael and C. Tze. (World Scientific, Delaware, 1984). I thank Fedele Lizzi for comments on the manuscript.

EFFECTIVE ACTIONS, DECOUPLING AND ANOMALIES IN CHIRAL GAUGE THEORIES

Eric D'Hoker
Physics Department
Columbia University
New York, New York 10027

Edward Farhi*
Center for Theoretical Physics
Laboratory for Nuclear Science &
Department of Physics
MIT
Cambridge, Massachusetts 02139

Abstract

We show that the Wess-Zumino term is a calculable consequence of decoupling a fermion in a chiral gauge theory. An anomaly free theory remains gauge invariant after decoupling a fermion. Decoupling alters the statistics and quantum numbers of stable solitons. If originally no stable solitons are present, decoupling may create stable solitons.

1. Decoupling of fermions with Yukawa Couplings: the effective action.

In theories containing only vector gauge interactions fermions can be given a Dirac mass term and the effects of heavy fermions at low energies are described by the "decoupling theorem" [1]. This theorem states that in Green functions with only light external particles, the only effect of the heavy fermions is the renormalization of the coupling constants of the original Lagrangian. In this sense, the effective action at low energies is given by the original action in which the fields of the heavy fermions have been omitted. In particular, no "new" terms appear in this effective action. Even though now a low energy theory, it is renormalizable.

In theories containing chiral gauge interactions, a Dirac mass term would violate gauge invariance. Instead, the chiral fermions can be given mass through Yukawa coupling to a Higgs field that acquires a non zero vacuum expectation value. This also gives mass to some of the gauge bosons. In this section,

This research was supported in part by the Dept. of Energy (DOE) under contracts DE-AC02-76 ER03069 and DE-AC-02-76 ER02271.

*Alfred P. Sloan Research Fellow

we shall examine the decoupling of anomalies in the presence of a fundamental Higgs field. We will show that a Wess-Zumino term (abbreviated WZ) dependent on the Higgs field and gauge fields alone is a calculable consequence of decoupling. If the theory before decoupling had an anomaly free set of fermions then decoupling of a fermion results in a low energy effective theory with an anomalous fermion content whose gauge non-invariance is compensated by the induced WZ [2].

Consider a chiral gauge theory based on the group G where the fermions form an anomaly free representation of G. We wish to decouple fermions ψ_L and ψ_R transforming under different N-dimensional representations r_L and r_R of G. The Lagrangian for this fermion is

$$\mathcal{L}_\psi = \bar{\psi}_L(i\partial\!\!\!/ - A\!\!\!/_L - qB\!\!\!/)\psi_L + \bar{\psi}_R(i\partial\!\!\!/ - A\!\!\!/_R - qB\!\!\!/)\psi_R$$

$$-\lambda\,\bar{\psi}_L\Phi\psi_R - \lambda\bar{\psi}_R\Phi^\dagger\psi_L \qquad (1)$$

where $A_L = A^a T^a_L$ and $A_R = A^a T^a_R$ are the gauge fields of G, T_L and T_R are NxN representation matrices of r_L and r_R, and we have included an explicit $U(1)_V$ gauge field B. The Higgs field Φ is an NxN matrix transforming under G as

$$\Phi \to e^{-i\alpha^a T^a_L}\,\Phi\, e^{i\alpha^b T^b_R} \,. \qquad (2)$$

We decouple ψ by letting the dimensionless Yukawa coupling get large keeping the vacuum expectation value $\langle\Phi\rangle = v1$ fixed. In this way we do not decouple any gauge bosons. All N components of ψ get equal mass[f1] λv.

To decouple the fermion ψ, we expand the effective action

$$W_\lambda = -\,i\,\ln \int \mathcal{D}\psi_L\,\mathcal{D}\psi_R\,\exp i\int d^4x\,\mathcal{L}_\psi \qquad (3)$$

in a power series in $1/\lambda v$ and retain only those terms which do not vanish as $\lambda v \to \infty$. This defines the low energy effective action W_∞. We have performed this expansion for the case where

$\Phi = vU$, with $U \varepsilon SU(N)$. Our results are the following[2].

W_∞ can be naturally written as the sum of a gauge invariant term W' and a gauge variant term W_{VAR}:

$$W_\infty(U, A_L, A_R, B) = W'(U, A_L, A_R, B) + W_{VAR}(U, A_L, A_R, B) \quad (4)$$

W_{VAR} is given by

$$W_{VAR} = q \int d^4x\, B_\lambda \{J^\lambda_{G.W.}(U, A_L, A_R, B) - \hat{R}^\lambda(A_L) + \hat{R}^\lambda(A_R)\}$$

$$+ \Gamma(U, A_L, A_R) \quad (5)$$

Here the Goldstone-Wilczek current[4] is defined by

$$J^\lambda_{G.W.}(U, A_L, A_R) = \frac{1}{24\pi^2} \varepsilon^{\lambda\mu\nu\rho} \, Tr(U^\dagger D_\mu U U^\dagger D_\nu U U^\dagger D_\rho U$$

$$- \frac{3i}{2} F_{L\mu\nu} D_\rho U U^\dagger - \frac{3}{2} i F_{R\mu\nu} U^\dagger D_\rho U) \quad (6)$$

and we also have[f2]

$$\hat{R}^\lambda(A) = \frac{1}{24\pi^2} \varepsilon^{\lambda\mu\nu\rho} \, Tr(A_\mu F_{\nu\rho} - \frac{i}{2} A_\mu A_\nu A_\rho) \quad (7)$$

and Γ is the usual Wess-Zumino term[5,6]. The expression for W' and Γ are rather lengthy and they can be found in[2]. W' contains renormalizations of couplings already present in the Lagrangian plus four derivative terms, not found in the original Lagrangian.

W_{VAR} is gauge-variant and it satisfies the same anomalous Ward identities as the theory defined by $\mathcal{L}_\psi$.(1) The anomalies associated with W_{VAR} cancel the anomalies of the remaining low energy fermions. Thus the theory stays gauge invariant after decoupling.

The effective theory however contains terms other than those present in the original low energy Lagrangian, unlike in the case of decoupling in vector gauge theories. These terms manifestly spoil renormalizability. In fact, the presence of the WZ alone is enough to render the theory non-renormalizable.

An interesting example [7] occurs if the original theory consists of an even number of left handed doublets under the gauge group SU(2). An even number of doublets is required to cancel the non-perturbative anomaly [8]. Suppose we decouple one doublet by introducing $\Phi(x) = vU(x)$ and two right handed SU(2) singlets. In this case we have

$$\Gamma(U) = \begin{Bmatrix} 0 & U \text{ trivial in } \pi_4(SU(2)) \\ \pi & U \text{ non-trivial} \end{Bmatrix} \mod 2\pi \ .$$

Under a gauge transformation which is non-trivial in $\pi_4(SU(2))$, $\Gamma(U) \to \Gamma(U) + \pi$. However, the low energy sector has an odd number of fermion doublets and under this gauge transformation they yield a factor of (-1) in the functional integral, which is compensated by the effect of $\Gamma(U)$, so that the total effective action is gauge invariant.

2. Decoupling and Solitons

Decoupling has a dramatic effect on the low energy spectrum of a chiral theory with scalar fields [7]. Suppose that the scalar field sector supports a topologically stable soliton much like the Skyrmion. Before decoupling, the fermionic sector of the theory is anomaly free, so there is no WZ, and the properly quantized solitons are bosons [6]. The solitons we consider have a size and an energy characteristic of the theory before decoupling: v. After decoupling we use the counterterms to guarantee that the scale of the low energy theory is still v and not m. This should guarantee that the soliton still has a size and an energy characteristic of v. Since the size of the soliton is much greater than $\frac{1}{m}$ it carries the $U(1)_V$ quantum number of the decoupled fermion [9,12]. Also, the decoupling results in the introduction of the term $\Gamma(U)$ in the low energy effective action. Because of this term, the properly quantized soliton is now a fermion. In addition, the term $\Gamma(U)$ determines the quantum numbers of the properly quantized soliton under the unbroken subgroup of G [10]. In the case of $G = SU(N)_L \times SU(N)_R$, the unbroken subgroup is $SU(N)_V$ and the lowest energy fermionic soliton with unit winding number transforms in the N-dimensional representation of $SU(N)_V$.

What if the theory does not support stable solitons before decoupling? We make an energetic argument [7], that a stable soliton is created by decoupling. Consider a winding number one configuration after decoupling. As long as its size is larger than 1/m it carries the fermion number of the decoupled state. If it shrinks to nothing or if it unwinds it no longer carries this fermion number. However, fermion number is conserved so for a winding number one configuration to shrink or unwind there must be a fermion number one object in the final state. Since m is presumed to be much larger than the energy of the initial configuration, the object is stabilized. This argument assumes that the Φ dynamics which result after decoupling is described by a Hamiltonian which is bounded from below by more than -m.

Let us consider the case of an SU(2) gauge theory with an even number of left handed doublets before decoupling. One can show that the theory has no gauge invariant states unless the total number of fermion doublets including fermionic solitons is even [11]. Thus, before decoupling, if the theory supports a stable soliton, it must be a boson. We now decouple one fermion doublet by sending its Yukawa coupling to infinity. The stable soliton is transformed into a fermion and the total number of fermion doublets in the low energy spectrum remains even. If before decoupling no stable soliton existed, decoupling may create a stable fermionic soliton as described above. In this case gauge invariance at the state level is maintained after decoupling as it was before.

Low energy solitons, which carry the fermion number of a decoupled state, can help resolve an apparent paradox concerning instanton mediated processes and decoupling. Instanton mediated processes violate separate fermion numbers but conserve the difference between any two fermion numbers. In any instanton mediated process all fermions in the theory must participate. If we decouple a single fermion then, without including the solitons, we would conclude that there are no low energy instanton mediated processes because the heavy fermion which must participate is not part of the low energy world. However, if we include the low energy soliton carrying the fermion number of the heavy state, then instanton processes can occur as long as the soliton appears in the initial or final state. In this way, decoupling does not necessarily lead to the suppression of instanton mediated processes.

References

1. T. Appelquist and Carrazzone, Phys. Rev.D11 (1975) 2856.
2. E. D'Hoker and E. Farhi, Nucl. Phys. B248 (1984) 59.
3. E. D'Hoker and J. Goldstone, Columbia Preprint (1985) 307.
4. J. Goldstone and F. Wilczek, Phys. Rev. Lett.47 (1981) 986.
5. J. Wess and B. Zumino, Phys. Lett. 37B (1971) 95.
6. E. Witten, Nucl. Phys. B223 (1984) 422, 433.
7. E. D'Hoker and E. Farhi, Nucl. Phys. B248 (1984) 77.
8. E. Witten, Phys. Lett. 117B (1982) 324.
9. E. D'Hoker and E. Farhi, Nucl. Phys. B241 (1984) 109.
10. E. Guadagnini, Nucl. Phys. B236 (1984) 35.
11. E. D'Hoker and E. Farhi, Phys. Lett. 134B (1984) 86.
12. R. Mac Kenzie and F. Wilczek, Phys.Rev. D30 (1984) 2194.

Footnotes

f1. The case when the N components of ψ get different masses has been treated for the case of $G = SU(2)_L \times SU(2)_R \times U(1)_V$ [3].

f2. There is an arbitrariness in W_{VAR}, corresponding to adding local polynomials in A and its derivatives to the Lagrangian. The form for $\hat{R}$ corresponds to a convention where all currents are decomposed in their left and right parts for each of which the anomaly is computed separately.

INTRODUCTION TO SIGMA MODEL ANOMALIES †

Philip Nelson
Lyman Laboratory of Physics
Harvard University
Cambridge, MA 02138

I'd like to tell you about two different kinds of results which A. Manohar, G. Moore, and I have recently been studying. [1][2][3]In each case the point is that some nonlinear sigma models coupled to chiral fermions are just bad. You can't just write them down at random and assume that they make quantum mechanical sense, just as you can't do this for chiral gauge theories. In each case a theory which was perfectly well-defined classically turns out to have quantum problems due to an anomaly.

One of our results deals with the specific case in which a sigma model with fermions arises as a result of dynamical symmetry breakdown from some group G to a subgroup H[3]. H may contain chiral symmetries protecting some fermions in a representation ρ_H of H. In this case it may be impossible to quantize the remaining fermions in a way which reproduces the anomalous Ward identities of *any* underlying strongly-interacting gauge theory, and so we conclude that this pattern of symmetry breakdown will not be realized in any such theory. The criterion in this case is *local* in character, since roughly speaking once we know how the sigma model in question behaves for field configurations close to the vacuum base point in the internal manifold, we can use symmetry to find how it behaves everywhere else.

If we drop the assumption that the internal space is homogeneous, then no particular local behavior can be excluded. Accordingly, in this broader class of models we get a weaker condition based only on the *global* topology of the configuration space. The analysis of this case is harder than the special case. An example of this type of situation is the compactified heterotic string[4], in which the internal space need have no symmetries at all. We

† supported in part by NSF contract PHY-82-15249

then find that permissible compactifications obey a topological condition. I'll begin with this global argument, since in fact it came first.

Recall that in gauge theory the problem with anomalies is that the fermion effective action $\Gamma_f[A]$ is not gauge-invariant on the space $\mathcal{A}$ of vector potentials. We can rephrase this by saying that $\Gamma_f[A]$ doesn't define a function $\Gamma_f[\bar{A}]$ on the true configuration space $\mathcal{C} \equiv \mathcal{A}/\mathcal{G}$ of vector potentials modulo gauge transformations. But it does come close. In fact the effective action does have a geometrical interpretation on $\mathcal{C}$, but only as a *section* of a (possibly twisted) line bundle over it[5][6][7]. In other words, there is an obstruction to defining $\Gamma_f[\bar{A}]$ which is like the obstruction to thinking of the wavesection for a Schrödinger particle near a magnetic monopole as an ordinary function. Since only bona fide functions can be integrated over $\mathcal{C}$, we cannot quantize the bosons in this theory. But since line bundles are classified by H^2, very little can go wrong: either the theory has a problem visible on some two-sphere in $\mathcal{C}$, or else it has none at all. Therefore we can without loss of generality consider not all of $\mathcal{C}$, but only two-parameter families in it.

If we can think of the gauge anomaly as an obstruction rather than as the failure of some kind of symmetry, then we can consider other theories, perhaps with no symmetries at all, which have complicated configuration spaces. These too will in general have anomalies obstructing their quantization.

Sigma models are examples of such theories. A bosonic nonlinear sigma model has degrees of freedom φ which are maps from (compactified) spacetime S^4 into some manifold M. To couple these "pions" to fermions in a geometrical way, consider the special case of supersymmetry. Here for every point x in spacetime $\psi(x)$ is a tangent vector to M at $\varphi(x)$, in order for the transformation law $\delta\varphi \propto \bar{\epsilon}\psi$ to make sense. For a given boson configuration φ, then, we paste together all the tangent spaces $TM|_{\varphi(x)}$ into one bundle called the *pullback* $\varphi^*(TM)$ over spacetime.

To complete this picture we must tensor in the spin bundle over spacetime. We also need to replace φ by a two-parameter family $\hat{\varphi}$, ie a function from $S^2 \times S^4 \to M$. Finally, we generalize TM, which was appropriate for supersymmetry, to an arbitrary bundle B over M. For example, in the CCWZ prescription[8] for writing down phenomenological lagrangians we will use $M = G/H$ and B will be associated to the bundle $G \to M$ by the representation ρ_H. Whatever the origin of B, we can now proceed to define a Dirac operator for the fermions in the presence of a background boson field φ, giving us a well-defined classical sigma model with fermions.

To quantize this system we begin with the fermions. Thus we have to make sense out of the functional integral $\exp[-\Gamma_f[\varphi]] = \int d\bar\psi\, d\psi\, \exp[-\int \bar\psi \not{D}_\varphi \psi]$. As usual we turn the functional integral into countably many ordinary integrals by choosing an eigenmode expansion $\{u^i_\varphi(x)\}$ for $\not{D}^\dagger\not{D}$ and $\{v^i_\varphi(x)\}$ for $\not{D}\not{D}^\dagger$. Thus u_φ's are an orthonormal *frame* for the Hilbert space $\mathcal{H}^+_\varphi$ of positive-chirality wavefunctions in the background φ; similarly the v's frame $\mathcal{H}^-_\varphi$.

But what frame are we to use? If we were to choose some other orthonormal $u^{i\prime}_\varphi = U^{ij}(\varphi)u^j_\varphi$, $v^{i\prime} = V^{ij}v^j$, then the value we computed for $\exp[-\Gamma_f[\varphi]]$ would change by the phase $\det(UV^{-1})$. [1] Indeed, all that is happening here is that we are trying to find the (functional) determinant of an operator $\not{D}_\varphi$ which maps one space $\mathcal{H}^+_\varphi$ to a *different* space $\mathcal{H}^-_\varphi$ and so has no determinant. What we have done amounts to framing both spaces and taking the determinant of the *matrix* representing our operator; while this works fine at one fixed φ, it leaves open the possibility that we may paint ourselves into a corner trying to extend the framing smoothly throughout $\mathcal{C}$.

Mathematically, this means that $\exp[-\Gamma_f[\varphi]]$ must be regarded as a section of a line bundle $\mathcal{D} = \mathrm{DET}\mathcal{H}^+ - \mathrm{DET}\mathcal{H}^-$, where $\mathrm{DET}\mathcal{H}$ means the bundle whose transition functions are the determinants of those of $\mathcal{H}$, and the subtraction indicates that the second factor's transition functions are to be inverted as above. $\mathcal{D}$ can be rigorously defined using a cutoff, whereupon it is called the "index of the family of Dirac operators" parametrized by $\mathcal{C}$ (or in our case, by a two-sphere in $\mathcal{C}$). Now the computation of the twist of $\mathcal{D}$ by the above definition may seem a hopeless task. Incredibly, however, it turns out to be a topological invariant given by the Atiyah-Singer index theorem [10][5][11][2] as

$$(\text{anomaly}) = \int_{S^2\times S^4} ch_3\,\hat\varphi^*(B).$$

For details on how to compute and interpret this invariant, see [2]. In particular, the het-

[1] This infinite-dimensional determinant turns out to be a local functional of φ — a Wess-Zumino term[9].

erotic string will be safe if its background Yang-Mills field strength equals its background Riemann curvature, since then the curvature form used to compute the Chern character has two cancelling pieces.

Thus the topology of the bundle B combines with that of the configuration space $\mathcal{C}$ to determine whether quantized fermions can exist at all in the given model.

Turning now to the case of dynamical symmetry breakdown to $M = G/H$, we now can and should ask more of a quantization than that it exist at all. Not only must we choose framings of $\mathcal{H}^{\pm}$ which *exist* globally (up to unimodular changes U, V), we must now require of them the right *variation* under symmetry transformations. We can phrase this in more familiar language if we work locally, so that there is no problem finding some framing of $\mathcal{H}^{\pm}$. We then choose any old framing, for example the one used in ordinary perturbation theory, and seek to fix it up. By the previous footnote, this amounts to finding a Wess-Zumino-type counterterm which modifies the anomalous current algebra of our model until it coincides with that of some underlying "preon" model.

Specifically, suppose the underlying model has fermions ("preons") transforming linearly in some representation ρ_G of G. Suppose our putative effective theory is a nonlinear sigma model with internal space G/H and residual fermions ("composite quarks") transforming in the representation ρ_H of H and constructed by the recipe of [8]. By the 't Hooft matching condition[12] we know that the H-anomalies of ρ_H must match those of $\rho_G|_H$, the restriction of ρ_G to H.

But what about the anomalies of G? In general the effective theory as we have quantized it will get them wrong. In general no local counterterm can be built from the "pion" fields which reproduces them. Can these two *conspire* to produce the correct Ward identities for all of G?

They can. Whenever the 't Hooft condition is satisfied we can write down a Wess-Zumino counterterm taking the G-variation of $\Gamma_f(\rho_H)$ to the desired variation of $\Gamma_f^{linear}(\rho_G)$ [3]. What is more, while the counterterm isn't globally defined, neither is $\Gamma_f(\rho_H)$, in such a way that the *sum* is global. Hence whenever the local condition applies and is satisfied, the global obstruction of the previous section vanishes too.

There is a quick and dirty argument for this result. To define the effective theory locally, we can use the prescription of [8] for the fermion effective action $\Gamma_f(\rho_H)$. We can conveniently describe the anomalous Ward identities for $\Gamma_f(\rho_H)$ by coupling the theory to external "flavor" gauge fields for G and discussing the anomalous variation of Γ_f under local G-transformations. Now consider adding the H-representation $\rho_G|_H$, and its complex conjugate. This does not change the anomalies, so we have

$$\Gamma_f(\rho_H) \doteq \Gamma_f(\rho_H + \overline{\rho}_G|_H) + \Gamma_f(\rho_G|_H) ,$$

where the symbol $\doteq$ means "has the same anomalous variation under G."

Recall that in the CCWZ prescription we begin by choosing a local section $s : G/H \rightarrow G$. For example, in [8] the section near the identity is $s_0(p) = e^{\xi \cdot X}$ where ξ are the normal coordinates of p and X^r are the broken generators. Define the function $h(p; g_0)$ by

$$g_0 s(p) = s(g_0 \cdot p) h(p; g_0)$$

where $h(p; g_0) \in H$. For the choice in [8] we thus have $h(p; g_0) = e^{u' \cdot T}$ where $u'(p; g_0)$ is defined by $g_0 e^{\xi \cdot X} = e^{\xi' \cdot X} e^{u' \cdot T}$ and T^a are the unbroken generators. Then under the transformation by g_0 the fermions rotate by $\rho_H(h(\varphi(x), g_0)$. But $\rho_H + \overline{\rho}_G|_H$ has no H-anomaly by hypothesis so the first term on the right hand side has no G-variation.

Moving on to the second term on the right, there the fermions correspond to those in the effective action of the underlying linear theory, $\Gamma_f^{linear}(\rho_G)$. Before we can conclude that $\Gamma_f(\rho_H) \doteq \Gamma_f^{linear}(\rho_G)$, however, we must investigate the transformation from the Fermi fields ψ in the CCWZ basis to fields Ψ transforming linearly under G. Following [8] this is

$$\rho_G(s(\varphi(x)))\,\psi(x) = \Psi(x) . \tag{1}$$

Since the fields Ψ transform in the same way as the underlying fermions the flavor anomalies are the same. As shown in [9] in the case of the chiral quark model, this change of variables contributes an anomalous Jacobian factor to Γ_f which can be compensated by the addition of a local counterterm, and so we expect

$$\Gamma_f(\rho_H) + F \doteq \Gamma_f^{linear}(\rho_G) . \tag{2}$$

Hence the addition of a local counterterm F should be sufficient to realize the G symmetry properly.

In general, the map s above will be defined only on a neighborhood $\mathcal{U} \subseteq G/H$, so we need to use a collection of maps $\{s_\alpha\}$ on patches $\{\mathcal{U}_\alpha\}$ covering G/H. These define a set of Γ_f^α, and by (1) a corresponding set of F^α. Since the right hand side of equation (2) is independent of s_α, we have that $\exp\left(-\Gamma_f^\alpha - F^\alpha\right)$ regarded as a section of a line bundle has trivial transition functions. Thus the global anomaly of [1] is absent.

A more convincing argument would simply construct F. This is what we do in [3]. We show that appropriate F's exist for any of the various lagrangians constructed in [8], as long as the 't Hooft condition is satisfied. In particular there is one choice which makes it plain that the global obstruction vanishes.

References

[1] G. Moore, P. Nelson, Phys. Rev. Lett. **53**(1984)1519.

[2] G. Moore, P. Nelson, to appear in Comm. Math. Phys. This paper contains a fuller bibliography than the one here.

[3] A. Manohar, G. Moore, P. Nelson, Phys. Lett. **152**(1985)68.

[4] D. Gross, J. Harvey, E. Martinec, R. Rohm, Phys. Rev. Lett. 54(1985)502; P. Candelas, G. Horowitz, A. Strominger, E. Witten, "Vacuum Configurations for Superstrings," preprint.

[5] I. Singer, Lectures at Santa Barbara, 1982, unpublished.

[6] M. Atiyah and I. Singer, Proc. Nat. Acad. Sci. USA **81** (1984) 2597.

[7] L. Alvarez-Gaumé and P. Ginsparg, Nucl. Phys **B243**(1984)449.

[8] S. Coleman, J. Wess, and B. Zumino, Phys. Rev. **177**(1969) 2239; C. Callan, S. Coleman, J. Wess, and B. Zumino, Phys. Rev. **177** (1969) 2247.

[9] A. Manohar and G. Moore, Nucl. Phys. **B243** (1984) 55.

[10] M. Atiyah, I. Singer, Ann. Math. **87**(1968)546.

[11] O. Alvarez, B. Zumino, and I. Singer, Comm. Math. Phys. **96**(1984)409.

[12] G. 't Hooft, in *Recent developments in gauge theories,* ed. G. 't Hooft et. al. (Plenum, New York, 1980).

INDUCED CHERN-SIMONS TERMS AT HIGH TEMPERATURES AND FINITE DENSITIES

A. N. Redlich
Department of Physics, Brandeis University, Waltham MA 02254

This talk is based upon work I did in collaboration with L.C.R. Wijewardhana.[1]

It is well known that at high temperatures, $T \to \infty$, a quantum field theory undergoes dimensional reduction to an effective theory of one lower dimension.[2,3,4,5] To understand how this dimensional reduction takes place (from here on, we restrict ourselves to a reduction from 4 to 3 dimensions), we write the thermal partition function as a Euclidean path integral

$$Z = \sum_n e^{-\beta E_n} = \mathrm{tr}\, e^{-\beta H} = \int d\phi\, d\bar{\psi} d\psi\; e^{-\int_0^\beta d\tau \int d^3x\, \mathscr{L}(\phi,\psi)} \tag{1}$$

in which the imaginary time variable τ, runs from 0 to $\beta = 1/T$; $\phi(\tau,x)$ $[\psi(\tau,x)]$ represents a set of bosonic (fermionic) fields which satisfy the periodic (antiperiodic) boundary conditions $\phi(0,x) = \phi(\beta,x)$ $[\psi(0,x) = -\psi(\beta,x)$. Because τ takes values in a compact space, we can decompose functions of τ into a sum over a discreet set of modes: $\phi(\tau,x) = \Sigma_n \phi_n(x)\, \exp(i2\pi n\tau/\beta)$; $\psi(\tau,x) = \Sigma_n \psi_n(x)\, \exp[i(2n+1)\pi\tau/\beta]$. The bosonic and fermionic propagators are

$$\frac{-i}{\left(\frac{2\pi n}{\beta}\right)^2 + \vec{k}^2 + m^2} \;\ldots\; \text{Bosons} \qquad\qquad \frac{i}{\left(\frac{(2n+1)\pi}{-i\beta}\right)\gamma^0 + \vec{k}\cdot\vec{\gamma} - m} \;\ldots\; \text{Fermions}\,. \tag{2}$$

Thinking of these propagators as an infinite set of three-dimensional propagators, one for each three-dimensional field, $\phi_n(x)$, $\psi_n(x)$, we see that at high temperatures all of the modes, except for the zero bosonic mode, become very heavy, with masses proportional to T. Therefore, if we are interested in an effective theory at high temperature, valid at length scales $l \gg 1/T$, we may "integrate out" all of these heavy fields, leaving us with an effective theory for the static, bosonic, zero modes $\phi_0(x)$:

$$Z \underset{T\to\infty}{\to} \int d\phi_0\, e^{-\int d^3x\, \mathscr{L}_{eff}(\phi_0(x))}\,. \tag{3}$$

Let us now specialize to a four-dimensional theory of two left-handed

SU(2) fermion doublets coupled to an SU(2) gauge field. This model is free of both perturbative and non-perturbative anomalies; its partition function is

$$Z = \int dA d\bar{\psi} d\psi \exp\{- \int_0^\beta d\tau \int d^3x [\frac{1}{2} \mathrm{tr}\, F^2 + \sum_{i=1}^{2} \bar{\psi}_L^i (i\partial\!\!\!/ - gA\!\!\!/ + i\mu_i \gamma^0)\psi_L^i]\} \ . \qquad (4)$$

The term $\sum_{i=1}^{2} \bar{\psi}^i (i\mu_i \gamma_0)\psi_L^i$ corresponds to adding chemical potentials, μ_i, for each fermion species, ψ_L^i: $Z = \mathrm{tr}\, e^{-\beta H} \rightarrow \mathrm{tr}\, e^{-\beta(H + \mu Q_L)}$. We ignore here the nonconservation of Q_L due to instantons because these effects are negligible in all realistic theories.[6] The property of μQ_L which for our purposes makes it a desirable addition to the action is its transformation properties under CP, since our goal here is to show that CP violating effects at high temperatures can induce a topological mass term (Chern-Simons term) for the gauge fields. μQ_L does effectively violate CP. Unfortunately, as I will discuss, for real chemical potentials, μ^i, it also effectively violates CTP (for imaginary μ^i only CP is violated). This should not be upsetting, since it does not imply that CTP is violated in the underlying interactions, only that we have set up an ensemble of particles which does not respect the symmetry.

We use finite temperature perturbation theory to calculate the parity odd portion of the one-loop fermionic effective action to leading order in 1/T:

$$-\ln \det(i\partial\!\!\!/ - gA\!\!\!/ + i\mu_i \gamma^0) =$$  + 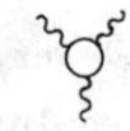 $+ O(1/T)$. (5)

At high temperatures, this gives us an effective theory for the spatial components of the gauge field A^i:

$$Z \underset{T\to\infty}{\rightarrow} \int dA' e^{-I_{eff}[A']} \qquad (6)$$

$$I_{eff}[A'] = \int d^3x \frac{1}{2} \mathrm{tr}\, F^2 + \sum_i (i\mu^i/T) W[A'] + \ldots \qquad (7)$$

$$W[A'] = \frac{ie^2}{16\pi^2} \int d^3x\, \varepsilon^{ijk} \mathrm{tr}[A_i' F_{jk}' - i \frac{2}{3} A_i' A_j' A_k'] \ . \qquad (8)$$

The dots in (7) include terms of even parity and terms which are not of leading order in 1/T; the three-dimensional gauge field is defined as $A^{i'} \equiv A_0^i/\sqrt{T}$; and the three-dimensional coupling constant is $e \equiv g\sqrt{T}$. We do not include the time component of the gauge field zero mode $A_0^0(x)$ because it acquires a mass of order[4] g^2T.

The effective three-dimensional theory (7) (ignoring the terms signified by the dots) has been extensively studied by Deser, Jackiw, and Templeton.[7] Of special interest to mathematicians because of its topological properties, the second term in (7), W[A'], is known as the Chern-Simons secondary characteristic class. It is odd under P and changes by an integer, W[A'] $\to$ W[A'] + n, under a homotopically non-trivial gauge transformation, A $\to$ $U_n^{-1}AU_n + U_n^{-1}\partial U_n$, with winding number n. W[A'] is also known as a topological mass term because it produces a mass for the gauge fields $A^{i'}$ proportional to the coefficient in front of W[A'].[7,8] In our model, the $(\text{mass})^2 = \left(\frac{e^2}{4\pi} i \sum_i \frac{\mu_i}{T}\right)^2$ is less (greater) than zero for real (imaginary) chemical potential. This is because for μ real the chemical potential term we added to the four-dimensional action was CTP violating. Since $A^{i'}$ actually represents the spatial, or magnetic, components of the original 4-d gauge field, the "mass" is to be interpreted as magnetic screening (antiscreening) for imaginary (real) chemical potentials, μ^i.

Why is this result interesting, or potentially interesting?

First, in QCD the "electric" component of the static gauge field $A_0^0(x)$ acquires a mass of order[4] g^2T (Debye screening), but the magnetic components $A_0^i(x)$ remain massless (at least in perturbation theory). A "magnetic mass" would be desirable, however, because it would act as an infrared cutoff and cure the severe infrared infinities which plague perturbation theory in 3-d[9]. Also, a finite screening length for the magnetic field (together with flux conservation $\nabla\cdot B=0$) would cause confinement of magnetic flux: monopole-antimonopole (M-$\bar{M}$) pairs produced in the early universe would be connected by thin flux tubes, which, it has been speculated,[10] would enhance M-$\bar{M}$ annihilation. Second, we have found an example in which fermions do not naively decouple at high temperature. Ordinary decoupling theorems predict the fermions should leave behind interactions which simply renormalize terms already present in the effective theory. Third, because W[A'] (8) changes by an integer n under a large gauge transformation, the coefficient $i\alpha$ of W[A'] in the action must be quantized so that $\exp(i\alpha\, W[A'])$, which appears in the functional integral, remains gauge-invariant.[7] It was hoped that this quantization condition would constrain some of the parameters of the original 4-d theory; it does not do so in our case. Finally, one of the justifications for studying topologically massive Yang-Mills theory was the possibility that it might arise as the high T limit of a 4-d theory. Nobody had, however, given an example in which this occurs.

Discussion: Unfortunately, from a physical standpoint our result is not satisfactory. For real chemical potential, we discover an antiscreening effect which at best can be interpreted as instability in our effective theory. At worst it is an indication that, from the standpoint of realistic physics, we have not correctly derived the effective high temperature theory. This point of view is strengthened by the fact that the quantization condition $\frac{i}{2\pi T}\Sigma_i\mu_i$ = integer cannot be satisfied here for real μ, which means our effective theory is not gauge invariant. It may be that ignoring instantons in 4-d is equivalent to restricting the 3-d theory to a single homotopy class, which would allow us to avoid the quantization condition. (For further comments see Ref.1,11.)

On the other hand, we have given an example in which fermions do not naively decouple. Furthermore, we have proven that CP violating effects can cause a Chern-Simons term to be induced at high temperatures. While in our model we must choose unphysical values of the parameters μ,T in order to obtain a consistent 3-d effective theory--one in which we get magnetic screening and the quantization condition is satisfied--it may be that for some other model, one will obtain a consistent theory for physical values of its parameters.

Postscript: As you might have guessed, W[A'] is induced because of the U(1) anomaly in the presence of SU(2) left gauge fields. To see this, consider the 4-d theory in Minkowski space at T=0, $\mu\neq 0$. At T=0, we give the fermions masses, m^i, (neglected at high T) by including the right handed components of the fermion fields. The term $\Sigma_i\mu_i\bar{\psi}^i\gamma^0\psi^i$ is rewritten as a coupling to a U(1) gauge field $B_i^\mu = (\mu_i,0,0,0)$: $\Sigma_i B_i^\mu\bar{\psi}^i\gamma_\mu\psi^i$. In the presence of SU(2) left gauge fields, A^μ, the U(1) current $J^{\mu i} = \bar{\psi}^i\gamma^\mu\psi^i$ is not conserved, and $\langle J^\mu\rangle \neq 0$. By expanding in powers of momenta p over m^i, we may use a well known result[12] for $\langle J^\mu\rangle$ in the presence of $SU(2)_L$ gauge fields. The induced one loop effective action is

$$I_{1L} = \int d^4x\, \frac{1}{2}\, B_i^\mu\langle J_\mu^i\rangle = \Sigma_i\mu^i \int_{-\infty}^{\infty} dx_0(-i)W[A(x_0)] + O(p/m)\ . \qquad (9)$$

At high temperatures, $\mu \int dx_0(-i)W[A] \to (\frac{\mu}{T})W[A']$.

REFERENCES

1. A. N. Redlich and L.C.R. Wijewardhana, Phys. Rev. Lett. (1985).
2. D. A. Kirzhnits and A. D. Linde, Phys. Lett. 42B, 471 (1972); S. Weinberg, Phys. Rev. D9, 3357 (1974).
3. L. Dolan and R. Jackiw, Phys. Rev. D9, 3320 (1974).
4. D. J. Gross, R. D. Pisarski, and L. G. Yaffe, Rev. Mod. Phys. 53, 43 (1981).
5. T. Appelquist and R. D. Pisarski, Phys. Rev. D23, 2305 (1981).
6. G. 'tHooft, Phys. Rev. Lett. D37, 8 (1976).
7. S. Deser, R. Jackiw, and S. Templeton, Phys. Rev. Lett. 48, 975 (1982); Ann. Phys. 140, 372 (1982).
8. W. Siegel, Nucl. Phys. D156, 135 (1979); R. Jackiw and S. Templeton, Phys. Rev. D23 2291 (1981); J. Schonfeld, Nucl. Phys. B185, 157 (1981).
9. A. D. Linde, Phys. Lett. B96, 289 (1980).
10. A. D. Linde, Phys. Lett. B96, 293 (1980); E. W. Kolb, Los Alamos Preprint.
11. A. J. Niemi and G. W. Semenoff, Phys. Rev. Lett. (1985).
12. J. Goldstone and F. Wilczek, Phys. Rev. Lett. 47 986 (1981).

Energy of the weak Skyrmion

R. MacKenzie*

Department of Physics
University of California
Santa Barbara, CA 93106

1. Introduction

The nonlinear σ-model[1] was conceived as a field theoretic way of obtaining the Goldberger-Treiman relation for the pion decay constant. Shortly thereafter, Skyrme[2] realized that, in today's language, the scalar sector of the model possesses solitons, which can be made stable against scaling by the inclusion in the Lagrangian of a four-derivative term (the so-called Skyrme term). He suggested the identification of the soliton (skyrmion) with the nucleon; thus a theory with only scalar fields would describe both pions and nucleons—an economical idea, the phenomenology of which has been studied by several authors.[3]

Skyrme's idea has recently found use in a different context, namely the Weinberg-Salam (WS) model.[4] Here the Higgs sector is equivalent to the σ-model. Skyrme's idea is especially appropriate here if a theory like technicolor[5] is responsible for the dynamics of the Higgs sector. As is the case with QCD, technicolor would be seen as a nonlinear σ-model at low energy. Assuming the same mechanism which generates the Skyrme term in the strong interaction case is also at work here,[6] the Higgs sector is then described by an energetically scaled-up version of the Skyrme Lagrangian. We can then make scaled-up conclusions: that a topologically stable soliton which is also stable against scaling exists in the WS model. This soliton has been called the *weak* skyrmion in order to differentiate it from its strong-interaction cousin; however here, for simplicity, we refer to it simply as the skyrmion.

Here I would like to discuss a slightly different situation, abandoning the notion of an underlying theory such as technicolor giving rise to a *nonlinear* σ-model. Namely, I will examine the case where the WS Higgs sector is weakly self-coupled, in which case it is described by the *linear* σ-model.[7] Strictly speaking, there are no solitons in this model. However, one can argue that in going from the nonlinear to the linear σ-model one demotes the topological stability of the soliton to mere *meta*stability: the scalar fields are no longer separated form the vacuum by an *infinite* energy barrier, but rather by a finite one.

The emphasis in this paper is on the important role of fermions in determining the properties of the skyrmion. In the next section the skyrmion is introduced and its topological properties are discussed. Thereafter I will discuss the addition of fermions to the model, which could have interesting effects. First it is shown that the skyrmion polarizes the Dirac sea, attaining one unit of fermion number (charge) per *heavy* fermion doublet. Next the question of the skyrmion energy is discussed, where the possibility exists that the skyrmion may be the *lightest* state with the fermion quantum numbers it induces. If this is the case, the fermions stabilize the otherwise topologically metastable skyrmion, and the skyrmion forms a "bag" which "contains" the fermions. I will conclude with a qualitative discussion of skyrmion decay in this situation — a possibility if the heavy fermions could decay weakly into light ones.

2. The Skyrmion

It is necessary at this point to introduce some notation. The scalar sector of the σ-model consists of a 4-tuplet $(\phi_0, \vec{\phi})$ of scalar fields with an O(4) invariant potential which breaks spontaneously the symmetry to O(3):

$$\mathcal{L}_H = \frac{1}{2}(\partial\phi_i)^2 - \lambda(\phi^2 - v^2)^2 \tag{1}$$

Three of the scalar fields are massless; the fourth has mass $\sim \sqrt{\lambda}v$.

In the nonlinear model ($\lambda \to \infty$, so $\phi^2 = v^2$ is a constraint) the set of finite-energy field configurations is disconnected, indicating the existence of solitons. The skyrmion is the winding number one soliton; an ansatz for a skyrmion of size R is

$$\phi_0 = v\frac{(r/R)^2 - 1}{(r/R)^2 + 1}$$

$$\vec{\phi} = v\frac{-2r/R}{(r/R)^2 + 1}\hat{r} \tag{2}$$

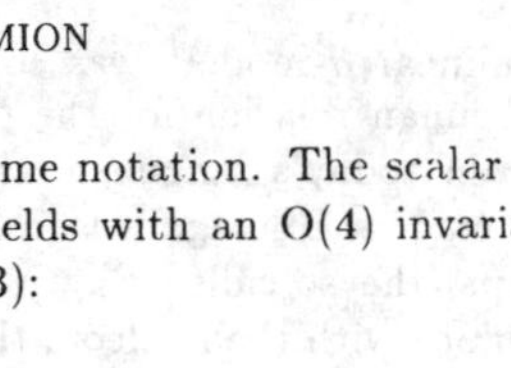

The topological stability/metastability of the skyrmion in the nonlinear/linear σ-model can be illustrated in a one-dimensional version of the σ-model. Consider therefore an O(2)-invariant doublet of scalar fields (ϕ_1, ϕ_2) in one dimension. This displays the essential features of the 3-dimensional model, while being easy to visualize. The potential can be viewed as a surface above the $\phi_1 - \phi_2$ plane — the usual "sombrero" or "wine-bottle" potential. Any particular field configuration, *i.e.*, functions $\phi_2(x), \phi_2(x)$, is then a curve on this surface parametrized by the position, x. In order for the configuration to be of finite energy both ends of the curve (corresponding to spatial $\pm\infty$) must lie on the circle $\phi_1^2 + \phi_2^2 = v^2$, where the potential is zero.

In order to maintain correspondence with the 3-dimensional model, an additional constraint must be put in by hand. In 3 dimensions spatial infinity is connected, so for finiteness of energy the fields must be independent of direction at spatial infinity. (For example, in the skyrmion ansatz $(\phi_0, \vec{\phi}) = (v, 0)$ everywhere at $r \to \infty$). There is no such requirement in 1 dimension since spatial infinity is *disconnected*; for correspondence, therefore, we must impose the artificial constraints $\phi_1(-\infty) = \phi_1(+\infty)$, $\phi_2(-\infty) = \phi_2(+\infty)$. Field configurations, then, are represented by *closed* curves on the potential surface, where one point on the curve, located on the circle $\phi_1^2 + \phi_2^2 = v^2$, corresponds to spatial $\pm\infty$.

It is easy to demonstrate the existence of solitons in the nonlinear model, where the potential is infinite except at $\phi_1^2 + \phi_2^2 = v^2$. In that case, maps from position space into field space are maps from S^1 to S^1, and are therefore characterized by their winding number, which is conserved.

In the linear model, however, field space is topologically a disc, not a circle, and any field configuration can be continuously deformed to the trivial one (*i.e.*, the vacuum, $\phi_1(x) = v$, $\phi_2(x) = 0$), maintaining finite energy at intermediate stages (see Fig. 1). It is clear, however, that $\phi_1 = \phi_2 = 0$ represents an energy barrier, so that a change of winding number is a tunnelling phenomenon; the soliton is topologically metastable. Also, in the nonlinear limit the energy barrier becomes infinite, resulting in topological stability.

(In both the nonlinear and linear model, the skyrmion can decay via tunnelling in the gauge field sector; these instanton effects are ignorably small.[8])

3. Fermion Number of the Weak Skyrmion

Let us now include fermions in the picture. In the WS model, the fermion masses arise from Yukawa coupling to the vacuum expectation value of the Higgs fields. Properly, the two members of each flavor doublet should have different coupling constants (*e.g.*, $m_u \neq m_d$, $m_e \neq m_\nu$, etc.); however, for calculational simplicity we equate the masses within each doublet. Below we will discuss the validity of this equal-mass approximation.

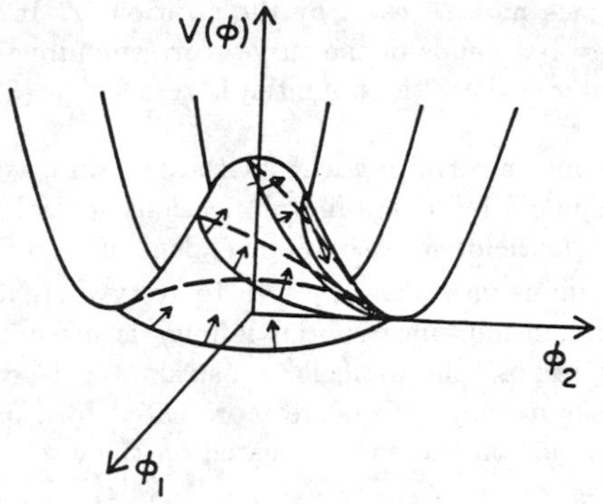

Figure 1: Tunneling of a scalar field configuration in the 1-dimensional linear theory.

In this approximation, the Higgs/fermion sector of the WS model is described by the Lagrangian

$$
\begin{aligned}
\mathcal{L} &= \mathcal{L}_H + \mathcal{L}_F \\
\mathcal{L}_H &= \frac{1}{2}(\partial_\mu \phi)^2 - V(\phi) \\
\mathcal{L}_F &= \bar{\psi}_j i\partial\!\!\!/ \psi_j - g_j \bar{\psi}_j(\phi_0 + i\gamma_5 \vec{\phi}\cdot\vec{\tau})\psi_j
\end{aligned}
\tag{3}
$$

where the index j labels the doublets.

A nontrivial scalar field configuration, *e.g.*, a skyrmion, breaks charge conjugation symmetry, and is capable of polarizing the Dirac sea. The skyrmion thereby obtains a charge.

The so-called adiabatic method can be used to compute the induced charge. Here, the scalar fields are imagined to evolve infinitely slowly from the vacuum to the skyrmion configuration. and the charge flow is computed as an expansion in gradients of the scalar field. From this method, one sees that the charge of the state reached adiabatically is one per fermion doublet. A closer look reveals that the skyrmion actually carries only the quantum numbers of *heavy* fermions, but not of light ones.[9] Here heaviness is set to the fermion Compton wavelength $\lambda_c = 1/m_f$: a *heavy* fermion is one for which $\lambda_c < R$.

To understand the role of the fermion mass in determining the charge of the skyrmion, it is helpful to consider the distribution of the polarization charge in the skyrmion background. Suppose we have just one fermion doublet, with Compton wavelength λ_c. The polarization can be envisioned as a cloud of fermion density induced on the skyrmion, whose integrated charge is one. The key point is that the fermion cloud cannot be confined to a region smaller than λ_c.

Imagine starting with a *wide* skyrmion and slowly shrinking it . For $R > \lambda_c$, the charge happily resides within the skyrmion. However, for $R < \lambda_c$, the charge is forced by quantum mechanical effects to occupy a volume *larger* than the skyrmion. Eventually, as R gets smaller, most of the charge lives *outside* the skyrmion. This means that this state is not the fermionic ground state. Indeed, most of the charge cloud feels the scalar field vacuum so the energy expenditure to keep the cloud occupied is roughly the fermion mass. What happens is that as the skyrmion size decreases, an energy level of the Dirac equation goes from negative to positive energy ; the state with the cloud occupied is no longer the ground state for $R \lesssim \lambda_c$.

If we do not invoke the equal-mass approximation, the situation is *slightly* more complicated physically, and *grossly* more complicated computationally. In that case, the fermion doublet has two associated Compton wavelengths, each of which governs half the charge. If the two Compton wavelengths are similar in magnitude, the above analysis is reasonable, and their average value would roughly give the scale at which an energy level crosses $E = 0$. However, if they are drastically different, they supply two distinct distance scales, and it is not at all obvious where the level crossing would occur. In particular, the equal-mass approximation is particularly questionable for leptons, where heavy charged leptons may still be paired with light (massless?) neutrinos. For quarks, on the other hand, there is (admittedly flimsy) circumstantial evidence that the approximation may be better: at least for the three known generations both members obey the same trend ($m_u < m_c < m_t$, $m_d < m_s < m_b$). With this in mind, I will hereafter make the equal-mass approximation, and refer to the fermions as quarks.

It is easy to extend the above picture to several doublets. The skyrmion polarizes a cloud of charge unity for each doublet, but only the clouds of heavy doublets are confined to the skyrmion. The light doublet's clouds are larger, and therefore unoccupied in the ground state of the skyrmion. Thus, the key result is that the skyrmion in its ground state has the quantum numbers of heavy, but not light, quarks.

4. Energy of the Weak Skyrmion

Interesting questions arise if one tries to calculate the skyrmion energy. At the classical level, no scalar field configuration is stable against scaling: the energy is a monotonically increasing function of the size of the configuration. However, the classical theory is not a valid description of arbitrarily small field configurations. This scaling argument (Derrick's theorem) does not indiscriminately preclude the existence of solitons, but only of classically-described solitons.

In this section we investigate the possibility that quarks stabilize the skyrmion against scaling, by computing quantum connections to the skyrmion energy.

The technique used is to calculate the effective action for the scalar fields, integrating out *heavy* quarks (here we assume there are N heavy doublets of mass m.) In terms of functional integrals,

$$e^{-S_{\text{eff}}(\phi)} = \int \mathcal{D}\psi^\dagger \mathcal{D}\psi e^{-S(\phi,\psi)} \tag{4}$$

The effective action can then be used to obtain the skyrmion energy. Hopefully the energy is minimized for $R > \lambda_c$, and the minimum energy is less than the energy of N quarks in the vacuum, Nm. The first condition ensures that the skyrmion does carry the quark quantum numbers, while the second states that the skyrmion forms a bag for the quarks. This situation will be explored more fully in the next section. Here, two approaches to calculating the effective action are outlined: an analytical calculation of 4-derivative terms in the effective Lagrangian, and a numerical calculation of the fermion determinant, currently in progress.

1. Gradient Expansion.[10] Here we write $\mathcal{L}_{\text{eff}}$ as an expansion in terms of gradients of the scalar fields, and compute the four-derivative terms to one fermion loop. This is an expansion in powers of λ_c/R, and thus is valid for $R \gg \lambda_c$.

For a skyrmion of size R, then, the two-derivative and four-derivative terms give an energy of the form

$$E \sim AR + B\frac{1}{R} \tag{5}$$

If this is minimized for $R \gg \lambda_c$, the skyrmion carries the fermion quantum numbers and is stabilized against scaling; if in addition the minimum energy is less than Nm, the skyrmion is a bag for the quarks.

There are ten four-derivative terms which have the correct symmetries; it turns out that seven of these vanish in the nonlinear limit $\phi^2 = v^2$. Thus much work can be saved since we can investigate scaling of the (nonlinear) skyrmion ansatz. It remains only to calculate the coefficients of the three remaining terms. This is accomplished by computing appropriate vertex functions to one quark loop. The details of this calculation are presented in refs. 10; the resulting skyrmion energy is

$$E[\phi] = \int d^3x \left\{ \frac{1}{2}(\partial\phi)^2 + \frac{N}{96\pi^2 v^4}\left[-2v^2\partial^2\phi_a\partial^2\phi_a\right.\right.$$

$$+3(\partial_i\phi_a\partial_i\phi_a)^2 - 2\partial_i\phi_a\partial_j\phi_a\partial_i\phi_b\partial_j\phi_b]\} \tag{6}$$

The minus signs in this expression are at first sight distressing, and after some thought fatal. A negative energy for any field configuration would indicate an instability of the vacuum, *i.e.*, a "bad" theory.

Substituting the skyrmion ansatz (2) into (6) yields the encouraging result that the corrections are positive; the skyrmion is stabilized against scaling (Fig. 4). It turns out that the minimum lies within the domain of validity of the gradient expansion, and that the skyrmion energy is less than that of N quarks in the scalar vacuum, for $Ng^2 \gg 1$.

Unfortunately, the corrections are not positive definite: for example, it is easy to see that the four-derivative terms are negative for the scalar field configuration $\phi = v(\cos x_1, \sin x_1, 0, 0)$. In the above limit, $Ng^2 \gg 1$, the energy of this configuration is negative so, while the skyrmion does form a bag, the vacuum is unstable, *i.e.*, the theory is bad. We must therefore look for bags outside the $Ng^2 \gg 1$ limit.

2. Numerical Calculation.[11] The functional integral (4) can be written as a fermion determinant in the usual way; for the skyrmion energy E_{sk} we find

$$e^{-E_{sk}t} = e^{-E_\phi t} \det\left(\frac{1+e^{-H_s t}}{1+e^{-H_v t}}\right) \tag{7}$$

where E_ϕ is the classical scalar field energy, t is imaginary time and H_s, H_v are the quark Hamiltonian in the skyrmion and vacuum scalar field configuration.

The determinant is to be evaluated for different skyrmion sizes, to investigate scaling stability. An important simplification of this calculation uses the symmetry of the skyrmion configuration. It is invariant under simultaneous space and isospin rotations. In other words, defining a generalized angular momentum $\vec{K} = \vec{L} + \vec{S} + \vec{T}$ (where $\vec{T}$ is isospin), we have

$$\left[H_{s,v}, \vec{K}\right] = 0 \tag{8}$$

The Hamiltonian, therefore, can be block diagonalized: it doesn't mix states of different $| k, k_z\rangle$.

$$H = H_{|0,0\rangle} \oplus H_{|1,1\rangle} \oplus H_{|1,0\rangle} \oplus H_{|1,-1\rangle} \oplus \ldots \tag{9}$$

Also, the matrices are independent of k_z, so the determinant in (7) can be written

$$\det = (\det_{|0,0\rangle})(\det_{|1,1\rangle})^3(\det_{|2,2\rangle})^5 \ldots \tag{10}$$

and presumably the interesting effects reside in the $|0,0\rangle$ sector. No conclusive results are available yet; the hope is that the skyrmion would be stabilized at $R \approx \lambda_c$, where the gradient expansion breaks down and yet the skyrmion may still carry the quark quantum numbers.

5. Weak Decay of the Skyrmion

Let us now investigate what happens if the skyrmion *does*, in fact, form a bag, *i.e.*, if its energy satisfies

$$E_{sk} < Nm \tag{11}$$

Recall that in the linear model we have been discussing the skyrmion is topologically *metastable*; it can tunnel to the vacuum. Equation (11) implies, however, that this tunnelling cannot occur, for energetic reasons. For simplicity, suppose $N = 1$, in which case the skyrmion contains one heavy quark. The tunnelling of the skyrmion to the vacuum must then liberate the quark, but the final energy of this would-be decay is *greater* than its initial energy, E_{sk}.

This argument indicates that when (11) is satisfied, the quarks prevent the tunnelling decay of the skyrmion.[12] Absolute stability of the skyrmion would still depend upon the quantum numbers of the heavy quarks being conserved. In the "real" world, light quarks exist, and we expect Cabibbo-type mixing between light and heavy quarks. In this case, the heavy quarks contained in the skyrmion could decay weakly to light quarks which would then escape from the bag. As a result, the skyrmion is no longer prevented from tunnelling.

A closer look at the energetics reveals some interesting features. Again supposing $N = 1$, we have argued above that the skyrmion cannot decay due to the quark; as I will now argue, the quark cannot decay due to the skyrmion.

To see this, it is helpful to think of the charge of the skyrmion in terms of the quark energy spectrum in the presence of the skyrmion. That the skyrmion charge is one is seen in hole theory as resulting from the fact that the number of energy levels of the Dirac sea in the skyrmion background is one greater than that in the vacuum. The decay of the heavy quark contained in the skyrmion to a light quark leaves one negative energy level vacant, increasing the skyrmion energy by roughly the mass of the heavy fermion: again energetics prevents the decay.

Neither the skyrmion tunnelling nor the quark decay can occur individually, but both can take place simultaneously. One needs the coincidental decay of the skyrmion and weak decay of the quark. The final products of this decay would be a light quark and presumably, one or more Higgs particles.

With many heavy quark doublets the situation is similar. If (11) is *strongly* satisfied, *i.e.*, if the skyrmion energy is *much* less than that of N quarks, the effect on the skyrmion decay could be dramatic. The weak decay of one heavy quark to a light one in conjunction with the skyrmion decay would leave us with an energy of at least $(N-1)m$, the mass of the remaining heavy fermions — greater than the initial energy. What is required is the coincidental weak decay of *all* (or many) of the heavy fermions and the decay of the skyrmion. This would be greatly suppressed compared to a naive calculation of the tunnelling rate, resulting in a much larger lifetime for the skyrmion.

REFERENCES

* Address after October 1, 1985: Department of Applied Mathematics and Theoretical Physics, University of Cambridge, Silver Street, Cambridge, U.K. CB3 9EW

1. Gell-Mann, M. and M. Lévy, Nuovo Cimento **16**, 705 (1960).

2. T. H.R. Skryme, Proc. Roy. Soc. A**247**, 260 (1958), A**252**, 236 (1959), A**260**, 127 (1960); Nucl. Phys. **31**, 556 (1962); J. Math. Phys. **12**, 1735 (1971).

3. G.S. Adkins, C.R. Nappi and E. Witten, Nucl. Phys. B**228**, 552 (1983); Adkins, G.S. and C.R. Nappi, Nucl. Phys. B**233**, 109 (1984); Phys. Lett. **137**B 251 (1984); Jackson, A.D. and M. Rho, Phys. Rev. Lett. **51**, 751 (1983); Rho, M., A.S. Goldhaber and G.E. Brown, Phys. Rev. Lett. **51**, **747** (1983).

4. Gipson, J.M. and H.C. Tze, Nucl. Phys. B**183**, 524 (1981); Gipson, J.M., Nucl. Phys. B**231**, 365 (1984); D'Hoker, E. and E. Farhi, Nucl. Phys. B**241**, 109 (1984).

5.. For a review see Farhi, E. and L. Susskind, Phys. Rep. **74**C, 277 (1981).

6. These terms were calculated as counterterms to make the Lagrangian finite to one loop by Appelquist, T. and C. Bernard, Phys. Rev. D**22**, 200 (1980).

7. Much of the material presented here is discussed in greater detail by MacKenzie, R., preprint NSF-ITP-84-135.

8. D'Hoker, E. and E. Farhi, Phys. Lett. **134**B, 86 (1984).

9. MacKenzie, R. and F. Wilczek, Phys. Rev. D**30**, 2260 (1984); D'Hoker, E. and E. Farhi, Ref. 4.

10. MacKenzie, R., F. Wilczek, and A. Zee, Phys. Rev. Lett. **53**, 2203 (1984); Aitchison, I.J.R. andC.M. Fraser, Phys. Lett. **146**B, 63 (1984).

11. MacKenzie, R. and F. Wilczek, in preparation.

12. A similar situation has been discussed in D'Hoker, E. and E. Farhi, Nucl. Phys. B**248**, 59. 77 (1984).

Some Consequences of the BWZW Anomaly for SU(3) Skyrmions*

L. C. Biedenharn

and

Yossef Dothan**

Physics Department, Duke University

Durham, NC 27706 USA

Witten[1] showed that a minimal chiral effective Lagrangian must be augmented by an anomaly term to accord with the discrete symmetries of QCD. From the topological nature of this term he demonstrated that, in the proper normalization, the anomaly has an integer coefficient N. Gauging the anomaly to account for $\pi^o \to \gamma + \gamma$ identifies N as the number of quark colors with N = 3.

The purpose of the present contribution is to present a different and more direct evaluation of N wholly within the framework of strong interactions[2,3].

Consider the anomaly term $N\Gamma$ in the effective action:

$$N\Gamma = \frac{N}{240\pi^2} \int_{M^5} \omega \tag{1}$$

where M^5 is a 5-dimensional region chosen so that its boundary is compactified space time: $\partial M^5 = S^3 \times S^1$. (Here S^3 is compactified space and S^1 is compactified time). The differential 5-form ω is expressible in terms of the SU(3) field-matrix U and its derivatives. Define μ a matrix of differential 1-forms:

$$\mu = -i\, U^\dagger\, dU \tag{2a}$$

Then

$$\omega = \mathrm{Tr}\,(\mu \wedge \mu \wedge \mu \wedge \mu \wedge \mu) \tag{2b}$$

Actually the field-matrix U is given only on the 4 dimensional boundary of M^5, and we must extend it to the interior of M^5. For a static solution, U does not depend on time. It is thus constant on each time circle S^1 in ∂M^5 and extends to $S^3 \times D^2$ being constant on each disc D^2, so that the corresponding 5-form ω vanishes identically. Consider next zero mode SU(3) transformations-Z(t)-about $U_1(x)$ defined to be a static energy minimizing solution of the field equations with baryon number B = 1:

$$U = Z(t)\; U_1(x)\; Z^\dagger(t) \tag{3}$$

Considering $U_1(x)$ as a point in field-matrix space, the adjoint action of Z on U_1 moves it in that space. However, for the static SU(3) solution gotten by injecting the static SU(2) solution in SU(3) (putting it in the left upper corner), there is a $U_Y(1)$ subgroup of SU(3) that leaves $U_1(x)$ invariant. Therefore, the manifold of static minimal energy solutions is $Y^7 = SU(3)/U_Y(1)$. Quantization of the zero modes involves quantum-mechanics on Y^7. The circle S^1 is mapped by Z(t) onto a circle in Y^7. Since the homology group $H_1(Y^7) = 0$ any circle in Y^7 is a boundary. Since the homotopy group $\pi_1(Y^7) = 0$, there is an extension Z(t,s) from the circle S^1 to the disc D^2. These observations allow the integral in (1) to be written as a product of the baryon number integral over S^3 and an exact 2-form integrated over D^2. Integration by parts converts the D^2 integral to an S^1 integral so that the anomaly term may be written as

$$N = \frac{NB}{\sqrt{3}} \int_{S^1} d\psi_8 , \qquad (4)$$

where ψ_8 is an angle coordinate on S^1.

This has two consequences: 1) the momentum conjugate to ψ_8 can be identified with $Y'/\sqrt{3}$ for the right action of SU(3) leading to

$$Y' = N\,B\,/3$$

In particular for B = 1 the integer N must be a multiple of 3. 2) The anomaly term now resembles a similar term in a Dirac monopole Lagrangian. Therefore the quantization involves the construction of wave-sections rather than wave functions[4].

To actually show that N = 3 one calculates the energy of the lowest lying states in the B = 1 sector, then the experimental fact that these are the $1/2^+$ octet states leads to the conclusion N = 3.

It was pointed out by O. Alvarez[5] that de Rham cohomology is the more important concept involved in topological quantization. For simple cases the homotopic considerations and the cohomological considerations may lead to the same conclusions. In this connection, it is our particular interest to note that for the present problem there are cohomologically two distinct SU(3)/U(1) manifolds (see appendix), which are homotopically indistinguishable.

We are very grateful to Prof. Jim Stasheff of the U.N.C. Mathematics Department for many helpful discussions and explanations.

Appendix

We give the de Rham cohomology groups for the manifold $SU(3)/U_Y(1)$, using the method of ref.[6]. The Poincaré polynomial for $SU(3)/U_Y(1)$ is given by

$$P = (1+t^3)\ (1-t^6)/(1-t^2) = (1+t^3)\ (1+t^2+t^4)$$

Reading off the cohomology groups we get

$$H^o = \mathbb{R} \quad H^1 = 0 \quad H^2 = \mathbb{R} \quad H^3 = \mathbb{R} \quad H^4 = \mathbb{R} \quad H^5 = \mathbb{R} \quad H^6 = 0 \quad H^7 = \mathbb{R}$$

Locally $SU(3)/U_Y(1)$ may be parametrized as $S^3 \times \mathbb{C}P^2$.

The topology is different if instead of $U_Y(1)$ generated by Y we consider the $U_T(1)$ subgroup generated by T_3. In this case we get:

$$P = (1+t^5)\ (1-t^4)/(1-t^2) = (1+t^5)\ (1+t^2)$$

Again reading off the cohomology groups we have

$$H^o = \mathbb{R} \quad H^1 = 0 \quad H^2 = \mathbb{R} \quad H^3 = 0 \quad H^4 = 0 \quad H^5 = \mathbb{R} \quad H^6 = 0 \quad H^7 = \mathbb{R}$$

Locally $SU(3)/U_T(1)$ may be parametrized as $S^2 \times S^5$.

References

1) E.Witten, Nucl. Phys. B223, 422, (1983); ibid B223, 433, (1985).
2) E.Guadagnini, Nucl. Phys. B236, 35, (1984).
3) L.C.Biedenharn, Y. Dothan and A.A.Stern, Phys. Letters B146, 289, (1984).
4) L.C.Biedenharn, Y. Dothan to be published in the Y. Ne'eman festschrift.
5) O.Alvarez, "Topological quantization and cohomology", LBL-18658 (Nov. 1984)
6) W.Greub, S.Halpern, R.Vanstone Connection Curvature and Cohomology Vol. III ch. XI, Academic Press, New York.

* Supported in part by the National Science Foundation.

** On leave from Tel-Aviv University, Tel-Aviv, Israel.

SYMPOSIUM ON ANOMALIES, GEOMETRY, TOPOLOGY

RELATED TOPICS

CHARLES GOEBEL

CHAIRMAN

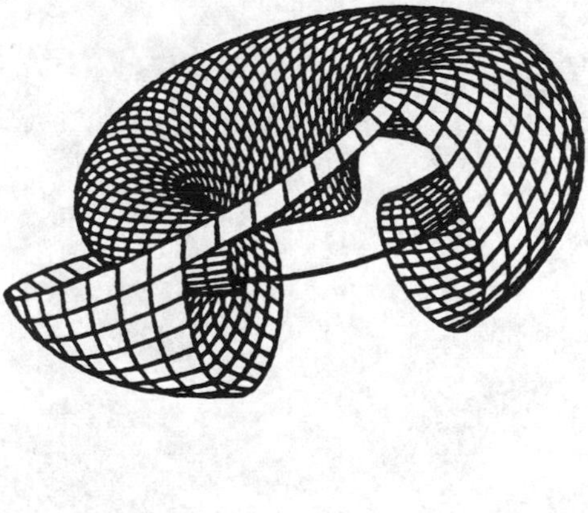

Can Isometries Tell Us About the Extra Dimensions

Freydoon Mansouri and Louis Witten

Physics Department, University of Cincinnati, Cincinnati, OH 45221

Abstract

We argue that the breakdown of the isometries of a higher dimensional theory to that of the final low energy theory provides a quantitative method of testing the extra dimensions.

Over the last decade or so, a general consensus seems to have emerged that theories at higher dimensions when supplemented with dimensional reduction provide a promising framework for a deeper understanding of physical phenomena at very high energies. A number of approaches have been pursued to implement this general idea. Notable among these are (i) superstring models, (ii) supergravity theories, (iii) direct construction of phenomenological models, and (iv) models of preons. These possibilities are, of course, not mutually exclusive. Currently, superstring models in ten dimensions with internal symmetries SO(32)[1] or $E_8 \times E_8$[2] appear to be the most viable theories at higher dimensions. This is not surprising if we recall the initial role played by the string models in reviving the old ideas of Kaluza and Klein[3]. Since the groups SO(32) and $E_8 \times E_8$ are large enough to accomodate grand unified models, such theories appear to provide a basis for the unification of particle physics and gravity as we know them today. If it turns out, however, that quarks and leptons begin to exhibit structure at scales far below the planck scale, then the basis for the unification of gravity and internal symmetries will of necessity have to shift from quarks and leptons to their constitutents. It might still be possible to make recourse to some sort of string theory to achieve unification at that level. But the internal symmetries carried by such strings would clearly have to be different.

Independently of any particular approach, if we wish to take the physical existence of the extra dimensions seriously, we must develop a systematic method for studying the effects of the extra dimensions. Any such method must provide, among other things, satisfactory answers to the following two questions: (1) Since there is no evidence for the existence of the extra dimensions at the shortest distances which can be probed at present, it must explain how this can be attributed to some intrinsic property of a higher dimensional theory. (2) It must provide a quantitative method for studying the consequences of the dependence on the extra dimensions.

In carrying out the above procedure, we must not lose sight of another feature of taking the extra dimensions seriously: the fundamental theory is the higher dimensional theory. Therefore, dimensional reduction must be carried out in such a way that the solutions to the resulting reduced theory will also be solutions to the original higher dimensional theory. To satisfy this condition, we have adopted a generalization of a work by Geroch[5] for dimensional reduction. Thus, from our point of view the first objective of a dimensional reduction would consist in showing explicitly how isometries remove the traces of extra dimensions from the reduced theory while ensuring that the solutions to the reduced theory are also solutions of the initial higher dimensional theory. The details of how this can be carried out has been given elesewhere[6]. Here we want to discuss a possible way of extracting information about the extra dimensions starting from a D-dimensional theory which, in the presence of isometries, looks like a d-dimensional theory with $d< D$. Just as the masslessness of certain quanta in a field theory can be attributed to the presence of symmetries, the non-appearance of the $(D - d)$ - dimensions can be attributed to the presence of an isometry of the original theory. Then if the extra dimensions really exist, it is reasonable to expect that the consequences of the dependence on these dimensions can be studied by breaking the isometry which is responsible for their non-appearance. In this context, as we shall see, the conventional notions of symmetry breaking would have to be considerably modified and enlarged.

It will be recalled that in conventional gauge theories, spontaneous symmetry breaking takes place at a stage when there is a clear distinction between space-time and internal space, so that it results in the reduction of the symmetry associated with internal degrees of freedom while keeping the space-time symmetry intact. Clearly, a straight-forward application of this technique to any dimensionally reduced theory in which the space-time and internal space have already been separated will not yield any information about the extra dimensions. To learn about these dimensions, one must go back to the original D-dimensional theory and consider all possible isometries of the manifold M. With one time and (D-1) space dimensions, the maximum number of the one parameter groups of isometries of M is limited by its structure group GL(DR). Since isometries are metric preserving transformations, this implies that the largest group of isometries of the manifold M is SO(1,D-1). The largest subgroup of this group which can be associated with an internal symmetry is determined by the choice of space--time. For example, in the fiber bundle solutions discussed in references (4) and (6), we wish to identify the d-dimensional base manifold, S, as the dimensionally reduced space-time. If we wish to retain the structure group SO(1,d-1) as the symmetry of such a space-time, then of the isometries of the manifold M, the part which can be devoted to internal symmetries is contained in the quotient SO(1,D-1)/SO (1,d-1). To be a local isometry, this quotient must itself be a group or contain a group. In this way, one arrives at SO(D-d) as the largest available isometry group for internal symmetry. If the initial D-dimensional theory is endowed with additional internal symmetry, G_I, then one would have to see how SO(1,D-1)X G_I is reduced in going from D to d. This is clearly the case in string models.

As mentioned above, if we start with an isometry group of the form SO(1,d-1) x SO(D-d) and proceed to subject SO(D-d) to spontaneous symmetry breaking, we will end up getting the grand unified models. In such an approach there is no room for the effects related to the extra dimensions. To see how the extra dimensions lead to physical consequences, we must allow for the possibility that the dimension, d, of the reduced manifold varies in the process of spontaneous symmetry breaking. Then, for fixed D, as d increases, the internal symmetry group, SO(D-d), is broken down to a smaller group and, simultaneously, the space-time symmetry group, SO(1,d-1) increases. This is as it should be because by taking one or more of the extra dimensions as real, we are considering a real world with a larger number of spacial dimensions and hence with a larger structure group.

For example, let us suppose that the dimensional reduction occurs in a series of steps such as $D \rightarrow d + 1 \rightarrow d$. Then in the transition $d + 1 \rightarrow d$, the isometry group SO(1,d) x SO(D-d-1) changes to SO(1,d-1) x SO(D-d). It is easy to see that, in general, SO(1,d-1) x SO(D-d) is not a subgroup of SO(1,d) x SO(D-d-1). Therefore, in this context, it is more appropriate to speak of "phase transitions" or "symmetry transmutations," than standard spontaneous symmetry breaking. Explicit methods of implementing such phase transitions are currently under investigation. We are hopeful that they will lead to model independent tests of the extra dimensions.

This work was supported in part by Department of Energy under contract NO. DE-AS-2-76ER02978 and by National Science Foundation under Grant NSF Phy. 8313410.

References

1. M. Green and J. Schwarz, Phys. Lett. 149B, 117 (1984).
2. D. Gross et al, Phys. Rev. lett. 54, 502 (1985).
3. F. Ardalan and F. Mansouri, Phys. Rev. D9, 3341 (1974) L. N. Chang, K. Macrae, and F. Mansouri, Phys. Lett. B57, 59 (1975) and Phys. Rev.-D13, 235 (1976).
4. F. Mansouri and L. Witten, Phys. Lett. 140B, 317 (1984), and reference cited therein.
5. R. Geroch, J. Math Phys. 12, 918 (1971), 13, 394 (1972).
6. See reference (4) and F. Mansouri and L. Witten, Proceedings of VIII Johns Hopkins Workshop on Current Problems in High Energy Particle Theory, ed. G. Domokos and S. Kovesi-Domokos, Domokos, World Scientific Publ., 1984.

16/16 SUPERGRAVITY COUPLED TO MATTER: THE LOW ENERGY LIMIT OF THE SUPERSTRING

Burt A. Ovrut†
Department of Physics, University of Pennsylvania
Philadelphia, Pennsylvania 19104

ABSTRACT

We analyze irreducible, N = 1 supergravity theories with 16 bosonic and 16 fermionic degrees of freedom. The Lagrangians for pure 16/16 supergravity, and for 16/16 supergravity coupled to arbitrary chiral superfields are constructed. These theories are shown to have natural SU(1,1) non-compact symmetry. The low energy field theory limit of the superstring is conjectured to be of this type.

The superfields of non-minimal (20/20), N = 1 supergravity [1], along with their lowest components are listed in Table 1. Fields $e_m{}^a$ and $\psi_m{}^\alpha$ are the graviton and gravitino respectively. Non-minimal supergravity is reduced to 16/16 supergravity by imposing the constraint [2]

$$T_\alpha = \mathcal{D}_\alpha \psi \tag{1}$$

where ψ is a real superfield. Eqn. (1), with the Bianchi identities, implies that

$$\mathcal{D}^{\alpha\dot\alpha} W_{\alpha\dot\alpha} = 0 \tag{2}$$

where

$$W_{\alpha\dot\alpha} = 2e^{-4n\psi}(G_{\alpha\dot\alpha} + \frac{1}{3}[\bar{\mathcal{D}}_{\dot\alpha} T_\alpha - \mathcal{D}_\alpha \bar{T}_{\dot\alpha}] - \frac{2}{3}(n-1)T_\alpha \bar{T}_{\dot\alpha}) \tag{3}$$

and n ($\neq 0, -\frac{1}{3}$) is a real number. It follows from Eqns. (1) and (2) that

$$c_a - \bar{c}_a = -2i\,\partial_a \psi$$
$$c_a + \bar{c}_a = -\,b_a - \frac{3}{2}e^{4n\psi} W_a + \text{fermions.} \tag{4}$$

These equations, along with Eqn. (2), reduce the bosonic degrees of freedom from 20 to 16. A related equation eliminates four fermionic degrees of freedom from the non-minimal supermultiplet. The superfields of 16/16 supergravity, along with their lowest components, are listed in Table 2. The super-

†On leave of absence from The Rockefeller University, New York, N.Y. 10021.

density for 16/16 supergravity is [3]

$$\mathcal{E}(\alpha) = \mathcal{E}^{o}\, e^{\alpha\bar{\Omega}+\beta(\alpha)\psi}\Big|_{\bar{\theta}=0} \tag{5}$$

where

$$\bar{\Omega} = 2(3n + 1)\,\frac{\bar{T}_{\dot{\alpha}}\bar{T}^{\dot{\alpha}}}{\bar{S}} \tag{6}$$

$$\beta(\alpha) = 2(3n + 1)(\alpha-1) \tag{7}$$

and

$$\begin{aligned} \mathcal{E}^{o} &= e(1 + \theta^{\alpha}\rho^{o}_{\alpha} + \theta^{2}f^{o}) \\ \rho^{o}_{\alpha} &= (\tfrac{13n-3}{2})T_{\alpha} + i(\sigma^{m}\bar{\psi}_{m})_{\alpha} \\ f^{o} &= -\tfrac{1}{2}(3n-1)S-4n(3n-1)T^{\alpha}T_{\alpha} + i(3n-1)(\bar{\psi}_{m}\sigma^{m})^{\alpha}T_{\alpha}-(\bar{\psi}_{m}\bar{\sigma}^{mn}\bar{\psi}_{n}) \end{aligned} \tag{8}$$

Parameter α is an arbitrary real number, and $e = \det e_{m}{}^{a}$. First we derive the component field Lagrangian for pure 16/16 supergravity. In terms of superfields this Lagrangian is given by

$$\mathcal{L}^{16}_{SG} = -\frac{1}{2}\int d^{2}\theta\, \mathcal{E}(\alpha)\bar{S} + \text{h.c.} \tag{9}$$

Expanding $\mathcal{E}(\alpha)$ and $\bar{S}$ into component fields, we find that the bosonic part of $\mathcal{L}^{16}_{SG}$ is

$$\begin{aligned} \mathcal{L}^{16}_{SG} = e\, e^{\beta(\alpha)\psi}\Big[&-\frac{1}{2}R + \sigma(n,\alpha)\bar{S}S + \frac{1}{3}b_{a}^{2}(1 + \frac{1}{2}(3n+1)(1-3\alpha)) \\ &+ A_{a}^{2}(\frac{3}{8}(3n+1)(1-3\alpha)) + b_{a}A^{a}(\frac{1}{2}(3n+1)(1-3\alpha)) \\ &+ (\partial_{a}\psi)^{2}(-2(3n+1)(2n-(6n+1)(1-\alpha)))\Big] \end{aligned} \tag{10}$$

where

$$\sigma(n,\alpha) = \frac{1}{4}(4n+\beta) \tag{11}$$

$$A_{a} = e^{4n\psi}W_{a}$$

and R is the scalar curvature. We implement the constraint in Eqn. (2) by adding a Lagrange multiplier,

$$e\lambda\,\mathcal{D}_{a}W^{a} \tag{12}$$

where λ is a real scalar field, to Eqn. (10). The Lagrangian can now be written as

$$\mathcal{L}^{16}_{SG} = e\, e^{\beta\psi} [-\frac{1}{2}R - \frac{1}{\gamma(n,\alpha)} (\partial_a\lambda)^2 e^{-2(4n+\beta)\psi}$$

$$- (\partial_a\psi)^2(2(2n+1)(2n-(6n+1)(1-\alpha)))] \qquad (13)$$

where

$$\gamma(n,\alpha) = - \frac{(3n+1)(1-3\alpha)}{2\sigma} \qquad (14)$$

Weyl rescale the fields to eliminate the factor in front of the term $-\frac{1}{2}$ R. The Lagrangian becomes

$$\mathcal{L}^{16}_{SG}/e = -\frac{1}{2}R - \frac{1}{\gamma} (\partial_a\lambda)^2 e^{-2(4n+\beta)\psi} \qquad (15)$$

$$-(\partial_a\psi)^2((3n+1)(1-3\alpha)(n+1)-(3n+1)\alpha))$$

Finally, make the field redefinitions

$$X = -\frac{\gamma}{2} e^{(4n+\beta)\psi} \qquad (16)$$

$$z = X + i\lambda \qquad (17)$$

The bosonic part of the pure 16/16 Lagrangian is then given by

$$\mathcal{L}^{16}_{SG}/e = -\frac{1}{2}R - \frac{\gamma}{(z+\bar{z})^2} \partial_a\bar{z}\, \partial^a z \qquad (18)$$

The Kahler potential (up to arbitrary Kahler transformations) is

$$K(z,\bar{z}) = -\frac{\gamma}{2} \ln (z+\bar{z})^2 \qquad (19)$$

Also, the z-field kinetic energy term is invariant under the SU(1,1) transformations

$$z \to \frac{\alpha z + i\beta}{i\xi z + \delta} \qquad (20)$$

where α, β, ξ, δ are real, and $\alpha\delta+\beta\xi = 1$. The potential energy of the z-field vanishes.

We now derive the component field Lagrangian for 16/16 supergravity coupled to arbitrary chiral superfields Φ^i. We denote the scalar and auxiliary component fields of Φ^i by A^i and F^i respectively. In terms of superfields, the super kinetic energy part of the Lagrangian is given by

$$\mathcal{L}^{16}_{SK} = -\frac{1}{8} \int d^2\theta\, \mathcal{E}(\alpha)\bar{\Delta}(e^{-a\bar{\Omega}+b\Omega+c\psi} f(\bar{\Phi}_{i*},\Phi^i)) + h.c. \qquad (21)$$

where

$$\bar{\Delta} = \bar{\mathcal{D}}_{\dot{\alpha}}\bar{\mathcal{D}}^{\dot{\alpha}} - 3(n+1)\bar{T}_{\dot{\alpha}}\bar{\mathcal{D}}^{\dot{\alpha}} - 2(n+1)\bar{S} \tag{22}$$

parameters a, b, and c are any real numbers, and f is an arbitrary function. For simplicity we take f to be real. Expand Eqn. (21) into component fields, and rewrite F^i in terms of a new field $\not{F}^i$. Then the bosonic part of $\mathcal{L}^{16}_{SK}$ is

$$\mathcal{L}^{16}_{SK} = e\, e^{(\beta+c)\psi}[\ldots + (3n+1)E\frac{c_a^{\ 2}}{S}\frac{\bar{c}_a^{\ 2}}{\bar{S}}] \tag{23}$$

where

$$E = 4(-a+\alpha)bf - (-a+b+\alpha)^2 f^{j*}(f^{-1})_{j*}{}^{i} f_i \tag{24}$$

$\mathcal{L}^{16}_{SK}$ will be singular in S and $\bar{S}$ unless we set E = 0. This can be achieved by taking

$$f = f^{j*}(f^{-1})_{j*}{}^{i} f_i$$

$$\alpha = a + b \tag{25}$$

Weyl rescale the fields so as to eliminate the factor in front of the term $-\frac{1}{2}R$, redefine field ψ as in Eqn. (16), and let

$$a = X + i\lambda \tag{26}$$

Also, take

$$1 = a + b = \frac{2}{3}$$

$$c = 0 \tag{27}$$

The sum of $\mathcal{L}^{16}_{SG}$ and $\mathcal{L}^{16}_{SK}$ is then given by

$$\begin{aligned}\mathcal{L}^{16}_{SG+SK}/e = &-\frac{1}{2}R - \frac{1}{\Lambda^2}(f_i{}^{j*} + \frac{1}{3\Lambda^2}f_i f^{j*})\,\partial_a\bar{A}_{j*}\partial^a A^i \\ &- \frac{1}{\Lambda^2}\frac{\gamma}{(a+\bar{a})^2}(1 + \frac{\gamma f}{18\Lambda^2})\,\partial_a\bar{a}\partial^a a \\ &+ \frac{1}{6\Lambda^4}\frac{\gamma}{(a+\bar{a})}(\bar{\alpha}^a\partial_a a + \alpha^a\partial_a\bar{a}) \\ &- \frac{1}{6\Lambda^4}\frac{\gamma}{(a+\bar{a})}(\alpha^a\partial_a a + \bar{\alpha}^a\partial_a\bar{a}) \\ &+ \frac{f}{36\Lambda^4}\frac{\gamma^2}{(a+\bar{a})^2}((\partial_a a)^2 + (\partial_a\bar{a})^2)\end{aligned} \tag{28}$$

where

$$\Lambda^2 = 1 - \frac{1}{3}f \tag{29}$$

$$\alpha^a = f_i \partial^a A^i \tag{30}$$

$$\gamma = \frac{1+3}{\sigma}, \quad \sigma = -\frac{1}{3}(1-3b(3n+1)) \tag{31}$$

Note that the last two terms in Eqn. (28) are not in hermitian form. Henceforth, for simplicity, assume that f is homogeneous of degree p. For $|f| \ll 1$ (an excellent approximation for $|A^i| \lesssim 1/10$), we find that, to leading order, the field redefinitions

$$z = a$$

$$Z^i = |a + \bar{a}|^{\gamma/6p} A^i \tag{32}$$

put the entire Lagrangian into hermitian form. Defining

$$v(Z^i, \bar{Z}_{i*}) = f(Z^i, \bar{Z}_{i*}) \quad , \tag{33}$$

the Lagrangian in Eqn. (28) becomes

$$\begin{aligned} \mathcal{L}^{16}_{SG + SK}/e = &- \frac{1}{2}R - g\,\partial_a \bar{z}\,\partial^a z - \mathscr{H}_i \partial_a \bar{z}\,\partial^a Z^i \\ &- \mathscr{H}^{i*} \partial_a z\,\partial^a \bar{Z}_{i*} - G_i^{\;j*}\,\partial_a \bar{Z}_{j*}\,\partial^a Z^i \end{aligned} \tag{34}$$

where

$$g = \gamma(z + \bar{z})^{-2} = \frac{\partial^2 K}{\partial \bar{z} \partial z}$$

$$\mathscr{H}_i = -\frac{\gamma}{3}|z + \bar{z}|^{-(\gamma/3+1)} \frac{\partial v}{\partial Z^i} = \frac{\partial^2 K}{\partial \bar{z} \partial Z^i} \tag{35}$$

$$G_i^{\;j*} = |z + \bar{z}|^{-\gamma/3} \frac{\partial^2 v}{\partial Z^i \partial \bar{Z}_{j*}} = \frac{\partial^2 K}{\partial \bar{Z}_{j*} \partial Z^i}$$

and

$$K = -\gamma \ell n(|z + \bar{z}| - \frac{1}{\gamma}|z + \bar{z}|^{-(\gamma/3-1)} v(Z^i, \bar{Z}_{i*})) \tag{36}$$

We emphasize that the form of Kahler potential K is completely determined from the theory.

In terms of superfields, the superpotential part of the Lagrangian is given by

$$\mathcal{L}^{16}_{SP} = \int d^2\theta\, \mathcal{E}(\alpha)\, W(\Phi^i) + \text{h.c.} \tag{37}$$

where W is an arbitrary function. Expand Eqn. (37) into component fields. Then the bosonic part of $\mathcal{L}^{16}_{SP}$ is

$$\mathcal{L}^{16}_{SP} = e\, e^{\beta\psi} [\, . \; . \; . + 2(3n+1)E' \frac{c_a^{\;2}}{\bar{S}} + h.c.] \tag{38}$$

where

$$E' = \alpha W - \frac{1}{2} (\alpha - a + b)\; f^{j*}(f^{-1})_{j*}{}^{i} W_i \tag{39}$$

$\mathcal{L}^{16}_{SP}$ will be singular in S and $\bar{S}$ unless we set $E' = 0$. This can be done by taking

$$f^{j*}(f^{-1})_{j*}{}^{i} W_i = \frac{\alpha}{b} W \tag{40}$$

The auxiliary fields $\not{A}\,(= 2\sigma S)$ and $\not{F}^{\,i}$ are found to be

$$\not{A} = \frac{2}{3} \left(\frac{1-3b}{3b}\right)\bar{W} \tag{41}$$

$$\not{F}^{\,i} = -\bar{W}^{j*}(f^{-1})_{j*}{}^{i} \tag{42}$$

It follows that the potential energy is given by

$$V/e = \gamma^{\gamma F} |z + \bar{z}|^{-2\gamma/3} \{\bar{W}^{i*} (v^{-1})_{i*}{}^{j} W_j + \frac{F^2}{\sigma} |z + \bar{z}|^{-\gamma/3} |W|^2\} \tag{43}$$

where

$$F = \frac{3b-1}{9b} \tag{44}$$

and $W = W(Z^i)$. For $b = -\frac{1}{6}$ superpotential $W = \tilde{c}$, where $\tilde{c}$ is an arbitrary constant. In this case, Eqn. (43) becomes

$$V/e = \frac{\gamma^{\gamma}}{\sigma} |z + \bar{z}|^{-\gamma} |\tilde{c}|^2 \tag{45}$$

and the gravitino mass is given by

$$m_{3/2} = \gamma^{\gamma/2} |z + \bar{z}|^{-\gamma/2} |\tilde{c}| \tag{46}$$

Hence, supergravity is spontaneously broken for $\tilde{c} \neq 0$. It is clear from Eqn. (43) that there are two possibilities for the vacuum state. The first is that the minimum of the function inside the brackets occurs for a non-vanishing value of this function. The $|z + \bar{z}|^{-\gamma/3}$ factor then assures that $z \to \infty$, and the vacuum is unstable. The second possibility is that the minimum occurs for vanishing value of this function. In this case, at tree level, z is undetermined, the vacuum is stable, and the theory has naturally vanishing cosmological constant. We have shown that the superstring satisfies the latter possibility.

TABLE I

Superfield	Lowest Component
$E_m{}^a$	$e_m{}^a$
$E_m{}^\alpha$	$\frac{1}{2}\psi_m{}^\alpha$
T_α	T_α
$G_{\alpha\dot\alpha}$	$-\frac{1}{3}b_{\alpha\dot\alpha}$
S	S
$\mathcal{D}_\alpha T_{\dot\alpha}(\bar{\mathcal{D}}_{\dot\alpha}T_\alpha)$	$c_{\alpha\dot\alpha}(-\bar{c}_{\alpha\dot\alpha})$
$\mathcal{D}_\alpha S$	λ_α

Table I. Superfields of non-minimal supergravity along with their lowest components.

TABLE 2

Superfield	Lowest Component
$E_m{}^a$	$e_m{}^a$
$E_m{}^\alpha$	$\frac{1}{2}\psi_m{}^\alpha$
T_α	T_α
$G_{\alpha\dot\alpha}$	$-\frac{1}{3}b_{\alpha\dot\alpha}$
S	S
ψ	ψ
$W_a(B_{mn})$	$W_a(N_{mn})$

Table II. Superfields of 16/16 supergravity, along with their lowest components. B_{mn} is the antisymmetric tensor superfield associated with W_a.

REFERENCES

1. P. Breitenlohner, Nucl. Phys. B124 (1977) 500; W. Siegal and J. Gates, Nucl. Phys. B147 (1979) 77.
2. G. Girardi, R. Grimm, M. Muller and J. Wess, Z. Phys. C26 (1984) 123; R. Grimm, M. Muller, and J. Wess, Z. Phys. C26 (1984) 427.
3. W. Lang, J. Louis, and B. Ovrut, Phys. Lett. B (1985) to appear.

Non-Antisymmetric Parallelizing Torsions in Kaluza-Klein Theories

Xizeng Wu

Center for Theoretical Physics
Laboratory for Nuclear Science and Department of Physics
Massachusetts Institute of Technology
Cambridge, Massachusetts 02139 U.S.A.

Abstract

We show how non-antisymmetric parallelizing torsions arise in Kaluza-Klein theories. As an example, a class of solutions of $D = 11$ supergravity is explicitly constructed, in which the extra dimensions are compactified to a squashed and parallelized seven-sphere and therefore the cosmological constant in four dimensions vanishes. Eight constant Killing spinors are found for these solutions. As a by-product, an explicit formula for the Cartan-Schouten parallelizing torsions is obtained, which is globally valid on S^7.

At this symposium, we have already heard much about attempts at searching a unification of all known interactions. As we can see, some mathematical findings gained decades ago might become relevant to the quest of unification. In this short talk, I am going to tell you another example of this kind of story.

About forty years ago, Cartan and Schouten studied the parallelizability of manifolds.[1] They found that among manifolds, only group manifolds and some odd-dimensional spheres (S^1, S^3 and S^7) can be parallelized by antisymmetric parallelizing torsions. In this talk I am trying to convince you that the idea about the parallelizability of manifolds is not only mathematically beautiful, but also useful for construction of Kaluza-Klein theories. I will also show you how not only antisymmetric parallelizing torsions, but also non-antisymmetric parallelizing torsions, arise in Kaluza-Klein theories.

Let us start with the $N = 1$ supergravity in eleven dimensions. The field equations are:[2,3]

$$\Gamma^{RST}\hat{D}_S(\hat{\omega})\psi_T = 0 \ , \tag{1}$$

$$D_T(\hat{\omega})\hat{F}^{TURS} = (24)^{-2}\epsilon^{MNPQVWXYUSR}\hat{F}_{MNPQ}\hat{F}_{UWXY} \ , \tag{2}$$

$$R_{TS}(\hat{\omega}) - \frac{1}{2}g_{TS}R(\hat{\omega}) = \frac{1}{24}[g_{TS}\hat{F}_{MNPQ}\hat{F}^{MNPQ} - 8\hat{F}_{MNPT}\hat{F}^{MNP}{}_S] \ , \tag{3}$$

where

$$\hat{D}_S(\hat{\omega})\psi_T = D_S(\hat{\omega})\psi_T + T_S{}^{MNPQ}\hat{F}_{MNPQ}\psi_T \ , \tag{4}$$

$$\hat{\omega}_{MRS} = \omega_{MRS}(e) + \frac{1}{2}i(2\overline{\psi}_M\Gamma_{[S}\psi_{R]} + \overline{\psi}_S\Gamma_M\psi_R) \ , \tag{5}$$

$$\hat{F}_{MNPQ} = F_{MNPQ} - 3\overline{\psi}_{[M}\Gamma_{NP}\psi_{Q]} \ , \tag{6}$$

$$F_{MNPQ} = 4\partial_{[M}A_{NPQ]} \ , \tag{7}$$

$$T^{SMNPQ} = (12)^{-2}(\Gamma^{SMNPQ} - 8\Gamma^{[MNP}\eta^{Q]S}) \ . \tag{8}$$

My conventions are those of ref. [3]. It was shown that through the spontaneous compactification a four-dimensional unified theory can be obtained. By now, some solutions in which seven of the dimensions are compactified have been proposed.[2] Unfortunately, as a common feature of these solutions, an anti-deSitter (AdS) space-time with an enormous cosmological constant is predicted for the four dimensional world. Of course, this feature seriously violates the phenomenology.

Recently, Duff and Orzalesi proposed a spin-torsion mechanism as a possible cure for this problem.[3] They pointed out that the fermionic bilinears can provide non-vanishing torsion tensors, which can be used to parallelize the compact manifold in the extra dimensions. The curvature tensor of the parallelized manifold vanishes and therefore this leads to a vanishing cosmological constant in four dimensions.

To implement this idea, let us seek solutions satisfying the following ansatz for the spontaneous compactification:

$$\langle g_{\mu\nu}\rangle = g_{\mu\nu}(x), \quad \langle g_{mn}\rangle = g_{mn}(y), \quad \langle\psi_M\rangle = \langle\hat{F}_{MNPQ}\rangle = \langle\overline{\psi}_\mu\Gamma_\nu\psi_\rho\rangle = 0, \tag{9}$$

and

$$S_{msr}(y) \equiv \frac{1}{2}i\langle\overline{\psi}_m\Gamma_s\psi_r\rangle \neq 0 \ . \tag{10}$$

Here, x and indices μ, ν, ρ are refered to the space-time, y and indices m, s, r to the extra dimensions, and M, N, P to eleven dimensions.

In this ansatz, the generalized Maxwell equation and Rarita-Schwinger equation are satisfied automatically. We are suppposed to solve

$$R_{\mu\nu}(e) = 0 \ , \tag{11}$$

$$R_{mn}(\hat{\omega}) = 0 \ , \tag{12}$$

where

$$\hat{\omega}_{mrs} = \hat{\omega}_{mrs}(e) + S_{msr} - S_{mrs} + S_{smr} \ . \tag{13}$$

So the four-dimensional space-time can be taken to be a Minkowski space-time, and of course, the cosmological constant vanishes.

Now the question is if eq. (12) really has solutions corresponding to a compact seven-dimensional space. At this point, Cartan's story comes in. A manifold is called parallelizable if it is possible to find n independent global vector fields on it. On a parallelizable manifold one can define a connection with a torsion such that the curvature tensor vanishes everywhere.[1] This sort of parallelism is called the absolute parallelism. Among the spheres, only S^1, S^3, and S^7 are parallelizable. If an absolute parallelism is consistent with the metric ($\nabla g = 0$) and if furthermore the autoparallels coincide with the metric geodesics, then the parallelism is called the Cartan-Schouten parallelism.[5] In this case, as happens for the Cartan-Schouten torsion on S^7, the parallelizing torsion is totally antisymmetric. In order to get a solution of $D = 11$ supergravity with a vanishing cosmological constant, we have to use a nonzero value for the fermion bilinear $\overline{\psi}_m\Gamma_s\psi_r$, see ref. [3]. For this fermion bilinear, we have the antisymmetry property

$$\overline{\psi}_m\Gamma_s\psi_r = -\overline{\psi}_r\Gamma_s\psi_m \ . \tag{14}$$

However, it does not appear natural that $\langle\overline{\psi}_m\Gamma_s\psi_r\rangle$ is totally antisymmetric, hence we look for cases where the parallelizing torsion is not totally antisymmetric. Therefore, a different parallelism should be used.

Suppose P is a point of S^7 and parametrized as $(y^1,\ldots,y^8)$ with

$$(y^1)^2+(y^2)^2+\ldots+(y^8)^2=1\ . \tag{15}$$

Let

$$\tilde{P}=y^1 0_1+\ldots+y^7 0_7+y^8\ ,$$

where $\{1,0_1,\ldots,0_7\}$ forms the Cayley algebra:[6,7]

$$0_a\cdot 0_b=f_{abc}0_c-\delta_{ab}\ . \tag{16}$$

Here, f_{abc} are antisymmetric constants and $f_{abc}=1$ for $(abc)=$ 123, 516, 624, 435, 471, 673, 572. The left multiplication $0_a\tilde{P}=\tilde{P}'$ induces a mapping from S^7 to S^7. We note that this mapping also defines a tangent vector $e_a(p)$ at P:

$$\begin{aligned} e_a{}^m(p)&=f_{anm}y^n+\delta_{am}y^8\ ,\\ e_a{}^8&=-y^a\ , \end{aligned} \tag{17}$$

where $a,\ m=1,\ 2,\ldots,\ 7$. If we impose a metric

$$g^{-1}=e_a\otimes e_a\ , \tag{18}$$

on S^7, then $\{e_a\}$ is a global orthonormal basis on S^7. The parallelizing connection can be defined vanishing in this basis:

$$\nabla_a e_b=0\ . \tag{19}$$

Therefore, the curvature tensor R_{abcd} vanishes everywhere on S^7, *i.e.*, S^7 is parallelized. But as is shown below, this torsion is totally antisymmetric, thus might not be related to a fermion bilinear, hence to a solution of $D=11$ supergravity with a vanishing cosmological constant. We observe that the symmetry of torsion is related to the symmetry of the metric. The metric given by eq. (18) is the maximally symmetric metric and its isometry is $SO(8)$. We can instead impose a metric with a smaller isometry, that is, we can squash S^7. A solution of $D=11$ supergravity with a squashed S^7 without torsion was proposed in ref. [8]. Here, we want to find a solution with a squashed and parallelized S^7. Let us consider a general metric

$$g^{-1}=\lambda_{ab}(y)e_a\otimes e_b\ , \tag{20}$$

on S^7, where λ_{ab} are functions on S^7. Define the parallelizing connection as shown in eq. (19), then we have an absolute parallelism. In order to have a consistent spin structure on S^7, we would require $\nabla g=0$. This requirement can be satisfied if and only if λ_{ab} are constants on S^7. So without loss of generality, we can impose the metric

$$g^{-1}=\lambda_a^{-1}e_a\otimes e_a\ , \tag{21}$$

on S^7, where all λ_a are constants, but not all are the same. In this case the isometry depends on λ_a, and always is a subgroup of $SO(8)$, thus S^7 is squashed. The non-antisymmetric parallelizing torsion is found to be[9]

$$\begin{aligned} T_{abc} = -4\left[\lambda_a\lambda_b^{-1}\lambda_c^{-1}\right]^{1/2}\{f_{ak'b}y^c y^{k'} \\ + f_{ak''c}y^b y^{k''} + f_{bck}f_{amk}y^m y^8 + f_{bck}y^k y^a \\ + f_{bca}(y_8)^2 - \frac{1}{2}f_{abc}\}, \quad \text{if } a \neq b \neq c; \end{aligned} \tag{22}$$

and

$$T_{abc} = 0, \quad \text{otherwise} \ . \tag{23}$$

Note that $T_{abc} = -T_{acb}$.

We now are back to solutions of $D = 11$ supergravity. If the fermionic bilinear satisfies

$$i\langle\overline{\psi}_c\Gamma_a\psi_b\rangle = T_{abc} \ , \tag{24}$$

where T_{abc} is given by eqs. (22), (23), then eqs. (9), (21), (24), and $g_{\mu\nu} = \eta_{\mu\nu}$ provide a class of solutions of $D = 11$ supergravity. For these solutions the eleven-dimensional space is spontaneously compactified to $M_4 \times S^7$, where M_4 is the four-dimensional Minkowskian space-time, and S^7 is squashed and parallelized.

In order to see what are the surviving supersymmetries in this case, let us consider the $N = 1$ supersymmetry transformations in $D = 11$ dimensions:[1]

$$\begin{aligned} \delta e_M^A &= -i\bar{\epsilon}\Gamma^A\psi_M \ , \\ \delta\psi_M &= D_M(\hat{\omega})\epsilon - id(\Gamma^{NPQR}{}_M + 8\Gamma^{PQR}\delta_M^N)\hat{F}_{NPQR}\epsilon \ , \\ \delta A_{MNP} &= \frac{3}{2}\bar{\epsilon}\Gamma_{[MN}\psi_{P]} \ , \end{aligned} \tag{25}$$

where ϵ is the supersymmetry transformation parameter, which generally is a function of the 4-coordinates x and 7-coordinates y. For our solutions, it is evident that

$$\langle\delta e_M^A\rangle = \langle\delta A_{MNP}\rangle = 0, \quad \langle\delta\psi_a\rangle = e_a^M\partial_m\epsilon \tag{26}$$

Suppose $\epsilon(x, y) = \epsilon_0(x)\eta(y)$. Evidently, there are eight constant and linear independent η satisfying eq. (26) while as $\epsilon_0(x)$ is arbitrary. This suggests that there are eight surviving supersymmetries in the four-dimensional effective theory. But the ansatz $\epsilon(x, y) = \epsilon_0(x)\eta(y)$ may fail to account for all the supersymmetry transformations in $D = 4$ dimensions. Actually, there is an indication that the ansatz $\epsilon(x, y) = \epsilon_0(x)\eta(y)$ is inconsistent with the massless states ansatz.[10] So what is the correct ansatz for $\epsilon(x, y)$ still is a puzzle, not only for this class of solutions, but also for others.[10]

Before closing, some remarks are in order. Firstly, as a byproduct, eqs. (22) and (23) also give an explicit formula for the Cartan-Schouten-Englert torsion by letting all λ_a be equal. This formula will be useful for the Englert solution.[4] Besides, it generalizes the torsion formula given in ref. [5], which is valid only at the northpole of S^7. Secondly, the isometries

of the solutions depend on λ_a and the latter on the specific mechanism providing non-vanishing fermionic bilinears. Thirdly, non-antisymmetric parallelizing torsions make their appearance also in other Kaluza-Klein theories. For example, if the extra dimensions are compactified to a group manifold equipped with a non-bi-invariant metric (*i.e.*. a squashed group manifold), then the manifold has to be parallelized by non-antisymmetric torsions for allowing existence of spin-half fermion zero modes. I do not have time to talk about this case and you are refered to ref. [11] for a detailed analysis.

Acknowledgement

I wish to thank Professors D. Freedman, R. Jackiw and C. H. Tze for discussions. This work was supported in part through funds provided by the U. S. Department of Energy (D.O.E.) under contract #DE-AC02-76ER0-3069.

References

1. E. Cartan and J. A. Schouten, *Proc. K. Akad. Wet Amsterdam* **29** 803,933 (1926).
2. E. Cremmer and B. Julia, *Phys. Lett.* **80B**, 48 (1978); M. J. Duff, *Nucl. Phys.* **219B**, 389 (1983).
3. M. J. Duff and C. A. Orzalesi, *Phys. Lett.* **122B**, 37 (1983).
4. F. Englert, *Phys. Lett.* **119B** 339 (1983); F. Englert, M. Rooman and P. Spindel, *Phys. Lett.* **127B** 47 (1983); B. Biran, F. Englert, B. deWitt and H. Nicolai, *Phys. Lett.* **124B**, 45 (1983).
5. F. Gürsey and C. H. Tze, *Phys. Lett.* **128B**, 191 (1983).
6. R. Hermann, *Spinor, Clifford, and Cayley Algebras* (R. Hermann, Brookline, MA, 1974).
7. M. Günaydin and F. Gürsey, *J. Math. Phys.* **14**, 1651 (1973).
8. M. A. Awada, M. J. Duff and C. N. Pope, *Phys. Rev. Lett.* **50**, 294 (1983).
9. X. Wu, *Phys. Lett.* **144B**, 51 (1984).
10. B. deWitt and H. Nicolai, preprint NIKHEF-H/83/8.
11. X. Wu, *Phys. Rev.* **29D** 2769 (1984).

Reduction in Coupling Parameter Space

Reinhard Oehme

The Enrico Fermi Institute and the Department of Physics
The University of Chicago, Chicago, Illinois 60637

Reductions in the number of coupling parameters of massless quantum field theories are considered on the basis of renormalization group invariance of the original and the reduced theories. We discuss here only reductions resulting in a single coupling parameter λ . The invariance requirement implies reduction equations for the independent coupling parameters $\lambda_0, \lambda_1, \ldots, \lambda_m$ of the original theory. Using $\lambda_0 = \lambda$ as the primary coupling, we have:

$$\lambda_k(\lambda) = \lambda f_k(\lambda) \ , \quad \beta_\lambda(\lambda\, df_k/d\lambda + f_k) = \beta_k, \quad k=1,\ldots m \ . \tag{1}$$

In the following we will find it convenient to write the β-functions as asymptotic series in the form

$$\beta_\lambda \simeq \sum_{n=o}^{\infty} \beta_{\lambda n}(f(\lambda))\lambda^{n+2}, \quad \beta_k \simeq \sum_{n=o}^{\infty} \beta_k^{(n)}(f(\lambda))\lambda^{n+2} \ .$$

We consider solutions of Eqs. (1) with λ_k/λ bounded and approaching f_k^0 for $\lambda \to 0$. The resulting equations for f_k^0 are

$$\beta_{\lambda 0}(f^0)f_k^0 - \beta_k^{(0)}(f^0) = 0 \ . \tag{2}$$

They have in many cases only a few characteristic solutions. Even though the original theory is assumed to be renormalizable with an asymptotic power series expansion in the couplings $\lambda, \lambda_1, \ldots, \lambda_m$, the reduced theory is, a priori, not guaranteed to have only integer powers of λ in the asymptotic expansion. We will see that there can appear logarithms and, in general solutions, also non-integer powers. But in all cases the reduced theory is well defined and "renormalized" in view of its embedding in the renormalizable original multi-parameter theory.

Of special interest are solutions of the reduction equations (1) which have asymptotic power series expansions $f_k \simeq f_k^0 + \sum_{n=1}^{\infty} \chi_k^{(n)}\lambda^n$. Then the coefficients satisfy equations of the form

$$M_{k\ell}^{(n)}\chi_\ell^{(n)} = \beta_{\lambda n}(f^0)f_k^0 - \beta_k^{(n)}(f^0) + X_k^{(n)} \ , \tag{3}$$

where $X_k^{(n)}$ depends only upon $\chi^{(1)}, \ldots, \chi^{(n-1)}$, and

$$M_{k\ell}^{(n)}(f^0) \equiv (\partial\beta_k^{(0)}/\partial f_\ell)(f^0) - (\partial\beta_{\lambda 0}/\partial f_\ell)(f^0)f_k^0 - (n+1)\beta_{\lambda 0}(f^0)\delta_{k\ell} \ . \tag{4}$$

The matrices $M^{(n)}(f^0)$ are determined by one-loop calculations. If det $M^{(n)}(f^0) \neq 0$ for all $n \geq 1$, the coefficients $\chi^{(n)}$ are uniquely determined and the reduced theory has a renormalized power series expansion in λ. We can thus use regular reparametrizations of the original theory in order to remove the $\chi^{(n)}$-terms so that $\lambda_k = \lambda f_k^0$ is exact (ignoring possible exponential contributions). Furthermore the terms $X^{(n)}$ in Eqs. (3) vanish, and we obtain the relation $\beta_{\lambda n}(f^0)f_k^0 - \beta_k^{(n)}(f^0) = 0$ for all $n \geq 0$. The reparametrization transformations are of the form

$$\lambda' = \lambda'(\lambda,\lambda_1,\ldots,\lambda_m) = \lambda + (a^{(20)}\lambda^2 + a_\ell^{(11)}\lambda_\ell\lambda) + \ldots \qquad (5)$$
$$\lambda'_k = \lambda'_k(\lambda,\lambda_1,\ldots,\lambda_m) = \lambda_k + (b_{krs}^{(20)}\lambda_r\lambda_s + b_{k\ell}^{(11)}\lambda_\ell\lambda) + \ldots$$

They leave the quantities f_k^0, $\beta_{\lambda 0}(f^0)$, $\beta_k^{(0)}(f^0)$, $M^{(n)}(f^0)$ invariant.

If det $M^{(n)}=0$ for some $n=N \geq 1$ and $\beta_{\lambda 0} \neq 0$, we find that in general the asymptotic power series must be supplemented by terms of the form $\lambda^n(\lg\lambda)^m$, $n \geq N$, $1 \leq m \leq \sigma(N)$. After reparametrization, we obtain for $\lambda \to 0$: $f_k = f_k^0 + d_k\lambda^N \lg\lambda + c_k\lambda^N + \ldots$, where $M_{k\ell}^{(N)}(f^0)c_\ell = 0$ and where c_ℓ contains arbitrary parameters, their number corresponding to the degeneracy of the eigenvalue. The remaining coefficients are determined. We have a well defined, "renormalized" theory with logarithmic terms in the asymptotic expansion for $\lambda \to 0$.

In the following we consider only reductions with det $M^{(n)} \neq 0$. As a simple example we mention the model with $L_{int} = i\sqrt{g}\bar{\psi}\gamma_5\psi\phi - (\lambda/4!)\phi^4$ (de Rafael, Stora; Zimmermann). Here g should be taken as the primary coupling. The reduction implies $g(\lambda) = \lambda f^0$ with $f_0^0 = 0$, $f_\pm^0 = (\pm\sqrt{145}-1)/48$ ($\lambda \gtrless 0$ respectively). Of particular interest are gauge theories with matter fields, which generally require additional Yukawa and quartic interactions in order to be renormalizable. Here we can use the reduction equations in order to express the corresponding extra coupling parameters λ_k in terms of the gauge coupling g. After reparametrization, the solutions $\lambda_k = g^2 f_k^0$, where they exist, give rise to reduced theories which one may call "minimally" coupled gauge theories with matter fields.

As examples, we consider the reduction of two models with four coupling parameters. The first model contains one Dirac - and two scalar fields, both in the adjoint representation of SU(2). The direct interaction part of the Lagrangian is given by

$$L_{dir} = - i\sqrt{\lambda_1}\,\varepsilon^{abc}\bar{\psi}^a(A^b + i\gamma_5 B^b)\psi^c - \qquad (6)$$
$$- \frac{1}{4}\lambda_2(A^aA^a + B^aB^a)^2 + \frac{1}{4}\lambda_3(A^aA^b + B^aB^b)^2$$

The reduction equations have four solutions which are asymptotic power series expansions in g^2 for $g^2 \to 0$. After reparametrizations, they are of the form

(a) $\lambda_1=\lambda_2=\lambda_3=g^2$ (N=2 extended supersymmetric Yang-Mills theory)

(b) $\lambda_1=g^2$, $\lambda_2=9/\sqrt{105}\ g^2$, $\lambda_3=7/\sqrt{105}\ g^2$ (non supersymmetric theory)

and two more theories (a') and (b') which are obtained from (a) and (b) by reversing the sign of the quartic couplings λ_2 and λ_3, and which are not supersymmetric. Note that there are no solutions with vanishing Yukawa coupling λ_1. The above four theories are the only ones with asymptotic power series expansions in g^2 and real coefficients. There are further "general" solutions of the reduction equations which involve non-integer powers of g^2. Among these there is one which has an asymptotic power series in g with $\lambda_k = g^2 + c_k g^3 + d_{1k} g^4 + d_{2k} g^5 + \cdots$, k=1,2,3. Here $c_1=0$, $c_2=a$, $c_3=3a$, where a is an arbitrary real parameter. The coefficients d_{mk} are determined for given a. This solution corresponds to a hard breaking of supersymmetry. It may be eliminated by requiring the symmetry $A^\mu \to -A^\mu$, $g \to -g$. If we also exclude negative infinite asymptotic behavior of the classical potential, we are left with the solutions (a) and (b) as "minimally" coupled theories. They are both asymptotically free.

The second model involves four Majorana spinors ψ_k k=1...4 and six scalars A_i, B_i, i=1,2,3, all in the adjoint representation of SU(2). For simplicity, we impose an SU(2) x SU(2) symmetry in addition. Then the direct interaction part of the Lagrangian is

$$\begin{aligned} L_{dir} = &-\frac{1}{2}\sqrt{\lambda_1}\,\varepsilon^{abc}\bar{\psi}_k^a\,(\alpha_{ikL}A_i^b + i\gamma_5\beta_{ikL}B_i^b)\psi_L^c \\ &-\frac{1}{4}\lambda_2(A_i^aA_i^a + B_i^aB_i^a)^2 + \frac{1}{4}\lambda_3(A_i^aA_i^b + B_i^aB_i^b)^2 \end{aligned} \tag{7}$$

where α_i and β_i are appropriate 4x4 matrices. For the model (7) the reduction equations have two real solutions corresponding to power series in g . After reparametrization, we obtain

(a) $\lambda_1=\lambda_2=\lambda_3=g^2$ (N=4 extended supersymmetric Yang-Mills theory)

(b) $\lambda_1=g^2$, $\lambda_2 = (0.757944\ldots)g^2$, $\lambda_3 = (0.352305\ldots)g^2$ (non-supersymmetric theory)

For both reduced theories (a) and (b), the β-function vanishes at least in the order g^4(one-loop). For the supersymmetric case (a) there are well known arguments for the vanishing of the β-function in every order of perturbation theory.

In all models mentioned above, the reduction scheme implies the existence of renormalized theories with one-coupling parameter and with power series expansions for $g^2 \to 0$, although symmetries like N=2 or N=4 extended supersymmetry remain to be verified in higher orders.

In general, the reduction process can lead to theories with one coupling parameter, well defined renormalized Green's functions, and the possibility of new symmetries. Such symmetries appear if the original multiparameter theory contains the appropriate kind and number of fields so that a given symmetry can be implemented by relating coupling parameters in accordance with the requirements of the renormalization group. Generally, in the same systems, we also find other solutions of the reduction equations which do not realize a possible symmetry.

The reduction of N=1 supersymmetric theories with $\beta_{g0}=0$ (one loop) is of particular interest in connection with possible "finiteness". Here we consider solutions of reduction equations expressing the super-Yukawa couplings d_{ijk} in terms of the gauge coupling. We have $d_{ijk}=g\, f_{ijk}(g)$, and for solutions which allow power series expansions, we can again reparametrize to get $d_{ijk} = g\, f^0_{ijk}$ with $f^0_{ijk} = f_{ijk}(0)$ being a solution of $\beta^{(0)}_{ijk}(f^0) = 0$. After reparametrization we obtain the relation $\beta^{(n)}_{ijk}(f^0) = \beta_{gn}(f^0) f^0_{ijk}$.

Besides the "special" solutions of the reduction equations, there usually exist also "general" solutions which contain arbitrary coefficients. If $\beta_{\lambda 0} \neq 0$ (one-loop) for the original theory, these solutions may involve non-integer powers of λ and again also logarithmic terms. On the other hand, if $\beta_{\lambda 0} = 0$, they differ from a special solution by terms which vanish exponentially or faster for $\lambda \to 0$. These general solutions are important for the problem of stability of the special solutions. Stability concerns the question whether, for a given special solution, all "neighboring" solutions have the same limit as the primary coupling λ approaches a fixed point like $\lambda = 0$. The questions of stability or instability can be discussed in detail. We have shown that the theorems of Ljapunov can be applied to the reduction equations in order to obtain stability criteria. Special solutions corresponding to supersymmetric theories with non-vanishing super Yukawa interactions are generally found to be unstable.

The reduction scheme described in this report has also phenomenological applications. For example, the use of reduction in the Higgs-sector of the Weinberg-Salam theory is being considered by J. Kubo and K. Sibold.

This report is based upon work done in collaboration with W. Zimmermann and K. Sibold. For references see: R. Oehme and W. Zimmermann, Max Planck Institut Report MPT-PAE/PTh 60/82 (1982), Commun. Math. Phys. 97, 569 (1985); R. Oehme, K. Sibold and W. Zimmermann, Phys. Lett. 147B, 115 (1984); 153B, 142 (1985); W. Zimmermann, Commun. Math. Phys. 97, 211 (1985).

The Global Structure of Supermanifolds

Jeffrey M. Rabin*

The Enrico Fermi Institute of the University of Chicago
5640 S. Ellis Ave., Chicago, IL 60637

ABSTRACT

The global topological structure of a general supermanifold is described. Many more topologies are possible than those which have found application in physics. Speculations are presented on the physical consequences of such exotic topologies in supergravity and superstring theories.

Supermanifolds are the geometric objects on which supergravity and superstring theories live. Discussions of supermanifolds in the physics literature treat their anticommuting dimensions in a purely formal manner, and also concentrate on local geometry rather than global issues. There is some confusion in the literature as to the very possibility of topologically nontrivial supermanifolds.

In this talk I will sketch Rogers' mathematically rigorous definition of supermanifold, which makes sense of both local geometry and global topology[1]. This definition is extremely general, including as special cases the supermanifolds of other authors[2]. It allows supermanifolds to have far more exotic global properties, however. I then summarize my work with Louis Crane on the global structure of a general Rogers supermanifold. Proofs and technical details can be found in Ref. 3. Finally I speculate on the physical properties of supergravity and superstring theories on topologically nontrivial supermanifolds.

A supermanifold is a geometric object having some commuting coordinates x^μ and some anticommuting coordinates θ^α. To construct such a thing, introduce a basis $v_1, v_2, \ldots, v_L$ for a Grassmann (exterior) algebra B_L satisfying $v_i v_j = -v_j v_i$. Next, write the most general even and odd elements of B_L as

$$x^\mu = x_0^\mu + x_{ij}^\mu v_i v_j + x_{ijk\ell}^\mu v_i v_j v_k v_\ell + \cdots$$

$$\theta^\alpha = \theta_i^\alpha v_i + \theta_{ijk}^\alpha v_i v_j v_k + \cdots .$$

Here the coefficients x_Γ^μ and θ_Γ^α are ordinary real (or, more generally, complex) numbers. A supermanifold is simply an ordinary real manifold with local coordinates x_Γ^μ and θ_Γ^α. However, functions on the manifold, <u>including the transi-</u>

*E. Fermi Fellow, work supported in part by the NSF (PHY-83-01221) and the DOE (DE-AC02-82-ER-40073).

tion functions giving the coordinate transformations relating overlapping charts, may not depend explicitly on the real coordinates. They must be functions of the combinations x^μ and θ^α only, possessing the Taylor expansions in these variables normally assumed of superfields. This constraint should be thought of as analogous to the analyticity constraint in complex manifold theory: functions of the complex coordinates $z^\mu = x^\mu + iy^\mu$ can depend only on z^μ, not on x^μ and y^μ separately.

In physics, one assumes that an infinite supply of independent Grassmann numbers is available if needed, corresponding to the algebra B_∞. For easier analysis, we consider B_L with L finite, although most of our results hold in the infinite-dimensional case.

In physical applications it is implicitly assumed that the "body coordinates" x_0^μ parametrize a real spacetime manifold, called the body of the supermanifold, while the remaining "soul coordinates" take all real values without restriction. Such supermanifolds are vector bundles over their bodies[2] and have no topology in the soul directions. But far more general structures are possible.

In general, a supermanifold has only a foliated structure, not a bundle structure. That is, a supermanifold is foliated by surfaces along which the body coordinates x_0^μ in any chart are constant. However these surfaces (leaves) need not all be diffeomorphic, and no body manifold (defined as a manifold intersecting every leaf transversely and exactly once) need exist. The existence of a body is a similar issue to the existence of a gauge-fixing surface transverse to the gauge orbits in a non-Abelian gauge theory. Indeed, the body of a supermanifold is essentially a gauge-fixing surface for local supersymmetry transformations.

There are severe restrictions on the types of leaves which are possible. The universal covering space of any particular leaf can be shown to admit a flat Riemannian metric. This implies, for example, that no compact and simply connected leaf can exist. Furthermore, each leaf can be shown to have an extensive network of additional foliations. Still, the topology of a leaf can be quite complicated, rather than trivial as in the vector bundle cases. For example, toroidal supermanifolds having toroidal leaves exist. The topology of the leaves is the precise version of the intuitive concept of "topology in the soul directions".

Global topological features of a supermanifold influence the properties of functions (superfields) defined on it. Since a superfield is a polynomial function of the soul coordinates, it can be analytically continued along leaves once it is given locally. For the usual vector bundle supermanifolds, any local superfield extends to a global one. This is not true when the leaves are topologically nontrivial. For example, one can show that a superfield is necessarily constant on any compact leaf. Roughly speaking, this is because a polynomial cannot be periodic or quasiperiodic. One can even manipulate the topology of the leaves so as to impose physically interesting constraints such as the constraint that a superfield be chiral.

What possible uses could supermanifolds with exotic global structures have in physics? I am 99% certain that only supermanifolds having bodies can be physically useful, since the body is identified with the physical spacetime manifold. The 1% hedge is because a body always exists locally and this may be sufficient for some purposes. Nontrivial topology is still possible when a body exists, and I have the following suggestions, in order from least to most speculative.

1) Berezin integration as used in supersymmetric theories is a formal operation with many of the properties of an integral but no measure-theoretic interpretation. A deeper understanding of the Berezin integral is desirable and might be achieved by trying to construct integrals over arbitrary supermanifolds.

2) A local supersymmetry transformation is interpreted geometrically as a small change in the embedding of the body in a supermanifold. If the supermanifold has nontrivial homotopy groups, there may be embeddings which cannot be deformed into one another. These would correspond to "large" SUSYs as opposed to the usual "small" ones, analogous to the distinction between large and small gauge transformations. This might lead to entirely new global phenomena in supergravity.

3) A supermanifold with nontrivial topology normally admits fewer independent global superfields than does flat superspace. A supergravity theory on such a supermanifold would have fewer degrees of freedom than usual, presumably corresponding to some type of SUSY-invariant constraints.

4) Finally, superstrings on exotic supermanifolds may have new winding numbers around loops in soul directions. There may also be restrictions on the functional dependence of superstring modes on compactified soul dimensions.

REFERENCES

1. A.Rogers, J. Math.Phys. 21, 1352 (1980).
2. D. A. Leites, Russian Math. Surveys 35, 1 (1980); B. S. DeWitt, Supermanifolds, Cambridge University Press, Cambridge 1984.
3. J. M. Rabin and L. Crane, University of Chicago preprints EFI 84-39, to appear in Comm. Math. Phys., and EFI 85-25, submitted to Comm. Math. Phys. See also C. P. Boyer and S. Gitler, Trans. Am. Math. Soc. 285, 241 (1984).

SOME ASPECTS OF THE SO(32) SUPERSTRING THEORY

Hiroshi Itoyama, Physics Department
Columbia University, New York, NY 10027
with Hai-cang Ren
Institute for Advanced Study, Princeton, NJ 08540

Developments of superstring theories [1] have recently reached a new stage with a startling breakthrough by Green and Schwarz [2]. Supersymmetric ten-dimensional Yang-Mills theory coupled to $N=1$ supergravity are free from gauge [3], gravitational and mixed [4] anomalies when the gauge group is SO(32) or $E_8 \times E_8$. Superstring theories based on these groups are likely to be mathematically consistent.

Following the Green and Schwarz discovery, Witten [5] has argued that, when the low energy gauge group is semi-simple, the field strength 3-form H defined globally ensures the absence of the four-dimensional anomalies. Here, we will see some additional aspects of the SO(32) theory [9] which arise when the gauge group is not semi-simple [6].

Let us first demonstrate that compactification of the ten-dimensional theory by topologically nontrivial configurations in six-dimensional Kaluza-Klein space K_6 naturally admits a low energy non-semisimple gauge group. The relevant homotopy group is $\pi_5(H)$ with H the subgroup whose gauge fields receive vacuum expectation values in the Kaluza-Klein space and therefore break SO(32) into the low energy gauge group G. For $H = SU(N)$ with $N \geq 3$, $\pi_5(SU(N)) = Z$ and instantonlike configurations may exist [7].

What is naturally embedded in SO(32) is not SU(N) but U(N), where $N \leq 16$. After the compactification by instantons, one is, therefore, left with the U(1) originated from U(N). The generators of G in the fundamental representation are embedded in SO(32) in the following manner:

$$t = \begin{pmatrix} t' & 0 \\ 0 & 0 \end{pmatrix} \quad \text{and} \quad \begin{pmatrix} 0 & 0 \\ 0 & C \end{pmatrix}, \text{ with } C = \begin{pmatrix} 0 & I \\ -I & 0 \end{pmatrix}, \tag{1}$$

where we have chosen a real basis $(\vec{x}_1, \vec{y}_1, \vec{x}_2, \vec{y}_2)$ of the 32-dimensional vector space on which the generators act. The $\vec{x}_i$ and $\vec{y}_i$ are N (or $16 - N$)-dimensional vectors.

A generic generator f of H resides in $\begin{pmatrix} 0 & 0 \\ 0 & f \end{pmatrix}$. It is easy to see that

$$\text{tr } f^3 t \neq 0 \quad \text{and} \quad \text{tr } ft = 0. \tag{2}$$

As we will see later, eq. (2) has a particular significance which is related to the anomaly cancellations in four dimensions. Also it should be noted that, in the adjoint representation, the U(1) current couples to other gauge fields through one-loop diagrams.

Starting from the expression by Green and Schwarz, one can readily obtain an expression for the anomaly after compactification [8]:

$$Q\Big|_{comp} = -20c\int_{M_4\times K_6} tr(\zeta d_{M_4} v)trtf^3 - 20c\int_{M_4\times K_6} tr(\theta d_{M_4}\omega_{M_4})trtf^3$$
$$+ 10c\int_{M_4\times K_6} \omega^1_{6Y}(d_{M_4}\zeta,a)H_{M_4}, \quad \text{where } c = \frac{i^6}{6!(2\pi)^6}. \qquad (3)$$

The arguments of gauge and Lorentz parameters ζ and θ are restricted to four dimensions. We call this a *compactified anomaly*. We have used the fact $H = dB - \omega^0_{3Y} - \omega^0_{3L}$. Also we have reduced the trace Tr in the adjoint representation to the trace tr in the fundamental representation. The Yang-Mills connection and curvature written in lower case are in the fundamental representation.

The compactified anomaly vanishes if the gauge group is semi-simple. Eq. (3) tells us that it is nonvanishing for the generator of U(1), whose embedding is of the variety shown in eq. (1).

Let us denote by $\not{D}_6$ the six-dimensional Dirac and Rarita-Schwinger operators generically. We will demonstrate that the nonzero massive modes contribute to the compactified anomaly when it is nonvanishing. Suppose that the anomalies of the low energy theory come solely from the zero modes [5] of $\not{D}_6$. Then straightforward calculations from the twelve-dimensional index theorem and its relation to anomalies [3] tell us the anomaly $Q^{(T)}$ evaluated with this assumption:

$$Q^{(T)} = -20c\int_{M_4\times K_6} (tr(\zeta f^3)d_{M_4} tr(vd_{M_4}v + \tfrac{1}{2}v^3) + \tfrac{1}{2}tr(\zeta d_{M_4}v^2)tr(f^3 v)$$
$$+ 2tr(\zeta d_{M_4}v)tr(f^3 d_{M_4}v) + \tfrac{1}{2}tr(\zeta v^2)tr(f^3 d_{M_4}v)$$
$$+ 2tr(tf^3)tr(\theta d_{M_4}\omega_{M_4}) + tr(\zeta f^3)trR^2_{M_4}). \qquad (4)$$

The dangerous part proportional to $\int_{K_6}(trR^2_K + trf^2)\int_{M_4} tr(f\hat{\omega}^1_{4Y})$ cancels thanks to Witten's argument that H should be globally well-defined. The remaining anomaly, which we call a *truncated anomaly*, is nonvanishing only when the gauge group includes the U(1) of the variety seen in eq. (1). Thanks to the above cancellation, it is possible to construct the counter term $S^{(T)}$ such that $\delta_{\zeta,\theta} S^{(T)} = Q^{(T)}$.

The compactified anomaly and the truncated anomaly do not agree, although they both satisfy the consistency condition. The zero modes of $\not{D}_6$ alone do not saturate the gauge and mixed anomalies of the non-semisimple group which are derived from the ten-dimensional theory. One may wonder if the difference of the two anomalies $Q^{(T)} - Q|_{comp} = \delta_{\zeta,\theta}(S^{(T)} - (S_1 + S_2 + S_3)|_{comp}) + \int d(\text{something})$ would correspond to a redefinition of the generating functional. A "new" generating functional is *not* invariant under the gauge transformations in the Kaluza-Klein space, however. This interpretation is not acceptable. The claim now follows.

The above situation is somewhat analogous to one aspect of the standard theory of electroweak interactions: One is left with the low energy anomalous interactions when one sends the mass of the charm quark to infinity.

A question remains whether this U(1) symmetry can stay local symmetry at low energy. According to Witten, the U(1) gauge boson becomes massive, absorbing the B degree of freedom. We feel, however, that the complete demonstration requires the evaluation of one-loop *gauge invariant* effective action consisting of the determinants and the counter terms. Both of them are alone anomalous by themselves.

The integration of the exact ten form, which is negligible for sure in the original theory, may become a topological obstruction after certain compactifications. The precise analysis requires careful expressions for the nonabelian anomaly for the gauge fields which lie in nontrivial fiber bundles.

Finally, we would like to summarize the mathematical procedure used to obtain formulae (3) and (4) schematically. The index for the product manifold is

$$\sum_i (n_+ - n_-)^{(C_i)}_{d,1/2} (n_+ - n_-)^{(L_i)}_{D-d,1/2} + (n_+ - n_-)_{d,3,2} (n_+ - n_-)_{D-d,3/2} .$$

One obtains the truncated anomaly when one applies the procedure of ref. 3 after the above decomposition of the index (D = 12, d = 6). The decomposition $M_{10} \to M_4 \times M_6$ after the procedure gives us, of course, the compactified anomaly. The above facts can be summarized as the following diagram:

Index theorem at D = 12 ⟶ Anomaly at D = 10
(compactification) ↓ (compactification) ↓
Index theorem at D = 6 + 6 ⟶ Truncated anomaly ≠ Compactified anomaly

References

[1] J. H. Schwarz, Phys. Rep. 89, 223 (1982); M. B. Green, Surveys in High Energy Physics 3, 127 (1982).

[2] M. B. Green and J. H. Schwarz, CALT-68-1182.

[3] B. Zumino, Wu Yong-shi and A. Zee, Nucl. Phys. B239, 447 (1984); B. Zumino, Les Houches Lectures (1983); R. Stora, Cargese Lectures (1983).

[4] L. Alvarez-Gaumé and E. Witten, Nucl. Phys. B234, 269 (1983).

[5] E. Witten, "Some properties of O(32) Superstrings," Princeton University preprint.

[6] H. Itoyama and H. C. Ren, Columbia-IAS preprint (December 1984), to appear in Phys. Rev. D.

[7] A different possibility based on a product manifold $M_1 \times M_2 \times M_3$ has been considered by Witten (ref. 5).

[8] For detailed notation, see ref. [6].

[9] It has now become clear that $E_8 \times E_8$ theory is phenomenologically superior.

Axial anomaly and Josephson effects in 1+1 dimensional models

Joe Kiskis
Department of Physics
University of California at Davis
Davis, California 95616

Massless electrons have an axial anomaly and nonrelativistic, superconducting electrons have Josephson effects. These are responses of the Dirac and Fermi seas to external electric fields and are quite similar. It is shown that the reason for this is that the Fermi sea is a regularization of the Dirac sea.

The phenomena are studied in one time and one space dimension. The spatial dimension has length L and the topology of a ring. We consider non-interacting electrons in an external electric field that is uniform in space but may vary in time. The details of this work and references to related papers can be found in ref. 1.

In a uniform electric field, we can take $A_0(t,x) = 0$ and $A_1(t,x) = A(t)$. The gauge invariants are the electric field $E(t) = -\partial_0 A$ and the phase $\delta = -\oint A \cdot dx\Big|_{t_0} = -LA(t_0)$. The time t_0 is arbitrarily chosen but fixed. The possible canonical momenta for the electrons are $2\pi n/L$ with $n = 0, \pm 1, \pm 2, \ldots$.

The energy levels of the Dirac equation are $(\frac{2\pi}{L}n-A)$ for right movers and $-(\frac{2\pi}{L}n-A)$ for left movers. The axial anomaly[2] can be seen[3] in the movement of filled and empty levels in the regulated Dirac sea as A changes from 0 to $-2\pi/L$.

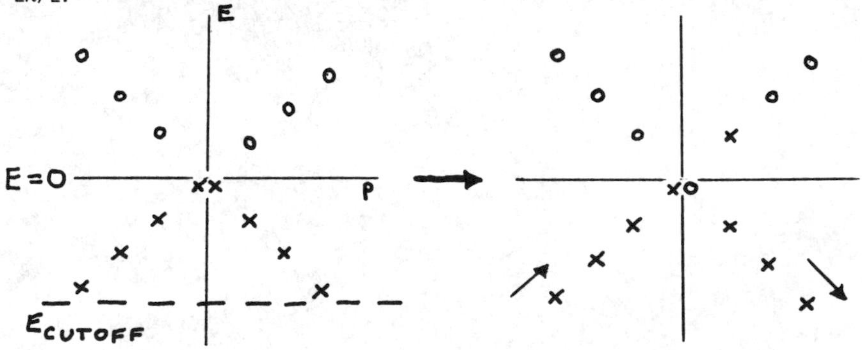

The number of occupied levels has not changed. Thus the charge density is independent of time, and electric charge is conserved. However, by considering the behavior around either $E = 0$ or $E = E_{cutoff}$, one finds that the electric current has increased by two units. Since the axial charge density is the electric current density, the axial charge is not conserved. A pair is produced. One can show that the electric current density is

$$j = -\frac{1}{\pi} A , \tag{1}$$

and that the time derivative of eq. 1 is equivalent to the usual expression for the anomalous divergence of the axial current.

The energy levels of the Schroedinger equation are $(\frac{2\pi}{L} n - A)^2$, and the response of the Fermi sea filled to $E_F = p_F^2/2m$ is

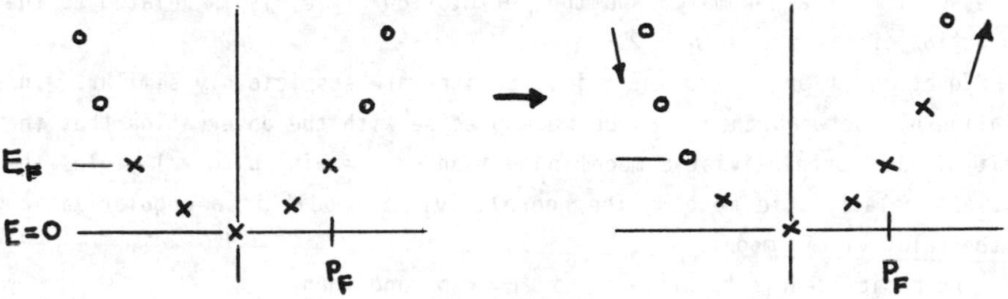

It is easy to show that the charge density $\rho = p_F/2\pi + 1/L$ does not change and that the current density is

$$j = -\frac{\rho}{m} A. \tag{2}$$

Equation 2 is central to superconductor phenomenology, and in ref. 1 the relationship of it to ac and dc Josephson effects is discussed. It is shown that simple assumptions on the effects of interactions modify eq. 2 at large A so that it reads

$$j = \frac{\rho}{m} \frac{1}{L} s(-LA) .$$

The form of $s(\cdot)$ is

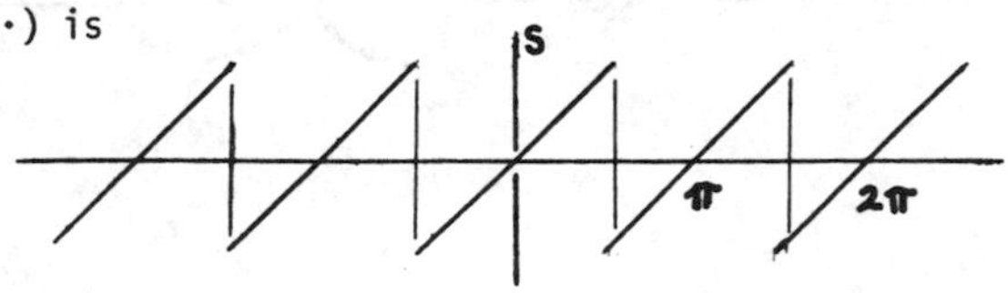

For zero electric field, there is a current

$$j = \frac{\rho}{m}\frac{1}{L}\, s(\delta)$$

that is essentially the dc Josephson effect. For a static electric field, there is a current

$$j = \frac{\rho}{m}\frac{1}{L}\, s(ELt)$$

that is essentially the ac Josephson effect.

In the nonrelativistic case, eq. 2 is the acceleration of charge by the electric field, and the permutation of energy levels is related to the periodicity of the Josephson effects. In the relativistic case, eq. 1 expresses the axial anomaly, and the permutation of levels is related to the production of pairs with $Q_5 = 2$.

Equations 1 and 2 and their implications are suspiciously similar. The relationship between them can be made precise with the observation that the limit of the nonrelativistic model $p_F \to \infty$ and $m \to \infty$ with $p_F/m = 1$ yields the massless relativistic model: The nonrelativistic model is a regularization of the relativistic model.

The basic idea is to write $p_{NR} = \pm p_F + p_R$ and then

$$E_{NR} = \frac{p_{NR}^2}{2m} = \frac{1}{2m}(\pm p_F + p_R)^2 = \pm\frac{p_F}{m}p_R + \frac{p_F^2}{2m} + \frac{p_R^2}{2m}$$

$$\to \pm\, p_R + \text{constant} = E_R + \text{constant}$$

In this limit, $\frac{\rho}{m} \to \frac{1}{\pi}$ so eq. 2 becomes eq. 1. The picture is

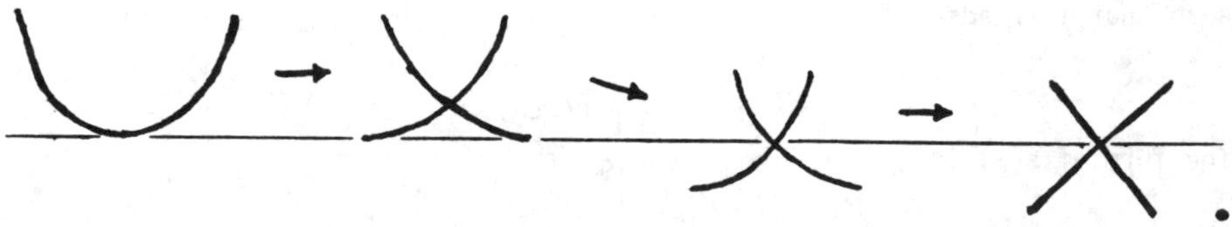

References

1. Joe Kiskis, Phys. Rev. D, in press.
2. S. Adler, Phys. Rev. 177,2426 (1969).
   J. Bell and R. Jackiw, Nuovo Cimento 60A,47 (1969).
3. N. Manton, Report No. NSF ITP 84-15.
   J. Bjorken, in Quantum Chromodynamics, Proceedings of the Summer Institute on Particle Physics, SLAC, 1979.
   M. Stone, Ann. Phys. 155,56 (1984)
   J. Ambjorn, J. Greensite, and C. Peterson, Nucl. Phys. B221,381 (1983).

BIFURCATION THEORY AND FERMION MASS GENERATION

by

Lay-Nam Chang
Virginia Polytechnic Institute & State University
Blacksburg, Va 24061

and

Ngee-Pong Chang
City College of the City University of New York
New York, N.Y. 10031

Even though the subject of our talk has nothing to do directly with anomaly, topology, or geometry, there is sufficient connection with a totally new direction in mathematics that we feel it warrants the attention of the participants of this symposium, who are experts in field theory as well as in mathematics.

Bifurcation theory[1] is a new branch of mathematics that studies mappings containing a parameter λ. As λ is varied, the behavior changes dramatically at certain critical values of λ_c, called bifurcation points. If $f(x, \lambda)$ is the mapping, then x is the **fixed point** of the mapping whenever x satisfies the equation

$$x = f(x, \lambda) \qquad (1)$$

For λ below some critical value, there may be only one **stable** fixed point at x=0, say. For λ above that critical value, **bifurcation** may occur and the mapping then yields two fixed points, one of which ($x \neq 0$) will be the new stable fixed point while the old fixed point at x = 0 becomes unstable.

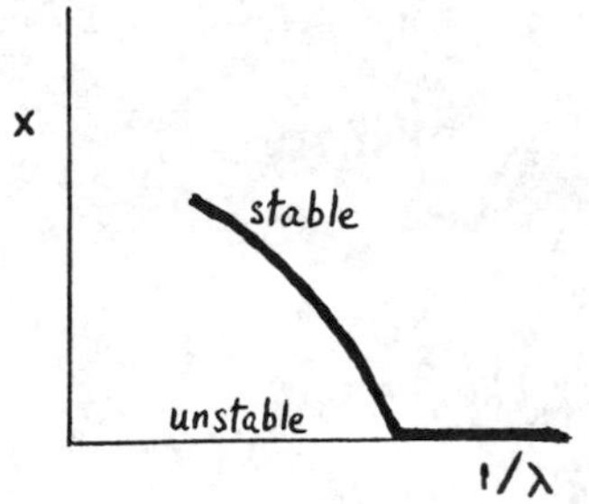

Fig. 1

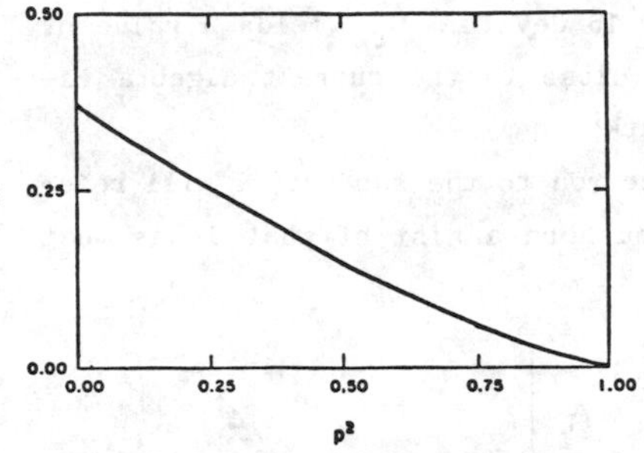

Fig. 2

In our continuing effort to apply Nambu-Jona-Lasinio[2] to the study of chiral symmetry breaking in QCD, we have come across a connection between Renormalisation Group and bifurcation theory that is new and intriguing.[3] We find that the dynamical symmetry breaking is dependent on p^2 momentum scale.

For p^2 GREATER than a threshold value, the system chooses the chiral <u>symmetric</u> state.

For p^2 LESS than the threshold, the system chooses the chiral <u>asymmetric</u> state.

The resulting effective mass of the fermion, for space-like p^2, is exactly the same as bifurcation theory would have it.

Note that whereas previous studies of phase transitions have involved temperature as an **external parameter**, in our study here of the zero temperature renormalisation field theory, the role of the **external parameter** is taken over by four momentum-squared. Dynamical symmetry breaking in field theory thus takes on a space-time dimension suggestive of the bag model, where chiral symmetry is taken to be preserved inside the bag, but is broken outside the bag.

As a direct result of fig. 2 above, the vacuum expectation value of $\langle\bar{\psi}\psi\rangle$ defined to be the limit as x approaches y of the two-point function for the fermion, becomes finite and calculable. It is

$$\langle\bar{\psi}\psi\rangle = -0.0398\, N_c\, \Lambda_c^3 \quad (2)$$

where Λ_c is the QCD invariant cut-off, and N_c is the number of colors. To compare with current algebra determinations, it is necessary to multiply eq. (2) by M, the dynamically generated mass, to find

$$M\langle\bar{\psi}\psi\rangle = -0.0470\, N_c\, \Lambda_c^4 \quad (3)$$

The combination on the left hand side of eq. (3) is commonly believed to be

RG-invariant. Using an accepted value of 0.15 GeV for Λ_c yields a value of 9.24×10^{-5} $(\mathrm{GeV})^4$, which is remarkably close to the current algebra estimate of 8.8×10^{-5} $(\mathrm{GeV})^4$ for the up quark.

Since this is a short talk to introduce you to the subject, I will refer you to ref. 3 for details, and only give you here a gist of what it is that led to this connection with bifurcation.

Consider first a chiral broken QCD theory, where in the tree Lagrangian the fermions are massive, with a running mass, m_r. Because m_r is dependent on renormalisation scale, it is not suitable as a physical parameter. Instead, we can parametrize by the two RG-invariant mass scales, Λ_c and M_o. The physically allowed region in the parameter space is shown on the right.

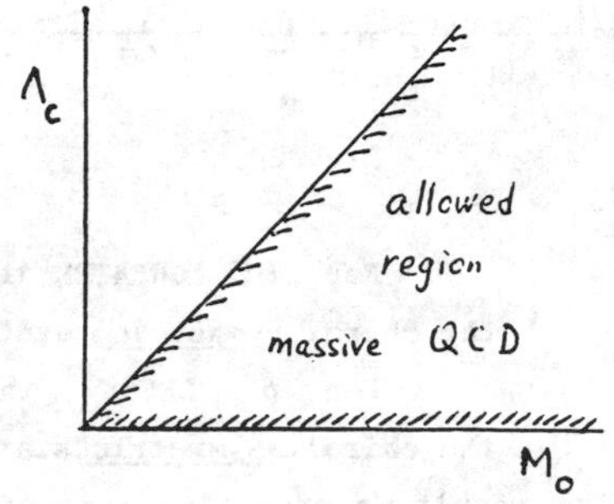

Fig. 3

The boundary of the allowed domain is described by

$$M_o = \Lambda_c e^{1/6} \tag{4}$$

and corresponds to the chiral symmetric limit of vanishing m_r. This fact enables us to study the dynamical symmetry breaking as the **limit** of a massive QCD theory.

For every point in the allowed domain of parameter space in fig.3, we can develop the renormalised perturbative series for the n-point functions of the theory, accurate to, say, 1 loop Renormalisation Group analysis. Take in particular the chiral-flip part of the two-point function for the fermion, M_p. The renormalised perturbative series, accurate to 1 loop Renormalisation Group, can be generated by the iterative equation

$$M_p = M_o \left\{ 1 + \frac{\lambda_o b}{2} \log\left[\frac{M_p^2}{M_c^2 e} \left(1 + \frac{p^2}{M_p^2}\right)^{\frac{M_p^2}{p^2}+1} \right] \right\}^{-\alpha} \tag{5}$$

where λ_o is given by

$$1/\lambda_o = \frac{b}{2} \log\left[M_o^2 / (\Lambda_c^2 e^{1/3}) \right] \tag{6}$$

Equation (5) is the crux of the matter as far as connection with bifurcation theory is concerned. For it is in the form of eq. (1), with M_o and Λ_c as **external parameters**.

By an application of the Leray-Schauder fixed point theorem[4], it can be shown that eq. (5) defines a complex function of p^2 that is analytic in a cut p^2 -plane, with the cut along the time-like p^2 axis. This is true **for every set of parameters within the allowed domain of fig. 3**. This is of course reassuring since perturbative analyticity has long been established for renormalised field theory order by order.

What happens when we now go to the boundary of Fig. 3 as the dynamical symmetry breaking limit ? For p^2 outside a certain fig leaf domain, the function M_p in fact chooses the chiral symmetric phase, viz. it **vanishes**. Inside the fig leaf domain, the function M_p opts for the chiral asymmetric phase.

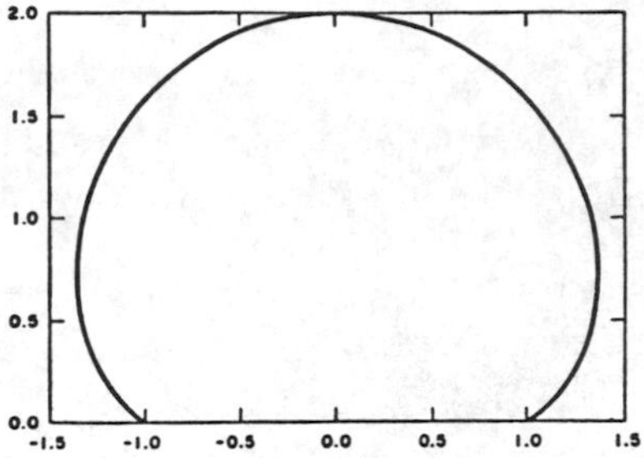

Fig. 4

This is to be contrasted with the gap equation in Nambu-Jona-Lasinio approach. There the gap equation by itself could not decide if the broken symmetry solution was in fact chosen by the system. Here bifurcation theory makes an outright choice, depending on the momentum range.

Clearly what we have described here is but a scratch in the full panoply of bifurcation theory. Questions of **chaos** spring to mind. In fig. 3 we have restricted ourselves only to the allowed region. If we analytically continue our parameters into the forbidden region, do we encounter period four and higher bifurcation, leading ultimately to chaos ? We would like to answer yes, but until we have carried out a full investigation, it must remain for now an intriguing conjecture.

REFERENCES

1. For an excellent exposition on the subject, see Lecture Notes by S.N. Chow, **Bifurcation theory and Dynamical Systems**, Lecture Notes No. 22, Math Dept,National University of Singapore,Kent Ridge, Singapore 0511.
2. Y. Nambu, G. Jona-Lasinio, Phys. Rev. 122, 345 (1961); **ibid** 124, 246 (1961).
3. L.N. Chang and N.P. Chang, " Bifurcation and Dynamical Symmetry Breaking in a RG-improved Field Theory", CCNY-HEP-84-11, to appear in Phys. Rev. Lett. June 1985.
4. D.R. Smart, Fixed point theorems, Cambridge University Press (1974). See Theorem 10.3.10 on p. 82.

SYMPOSIUM ON ANOMALIES, GEOMETRY, TOPOLOGY

PROGRAM

PARTICIPANTS

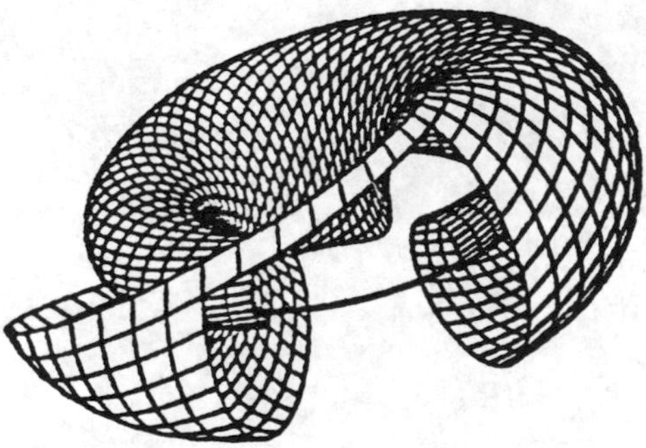

SYMPOSIUM ON ANOMALIES, GEOMETRY, TOPOLOGY

S

WEDNESDAY PROGRAM

MARCH 27, 1985
CARRIAGE GREENS INN

6:00-10:00PM	REGISTRATION
6:30-9:30PM	RECEPTION WITH BUFFET

THURSDAY PROGRAM

MARCH 28, 1985
HIGH ENERGY PHYSICS AUDITORIUM
ARGONNE NATIONAL LABORATORY

8:30AM	REGISTRATION AT ARGONNE
9:00AM	OPENING REMARKS
9:10AM	O. ALVAREZ: ANOMALIES AND COHOMOLOGY
10:00AM	M.F. ATIYAH: TOPLOGICAL ASPECTS OF ANOMALIES
10:50AM	COFFEE BREAK
11:10AM	G. 'T HOOFT: ON THE QUANTUM STRUCTURE OF BLACK HOLES
12:00AM	J.H. SCHWARZ: SUPERSTRINGS
12:50AM	LUNCH
1:15PM	SPECIAL TOPICS SESSIONS (PARALLEL)

A: SUPERSTRINGS I (D. FRIEDAN)

2:30PM	M. GREEN: ASPECTS OF SUPERSTRINGS
3:10PM	V. KAC: 112 CONSTRUCTIONS OF THE BASIC REPRESENTATION OF THE LOOP GROUP OF E_8
3:50PM	COFFEE BREAK
4:10PM	D. GROSS: HETEROTIC STRING I
4:50PM	T. BANKS: GAUGE INVARIANT STRING THEORY

B: ANOMALY STRUCTURE I (P. GINSPARG)

2:30PM	B. GROSSMAN: ON THE 3RD COCYCLE IN GAUGE THEORIES
3:00PM	Y.S. WU: COHOMOLOGY OF GAUGE FIELDS AND ABELIAN GAUGE STRUCTURE INSIDE NON-ABELIAN THEORIES
3:30PM	L. BAULIEU: LOCAL SUPERSYMMETRY AND EVANESANCE OF ANOMALIES
4:00PM	COFFEE BREAK
4:20PM	D. NEMESCHANSKY: HOLONOMY ANOMALIES
4:50PM	H.-Y. GUO: GENERALIZED CHERN-SIMONS CECH-deRHAM COMPLEX AND GAUGE GROUP COHOMOLOGIES

6:00PM	COCKTAILS AND DINNER (CARRIAGE GREENS INN)
8:30PM	PHILOSOPHY, STRINGS, AND THE ANSWER *42* (P.G.O. FREUND)

FRIDAY PROGRAM

MARCH 29, 1985
KENT AUDITORIUM
UNIVERSITY OF CHICAGO

9:00AM	E. WITTEN: GLOBAL GRAVITATIONAL ANOMALIES
9:50AM	J.R. SCHRIEFFER: FRACTIONAL CHARGE AND TOPOLOGICAL KINKS
10:40AM	COFFEE BREAK
11:00AM	B. ZUMINO: COHOMOLOGY AND ANOMALIES
11:50AM	LUNCH
2:00PM	SPECIAL TOPICS SESSIONS (PARALLEL)

A: SUPERSTRINGS II (S. SHENKER)

2:00PM	L. BRINK: UNIQUENESS OF SUPERSTRING ACTIONS
2:40PM	J. HARVEY: HETEROTIC STRINGS II
3:20PM	COFFEE BREAK
3:40PM	W. SIEGEL: COVARIANT APPROACH TO SUPERSTRINGS
4:20PM	M. KAKU: COVARIANT QUANTIZATION OF SUPERSTRINGS
4:50PM	M. BOWICK: SUPERSTRINGS AT HIGH TEMPERATURE
5:00PM	J.L. GERVAIS: POLYAKOV STRING
5:20PM	B. ZWIEBACH: GHOST-FREE R^2 ACTIONS FROM STRING THEORY

B: CHARGE FRACTIONALIZATION (A. NIEMI)

2:00PM	H. PANAGOPOULOS: CHIRAL ANOMALIES IN A MONOPOLE BACKGROUND
2:30PM	D. BOYANOVSKY: FRACTIONAL CHARGE IN A NUT SHELL
3:00PM	R. AKHOURY: "HIDDEN" SUPERSYMMETRY AND FERMION FRACTIONALIZATION
3:30PM	COFFEE BREAK
3:50PM	M. STONE: TOPOLOGY AND TWIST IN ^{3}He – A
4:20PM	G. SEMENOFF: INDEX THEORY ANALYSIS OF FERMION FRACTIONIZATION
4:50PM	A. NIEMI: OTHER USES OF CHARGE FRACTIONIZATION

C: GENERAL TOPICS (C. GOEBEL)

2:00PM	F. MANSOURI: ISOMETRIES IN DIMENSIONAL REDUCTION
2:20PM	B. OVRUT: 16/16 N=1 SUPERGRAVITY AND SUPERSTRINGS
2:45PM	X. WU: NONCANONICAL TORSION IN KALUZA- KLEIN THEORIES
3:00PM	R. OEHME: REDUCTION IN COUPLING PARAMETER SPACE
3:15PM	COFFEE BREAK
3:35PM	J. RABIN: THE GLOBAL STRUCTURE OF SUPERMANIFOLDS
3:50PM	H. ITOYAMA: ANOMALY CANCELATIONS AND COMPACTIFICATIONS IN THE SO(32) SUPERSTRING THEORY
4:05PM	J. KISKIS: AXIAL ANOMALY AND THE AC JOSEPHSON EFFECT IN 1+1 DIMENSIONAL MODELS
4:20PM	M. BANDER: ON RANDOM SURFACES ON THE LATTICE
4:35PM	L.N. & N.P. CHANG: BIFURCATION AND DYNAMICAL SYMMETRY BREAKING

6:00PM	RECEPTION (NORTH LOUNGE OF REYNOLDS CLUB, U.C.)
7:00PM	BANQUET (HUTCHINSON COMMONS, U.C.)
9:00PM	RECITAL: VOICE AND PIANO (MANDEL HALL, U.C.) ELSA CHARLSTON, SOPRANO ABRAHAM STOKMAN, PIANO

SATURDAY PROGRAM

MARCH 30, 1985
HIGH ENERGY PHYSICS AUDITORIUM
ARGONNE NATIONAL LABORATORY

9:00AM	L. ALVAREZ-GAUME: FINITENESS IN SIGMA MODELS
9:50AM	I.M. SINGER: MORE ON ANOMALIES
10:40AM	COFFEE BREAK
11:00AM	R. JACKIW: OVERVIEW OF TOPOLOGICAL ANALYSIS IN QUANTUM GAUGE THEORIES
11:50AM	LUNCH
1:15PM	SPECIAL TOPICS SESSIONS (PARALLEL)

A: COMPACTIFICATION (A. STROMINGER)

1:15PM	G. HOROWITZ: VACUUM CONFIGURATIONS FOR SUPERSTRINGS
1:50PM	S.T. YAU: RICCI FLAT METRICS ON KAHLER MANIFOLDS
2:25PM	COFFEE BREAK
2:40PM	M. DINE: SUPERSYMMETRY BREAKING IN SUPERSTRINGS
3:10PM	P. FRAMPTON: SUPERSYMMETRY PHENOMENOLOGY
3:20PM	B. SCHELLEKENS: SOME COMPACTIFICATIONS OF SUPERSTRINGS
3:30PM	E. WITTEN: VACUUM CONFIGURATIONS FOR SUPERSTRINGS

B: EFFECTIVE LAGRANGIANS (E. FARHI)

1:15PM	C. NAPPI: SOME NEW RESULTS ON SKYRMIONS
1:45PM	A. BALACHANDRAN: QUANTIZATION AMBIGUITIES IN CHIRAL MODELS
2:15PM	E. D'HOKER: DECOUPLING IN CHIRAL GAUGE THEORIES
2:45PM	COFFEE BREAK
3:00PM	P. NELSON: ANOMALIES IN SIGMA MODELS
3:30PM	A.N. REDLICH: CHERN SIMONS TERMS INDUCED AT FINITE TEMPERATURE
4:00PM	R. MACKENZIE: ENERGY OF THE WEAK SKYRMION

C: ANOMALY STRUCTURE II (P. GINSPARG)

1:15PM	C. VIALLET: NEW RESULTS IN BRS COHOMOLOGY
1:45PM	J. STASHEFF: THE deRAHM BAR CONSTRUCTION: AN INTERPRETATION OF ZUMINO, FADEEV, ETC
2:20PM	S. JO: ANOMALOUS COMMUTATORS IN NON-ABELIAN THEORIES
2:40PM	COFFEE BREAK
3:00PM	J. THIERRY-MIEG: GEOMETRICAL PROPERTIES OF GHOSTS AND ANTI-GHOSTS
3:30PM	B. HOU: HIGHER CO-CYCLES AND ANOMALIES
4:00PM	P. PASTI: ABJ ANOMALIES IN SUPERSYMMETRIC THEORIES

4:30PM	AIRPORT TRANSPORTATION

Symposium on Anomalies, Geometry, Topology

Participants

Abdalla, E.	Freie Universität Berlin
Accetta, F.	University of Chicago
Akhoury, R.	UCLA
Albright, C.	Northern Illinois University
Allen, T.	Caltech
Alvarez, J.	Purdue University
Alvarez, O.	U.C. Berkeley
Alvarez-Gaumé, L.	Harvard University
Atiyah, M.F.	Oxford University
Atkinson, G.	University of Maryland
Axelrod, A.	Florida State University
Bagger, J.	Harvard University/ SLAC
Bagneid, A.	Purdue University
Bai, G.	Syracuse University
Balachandran, A.	Syracuse University
Bander, M.	U.C. Irvine
Banks, T.	University of Tel-Aviv
Bars, I.	University of Southern California
Bardeen, W.	Fermilab
Baulieu, L.	Université Paris VI
Becchi, C.	University of Genoa
Bechhoefer, J.	University of Chicago
Berkovits, N.	U.C. Berkeley
Biedenharn, L.	Duke University
Bincer, A.	University of Wisconsin
Bodwin, G.	Argonne National Laboratory
Bowick, M.	Yale University
Boyanovsky, D.	SLAC
Braaten, E.	Northwestern University
Brekke, L.	University of Chicago
Brink, L.	Göteborg University
Burges, C.	M.I.T.
Burns, D.	University of Michigan
Buser, R.	Caltech
Caldi, D.	University of Southern California
Candelas, P.	University of Texas at Austin
Capps, R.	Purdue University
Carson, L.	Northwestern University
Carter, M	Stanford University
Chan, L.	University of Notre Dame

Chan, L.	Louisiana State University
Chang, D.	University of Maryland
Chang, L.N.	Virginia Polytechnic Institute
Chang, N.P.	City College of C.U.N.Y.
Chao, Y.	University of Michigan
Chattopadhay, U.	University of Maryland
Cho, H.	Brown University
Chodos, A.	Yale University
Chow, D.	University of Wisconsin
Clark, T.	Purdue University
Cohn, J.	University of Chicago
Collins, J.	Illinois Institute of Technology
Cordes, S.	Princeton University
Cotta-Ramusino, P.	University of Milano
Curtright, T.	University of Florida
D'Hoker, E.	Columbia University
Das, A.	University of Rochester
Deo, N.	Purdue University
Deser, S.	Brandeis University
Dine, M.	Institute for Advanced Study
Dixon, L.	Princeton University
Dolan, L.	Rockefeller University
Dothan, Y.	Duke University
Dunietz, I.	University of Chicago
Eastaugh, A.	S.U.N.Y. - Stony Brook
Fairlie, D.	University of Durham
Farhi, E.	M.I.T.
Feng, J.	Caltech
Fields, T.	Argonne National Laboratory
Finkelstein, R.	UCLA
Flores, E.	University of Michigan
Fradkin, E.	University of Illinois at Urbana
Frampton, P.	University of North Carolina
Freed, D.	M.I.T.
Freedman, D.	M.I.T.
Freund, P.G.O.	University of Chicago
Friedan, D.	University of Chicago
Frieman, J.	University of Chicago
Fulling, S.	Texas A. and M. University
Fulp, R.	North Carolina State University
Gabriel, M.	Purdue University
Gaitan, F.	University of Illinois at Urbana
Gates, J.	M.I.T.
Gegenberg, D.	Simon Fraser University
Gersdorff, H.	Fermilab
Gervais, J.	Ecole Normale Supérieure
Getzler, E.	Harvard University
Ginsparg, P.	Harvard University

Goebel, C.	University of Wisconsin
Goff, W.	University of Illinois
Goldberg. G.	University of Michigan
Gonsalves, R.	S.U.N.Y. - Buffalo
Grady, M.	Argonne National Laboratory
Green, M.	Queen Mary College
Greenberg, O.W.	Fermilab/ University of Maryland
Greenspoon, A.	Mathematical Reviews
Grisaru, M.	Brandeis University
Gross, D.	Princeton University
Grossman, B.	Rockefeller University
Gunaydin, M.	Lawrence Livermore Laboratory
Guo, H.Y.	ITP - Academia Sinica
Gürsey, F.	Yale University
Ha, Y.	Rockefeller University
Hadjitheodoridis, S.	Brown University
Hamidi, S.	Caltech
Harvey, J.	Princeton University
Hatfield, B.	University of Illinois at Urbana
Hill, A.	University of Michigan
Hill, C.	Fermilab
Hodges, H.	University of Chicago
Hoek, T.	Rutherford Appleton Laboratory
Holman, R.	University of Florida
Honan, T.	University of Maryland
't Hooft, G.	University of Utrecht
Horowitz, G.	U.C. Santa Barbara
Hosotani, Y.	University of Minnesota
Hou, B.	Northwest University, Xian
Issaevitch, T.	University of Illinois
Itoyama, H.	Columbia University
Jackiw, R.	M.I.T.
Jaeger, G.	University of Wisconsin
Jasinschi, R.	Harvard University
Jo, S.	M.I.T.
Jones, K.	Nuclear Physics
Jourjine, A.	University of Wisconsin
Jovanovic, D.	Fermilab
Julia, B.	Ecole Normale Supérieure
Kac, V.	M.I.T.
Kagan, A.	University of Chicago
Kaku, M.	City College of C.U.N.Y.
Kalivas, N.	Oxford University
Kaplunovsky, V.	Princeton University
Karabali, D.	Yale University
Karatas, D.	Illinois Institute of Technology
Kastor, D.	University of Chicago

Katsumata, H.	University of Michigan
Kauffman, L.	University of Illinois at Chicago
Kaufman, B.	University of Michigan
Kephart, T.	Purdue University
Killingback, T.	Princeton University
Kim, Y.	University of Michigan
Kiridsis, E.	Caltech
Kiskis, J.	U.C. Davis
Kitazawa, Y.	University of Chicago
Kogut, J.	University of Illinois at Urbana
Kovacs, E.	Argonne National Laboratory
Kunstatter, G.	University of Toronto
Kuo, T.	Purdue University
Lam, H.	McGill University
Lee, I.	Ohio State University
Lee, S.	Academia Sinica
Leung, C.	Fermilab
Li, D.	City College of C.U.N.Y.
Li, K.	University of Illinois
Li, X.	DESY
Lina, J.	University of Montreal
Liu, J.	University of Notre Dame
Liu, K.	University of Kentucky
Lizzie, F.	Syracuse University
Lott, J.	Harvard University
Love, S.	Purdue University
MacKenzie, R.	U.C. Santa Barbara
Mahanthappa, K.	University of Colorado
Manes, J.	Lawrence Berkeley Laboratory
Mann, R.	University of Toronto
Manohar, A.	Harvard University
Mansouri, F.	University of Cincinnati
Marcus, N.	Lawrence Berkeley Laboratory
Martinec, E.	Princeton University
Matsuki, T.	Lousiana State University
Matsuoka, H.	Argonne National Laboratory
McCabe, J.	University of Florida
McGlinn, B.	University of Notre Dame
McKeon, G.	University of Western Ontario
Mezincescu, L.	University of Texas at Austin
Migneron, R.	University of Western Ontario
Moore, G.	Harvard University
Mtingwa, S.	Fermilab
Mueller, M.	Insititute for Advanced Study
Muzinich, I.	Cornell University/ Brookhaven
Myers, R.	Princeton University
Nair, V.	Institute for Advanced Study

Nakagawa, N.	Purdue University
Nambu, Y.	University of Chicago
Nappi, C.	Princeton University
Nelson, C.	S.U.N.Y. - Binghamton
Nelson, P.	Harvard University
Nemeschansky, D.	SLAC
Nemirovsky, A.	University of Chicago
Nepomechie, R.	University of Washington
Ng, J.	University of North Carolina
Niemi, A.	Institutê for Advanced Study
O'Connor, D.	University of Maryland
O'Connor, M.	University of Illinois at Urbana
Oakes, R.	Northwestern University
Oh, P.	University of Chicago
Oliensis, J.	Argonne National Laboratory
Olness, F.	University of Wisconsin
Olson, D.	University of Illinois at Urbana
Ovrut, B.	University of Pennsylvania
Palmeri, J.	University of Illinois
Panagopoulos, H.	University of Montreal
Pantziris, A.	Brown University
Paolo, P.	University of Padova
Parke, S.	Fermilab
Periwal, W.	Princeton University
Pernici, M.	S.U.N.Y. - Stony Brook
Pilch, K.	S.U.N.Y. - Stony Brook
Pisarski, R.	Fermilab
Polchinski, J.	University of Texas at Austin
Polonyi, J.	University of Illinois at Urbana
Polychronakos, A.	Caltech
Preitschopf, C.	Stanford University
Qian, S.	Illinois Institute of Technology
Qiu, Z.	University of Chicago
Rabin, J.	University of Chicago
Rajeev, S.	M.I.T.
Ralston, J.	University of Kansas
Ramaswami, S.	University of Illinois at Urbana
Rao, S.	Fermilab
Redlich, A.N.	Brandeis University
Rhie, S.	Stanford University
Riegert, R.	U.C. San Diego
Riggs, H.	University of Chicago
Rocek, M.	S.U.N.Y. - Stony Brook
Rodgers, V.	Syracuse University
Rodriquez, J.	University of Illinois
Rohm, R.	Princeton University
Rosner, J.	University of Chicago
Rubin, M.	Fermilab

Ruiz-Altaba, M.	University of Florida
Samuel, M.	Oklahoma State University
Sarcevic, I.	University of Minnesota
Sasaki, R.	Hiroshima University
Schechter, J.	Syracuse University
Schellekens, A.B.	S.U.N.Y. - Stony Brook
Schmidt, J.	University of Wisconsin
Schrieffer, J.R.	ITP - Santa Barbara
Schwarz, J.H.	Caltech
Seckel, D.	Fermilab
Segert, J.	Princeton University
Seki, R.	California State University
Semenoff, G.	University of British Columbia
Sen, A.	Fermilab
Sexton, J.	Fermilab
Shapiro, J.	Rutgers University
Shenker, S.	University of Chicago
Sherry, T.	University of Western Ontario
Shigemitsu, J.	Ohio State University
Sidenius, J.	Niels Bohr Institute
Siegel, W.	U.C. Berkeley
Sinclair, D.	Argonne National Laboratory
Singer, I.M.	M.I.T.
Siopsis, G.	Caltech
Sivers, D.	Argonne National Laboratory
Slansky, R.	Los Alamos National Laboratory
Sloan, J.	Princeton University
Smith, S.	University of Illinois at Chicago
Solomon, S.	Caltech
Sommerfield, C.	Yale University
Song, X.	Beijing University
Sonoda, H.	Caltech
Staebler, G.	Virginia Polytechnic Institute
Stasheff, J.	University of North Carolina
Stephens, C.	University of Maryland
Stern, A.	University of Oregon
Stone, M.	University of Illinois at Urbana
Strobel, E.	Purdue University
Strominger, A.	Institute for Advanced Study
Talmadge, C.	Purdue University
Taylor, C.	Rutgers University
Taylor, T.	Fermilab
Thacker, H.	Fermilab
Thierry-Mieg, J.	Lawrence Berkeley Laboratory
Thurber, J.	Purdue University
Topiwala, P.	University of Michigan
Torner, J.	Illinois Institute of Technology

Traschen, J.	University of Chicago
Trivedi, A.	University of Chicago
Tsokos, K.	University of Maryland
Tucci, R.	Argonne National Laboratory
Tung, W.K.	Illinois Institute of Technology
Tye, H.	Cornell University
Tze, C.	Yale University
Uhlenbeck, K.	University of Chicago
van Baal, P.	S.U.N.Y. - Stony Brook
Vaughn, M.	Northeastern University
Vepstas, L.	ITP - Santa Barbara
Viallet, C.	Univ. Pierre and Marie Curie
Vinet, L.	Université de Montreal
Visnjic, V.	University of Minnesota
Wada, W.	Ohio State University
Wald, R.	University of Chicago
Warner, N.	Caltech
Warr, B.	Caltech
Wheeler, J.	University of Chicago
White, A.	Argonne National Laboratory
Wijewardhana, L.	Yale University
Willcox, C.	Argonne National Laboratory
Windey, P.	Lawrence Berkeley Laboratory
Wirzba, A.	ITP - Santa Barbara
Witten, E.	Princeton University
Witten, L.	University of Cincinnati
Woit, P.	S.U.N.Y. - Stony Brook
Wong, B.	Simon Fraser University
Wu, Y.S.	University of Washington
Wu, X.	M.I.T.
Yahalom, A.	SLAC
Yamawaki, M.	City College of C.U.N.Y.
Yau, S.T.	U.C. San Diego
Yost, S.	Princeton University
Zachos, C.	Argonne National Laboratory
Zahed, S.	ITP - Santa Barbara
Zeller, D.	University of Chicago
Zhang, S.	S.U.N.Y. - Stony Brook
Zumino, B.	U.C. Berkeley
Zwieback, B.	U.C. Berkeley